INSTRUCTOR'S SOLUTIONS MANUAL

Gary P. Egan

Monroe Community College

Aimee L. Calhoun

Monroe Community College

to accompany

A Survey of Mathematics with Applications

Sixth Edition and Expanded Sixth Edition

Allen R. Angel

Stuart R. Porter

Addison
Wesley

Boston San Francisco New York
London Toronto Sydney Tokyo Singapore Madrid
Mexico City Munich Paris Cape Town Hong Kong Montreal

Reproduced by Addison Wesley Longman Publishing Company Inc. from camera-ready copy supplied by the authors.

Copyright © 2001 Addison Wesley Longman.

ISBN   0-201-61324-7

2 3 4 5 6 7 8 9 10 VG 03 02 01

ACKNOWLEDGMENTS

We would like to thank Allen Angel, Christine Dunn, and Dennis Runde, the authors of *A Survey of Mathematics with Applications*, for their support and encouragement; Julie Vincelli from Julmar Secretarial Service for her assistance; and Rachel Reeve from Addison Wesley Longman.

Gary Egan
Aimee Calhoun

I would like to thank my loving wife Claudia and my daughters Kelsey and Emily for their incredible patience during the preparation of this manual.

Gary Egan

Special thanks to my husband, Justin, for his help and believing in me. The sacrifices he made mean so much.

Aimee Calhoun

Table of Contents

CHAPTER 1   CRITICAL THINKING SKILLS
1.1   Inductive Reasoning   1
1.2   Estimation   3
1.3   Problem Solving   4
        Review Exercises   10
        Chapter Test   13
        Group Projects   14

CHAPTER 2   SETS
2.1   Set Concepts   15
2.2   Subsets   17
2.3   Venn Diagrams and Set Operations   18
2.4   Venn Diagrams with Three Sets and Verification of Equality of Sets   22
2.5   Applications of Sets   30
2.6   Infinite Sets   34
        Review Exercises   35
        Chapter Test   38
        Group Projects   39

CHAPTER 3   LOGIC
3.1   Statements and Logical Connectives   41
3.2   Truth Tables for Negation, Conjunction, and Disjunction   43
3.3   Truth Tables for the Conditional and Biconditional   50
3.4   Equivalent Statements   57
3.5   Symbolic Arguments   67
3.6   Eurler Circles and Syllogistic Arguments   75
        Review Exercises   78
        Chapter Test   82
        Group Projects   84

CHAPTER 4   SYSTEMS OF NUMERATION
4.1   Additive, Multiplicative, and Ciphered Systems of Numeration   87
4.2   Place-Value or Positional-Value Numeration Systems   89
4.3   Other Bases   92
4.4   Computation in Other Bases   97
4.5   Early Computational Methods   100
        Review Exercises   104
        Chapter Test   107
        Group Projects   108

CHAPTER 5   NUMBER THEORY AND THE REAL NUMBER SYSTEM
5.1   Number Theory   109
5.2   The Integers   113
5.3   The Rational Numbers   115
5.4   The Irrational Numbers and the Real Number System   121
5.5   Real Numbers and Their Properties   124
5.6   Rules of Exponents and Scientific Notation   126
5.7   Arithmetic and Geometric Sequences   129
5.8   Fibonacci Sequence   131
        Review Exercises   133
        Chapter Test   137
        Group Projects   138

CHAPTER 6   ALGEBRA, GRAPHS, AND FUNCTIONS
6.1   Order of Operations   **139**
6.2   Linear Equations in One Variable   **141**
6.3   Formulas   **151**
6.4   Applications of Linear Equations in One Variable   **161**
6.5   Variation   **166**
6.6   Linear Inequalities   **170**
6.7   Graphing Linear Equations   **176**
6.8   Linear Inequalities in Two Variables   **188**
6.9   Solving Quadratic Equations By Using Factoring and By Using the Quadratic Formula   **194**
6.10   Functions and Their Graphs   **199**
Review Exercises   **210**
Chapter Test   **222**
Group Projects   **225**

CHAPTER 7   SYSTEMS OF LINEAR EQUATIONS AND INEQUALITIES
7.1   Systems of Linear Equations   **227**
7.2   Solving Systems of Equations by the Substitution and Addition Methods   **233**
7.3   Matrices   **242**
7.4   Solving Systems of Equations by Using Matrices   **249**
7.5   Systems of Linear Inequalities   **252**
7.6   Linear Programming   **255**
Review Exercises   **258**
Chapter Test   **263**
Group Projects   **266**

CHAPTER 8   THE METRIC SYSTEM
8.1   Basic Terms and Conversions Within the Metric System   **267**
8.2   Length, Area, and Volume   **269**
8.3   Mass and Temperature   **270**
8.4   Dimensional Analysis and Conversions to and from the Metric System   **272**
Review Exercises   **278**
Chapter Test   **280**
Group Projects   **282**

CHAPTER 9   GEOMETRY
9.1   Points, Lines, Planes, and Angles   **283**
9.2   Polygons   **287**
9.3   Perimeter and Area   **291**
9.4   Volume   **296**
9.5   The Mobius Strip, Klein Bottle, and Maps   **301**
9.6   Non-Euclidean Geometry and Fractal Geometry   **302**
Review Exercises   **304**
Chapter Test   **306**
Group Projects   **307**

CHAPTER 10   MATHEMATICAL SYSTEMS
10.1   Groups   **309**
10.2   Finite Mathematical Systems   **310**
10.3   Modular Arithmetic   **314**
Review Exercises   **320**
Chapter Test   **323**
Group Projects   **325**

CHAPTER 11   CONSUMER MATHEMATICS

11.1   Percent   **327**
11.2   Personal Loans and Simple Interest   **331**
11.3   Compound Interest   **336**
11.4   Installment Buying   **339**
11.5   Buying a House with a Mortgage   **346**
         Review Exercises   **351**
         Chapter Test   **355**
         Group Projects   **356**

CHAPTER 12   PROBABILITY

12.1   The Nature of Probability   **357**
12.2   Theoretical Probability   **358**
12.3   Odds   **361**
12.4   Expected Value (Expectation)   **366**
12.5   Tree Diagrams   **369**
12.6   "Or" and "And" Problems   **380**
12.7   Conditional Probability   **386**
12.8   The Counting Principle and Permutations   **389**
12.9   Combinations   **392**
12.10   Solving Probability Problems by Using Combinations   **394**
12.11   Binomial Probability Formula   **398**
         Review Exercises   **400**
         Chapter Test   **404**
         Group Projects   **406**

CHAPTER 13   STATISTICS

13.1   Sampling Techniques   **407**
13.2   The Misuses of Statistics   **408**
13.3   Frequency Distributions   **412**
13.4   Statistical Graphs   **414**
13.5   Measures of Central Tendency   **422**
13.6   Measures of Dispersion   **426**
13.7   The Normal Curve   **432**
13.8   Linear Correlation and Regression   **436**
         Review Exercises   **448**
         Chapter Test   **454**

CHAPTER 14   GRAPH THEORY

14.1   Graphs, Paths, and Circuits   **457**
14.2   Euler Paths and Euler Circuits   **460**
14.3   Hamilton Paths and Hamilton Circuits   **465**
14.4   Trees   **471**
         Review Exercises   **483**
         Chapter Test   **488**

CHAPTER 15   VOTING AND APPORTIONMENT

15.1   Voting Systems   **491**
15.2   Flaws of Voting   **505**
15.3   Apportionment Methods   **509**
15.4   Flaws of Apportionment Methods   **515**
         Review Exercises   **519**
         Chapter Test   **524**

APPENDIX   **527**

CHAPTER ONE

CRITICAL THINKING SKILLS

Exercise Set 1.1

1. a) 1, 2, 3, 4, 5, ...
   b) counting numbers

2. a) It means that when we evaluate
      a ÷ b, the remainder is 0.
   b) 4, 8, 12
   c) 9, 18, 27

3. When a scientist or mathematician makes a prediction based on specific observations it is called a conjecture.

4. Inductive reasoning is the process of reasoning to a general conclusion through observation of specific cases.

5. Deductive reasoning is the process of reasoning to a specific conclusion from a general statement.

6. A counterexample is a specific case that satisfies the conditions of the conjecture but shows the conjecture is false.

7. Inductive reasoning: a general conclusion from observation of specific cases.

8. Inductive reasoning: a general conclusion from observation of specific cases.

9. 1 5(1+ 4) 10(4+6) 10(6+4) 5(4+1) 1

10. 5 x 9 = 45

11. 1 + 2 + 3 + 4 + 5 + 6 = 21

12. 11 x 14 = 154

13. Δ

14.

15.

16.

17. 13, 15, 17 (Add 2 to previous number)

18. -3, -7, -11 (Subtract 4 from previous number)

19. -1, 1, -1 (Alternate -1 and 1)

20. -5, -7, -9 (Subtract 2 from previous number)

21. $\dfrac{1}{16}, \dfrac{1}{32}, \dfrac{1}{64}$ (Multiply previous number by $\dfrac{1}{2}$)

22. 162, -486, 1458 (Multiply previous number by −3)

23. 36, 49, 64 (The numbers in the sequence are the squares of the counting numbers.)

24. 48, 63, 80 (35 + 13 = 48, 48 + 15 = 63, 63 + 17 = 80)

25. 34, 55, 89 (Each number in the sequence is the sum of the previous two numbers.)

26. $\dfrac{80}{81}, \dfrac{-160}{243}, \dfrac{320}{729}$ (Multiply previous number by $\dfrac{-2}{3}$)

27. a) Answers will vary.

   b) The sum of the digits is 9.

   c) The sum of the digits in the product when a one or two digit number is multiplied by 9 is 9.

28. Y: There are three letters in the pattern. 39 x 3 = 117, so the 117th entry is the second R in the pattern. Therefore, the 118th entry is Y.

29. a) 36, 49, 64

   b) Square the numbers 6, 7, 8, 9 and 10

   c) 8 x 8 = 64   9 x 9 = 81

   72 is not a square number since it falls between the two square numbers 64 and 81.

30. a) 28 and 36

   b) To find the 7th triangular number, add 7 to the 6th triangular number. To find the 8th triangular number, add 8 to the 7th triangular number. To find the 9th triangular number, add 9 to the 8th triangular number. To find the 10th triangular number, add 10 to the 9th triangular number. To find the 11th triangular number, add 11 to the 10th triangular number.

   c) 36 + 9 = 45   45 + 10 = 55   55 + 11 = 66   66 + 12 = 78

   72 is not a triangular number since it falls between the two triangular numbers 66 and 78.

31. blue: 1, 5, 7, 10, 12   purple: 2, 4, 6, 9, 11   yellow: 3, 8

32. a) 19 (Each new row has two additional triangles.)

   b) 1 + 3 + 5 + 7 + 9 + 11 + 13 + 15 + 17 + 19 = 100

33. a) 8% because 6.5% + 1.5% = 8%

   b) A general conclusion was made based on observations of specific cases. (1.5% was gained in each of the two previous years.)

34. a) $48,423 - $34,213 = $14,210, $48,423 + $14,210 = $62,633 ≈ $62,600

   b) $21,000 - $14,725 = $6275, $21,000 + $6275 = $27,275

   c) We are assuming about the same rate of growth as in the previous 20 years.

35.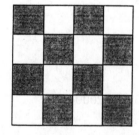

36.

37. a) You should obtain the original number.

   b) You should obtain the original number.

   c) Conjecture: The result is always the original number.

   d) n, $3n$, $3n+6$, $\dfrac{3n+6}{3} = \dfrac{3n}{3} + \dfrac{6}{3} = n+2$, $n+2-2 = n$

38. a) You should obtain twice the original number.

   b) You should obtain twice the original number.

   c) Conjecture: The result is always twice the original number.

   d) n, $6n$, $6n+3$, $\dfrac{6n+3}{3} = \dfrac{6n}{3} + \dfrac{3}{3} = 2n+1$, $2n+1-1 = 2n$

39. a) You should obtain the number 5.

   b) You should obtain the number 5.

   c) Conjecture: No matter what number is chosen, the result is always the number 5.

   d) n, $n+1$, $n+n+1 = 2n+1$, $2n+1+9 = 2n+10$, $\dfrac{2n+10}{2} = \dfrac{2n}{2} + \dfrac{10}{2} = n+5$, $n+5-n = 5$

40. a) You should obtain the number 0.

b) You should obtain the number 0.

c) Conjecture: No matter what number is chosen, the result is always the number 0.

d) n, $n+10$, $\dfrac{n+10}{5}$, $5\left(\dfrac{n+10}{5}\right) = n+10$, $n+10-10 = n$, $n-n = 0$

41. 50 x 50 = 2500 is one example.

42. 10 + 20 + 30 = 60 is one example.

43. 7 is a counting number. The sum of 7 and 3 is 10. 10 divided by 2 is 5, which is not even.

44. 1 and 3 are counting numbers. The product of 1 and 3 is 3, which is not divisible by 2.

45. The product of 5 multiplied by itself is 25, which is not even.

46. The sum of the odd numbers 3 and 7 is 10, which is not divisible by 4.

47 a) The sum of the measures of the angles should be $180°$.

b) Yes, the sum of the measures of the angles should be $180°$.

c) The sum of the measures of the interior angles of a triangle is $180°$.

48 a) The sum of the measures of the angles should be $360°$.

b) Yes, the sum of the measures of the angles should be $360°$.

c) The sum of the measures of the interior angles of a quadrilateral is $360°$.

49. 129, the numbers in positions are found as follows: a   b

c   a + b + c

50. 1881, 8008, 8118 (They look the same when looked at in a mirror.)

Exercise Set 1.2

(Note: Answers in this section will vary depending on how you round your numbers. The answers may differ from the answers in the back of the textbook. All answers are approximate.)

1. 333 + 296.4 + 93.5 + 20.4 + 315.9

$\rightarrow$ 333 + 296 + 94 + 20 + 316 = 1059

2. 2.53 + 202.6 + 156.9 + 189 + 0.23 + 416 $\rightarrow$

3 + 203 + 157 + 189 + 0 + 416 = 968

3. 297,700 x 4087 $\rightarrow$ 300,000 x 4000

= 1,200,000,000

4. 1854 x 0.0096 $\rightarrow$ 1854 x 0.01 = 18.54

5. $\dfrac{405}{0.049} \rightarrow \dfrac{400}{0.05} = 8000$

6. 196.43 - 85.964 $\rightarrow$ 196 - 86 = 110

7. 0.048 x 1964 $\rightarrow$ 0.05 x 2000 = 100

8. 9% of 2164 $\rightarrow$ 10% of 2000

= 0.10 x 2000 = 200

9. 31,640 x 79,264 $\rightarrow$ 32,000 x 79,000

= 2,528,000,000

10. $\dfrac{0.0498}{0.00052} \rightarrow \dfrac{0.05}{0.0005} = 100$

11. 592 x 2070 x 992.62 $\rightarrow$ 600 x 2000 x 1000

= 1,200,000,000

12. $\dfrac{296.3}{0.0096} \rightarrow \dfrac{300}{0.01} = 30,000$

13. 12.1 miles per week x 52 weeks $\rightarrow$

12 miles per week x 52 weeks = 624 miles

14. 28 x $0.33 $\rightarrow$ 30 x $0.30 = $9

15. $\dfrac{\$68.90}{29} \rightarrow \dfrac{\$70}{30} \approx \$2.33$

16. 1690 miles x 12 $\rightarrow$ 1700 x 12 = 20,400 miles

17. 42.8 hours x $7.95 per hour

$\rightarrow$ 43 hours x $8 per hour = $344

18. 7% of $789 $\rightarrow$ 7% of $800

= 0.07 x $800 = $56

19. 167 + 203 + 137 $\rightarrow$ 170 + 200 + 140 = 510 lbs.

20. $\dfrac{3.84}{5} \rightarrow \dfrac{4}{5} = 0.8$ lb.

21. $\dfrac{1}{4}$ of $102,272 $\rightarrow$ $\dfrac{1}{4} \times \$102,000 = \$25,500$

22. 32,090 - 18,928 $\rightarrow$ 32,100 - 18,900

= 13,200 lbs.

23. $\dfrac{24,300}{8} \rightarrow \dfrac{24,000}{8} = 3000$ lbs.

24. 18 x 3.92 $\rightarrow$ 18 x 4 = 72 lbs.

25. 1690 x 2 (round trip) x 2 (round trips per month) x 12 (months) → 1700 x 2 x 2 x 12
    = 81,600 miles

26. 15% of $38.60 → 15% of $40
    = 0.15 x $40 = $6

27. Team A: 189 + 172 + 191 → 190 + 170 + 190
    = 550
    Team B: 183 + 229 + 167 → 180 + 230 + 170
    = 580, 580 − 550 = 30 lbs.

28. 80 Mexican pesos = 80 x $0.302 U.S. dollars
    → 80 x $0.30 = $24 U.S. dollars
    $50 - $24 = $26

29. 3.8 x (60 ft. x 80.2 ft.) → 4 x (60 x 80)
    = 19,200 grubs

30. $892 + 6($42) + 6($97) + 6($90)
    → $900 + 6($40) + 6($100) + 6($90)
    = $900 + $240 + $600 + $540 = $2280

31. a) ≈ 2.5 miles
    b) ≈ 4 kilometers

32. a) ≈ 17 miles
    b) ≈ 27 kilometers

33. a) 24% of $41,105 → 24% of $41,000
    = 0.24 x $41,000 = $9840
    b) 39% of $41,105 → 39% of $41,000
    = 0.39 x $41,000 = $15,990

34. a) 28.1% of $599 → 30% of $600
    = 0.30 x $600 = $180
    b) 6.4% of $599 → 6% of $600
    = 0.06 x $600 = $36
    c) 0.2% of $599 → 0.2% of $600
    = 0.002 x $600 = $1.20

35. a) ≈ 4 million
    b) ≈ 98 million
    c) ≈ 98 - 39 = 59 million
    d) ≈ 20 + 80 + 80 + 60 + 40 = 280 million

36. a) ≈ 19%
    b) ≈ 25%
    c) ≈ 28% of 180 lbs. = 0.28 x 180 = 50 lbs.

37. a) luxury cars, minivans, large cars
    b) 30% of $18,209 → 30% of $18,200
    = 0.30 x $18,200 = $5460
    c) 43% of $27,937 → 40% of $30,000
    = 0.40 x $30,000 = $12,000

38. a) 2(410) + 4(545) → 2(400) + 4(550)
    = 800 + 2200 = 3000 calories
    b) running: 4(920) → 4(925) = 3700 calories
    casual bike riding: 4(300) = 1200 calories,
    3700 - 1200 = 2500 calories
    c) jogging: 3(545) → 3(550) = 1650 calories
    bicycling: 3(545) → 3(550) = 1650 calories,
    1650 + 1650 = 3300 calories per week,
    3300(52 weeks) → 3300(50) = 165,000 calories

39. about 20

40. about 32

41. ≈ 90

42. ≈ 450

43. ≈ 150°

44. ≈ 315°

45. ≈ 10%

46. ≈ 25%

47. ≈ 9 square units

48. ≈ 12 square units

49. ≈ 45 ft.

50. ≈ 16 ft.

Exercise Set 1.3

1. $\dfrac{1\ in.}{4.5\ ft.} = \dfrac{7.5\ in.}{x\ ft.}$

    $1x = 7.5(4.5)$

    $x = 33.75\ ft.$

2. $\dfrac{1\ in.}{12\ ft.} = \dfrac{x\ in.}{82\ ft.}$

    $12x = 82(1)$

    $\dfrac{12x}{12} = \dfrac{82}{12}$

    $x = \dfrac{82}{12} = 6\dfrac{10}{12} = 6\dfrac{5}{6}\ in.\ or \approx 6.83\ in.$

3. $\dfrac{3\ ft.}{1.2\ ft.} = \dfrac{48.4\ ft.}{x\ ft.}$

$3x = 48.4(1.2)$

$\dfrac{3x}{3} = \dfrac{58.08}{3}$

$x = 19.36\ ft.$

4. $\dfrac{40\ lbs.}{6000\ ft.^2} = \dfrac{x\ lbs.}{22{,}000\ ft.^2}$

$6000x = 22{,}000(40)$

$\dfrac{6000x}{6000} = \dfrac{880{,}000}{6000}$

$x = \dfrac{880{,}000}{6000} \approx 146.7\ lbs.$

5. $\$1.70 + \$.15\left(5 - \dfrac{1}{8}\right)(8)$

$= \$1.70 + \$.15\left(4\dfrac{7}{8}\right)(8)$

$= \$1.70 + \$.15\left(\dfrac{39}{8}\right)(8)$

$= \$1.70 + \$.15(39) = \$1.70 + \$5.85 = \$7.55$

6. $\dfrac{3\ oz.}{1\ gal.} = \dfrac{x\ oz.}{2.5\ gal.}$

$1x = 2.5(3)$

$x = 7.5\ oz.$

7. a) ≈ 38 cents per pound

b) $22{,}000(\$.55) = \$12{,}100$

$22{,}000(\$.38) = \$8360$ break-even point

$\$12{,}100 - \$8360 = \$3740$

c) $22{,}000(\$.10) = \$2200$

$22{,}000(\$.38) = \$8360$ break-even point

$\$2200 - \$8360 = -\$6160$ or loss of $6160

8. a) $\$2.25 + \$1.75 + \$1.75 + \$.75 = \$6.5$ billion

b) $\$6.5$ billion $= \$6{,}500{,}000{,}000$

$\rightarrow \dfrac{\$6{,}500{,}000{,}000}{273{,}300{,}000} \approx \$23.78$

9. $\dfrac{(mach)3}{2310\ mph} = \dfrac{(mach)1}{x\ mph}$

$3x = 1(2310)$

$\dfrac{3x}{3} = \dfrac{2310}{3}$

$x = 770\ mph$

10. $5[\$2.50 + \$1.00\,(7\ hrs.\ per\ day)]$

$= 5[\$2.50 + \$7.00] = 5(\$9.50) = \$47.50$

savings: $\$47.50 - \$35.00 = \$12.50$

11. a) weekly rate: $70
daily rate: $18(5) = $90
savings: $90 - $70 = $20
b) weekly rate: $50
daily rate: $12(5) = $60
The weekly rate is cheaper by $60 - $50 = $10.
c) $4 for first hour + $2 (6 remaining hours)
= $4 + $12 = $16

12. $\$120 + \$80(15) = \$120 + \$1200 = \$1320$
savings: $1320 - $1250 = $70

13. $\$3.75 + (21 - 3)(\$0.50) = \$3.75 + 18(\$0.50)$

$= \$3.75 + \$9 = \$12.75$

14. Let $x = $ Bill's grade on the fifth exam

$\dfrac{77 + 93 + 90 + 76 + x}{5} = \dfrac{80}{1}$

$(336 + x)(1) = 80(5)$

$336 + x = 400$

$\underline{-336 \qquad -336}$

$x = 64$

15. $\dfrac{\$23{,}000{,}000}{32} = \$718{,}750$

16. a) $10 \cdot 10 \cdot 10 \cdot 10 = 10{,}000$

b) 1 in 10,000

17. a) $\dfrac{460}{50} = 9.2$ min.

    b) $\dfrac{1550}{25} = 62$ min.

    c) $\dfrac{1400}{35} = 40$ min.

    d) $\dfrac{1550}{25} + \dfrac{2200}{25} = \dfrac{3750}{25} = 150$ min.

18. $38,687.0 \; mi. - 38,451.4 \; mi. = 235.6 \; mi.$

    $\dfrac{235.6 \; mi.}{12.6 \; gal.} \approx 18.7 \; \dfrac{mi.}{gal.}$

19. a) 11% of 273,300,000

    $= 0.11(273,300,000) = 30,063,000$

    b) 10% of 970,000 $= 0.10(970,000) = 97,000$

    c) 3% of 970,000 $= 0.03(970,000) = 29,100$

20. a) $20 \times \$5.40 \times 52 = \$5616$

    b) Let $x =$ the number of weeks

    $20(5.40x) = 750$

    $\dfrac{108x}{108} = \dfrac{750}{108}$

    $x \approx 7$ weeks

21. by mail: $(\$52.80 + \$5.60 + \$8.56) \times 4 = \$267.84$

    tire store:

    $\$324 + \$324(.08) = \$324 + \$25.92 = \$349.92$

    savings: $\$349.92 - \$267.84 = \$82.08$

22. Note: $(1 \; yd.)^2 = (3 \; ft.)^2 = 9 \; ft.^2$

    $\dfrac{2400 \times 9}{350} = \dfrac{21,600}{350} \approx 62 \; gal.$

23. a) $\$620(.12) = \$74.40$

    b) $\$1200(.22) = \$264$

    c) $\$1200 - \$1000 = \$200$ loss

    profit $= \$264 - \$200 = \$64$

24. a) $.1 \; cm.^3 \times 60 \; sec. \times 60 \; min. \times 24 \; hr.$

    $\times 365 \; days = 3,153,600 \; cm.^3$

    b) $30 \; cm. \times 20 \; cm. \times 20 \; cm. = 12,000 \; cm.^3$

    $.1 \; cm.^3 \times 60 \; sec. \times 60 \; min. \times 24 \; hr. = 8640$

    $\dfrac{12,000}{8640} \approx 1.4 \; days$

25. Let $x =$ the amount above $42,350

    $\$10,200 - \$6,352.50 = \$3847.50$

    $\dfrac{.28x}{.28} = \dfrac{\$3847.50}{.28}$

    $x \approx \$13,741.07$

    $\$42,350 + \$13,741.07 = \$56,091.07$

26. a) $1 \; oz. \times 60 \; min. \times 24 \; hr. \times 365 \; days$

    $= 525,600 \; oz.$, $\dfrac{525,600}{128} = 4106.25 \; gal.$

    b) $\dfrac{4106.25}{1000} \times \$5.20 = 4.10625 \times \$5.20 \approx \$21.35$

27. a) 2 day service: $\$11.75 \times 52 = \$611$

    priority overnight: $\$28 \times 52 = \$1456$

    savings: $\$1456 - \$611 = \$845$

    b) express mail: $\$17.25 \times 52 = \$897$

    next day air: $\$25.75 \times 52 = \$1339$

    savings: $\$1339 - \$897 = \$442$

28. a) $\dfrac{15,000}{15.8} - \dfrac{15,000}{16.4} \approx 949.367 - 914.634$

    $= 34.733 \; gal.$

    b) $34.733 \times \$1.20 \approx \$41.68$

    c) $140,000,000 \times 34.733 = 4,862,620,000$

    $\approx 4,863,000,000 \; gal.$

29. a) $\$150 + \$75 + \$40 \,(12 \text{ months})$

    $= \$150 + \$75 + \$480 = \$705$

    b) $\$150 + \$125 + \$40 \,(12 \text{ months})$

    $= \$150 + \$125 + \$480 = \$755$

    c) 50 (5 compared to 0.1)

30. Less:

    Let $x =$ the original price of the car

    price after increase: $x + .20x = 1.20x$

    price after decrease: $1.20x - .20(1.20x)$

    $= 1.20x - .24x = .96x$

31. cost after 1 year: $450 + \$450(.06)$

  $= \$450 + \$27 = \$477$

  cost after 2 years: $\$477 + \$477(.06)$

  $= \$477 + \$28.62 = \$505.62$

32. a) $\$498 + \$598 + 4(\$15)$

  $= \$498 + \$598 + \$60 = \$1156$

  $\$1156 - \$772 = \$384$

  b) $\dfrac{\$772}{\$1156} \approx 67\%$

33. a) $\dfrac{\$200}{\$41} \approx 4.9$ The maximum number of 10-packs is 4.

  $\$200 - (4 \times \$41) = \$200 - \$164 = \$36$, $\dfrac{\$36}{\$17} \approx 2.1$ Deirdre can also buy two 4-packs.

10-packs	4-packs	Number of rolls	Cost
4	2	48	$198
3	4	46	$191
2	6	44	$184
1	9	46	$194
0	11	44	$187

  Maximum number of rolls of film is 48.

  b) $198 when she purchases four 10-packs and two 4-packs.

34. a) $\dfrac{\$50}{\$5.76} \approx 8.7$ The maximum number of 4-packs of 36-exposures is 8.

  $\$50 - (8 \times \$5.76) = \$50 - \$46.08 = \$3.92$,   Erika cannot buy any 24-exposures.

4-packs of 36-exp.	4-packs of 24-exp.	Number of exposures	Cost
8	0	288	$46.08
7	2	300	$48.48
6	3	288	$46.80
5	5	300	$49.20
4	6	288	$47.52
3	8	300	$49.92
2	9	288	$48.24
1	10	276	$46.56
0	12	288	$48.96

  2 packs of 24-exposures and 7 packs of 36-exposures, or 5 packs of 24-exposures and 5 packs of 36-exposures, or 8 packs of 24-exposures and 3 packs of 36-exposures

  b) 300 exposures in each case

  c) $48.48 when she purchases 2 packs of 24-exposures and 7 packs of 36-exposures

35. a) water/milk: $3(1) = 3$ cups   salt: $3\left(\dfrac{1}{8}\right) = \dfrac{3}{8}$ tsp.

   cream: $3(3) = 9$ tbsp. $= \dfrac{9}{16}$ cup (because 16 tbsp. = 1 cup)

   b) water/milk: $\dfrac{2 + 3.75}{2} = \dfrac{5.75}{2} = 2.875$ cups $= 2\dfrac{7}{8}$ cups

   salt: $\dfrac{.25 + .5}{2} = \dfrac{.75}{2} = .375$ tsp. $= \dfrac{3}{8}$ tsp.   cream: $\dfrac{.5 + .75}{2} = \dfrac{1.25}{2} = .625$ cups $= \dfrac{5}{8}$ cup

   c) water/milk: $3\dfrac{3}{4} - 1 = \dfrac{15}{4} - \dfrac{4}{4} = \dfrac{11}{4} = 2\dfrac{3}{4}$ cups

   salt: $\dfrac{1}{2} - \dfrac{1}{8} = \dfrac{4}{8} - \dfrac{1}{8} = \dfrac{3}{8}$ tsp.   cream: $\dfrac{3}{4} - \dfrac{3}{16} = \dfrac{12}{16} - \dfrac{3}{16} = \dfrac{9}{16}$ cup = 9 tbsp.

   d) Differences exist in water/milk because the amount for 4 servings is not twice that for 2 servings.
   Differences also exist in Cream of Wheat because $\dfrac{1}{2}$ cup is not twice 3 tbsp.

36. a) rice: $\dfrac{1}{2}(4) = 2$ cups   b) rice: $1(2) = 2$ cups

   water: $1\dfrac{1}{3}(4) = \dfrac{4}{3}(4) = \dfrac{16}{3} = 5\dfrac{1}{3}$ cups   water: $2\dfrac{1}{4}(2) = \dfrac{9}{4}(2) = \dfrac{18}{4} = 4\dfrac{2}{4} = 4\dfrac{1}{2}$ cups

   salt: $\dfrac{1}{4}(4) = 1$ tsp.   salt: $\dfrac{1}{2}(2) = 1$ tsp.

   butter/margarine: $1(4) = 4$ tsp.   butter/margarine: $2(2) = 4$ tsp.

   c) rice: $\dfrac{1}{2} + 1\dfrac{1}{2} = \dfrac{1}{2} + \dfrac{3}{2} = \dfrac{4}{2} = 2$ cups

   water: $1\dfrac{1}{3} + 3\dfrac{1}{3} = \dfrac{4}{3} + \dfrac{10}{3} = \dfrac{14}{3} = 4\dfrac{2}{3}$ cups

   salt: $\dfrac{1}{4} + \dfrac{3}{4} = \dfrac{4}{4} = 1$ tsp.

   butter/margarine: 1 tsp. + 1 tbsp. = 1 tsp. + 3 tsp. = 4 tsp.

   d) Differences exist in water because the amount for 4 servings is not twice that for 2 servings.

37. $1\ ft.^2$ would be 12 in. by 12 in. Thus,
   $1\ ft.^2 = 12\ in. \times 12\ in. = 144\ in.^2$

38. $1\ ft.^3 = 12\ in. \times 12\ in. \times 12\ in. = 1728\ in.^3$

39. Area of original rectangle = lw
   Area of new rectangle = $(2l)(2w) = 4lw$
   Thus, if the length and width of a rectangle are doubled, the area is 4 times as large.

40. Volume of original cube = lwh
   Volume of new cube $= (2l)(2w)(2h) = 8lwh$
   Thus, if the length, width, and height of a cube are doubled, the volume is 8 times as large.

41. $7 + 7 - (7 \div 7) = 13$

42. $\dfrac{24}{4} \times \dfrac{24}{4} = 6 \times 6 = 36$ squares

43.
$$\frac{60}{4} = 15$$

Zebras	Number of Zebra Feet	Cranes	Number of Crane Feet	Number of Heads
15	60	0	0	15
14	56	2	4	16
13	52	4	8	17
12	48	6	12	18

Therefore, there are 12 zebras and 6 cranes.

44. $10; 2002, 2112, 2222, 2332, 2442, 2552,$
$2662, 2772, 2882, 2992$

45. a) $(4 \times 4) + (3 \times 3) + (2 \times 2) + (1 \times 1)$
$= 16 + 9 + 4 + 1 = 30$
b) $(7 \times 7) + (6 \times 6) + (5 \times 5) + 30$
$= 49 + 36 + 25 + 30 = 140$

46. The value of the dress plus the $55 change.

47. a) Place the object, 1 g., and 3 g. on one side
and 9 g. on the other side.
b) Place the object, 9 g., and 3 g. on
one side and 27 g. and 1 g. on the other side.

48.

8	6	16
18	10	2
4	14	12

49.

15	1	11
5	9	13
7	17	3

50. $28, 16, 44$ The sum of the four corner entries is
4 times the number in the center of the middle
row.

51. $21, 12, 33$ Multiply the number in the center of
the middle row by 3.

52. $63, 36, 99$ Multiply the number in the
center of the middle row by 9.

53. $3 \times 2 \times 1 = 6$ ways

54. $(5 \times 5) + (4 \times 4) + (3 \times 3) + (2 \times 2) + (1 \times 1)$
$= 25 + 16 + 9 + 4 + 1 = 55$

55. $35 - 15 = 20$

56. Each shakes with 4 people.

57.

	7	
3	1	4
5	8	6
	2	

Other answers are possible, but 1 and
8 must appear in the center.

58.

59.

1	2	3	4	5
2	3	4	5	1
3	4	5	1	2
4	5	1	2	3
5	1	2	3	4

Other answers are possible.

60. With umbrella policy

Mustang: $695 - $60 = $635

Escort: $650 × .36 = $234 reduction

$650 - $234 = $416

Total for umbrella policy: $635 + $416

+$392 = $1443

Without umbrella policy: $695 + $650 = $1345

$1443 - $1345 = $98

61. Mary is the skier.

62. $16 + 16 + 4 + 4 + 4 = 44$

63. Areas of the colored regions are:

$1 \times 1, 1 \times 1, 2 \times 2, 3 \times 3, 5 \times 5, 8 \times 8, 13 \times 13,$

21×21 ; $1 + 1 + 4 + 9 + 25 + 64 + 169 + 441$

$= 714$ square units

Review Exercises

1. 23, 28, 33 (Add 5 to previous number)

2. 25, 36, 49 (Next three perfect squares)

3. 64, -128, 256 (Multiply previous number by –2)

4. 25, 32, 40 (19 + 6 = 25, 25 + 7 = 32, 32 + 8 = 40)

5. 10, 4, - 3 (15 - 5 = 10, 10 - 6 = 4, 4 - 7 = -3)

6. $\frac{3}{8}, \frac{3}{16}, \frac{3}{32}$ (Multiply previous number by $\frac{1}{2}$)

7.

8.

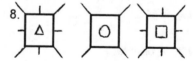

9. a) The original number and the final number are the same.

b) The original number and the final number are the same.

c) Conjecture: The final number is the same as the original number.

d) $n, 2n, 2n + 10, \frac{2n + 10}{2} = \frac{2n}{2} + \frac{10}{2} = n + 5, n + 5 - 5 = n$

10. This process will always result in an answer of 3. $n, n + 5, 6(n + 5) = 6n + 30, 6n + 30 - 12$

$= 6n + 18, \frac{6n + 18}{2} = \frac{6n}{2} + \frac{18}{2} = 3n + 9, \frac{3n + 9}{3} = \frac{3n}{3} + \frac{9}{3} = n + 3, n + 3 - n = 3$

11. $6^2 - 4^2 = 36 - 16 = 20$, 20 is an even number.

(Note: Answers for Ex. 12 - 25 will vary depending on how you round your numbers. The answers may differ from the answers in the back of the textbook. All answers are approximate.)

12. 204,600 x 1963 → 205,000 x 2000
     = 410,000,000

13. $\dfrac{19,254.5}{524.3} \rightarrow \dfrac{19,000}{500} = 38$

14. 346 .2 + 96.402 + 1.04 + 897 + 821 →
     350 + 100 + 1 + 900 + 800 = 2151

15. 21% of 1012 → 20% of 1000
     = .20 x 1000 = 200

16. Answers will vary.

17. 8 x $12.99 → 8 x $13 = $104

18. 6% of $202 → 6% of 200 = .06 x 200 = $12

19. $\dfrac{1.1\,mi.}{22\,min.} \rightarrow \dfrac{1\,mi.}{20\,min.} = \dfrac{3\,mi.}{60\,min.} = 3\,mph$

20. $2.49 + $0.79 + $1.89 + $0.10 + $2.19 + $6.75
     → $2 + $1 + $2 + $0 + $2 + $7 = $14.00

21. $5\,in. = \dfrac{20}{4}\,in. = 20\left(\dfrac{1}{4}\right)in. = 20(0.1)mi. = 2mi.$

22. 80 – 12 = 68

23. 5300 + 570 + 80 = 5950

24. 13 square units

25. length = 1.75 in. , 1.75(12.5) ≈ 22 ft.
     height = .625 in. , .625(12.5) ≈ 8 ft.

26. dialed direct: $1.20 + 14($0.30)
     = $1.20 + $4.20 = $5.40
     savings: $7.50 - $5.40 = $2.10

27. $2 + 7($0.90) = $2 + $6.30 = $8.30
     change: $10 - $8.30 = $1.70

28. 4($3.45) = $13.80 for four six-packs
     savings: $13.80 - $12.60 = $1.20

29. Eurich's: $2\,hr. = 120\,min., \dfrac{120}{15} = 8$, $8 \times \$10 = \$80$

     Starr's: $2\,hr. = 120\,min., \dfrac{120}{30} = 4$, $4 \times \$25 = \$100$

     Eurich's is better by $20 .

30. $\$1.35 + \left[\left(10 - \dfrac{1}{5}\right)(5)\right]\$.20$

     $= \$1.35 + \left[\left(\dfrac{50}{5} - \dfrac{1}{5}\right)(5)\right]\$.20$

     $= \$1.35 + \left[\dfrac{49}{5}(5)\right]\$.20$

     $= \$1.35 + 49 \times \$.20 = \$1.35 + \$9.80$

     $= \$11.15$

31. 10% of $530 = 0.10 x $530 = $53
     $53 x 7 = $371
     savings: $371 - $60 = $311

32. $\dfrac{1.5\,mg.}{10\,lbs.} = \dfrac{x\,mg.}{47\,lbs.}$

     $10x = 47(1.5)$

     $\dfrac{10x}{10} = \dfrac{70.5}{10}$

     $x = 7.05\,mg.$

33. $3800 - 0.30($3800) = $3800 - $1140
     = $2660 take-home
     25% of $2660 = .25 x $2660 = $665

34. 9 a.m. Eastern is 6 a.m. Pacific, from
     6 a.m. Pacific to 1:35 p.m. Pacific
     is 7 hr. 35 min. , 7 hr. 35 min. - 50 min. stop
     = 6 hr. 45 min.

35. 3 p.m. - 4 hr. = 11 a.m.
     July 26, 11 a.m.

36. a) $1\,in. \times 1\,in. = 2.54\,cm. \times 2.54\,cm.$

    $= 6.4516\,cm.^2 \approx 6.45\,cm.^2$

    b) $1\,in. \times 1\,in. \times 1\,in. = 2.54\,cm. \times 2.54\,cm.$

    $\times\,2.54\,cm. = 16.387064\,cm.^3 \approx 16.39\,cm.^3$

    c) $\dfrac{1\,in.}{2.54\,cm.} = \dfrac{x\,in.}{1\,cm.}$

    $2.54x = 1(1)$

    $\dfrac{2.54x}{2.54} = \dfrac{1}{2.54}$

    $x \approx .39\,in.$

37. Each figure has an additional two dots. To get the hundredth figure, 97 more figures must be drawn, 97(2) = 194 dots added to the third figure. Thus, 194 + 7 = 201.

38.

21	7	8	18
10	16	15	13
14	12	11	17
9	19	20	6

39.

23	25	15
13	21	29
27	17	19

40. 59 min., 59 sec. Since it doubles every second, the jar was half full 1 second earlier than 1 hour.

41. 6

42. Nothing. Each friend paid $9 for a total of $27; $25 to the hotel, $2 to the clerk.
    $25 for the room + $3 for each friend + $2 for the clerk = $30

43. Let $x =$ total weight of the four women

    $\dfrac{x}{4} = 130,\ x = 520,\ \dfrac{520 + 180}{5} = \dfrac{700}{5} = 140\,lbs.$

44. Yes, 3 quarters and 4 dimes, or 1 half dollar, 1 quarter and 4 dimes, or 1 quarter and 9 dimes.
    Other answers are possible.

45. $6\,cm. \times 6\,cm. \times 6\,cm. = 216\,cm.^3$

46. Place six coins in each pan with one coin off to the side. If it balances, the heavier coin is the one on the side. If the pan does not balance, take the six coins on the heavier side and split them into two groups of three. Select the three heavier coins and weigh two coins. If the pan balances, it is the third coin. If the pan does not balance, you can identify the heavier coin.

47. $\dfrac{n(n+1)}{2} = \dfrac{500(501)}{2} = \dfrac{250,500}{2} = 125,250$

48. 16 blue: 4 green → 8 blue, 2 yellow → 5 blue, 2 white → 3 blue

49. 90: 101, 111, 121, 131, 141, 151, 161, 171, 181, 191,...

50. The fifth figure will be an octagon with equal sides. Inside the octagon will be a 7-sided figure with each side of equal length. The figure will have one antenna. The nth figure will have n + 3 sides of equal length. Inside the figure will be a figure of n + 2 sides of equal length. If n is an odd number, it will have one antenna. If n is an even number, it will have 2 antennas.

51. 61: The sixth figure will have 6 rows of 6 tiles and 5 rows of 5 tiles (6 x 6 + 5 x 5 = 36 + 25 = 61)

52. Some possible answers are given below. There are other possibilities.

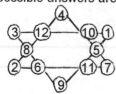 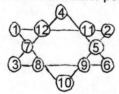 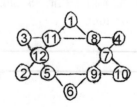

53. a) 2

b) There are 3 choices for the first spot. Once that person is standing, there are 2 choices for the second spot and 1 for the third. Thus, 3 x 2 x 1 = 6.

c) 4 x 3 x 2 x 1 = 24

d) 5 x 4 x 3 x 2 x 1 = 120

e) n x (n - 1) x (n - 2) x (n - 3) x ... x 2 x 1 = n! where n is the number of people in line.

Chapter Test

1. 18, 21, 24   (Add 3 to previous number)

2. $\dfrac{1}{81}, \dfrac{1}{243}, \dfrac{1}{729}$ (Multiply previous number by $\dfrac{1}{3}$)

3. a) The result is the original number plus 1.

b) The result is the original number plus 1.

c) Conjecture: The result will always be the original number plus 1.

d) $n, 5n, 5n + 10, \dfrac{5n + 10}{5} = \dfrac{5n}{5} + \dfrac{10}{5} = n + 2, n + 2 - 1 = n + 1$

(Note: Answers for Ex. 4 - 7 will vary depending on how you round your numbers. The answers may differ from the answers in the back of the textbook. All answers are approximate.)

4. $0.00417 \times 990,000 \rightarrow$
   $0.004 \times 1,000,000 = 4000$

5. $\dfrac{91,000}{0.00302} \rightarrow \dfrac{90,000}{0.003} = 30,000,000$

6. 7 square units

7. a) 25% - 7% = 18%

b) 25% - 9% = 16%

8. Let $x =$ number of therms used

$7.42 + .62(x - 3) = 100.42$

$7.42 + .62x - 1.86 = 100.42$

$5.56 + .62x = 100.42$

$\underline{-5.56 \qquad\qquad - 5.56}$

$\dfrac{.62x}{.62} = \dfrac{94.86}{.62}$

$x = 153$ therms

9. $\dfrac{\$15}{\$3.60} \approx 4.167$ The maximum number of

6-packs is **4**.

$\$15 - (4 \times \$3.60) = \$15 - \$14.40 = \$.60$

Thus, no individual cans can be purchased.

6-packs	Indiv. Cans	Number of cans
4	0	24
3	4	22
2	8	20
1	12	18
0	16	16

Maximum number of cans is 24.

10. 1 cut yields 2 equal pieces. Cut each of these 2 equal pieces to get 4 equal pieces.

3 cuts $\rightarrow$ 3(2.5 min.) = 7.5 min.

11. 2.5 in. by 1.8 in. $\rightarrow$ 2.5 x 12 by 1.8 x 12
= 30 in. by 21.6 in. $\approx$ 30 in. by 22 in.

12. $12.75 x 40 = $510

$12.75 x 1.5 x 10 = $191.25

$510 + $191.25 = $701.25

$701.25 - $652.25 = $49

13.

40	15	20
5	25	45
30	35	10

14. Christine drove the first 15 miles at 60 mph which took $\frac{15}{60} = \frac{1}{4}$ hr., and the second 15 miles at 30 mph which took $\frac{15}{30} = \frac{1}{2}$ hr. for a total time of $\frac{3}{4}$ hr. If she drove the entire 30 miles at 45 mph, the trip would take $\frac{30}{45} = \frac{2}{3}$ hr. (40 min.) which is less than $\frac{3}{4}$ hr. (45 min.).

15. 2 x 6 x 8 x 9 x 13 = 11,232; 11 does not divide 11,232

16. 243: 260 - 17 = 243, 234 + 9 =243, 274 - 31 = 243

17. a) 3 x $3.99 = $11.97

    b) 9($1.75 x .75) ≈ $11.81

    c) $11.97 - $11.81 = $0.16 Using the coupon is least expensive by $0.16.

18. 8: $ → on   * → off

    $$$$, $$$*, $$*$, $*$$, *$$$, *$*$, *$$*, $*$*

Group Projects

1. a) $\frac{\$325}{3} \approx \$108$

   b) Let $x =$ amount before tax

   $$x + .07x = 325$$

   $$\frac{1.07x}{1.07} = \frac{325}{1.07}$$

   $$x \approx \$303.74$$

   $$\frac{\$303.74}{3} \approx \$101.25$$

   c) Inductive reasoning - arriving at a general conclusion from specific cases.

   d) combination set: $62 - ($62 x .10) = $62 - $6.20 = $55.80

      individual set: 2 x $36 = $72, $72 - ($72 x .20) = $72 - $14.40 = $57.60

      Therefore, the combination set is cheaper.

   e) combintion with tax: $55.80 x 1.07 ≈ $59.71

      individual set with tax: $57.60 x 1.07 ≈ $61.63

      $61.63 - $59.71 = $1.92

2. a) – d) Answers will vary.

   e) 400 mi. ÷ 50 mi./hr. = 8 hrs.,   9 a.m. + 8 hrs. = 5 p.m.

   f) – h) Answers will vary.

3.

Order	Name	Apparel
1	Ernie	holster
2	Zeke	vest
3	Jed	chaps
4	Tex	stetson

CHAPTER TWO

SETS

Exercise Set 2.1

1. A **set** is a collection of objects.
2. An **ellipsis** is three dots in a set indicating the elements continue in the same manner.
3. Description: The set of even counting numbers less than 7.
   Roster form: {2, 4, 6}
   Set-builder notation: {x|x ∈ N and x < 7}
4. An **infinite** set is a set that is not finite.
5. A set is **finite** if it either contains no elements or the number of elements in the set is a natural number.
6. Set A is **equal** to set B, symbolized by A = B, if and only if they contain exactly the same elements.
7. Two sets are **equivalent** if they contain the same number of elements.
8. The **cardinal number** of a set A, symbolized by n(A), is the number of elements in set A.
9. N = {1, 2, 3, 4, 5, ...}
10. Set A and set B can be placed in **one-to-one correspondence** if every element of set A can be matched with exactly one element of set B and every element of set B can be matched with exactly one element of set A.
11. A **universal set**, symbolized by U, is a set that contains all the elements for any specific discussion.
12. The set that contains no elements is called the **empty set or null set**, and is symbolized by { } or ∅.

13. Not well defined, "best" is interpreted differently by different people.
14. Not well defined, "large" is interpreted differently by different people.
15. Well defined, contents can be clearly determined.
16. Well defined, contents can be clearly determined.
17. Well defined, contents can be clearly determined.
18. Not well defined, "interesting" is interpreted differently by different people.

19. Infinite, number of elements in the set is not a natural number.
20. Infinite, number of elements in the set is not a natural number.
21. Finite, number of elements in the set is a natural number.
22. Infinite, number of elements in the set is not a natural number.
23. Infinite, number of elements in the set is not a natural number.
24. Finite, number of elements in the set is a natural number.
25. {Nebraska, Nevada, New Hampshire, New Jersey, New Mexico, New York, North Carolina, North Dakota}
26. {North America, South America, Europe, Asia, Africa, Australia, Antarctica}

27. {11, 12, 13, 14, ..., 177}
28. B = {2, 4, 6, 8,10, ...}
29. C = {4}
30. { } or ∅
31. { } or ∅
32. {Alaska, Hawaii}
33. E = {6, 7, 8, 9, ..., 71}
34. {Mark McGwire}

35. A = {x | x ∈ N and x < 10}
    or A = {x| x∈ N and x ≤ 9}

36. B = {x | x ∈ N and 4 ≤ x ≤ 8}

37. C = {x | x ∈ N and x is a multiple of 3}

38. D = {x | x ∈ N and x is a multiple of 5}

39. E = {x | x ∈ N and x is odd}

40. A = {x | x is Labor Day}

41. C = {x | x is one of the three manufacturers of calculators with the greatest sales in the United States}

42. F = {x | x ∈ N and 15 ≤ x ≤ 100}

43. A is the set of natural numbers less than or equal to 7.

44. D is the set of natural numbers that are multiples of 4.

45. L is the set of Great Lakes in the U.S.

46. S is the set of seven dwarfs from the movie Snow White.

47. B is the set of the five tallest buildings in the U.S.

48. C is the set of companies that make computers.

49. E is the set of natural numbers greater than 5 and less than or equal to 12.

50. T is the set of singers who make up the 3 Tenors.

51. False, {b} is a set and not an element of the set.

52. True, b is an element of the set.

53. False, h is not an element of the set.

54. True, Mickey Mouse is an element of the set.

55. False, 3 is an element of the set.

56. False, the capital of Hawaii is Honolulu, not Maui.

57. True, Titanic is an element of the set.

58. False, 2 is an even natural number.

59. n(A) = 4

60. n(B) = 6

61. n(C) = 0

62. n(D) = 5

63. Both, A and B contain exactly the same elements.

64. Equivalent, both sets contain the same number of elements, 3.

65. Neither, the sets have a different number of elements.

66. Neither, not all dogs are collies.

67. Equivalent, both sets contain the same number of elements, 3.

68. Equivalent, both sets contain the same number of elements, 50.

69. a) A is the set of natural numbers greater than 2. B is the set of all numbers greater than 2.
    b) Set A contains only natural numbers, while set B contains other types of numbers, including fractions and decimal numbers.
    c) A = {3, 4, 5, 6, ...}
    d) No, set B cannot be written in roster form since we cannot list all the elements in set B.

70. a) A is the set of natural numbers greater than 2 and less than or equal to 5. B is the set of numbers greater than 2 and less than or equal to 5.
    b) Set A contains only natural numbers, while set B contains other types of numbers, including fractions and decimal numbers.
    c) A = {3, 4, 5}
    d) No, set B cannot be written in roster form since there is no smallest number that is greater than 2.

71. Cardinal, 19 tells how many.

72. Ordinal, 25 tells the relative position of the chart.

73. Ordinal, sixteenth tells Lincoln's relative position.

74. Cardinal, 35 tells how many dollars she spent.

75. Answers will vary.

76. Answers will vary. Examples: The set of people in the class who were born on the moon. The set of automobiles that get 400 miles on a gallon of gas. The set of fish that can talk.

77. Answers will vary.
78. a) Answers will vary. Examples: The set of actors, the set of men, the set of men in the movie, Meet Joe Black, the set of men in the movie, Fight Club, the set of men mentioned in Shania Twain's song, That Don't Impress Me Much.
    b) The set of all the people in the world.

Exercise Set 2.2

1. Set A is a **subset** of set B, symbolized by $A \subseteq B$, if and only if all the elements of set A are also elements of set B.
2. Set A is a **proper subset** of set B, symbolized by $A \subset B$, if and only if all the elements of set A are also elements of set B and set A $\neq$ set B.
3. If $A \subseteq B$, then every element of set A is also an element of set B. If $A \subset B$, then every element of set A is also an element of set B and set A $\neq$ set B.
4. 2^n
5. $2^n - 1$
6. No, if two sets are equal they cannot be proper subsets.

7. False, English is an element, not a subset.
8. False, { } is a subset, not an element.
9. True, { } is a subset of every set.
10. False, red is an element, not a proper subset.
11. True, 5 is not an element of {2, 4, 6}.
12. False, Pete and Mike are not in the second set.
13. False, the set {∅} contains the element ∅.
14. True, {1} is a subset of {1, 5, 9}.
15. True, { } and ∅ each represent the empty set.
16. False, 0 is a number and { } is a set.
17. False, the set {0} contains the element 0.
18. True, {1, 5, 9} is a subset of {1, 9, 5}.
19. False, {5} is a subset, not an element.
20. True, {3, 5, 9} = {3, 9, 5}.
21. False, no set is a proper subset of itself.
22. True, the elements of the set are themselves sets.
23. True, {apple, orange, plum} is a subset of {plum, orange, apple}.
24. True, {b, a, t} is a subset of {t, a, b}.
25. $B \subseteq A, B \subset A$
26. $A = B, A \subseteq B, B \subseteq A$
27. $A \subseteq B, A \subset B$
28. none
29. $B \subseteq A, B \subset A$
30. $B \subseteq A, B \subset A$
31. $A = B, A \subseteq B, B \subseteq A$
32. $A \subseteq B, A \subset B$
33. { } is the only subset.
34. { }, {O}
35. { }, {car}, {boat}, {car, boat}
36. { }, {apple}, {peach}, {banana}, {apple, peach}, {apple, banana}, {peach, banana}, {apple, peach, banana}
37. a) { }, {a}, {b}, {c}, {d}, {a, b}, {a, c}, {a, d}, {b, c}, {b, d}, {c, d}, {a, b, c}, {a, b, d}, {a, c, d}, {b, c, d}, {a, b, c, d}
    b) All the sets in part a) are proper subsets of A except {a, b, c, d}.
38. a) $2^8 = 2 \times 2 \times 2 \times 2 \times 2 \times 2 \times 2 \times 2 = 256$
    b) $2^8 - 1 = 256 - 1 = 255$
39. True, every proper subset is a subset.
40. False, A could be equal to B.
41. False, no set is a proper subset of itself.
42. True, every set is a subset of itself.
43. True, ∅ is a proper subset of every set except itself.
44. True, ∅ is a subset of every set.
45. True, every set is a subset of the universal set.
46. False, a set cannot be a proper subset of itself.

47. True, $\varnothing$ is a proper subset of every set except itself and U $\neq \varnothing$.

48. False, the only subset of $\varnothing$ is itself and U $\neq \varnothing$.

49. True, $\varnothing$ is a subset of every set.

50. False, U is not a subset of $\varnothing$. (See answer for #48.)

51. The number of options is equal to the number of subsets of {RAM, modem, video card, hard drive, processor, sound card}, which is $2^6 = 2 \times 2 \times 2 \times 2 \times 2 \times 2 = 64$.

52. The number of variations is equal to the number of subsets of the set, which is $2^6 = 64$.

53. The number of variations is equal to the number of subsets of the set, which is
$2^7 = 2 \times 2 \times 2 \times 2 \times 2 \times 2 \times 2 = 128$.

54. The number of variations is equal to the number of subsets of the set, which is $2^7 = 128$.

55. E = F since they are both subsets of each other.

56. Count the number of boys then count the number of girls. If the number is the same, then they are equivalent.

57. a) Yes, because a is a member of set D.
b) No, c is an element of set D.
c) Yes, each element of {a, b} is an element of set D.

58. a) Each person has 2 choices, namely yes or no. $2 \times 2 \times 2 \times 2 = 16$
b) YYYY, YYYN, YYNY, YNYY, NYYY, YYNN, YNYN, YNNY, NYNY, NNYY, NYYN, YNNN, NYNN, NNYN, NNNY, NNNN
c) 5 out of 16

Exercise Set 2.3

1.
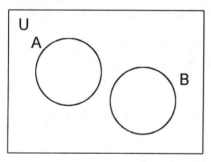

2.
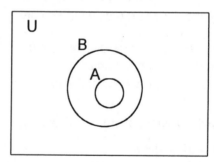

3.
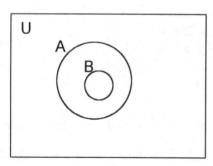

4.
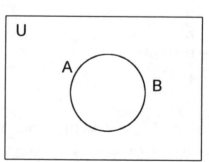

5.
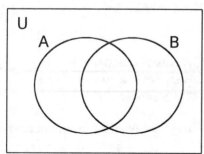

6. Determine the elements that are in the universal set that are not in set A.
7. Combine the elements from set A and set B into one set. List any element that is contained in both sets only once.
8. Take the elements common to both set A and set B.
9. a) Or is generally interpreted to mean union.
   b) And is generally interpreted to mean intersection.
10. $n(A \cup B) = n(A) + n(B) - n(A \cap B)$
11. Region II, the intersection of the two sets.
12. Region IV which contains any element not belonging to either set.

13.

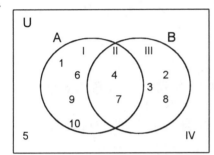

14.

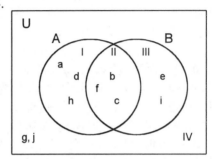

15.

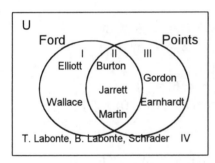

16.

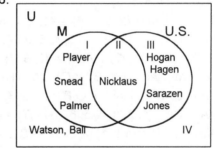

17. The set of U.S. senators who did not vote in favor of the Hartley-Domingo bill.
18. The set of marbles in the box that contain no blue coloring.
19. The set of universities in the U.S. that do not have the word State in their name.
20. The set of universities in the U.S. that do not have the word South in their name.
21. The set of universities in the U.S. that have the word State or the word South in their name.
22. The set of universities in the U.S. that have the words State and South in their name.
23. The set of universities in the U.S. that have the word State in their name and do not have the word South in their name.
24. The set of universities in the U.S. that have the word State in their name or do not have the word South in their name.
25. The set of U.S. corporations whose headquarters are in the state of New York and whose chief executive officer is a woman.
26. The set of U.S. corporations whose headquarters are in the state of New York or that employs at least 100 people.
27. The set of U.S. corporations whose chief executive officer is a woman and who do not employ at least 100 people.
28. The set of U.S. corporations whose headquarters are in the state of New York or whose chief executive officer is a woman or that employs at least 100 people.
29. The set of U.S. corporations whose headquarters are in the state of New York and whose chief executive officer is a woman and who employs at least 100 people.

30. The set of U.S. corporations whose headquarters are not in the state of New York or who do not employ at least 100 people.

31. B = {a, f, g, h, r}

32. A = {a, b, c, h, t, w}

33. U = {a, b, c, f, g, h, m, p, r, t, w, z}

34. A ∩ B = {a, b, c, h, t, w} ∩ {a, f, g, h, r} = {a, h}

35. A ∪ B = {a, b, c, h, t, w} ∪ {a, f, g, h, r} = {a, b, c, f, g, h, r, t, w}

36. (A ∪ B)' From #35, A ∪ B = {a, b, c, f, g, h, r, t, w}. (A ∪ B)' = {a, b, c, f, g, h, r, t, w}' = {m, p, z}

37. (A ∩ B)' From #34, A ∩ B = {a, h}. (A ∩ B)' = {a, h}' = {b, c, f, g, m, p, r, t, w, z}

38. A' ∩ B = {a, b, c, h, t, w}' ∩ {a, f, g, h, r} = {f, g, m, p, r, z} ∩ {a, f, g, h, r} = {f, g, r}

39. A = {L, Δ, @, *, $}

40. B = {*, $, R, □}

41. U = {L, Δ, @, *, $, R, □, ∞, Σ, Z}

42. A ∪ B = {L, Δ, @, *, $} ∪ {*, $, R, □} = {L, Δ, @, *, $, R, □}

43. A ∩ B = {L, Δ, @, *, $} ∩ {*, $, R, □} = {*, $}

44. A ∪ B' = {L, Δ, @, *, $} ∪ {*, $, R, □}' = {L, Δ, @, *, $} ∪ {L, Δ, @, ∞, Σ, Z} = {L, Δ, @, *, $, ∞, Σ, Z}

45. A' ∩ B = {L, Δ, @, *, $}' ∩ {*, $, R, □} = {R, □, ∞, Σ, Z} ∩ {*, $, R, □} = {R, □}

46. (A ∪ B)' From #42, A ∪ B = {L, Δ, @, *, $, R, □}. (A ∪ B)' = {L, Δ, @, *, $, R, □}' = {∞, Σ, Z}

47. A ∪ B = {1, 2, 4, 5, 8} ∪ {2, 3, 4, 6} = {1, 2, 3, 4, 5, 6, 8}

48. A ∩ B = {1, 2, 4, 5, 8} ∩ {2, 3, 4, 6} = {2, 4}

49. B' = {2, 3, 4, 6}' = {1, 5, 7, 8}

50. A ∪ B' = {1, 2, 4, 5, 8} ∪ {2, 3, 4, 6}' = {1, 2, 4, 5, 8} ∪ {1, 5, 7, 8} = {1, 2, 4, 5, 7, 8}

51. (A ∪ B)' From #47, A ∪ B = {1, 2, 3, 4, 5, 6, 8}. (A ∪ B)' = {1, 2, 3, 4, 5, 6, 8}' = {7}

52. A' ∩ B' = {1, 2, 4, 5, 8}' ∩ {2, 3, 4, 6}' = {3, 6, 7} ∩ {1, 5, 7, 8} = {7}

53. (A ∪ B)' ∩ B From #51, (A ∪ B)' = {7}. (A ∪ B)' ∩ B = {7} ∩ {2, 3, 4, 6} = { }

54. (A ∪ B) ∩ (A ∪ B)' From #47, A ∪ B = {1, 2, 3, 4, 5, 6, 8} and from #51, (A ∪ B)' = {7}.
    (A ∪ B) ∩ (A ∪ B)' = {1, 2, 3, 4, 5, 6, 8} ∩ {7} = { }

55. (B ∪ A)' ∩ (B' ∪ A') From #51, (A ∪ B)' = (B ∪ A)' = {7}.
    (B ∪ A)' ∩ (B' ∪ A') = {7} ∩ ({2, 3, 4, 6}' ∪ {1, 2, 4, 5, 8}') = {7} ∩ ({1, 5, 7, 8} ∪ {3, 6, 7})
    = {7} ∩ {1, 3, 5, 6, 7, 8} = {7}

56. A' ∪ (A ∩ B) From #48, A ∩ B = {2, 4}. A' ∪ (A ∩ B) = {1, 2, 4, 5, 8}' ∪ {2, 4} = {3, 6, 7} ∪ {2, 4}
    = {2, 3, 4, 6, 7}

57. A' = {a, c, d, f, g, i}' = {b, e, h, j, k}

58. B ∪ C = {b, c, d, f, g} ∪ {a, b, f, i, j} = {a, b, c, d, f, g, i, j}

59. A ∩ C = {a, c, d, f, g, i} ∩ {a, b, f, i, j} = {a, f, i}

60. A' ∪ B = {a, c, d, f, g, i}' ∪ {b, c, d, f, g} = {b, e, h, j, k} ∪ {b, c, d, f, g} = {b, c, d, e, f, g, h, j, k}

61. (A ∩ C)' From #59, A ∩ C = {a, f, i}. (A ∩ C)' = {a, f, i}' = {b, c, d, e, g, h, j, k}

62. (A ∩ C) ∪ B From #59, A ∩ C = {a, f, i}. (A ∩ C) ∪ B = {a, f, i} ∪ {b, c, d, f, g} = {a, b, c, d, f, g, i}

63. A ∪ (C ∩ B)' = {a, c, d, f, g, i} ∪ ({a, b, f, i, j} ∩ {b, c, d, f, g})' = {a, c, d, f, g, i} ∪ {b, f}'
    = {a, c, d, f, g, i} ∪ {a, c, d, e, g, h, i, j, k} = {a, c, d, e, f, g, h, i, j, k}

64. A ∪ (C' ∪ B') = {a, c, d, f, g, i} ∪ ({a, b, f, i, j}' ∪ {b, c, d, f, g}')
    = {a, c, d, f, g, i} ∪ ({c, d, e, g, h, k} ∪ {a, e, h, i, j, k}) = {a, c, d, f, g, i} ∪ {a, c, d, e, g, h, i, j, k}
    = {a, c, d, e, f, g, h, i, j, k}

65. A' ∩ (B ∩ C) From #63, B ∩ C = {b, f}. A' ∩ (B ∩ C) = {a, c, d, f, g, i}' ∩ {b, f}
    = {b, e, h, j, k} ∩ {b, f} = {b}

66. $(C \cap B) \cap (A' \cap B)$ From #63, $C \cap B = \{b, f\}$. $(C \cap B) \cap (A' \cap B)$
    $= \{b, f\} \cap (\{a, c, d, f, g, i\}' \cap \{b, c, d, f, g\}) = \{b, f\} \cap (\{b, e, h, j, k\} \cap \{b, c, d, f, g\}) = \{b, f\} \cap \{b\} = \{b\}$

For exercises 67 - 80: U = {1, 2, 3, 4, 5, 6, 7, 8, 9}, A = {1, 3, 5, 7, 9}, B = {2, 4, 6, 8}, C = {1 ,2, 3, 4, 5}

67. $A \cap B = \{1, 3, 5, 7, 9\} \cap \{2, 4, 6, 8\} = \{\ \}$
68. $A \cup B = \{1, 3, 5, 7, 9\} \cup \{2, 4, 6, 8\} = \{1, 2, 3, 4, 5, 6, 7, 8, 9\} = U$
69. $A' \cup B = \{1, 3, 5, 7, 9\}' \cup \{2, 4, 6, 8\} = \{2, 4, 6, 8\} \cup \{2, 4, 6, 8\} = \{2, 4, 6, 8\} = B$
70. $(B \cup C)' = (\{2, 4, 6, 8\} \cup \{1, 2, 3, 4, 5\})' = \{1, 2, 3, 4, 5, 6, 8\}' = \{7, 9\}$
71. $A \cap C' = \{1, 3, 5, 7, 9\} \cap \{1, 2, 3, 4, 5\}' = \{1, 3, 5, 7, 9\} \cap \{6, 7, 8, 9\} = \{7, 9\}$
72. $A \cap B' = \{1, 3, 5, 7, 9\} \cap \{2, 4, 6, 8\}' = \{1, 3, 5, 7, 9\} \cap \{1, 3, 5, 7, 9\} = \{1, 3, 5, 7, 9\} = A$
73. $(B \cap C)' = (\{2, 4, 6, 8\} \cap \{1, 2, 3, 4, 5\})' = \{2, 4\}' = \{1, 3, 5, 6, 7, 8, 9\}$
74. $(A \cup B) \cap C$ From #68, $A \cup B = \{1, 2, 3, 4, 5, 6, 7, 8, 9\}$.
    $(A \cup B) \cap C = \{1, 2, 3, 4, 5, 6, 7, 8, 9\} \cap \{1, 2, 3, 4, 5\} = \{1, 2, 3, 4, 5\} = C$
75. $(C \cap B) \cup A$ From #73, $C \cap B = \{2, 4\}$. $(C \cap B) \cup A = \{2, 4\} \cup \{1, 3, 5, 7, 9\} = \{1, 2, 3, 4, 5, 7, 9\}$
76. $(C \cup A) \cap B = (\{1, 2, 3, 4, 5\} \cup \{1, 3, 5, 7, 9\}) \cap \{2, 4, 6, 8\} = \{1, 2, 3, 4, 5, 7, 9\} \cap \{2, 4, 6, 8\} = \{2, 4\}$
77. $(A' \cup C) \cap B = (\{1, 3, 5, 7, 9\}' \cup \{1, 2, 3, 4, 5\}) \cap \{2, 4, 6, 8\} = (\{2, 4, 6, 8\} \cup \{1, 2, 3, 4, 5\}) \cap \{2, 4, 6, 8\}$
    $= \{1, 2, 3, 4, 5, 6, 8\} \cap \{2, 4, 6, 8\} = \{2, 4, 6, 8\} = B$
78. $(A \cap B') \cup C$ From #72, $A \cap B' = \{1, 3, 5, 7, 9\}$. $(A \cap B') \cup C = \{1, 3, 5, 7, 9\} \cup \{1, 2, 3, 4, 5\}$
    $= \{1, 2, 3, 4, 5, 7, 9\}$
79. $(A \cup B)' \cap C$ From #68, $A \cup B = \{1, 2, 3, 4, 5, 6, 7, 8, 9\}$.
    $(A \cup B)' \cap C = \{1, 2, 3, 4, 5, 6, 7, 8, 9\}' \cap \{1, 2, 3, 4, 5\} = \{\ \} \cap \{1, 2, 3, 4, 5\} = \{\ \}$
80. $(A \cap C)' \cap B = (\{1, 3, 5, 7, 9\} \cap \{1, 2, 3, 4, 5\})' \cap \{2, 4, 6, 8\} = \{1, 3, 5\}' \cap \{2, 4, 6, 8\}$
    $= \{2, 4, 6, 7, 8, 9\} \cap \{2, 4, 6, 8\} = \{2, 4, 6, 8\} = B$

81. A set and its complement will always be disjoint since the complement of a set is all of the elements in the universal set that are not in the set. Therefore, a set and its complement will have no elements in common. For example, if U = {1, 2, 3, 4, 5, 6} and A = {1, 2, 5}, then A' = {3, 4, 6}.
    $A \cap A' = \{1, 2, 5\} \cap \{3, 4, 6\} = \{\ \}$
82. $n(A \cap B) = 0$ when A and B are disjoint. For example, if U = {1, 2, 3, 4, 5, 6}, A = {1, 2, 5}, B = {3, 4}, then
    $A \cap B = \{\ \}$. $n(A \cap B) = 0$
83. Let A = {students on the baseball team} and B = {students on the football team}.
    $n(A \cup B) = n(A) + n(B) - n(A \cap B) = 16 + 35 - 7 = 44$
84. Let A = {visitors who visited the Hollywood Bowl} and B = {visitors who visited Disneyland}.
    $n(A \cup B) = n(A) + n(B) - n(A \cap B) = 27 + 38 - 16 = 49$
85. a) $A \cup B = \{a, b, c, d\} \cup \{b, d, e, f, g, h\} = \{a, b, c, d, e, f, g, h\}$, $n(A \cup B) = 8$,
    $A \cap B = (a, b, c, d) \cap \{b, d, e, f, g, h\} = \{b, d\}$, $n(A \cap B) = 2$.
    $n(A) + n(B) - n(A \cap B) = 4 + 6 - 2 = 8$
    Therefore, $n(A \cup B) = n(A) + n(B) - n(A \cap B)$.
    b) Answers will vary.
    c) Elements in the intersection of A and B are counted twice in n(A) + n(B).
86. $A \cap B'$ defines Region I. $A \cap B$ defines Region II. $B \cap A'$ defines Region III.
    $A' \cap B'$ or $(A \cup B)'$ defines Region IV.
87. $A \cup B = \{1, 2, 3, 4, ...\} \cup \{4, 8, 12, 16, ...\} = \{1, 2, 3, 4, ...\} = A$
88. $A \cap B = \{1, 2, 3, 4, ...\} \cap \{4, 8, 12, 16, ...\} = \{4, 8, 12, 16, ...\} = B$
89. $B \cap C = \{4, 8, 12, 16, ...\} \cap \{2, 4, 6, 8, ...\} = \{4, 8, 12, 16, ...\} = B$
90. $B \cup C = \{4, 8, 12, 16, ...\} \cup \{2, 4, 6, 8, ...\} = \{2, 4, 6, 8, ...\} = C$
91. $A \cap C = \{1, 2, 3, 4, ...\} \cap \{2, 4, 6, 8, ...\} = \{2, 4, 6, 8, ...\} = C$
92. $A' \cap C = \{1, 2, 3, 4, ...\}' \cap \{2, 4, 6, 8, ...\} = \{0\} \cap \{2, 4, 6, 8, ...\} = \{\ \}$

93. B' ∩ C = {4, 8, 12, 16, ...}' ∩ {2, 4, 6, 8, ...} = {0, 1, 2, 3, 5, 6, 7, 9, 10, 11, 13, 14, 15, ...} ∩ {2, 4, 6, 8, ...}
    = {2, 6, 10, 14, 18, ...}

94. (B ∪ C)' ∪ C From #90, B ∪ C = C. (B ∪ C)' ∪ C = C' ∪ C = {2, 4, 6, 8, ...}' ∪ {2, 4, 6, 8, ...}
    = {0, 1, 2, 3, 4, ...} = U

95. (A ∩ C) ∩ B' From #91, A ∩ C = C. (A ∩ C) ∩ B' = C ∩ B'.
    From #93, B' ∩ C = C ∩ B' = {2, 6, 10, 14, 18, ...}

96. U' ∩ (A ∪ B) From #87, A ∪ B = A. U' ∩ (A ∪ B) = U' ∩ A = { } ∩ {1, 2, 3, 4, ...} = { }

97. A ∪ A' = U

98. A ∩ A' = { }

99. A ∪ ∅ = A

100. A' ∪ U = U

101. A ∩ ∅ = ∅

102. A ∪ U = U

103. A ∩ U = A

104. A ∩ U' = A ∩ { } = { }

105. If A ∩ B = B, then B ⊆ A.

106. If A ∪ B = B, then A ⊆ B.

107. If A ∩ B = ∅, then A and B are disjoint sets.

108. If A ∪ B = A, then B ⊆ A.

109. If A ∩ B = A, then A ⊆ B.

110. If A ∪ B = ∅, then A = ∅ and B = ∅.

111. A - B = {b, c, e, f, g, h} - {a, b, c, g, i} = {e, f, h}

112. B - A = {a, b, c, g, i} - {b, c, e, f, g, h} = {a, i}

113. A' - B = {b, c, e, f, g, h}' - {a, b, c, g, i}
     = {a, d, i, j, k} - {a, b, c, g, i} = {d, j, k}

114. A - B' = {b, c, e, f, g, h} - {a, b, c, g, i}'
     = {b, c, e, f, g, h} - {d, e, f, h, j, k} = {b, c, g}

115. A - B = {2, 4, 5, 7, 9, 11, 13} - {1, 2, 4, 5, 6, 7, 8, 9,11} = {13}

116. B - A = {1, 2, 4, 5, 6, 7, 8, 9, 11} - {2, 4, 5, 7, 9, 11, 13} = {1, 6, 8}

117. (A - B)' From # 115, A - B = {13}.
     (A - B)' = {13}'
     = {1, 2, 3, 4, 5, 6, 7, 8, 9, 10, 11, 12, 14, 15}

118. A - B' = {2, 4, 5, 7, 9, 11, 13} - {1, 2, 4, 5, 6, 7, 8, 9, 11}' = {2, 4, 5, 7, 9, 11, 13} - {3, 10, 12, 13, 14, 15} = {2, 4, 5, 7, 9, 11}

119. (B - A)' From #116, B - A = {1, 6, 8}.
     (B - A)' = {1, 6, 8}' = {2, 3, 4, 5, 7, 9, 10, 11, 12, 13, 14, 15}

120. A ∩ (A - B) From #115, A - B = {13}.
     A ∩ (A - B) = {2, 4, 5, 7, 9, 11, 13} ∩ {13}
     = {13}

Exercise Set 2.4

1. Region V, the intersection of all three sets.

2. Regions II, IV, VI

3. A ∩ B is represented by regions II and V. If A ∩ B contains 10 elements and region V contains 6 elements, then region II contains 10 - 6 = 4 elements.

4. B ∩ C is represented by regions V and VI. If B ∩ C contains 12 elements and region V contains 4 elements, then region VI contains 12 - 4 = 8 elements.

5. (A ∪ B)' = A' ∩ B', (A ∩ B)' = A' ∪ B'

6. a) Yes.

   $A \cup B = \{1, 4, 5\} \cup \{1, 4, 5\} = \{1, 4, 5\}$

   $A \cap B = \{1, 4, 5\} \cap \{1, 4, 5\} = \{1, 4, 5\}$

   b) No, one specific case cannot be used as proof.

   c)

$A \cup B$		$A \cap B$	
Set	Regions	Set	Regions
A	I, II	A	I, II
B	II, III	B	II, III
$A \cup B$	I, II, III	$A \cap B$	II

Since the two statements are not represented by the same regions, $A \cup B \neq A \cap B$ for all sets A and B.

7.

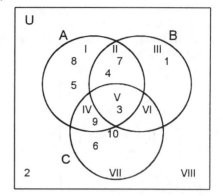

8.

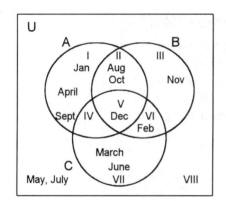

9.

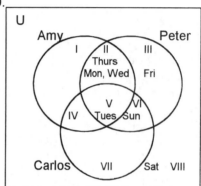

. 10.

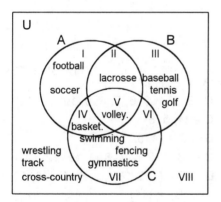

11.

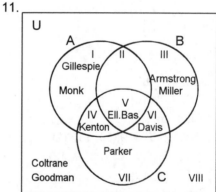

12.

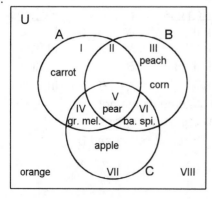

13.

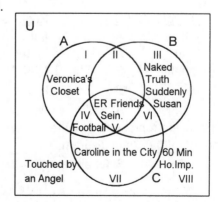

14. A = {Germany, Norway, Russia, Austria, Canada}, B = {Germany, Norway, Russia, Canada, U.S.}, C = {Germany, Austria, Finland}, A: at least 15 medals, B: at least 6 gold, C: at least 6 bronze

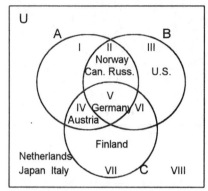

15. Levis, V

16. Tommy Hilfiger, VII

17. Nike, VI

18. London Fog, VI

19. Fruit of the Loom, IV

20. Reebok, V

21. Victoria's Secret, VII

22. Hanes Her Way, V

23. L.L. Bean, VI

24. Nike, IV

25. Levis, V

26. Tommy Hilfiger, VII

27. VI

28. III

29. IV

30. VIII

31. I

32. III

33. V

34. III

35. II

36. VIII

37. VII

38. VI

39. I

40. VII

41. VIII

42. V

43. VI

44. III

45. A = {1, 2, 3, 4, 5, 6}

46. B = {3, 4, 5, 7, 8, 9, 12}

47. C = {4, 5, 6, 7, 8, 10}

48. U = {1, 2, 3, 4, 5, 6, 7, 8, 9, 10, 11, 12}

49. A ∩ B = {3, 4, 5}

50. A ∩ C = {4, 5, 6}

51. (B ∩ C)' = {1, 2, 3, 6, 9, 10, 11, 12}

52. A ∩ B ∩ C = {4, 5}

53. A ∪ B = {1, 2, 3, 4, 5, 6, 7, 8, 9, 12}

54. B ∪ C = {3, 4, 5, 6, 7, 8, 9, 10, 12}

55. (A ∪ C)' = {9, 11, 12}

56. A ∪ B ∪ C = {1, 2, 3, 4, 5, 6, 7, 8, 9, 10, 12}

57. A' = {7, 8, 9, 10, 11, 12}

58. (A ∪ B ∪ C)' = {11}

59. (A ∪ B)'   A' ∩ B'

Set	Regions	Set	Regions
A	I, II	A	I, II
B	II, III	A'	III, IV
A ∪ B	I, II, III	B	II, III
(A ∪ B)'	IV	B'	I, IV
		A' ∩ B'	IV

Both statements are represented by the same region, IV, of the Venn diagram. Therefore, (A ∪ B)' = A' ∩ B' for all sets A and B.

60. (A ∪ B)'   A' ∩ B

Set	Regions	Set	Regions
A	I, II	A	I, II
B	II, III	A'	III, IV
A ∪ B	I, II, III	B	II, III
(A ∪ B)'	IV	A' ∩ B	III

Since the two statements are not represented by the same regions, (A ∪ B)' ≠ A' ∩ B for all sets A and B.

61. A' ∪ B'   A ∩ B

Set	Regions	Set	Regions
A	I, II	A	I, II
A'	III, IV	B	II, III
B	II, III	A ∩ B	II
B'	I, IV		
A' ∪ B'	I, III, IV		

Since the two statements are not
represented by the same regions,
A' ∪ B' ≠ A ∩ B for all sets A and B.

62. (A ∪ B)'   (A ∩ B)'

Set	Regions	Set	Regions
A	I, II	A	I, II
B	II, III	B	II, III
A ∪ B	I, II, III	A ∩ B	II
(A ∪ B)'	IV	(A ∩ B)'	I, III, IV

Since the two statements are not
represented by the same regions,
(A ∪ B)' ≠ (A ∩ B)' for all sets A and B.

63. A' ∪ B'   (A ∪ B)'

Set	Regions	Set	Regions
A	I, II	A	I, II
A'	III, IV	B	II, III
B	II, III	A ∪ B	I, II, III
B'	I, IV	(A ∪ B)'	IV
A' ∪ B'	I, III, IV		

Since the two statements are not
represented by the same regions,
A' ∪ B' ≠ (A ∪ B)' for all sets A and B.

64. A ∩ B'   A' ∪ B

Set	Regions	Set	Regions
A	I, II	A	I, II
B	II, III	A'	III, IV
B'	I, IV	B	II, III
A ∩ B'	I	A' ∪ B	II, III, IV

Since the two statements are not
represented by the same regions,
A ∩ B' ≠ A' ∪ B for all sets A and B.

65. (A ∩ B')'   A' ∪ B

Set	Regions	Set	Regions
A	I, II	A	I, II
B	II, III	A'	III, IV
B'	I, IV	B	II, III
A ∩ B'	I	A' ∪ B	II, III, IV
(A ∩ B')'	II, III, IV		

Both statements are represented by the
same regions, II, III, IV, of the Venn
diagram. Therefore, (A ∩ B')' = A' ∪ B for
all sets A and B.

66. A' ∩ B'   (A' ∩ B')'

Set	Regions	Set	Regions
A	I, II	A	I, II
A'	III, IV	A'	III, IV
B	II, III	B	II, III
B'	I, IV	B'	I, IV
A' ∩ B'	IV	A' ∩ B'	IV
		(A' ∩ B')'	I, II, III

Since the two statements are not
represented by the same regions,
A' ∩ B' ≠ (A' ∩ B')' for all sets A and B.

67.   A ∪ (B ∩ C)

Set	Regions
B	II, III, V, VI
C	IV, V, VI, VII
B ∩ C	V, VI
A	I, II, IV, V
A ∪ (B ∩ C)	I, II, IV, V, VI

(A ∪ B) ∩ C

Set	Regions
A	I, II, IV, V
B	II, III, V, VI
A ∪ B	I, II, III, IV, V, VI
C	IV, V, VI, VII
(A ∪ B) ∩ C	IV, V, VI

Since the two statements are not represented by the same regions,
A ∪ (B ∩ C) ≠ (A ∪ B) ∩ C for all sets A, B, and C.

68. $A \cup (B \cap C)$ $\qquad\qquad\qquad\qquad\qquad$ $(B \cap C) \cup A$

Set	Regions	Set	Regions
B	II, III, V, VI	B	II, III, V, VI
C	IV, V, VI, VII	C	IV, V, VI, VII
$B \cap C$	V, VI	$B \cap C$	V, VI
A	I, II, IV, V	A	I, II, IV, V
$A \cup (B \cap C)$	I, II, IV, V, VI	$(B \cap C) \cup A$	I, II, IV, V, VI

Both statements are represented by the same regions, I, II, IV, V, VI, of the Venn diagram. Therefore, $A \cup (B \cap C) = (B \cap C) \cup A$ for all sets A, B, and C.

69. $A \cap (B \cup C)$ $\qquad\qquad\qquad\qquad\qquad$ $(B \cup C) \cap A$

Set	Regions	Set	Regions
B	II, III, V, VI	B	II, III, V, VI
C	IV , V, VI, VII	C	IV, V, VI, VII
$B \cup C$	II, III, IV, V, VI, VII	$B \cup C$	II, III, IV, V, VI, VII
A	I, II, IV, V	A	I, II, IV, V
$A \cap (B \cup C)$	II, IV, V	$(B \cup C) \cap A$	II, IV, V

Both statements are represented by the same regions, II, IV, V, of the Venn diagram. Therefore, $A \cap (B \cup C) = (B \cup C) \cap A$ for all sets A, B, and C.

70. $A' \cup (B \cap C)$ $\qquad\qquad\qquad\qquad\qquad$ $A \cap (B \cup C)'$

Set	Regions	Set	Regions
B	II, III, V, VI	B	II, III, V, VI
C	IV, V, VI, VII	C	IV, V, VI, VII
$B \cap C$	V, VI	$B \cup C$	II, III, IV, V, VI, VII
A	I, II, IV, V	$(B \cup C)'$	I, VIII
A'	III, VI, VII, VIII	A	I, II, IV, V
$A' \cup (B \cap C)$	III, V, VI, VII, VIII	$A \cap (B \cup C)'$	I

Since the two statements are not represented by the same regions,
$A' \cup (B \cap C) \neq A \cap (B \cup C)'$ for all sets A, B, and C.

71. $A \cap (B \cup C)$ $\qquad\qquad\qquad\qquad\qquad$ $(A \cap B) \cup (A \cap C)$

Set	Regions	Set	Regions
B	II, III, V, VI	A	I, II, IV, V
C	IV, V, VI, VII	B	II, III, V, VI
$B \cup C$	II, III, IV, V, VI, VII	$A \cap B$	II, V
A	I, II, IV, V	C	IV, V, VI, VII
$A \cap (B \cup C)$	II, IV, V	$A \cap C$	IV, V
		$(A \cap B) \cup (A \cap C)$	II, IV, V

Both statements are represented by the same regions, II, IV, V, of the Venn diagram. Therefore, $A \cap (B \cup C) = (A \cap B) \cup (A \cap C)$ for all sets A, B, and C.

72. $A \cup (B \cap C)$ $(A \cup B) \cap (A \cup C)$

Set	Regions	Set	Regions
B	II, III, V, VI	A	I, II, IV, V
C	IV, V, VI, VII	B	II, III, V, VI
B ∩ C	V, VI	A ∪ B	I, II, III, IV, V, VI
A	I, II, IV, V	C	IV, V, VI, VII
A ∪ (B ∩ C)	I, II, IV, V, VI	A ∪ C	I, II, IV, V, VI, VII
		(A ∪ B) ∩ (A ∪ C)	I, II, IV, V, VI

Both statements are represented by the same regions, I, II, IV, V, VI, of the Venn
diagram. Therefore, $A \cup (B \cap C) = (A \cup B) \cap (A \cup C)$ for all sets A, B, and C.

73. $A \cap (B \cup C)'$ $A \cap (B' \cap C')$

Set	Regions	Set	Regions
B	II, III, V, VI	B	II, III, V, VI
C	IV, V, VI, VII	B'	I, IV, VII, VIII
B ∪ C	II, III, IV, V, VI, VII	C	IV, V, VI, VII
(B ∪ C)'	I, VIII	C'	I, II, III, VIII
A	I, II, IV, V	B' ∩ C'	I, VIII
A ∩ (B ∪ C)'	I	A	I, II, IV, V
		A ∩ (B' ∩ C')	I

Both statements are represented by the same region, I, of the Venn diagram.
Therefore, $A \cap (B \cup C)' = A \cap (B' \cap C')$ for all sets A, B, and C.

74. $(A \cup B) \cap (B \cup C)$ $B \cup (A \cap C)$

Set	Regions	Set	Regions
A	I, II, IV, V	A	I, II, IV, V
B	II, III, V, VI	C	IV, V, VI, VII
A ∪ B	I, II, III, IV, V, VI	A ∩ C	IV, V
C	IV, V, VI, VII	B	II, III, V, VI
B ∪ C	II, III, IV, V, VI, VII	B ∪ (A ∩ C)	II, III, IV, V, VI
(A ∪ B) ∩ (B ∪ C)	II, III, IV, V, VI		

Both statements are represented by the same regions, II, III, IV, V, VI, of the Venn
diagram. Therefore, $(A \cup B) \cap (B \cup C) = B \cup (A \cap C)$ for all sets A, B, and C.

75. $(A \cup B)' \cap C$ $(A' \cup C) \cap (B' \cup C)$

Set	Regions	Set	Regions
A	I, II, IV, V	A	I, II, IV, V
B	II, III, V, VI	A'	III, VI, VII, VIII
A ∪ B	I, II, III, IV, V, VI	C	IV, V, VI, VII
(A ∪ B)'	VII, VIII	A' ∪ C	III, IV, V, VI, VII, VIII
C	IV, V, VI, VII	B	II, III, V, VI
(A ∪ B)' ∩ C	VII	B'	I, IV, VII, VIII
		B' ∪ C	I, IV, V, VI, VII, VIII
		(A' ∪ C) ∩ (B' ∪ C)	IV, V, VI, VII, VIII

Since the two statements are not represented by the same regions, $(A \cup B)' \cap C \neq (A' \cup C) \cap (B' \cup C)$
for all sets A, B, and C.

76. $(C \cap B)' \cup (A \cap B)'$ $A \cap (B \cap C)$

Set	Regions	Set	Regions
C	IV, V, VI, VII	B	II, III, V, VI
B	II, III, V, VI	C	IV, V, VI, VII
$C \cap B$	V, VI	$B \cap C$	V, VI
$(C \cap B)'$	I, II, III, IV, VII, VIII	A	I, II, IV, V
A	I, II, IV, V	$A \cap (B \cap C)$	V
$A \cap B$	II, V		
$(A \cap B)'$	I, III, IV, VI, VII, VIII		
$(C \cap B)' \cup (A \cap B)'$	I, II, III, IV, VI, VII, VIII		

Since the two statements are not represented by the same regions, $(C \cap B)' \cup (A \cap B)' \neq A \cap (B \cap C)$ for all sets A, B, and C.

77. a) $(A \cup B) \cap C = (\{1, 2, 3, 4\} \cup \{3, 6, 7\}) \cap \{6, 7, 9\} = \{1, 2, 3, 4, 6, 7\} \cap \{6, 7, 9\} = \{6, 7\}$
$(A \cap C) \cup (B \cap C) = (\{1, 2, 3, 4\} \cap \{6, 7, 9\}) \cup (\{3, 6, 7\} \cap \{6, 7, 9\}) = \varnothing \cup \{6, 7\} = \{6, 7\}$
Therefore for the specific sets, $(A \cup B) \cap C = (A \cap C) \cup (B \cap C)$.
b) Answers will vary.
c) $(A \cup B) \cap C$ $(A \cap C) \cup (B \cap C)$

Set	Regions	Set	Regions
A	I, II, IV, V	A	I, II, IV, V
B	II, III, V, VI	C	IV, V, VI, VII
$A \cup B$	I, II, III, IV, V, VI	$A \cap C$	IV, V
C	IV, V, VI, VII	B	II, III, V, VI
$(A \cup B) \cap C$	IV, V, VI	$B \cap C$	V, VI
		$(A \cap C) \cup (B \cap C)$	IV, V, VI

Both statements are represented by the same regions, IV, V, VI, of the Venn diagram.
Therefore, $(A \cup B) \cap C = (A \cap C) \cup (B \cap C)$ for all sets A, B, and C.

78. a) $(A \cup C)' \cap B = (\{a, c, d, e, f\} \cup \{a, b, c, d, e\})' \cap \{c, d\} = \{a, b, c, d, e, f\}' \cap \{c, d\}$
   $= \{g, h, i\} \cap \{c, d\} = \varnothing$

$(A \cap C)' \cap B = (\{a, c, d, e, f\} \cap \{a, b, c, d, e\})' \cap \{c, d\} = \{a, c, d, e\}' \cap \{c, d\} = \{b, f, g, h, i\} \cap \{c, d\} = \varnothing$.
Therefore, for the specific sets, $(A \cup C)' \cap B = (A \cap C)' \cap B$.
b) Answers will vary.
c) $(A \cup C)' \cap B$ $(A \cap C)' \cap B$

Set	Regions	Set	Regions
A	I, II, IV, V	A	I, II, IV, V
C	IV, V, VI, VII	C	IV, V, VI, VII
$A \cup C$	I, II, IV, V, VI, VII	$A \cap C$	IV, V
$(A \cup C)'$	III, VIII	$(A \cap C)'$	I, II, III, VI, VII, VIII
B	II, III, V, VI	B	II, III, V, VI
$(A \cup C)' \cap B$	III	$(A \cap C)' \cap B$	II, III, VI

Since the two statements are not represented by the same regions, $(A \cup C)' \cap B \neq (A \cap C)' \cap B$ for all sets A, B, and C.

79.

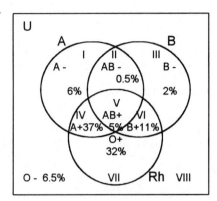

80.

Region	Set	Region	Set
I	$A \cap B' \cap C'$	V	$A \cap B \cap C$
II	$A \cap B \cap C'$	VI	$A' \cap B \cap C$
III	$A' \cap B \cap C'$	VII	$A' \cap B' \cap C$
IV	$A \cap B' \cap C$	VIII	$A' \cap B' \cap C'$

81.a)   A: Male, B: College degree, C: Greater than $30,000

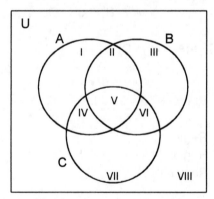

b)   Region V; $A \cap B \cap C$
c)   Region VI; $A' \cap B \cap C$
d)   Region I; $A \cap B' \cap C'$

82. a)

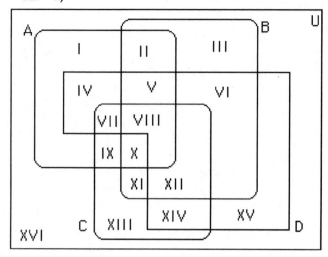

b)

Region	Set	Region	Set
I	$A \cap B' \cap C' \cap D'$	IX	$A \cap B' \cap C \cap D'$
II	$A \cap B \cap C' \cap D'$	X	$A \cap B \cap C \cap D'$
III	$A' \cap B \cap C' \cap D'$	XI	$A' \cap B \cap C \cap D'$
IV	$A \cap B' \cap C' \cap D$	XII	$A' \cap B \cap C \cap D$
V	$A \cap B \cap C' \cap D$	XIII	$A' \cap B' \cap C \cap D'$
VI	$A' \cap B \cap C' \cap D$	XIV	$A' \cap B' \cap C \cap D$
VII	$A \cap B' \cap C \cap D$	XV	$A' \cap B' \cap C' \cap D$
VIII	$A \cap B \cap C \cap D$	XVI	$A' \cap B' \cap C' \cap D'$

83. $n(A \cup B \cup C) = n(A) + n(B) + n(C) - 2n(A \cap B \cap C) - n(A \cap B \cap C') - n(A \cap B' \cap C)$
    $- n(A' \cap B \cap C)$

Exercise Set 2.5

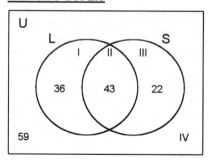

1. a) 36, Region I
   b) 22, Region III
   c) 59, Region IV

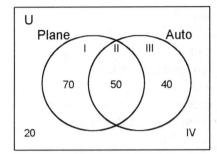

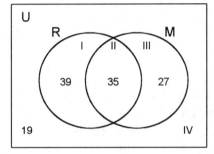

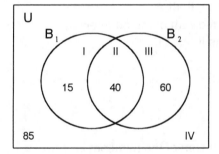

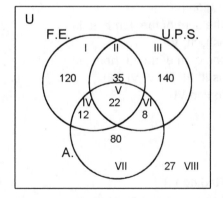

2. a) 70, Region I
   b) 40, Region III
   c) 20, Region IV

3. a) 39, Region I
   b) 27, Region III
   c) 101, the sum of the numbers in
   Regions I, II, III

4. a) 15, Region I
   b) 85, Region IV
   c) No, 100 out of 200 is not a majority.

5. a) 27, Region VIII
   b) 80, Region VII
   c) 340, the sum of the numbers in
   Regions I, III, VII
   d) 55, the sum of the numbers in
   Regions II, IV, VI
   e) 337, the sum of the numbers in
   Regions I, II, III, IV, V, VI

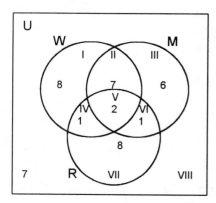

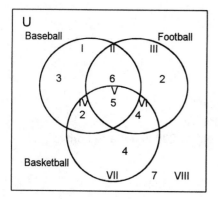

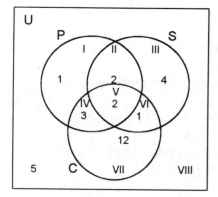

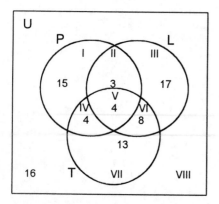

6. a) 7, Region VIII
   b) 22, the sum of the numbers in Regions I, III, VII
   c) 9, the sum of the numbers in Regions II, IV, VI
   d) 7, Region II
   e) 15, the sum of the numbers in Regions III, VI, VII

7. a) 2, Region III
   b) 6, Region II
   c) 22, the sum of the numbers in Regions I, II, III, IV, V, VI
   d) 11, the sum of the numbers in Regions I, II, III
   e) 12, the sum of the numbers in Regions II, IV, VI

8. a) 8, the sum of the numbers in Regions II, IV, V, VI
   b) 1, Region I
   c) 17, the sum of the numbers in Regions I, III, VII
   d) 24, the sum of the numbers in Regions II, III, IV, V, VI, VII
   e) 1, Region VI

9. a) 13, Region VII
   b) 45, the sum of the numbers in Regions I, III, VII
   c) 64, the sum of the numbers in Regions I through VII
   d) 15, the sum of the numbers in Regions II, IV, VI
   e) 16, Region VIII

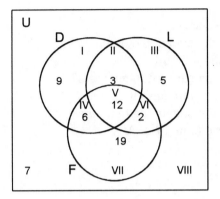

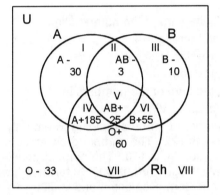

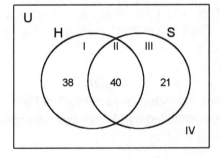

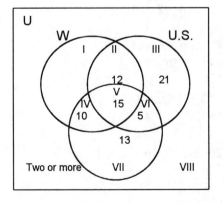

10. a) 5, Region III
    b) 19, Region VII
    c) 2, Region VI
    d) 26, the sum of the numbers in
    Regions III, VI, VII
    e) 7, Region VIII

11. a) 185, Region IV
    b) 10, Region III
    c) 25, Region V
    d) 401, the sum of the numbers in
    Regions I through VIII

12. No. The sum of the numbers in the Venn
    diagram is 99. Molly claims she surveyed
    100 people.

13. The Venn diagram shows the number of cars
    driven by women is 37, the sum of the
    numbers in Regions II, IV, V. This exceeds
    the 35 women the agent claims to have
    surveyed.

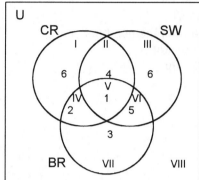

14. a) 6, Region III
    b) 15, the sum of the numbers in Regions I, III, VII
    c) 27, the sum of the numbers in Regions I through VII
    d) 18, the sum of the numbers in Regions II, III, IV, V, VI

15. a) 410, the sum of the numbers in Regions I through VII
    b) 35, Region V
    c) 90, Region VIII
    d) 50, the sum of the numbers in Regions II, IV, VI.

    The number of farmers growing wheat only, Region I, is 125. The number growing corn only, Region III, is 110. The number growing oats only, Region VII, is 90. 60 farmers grew wheat and corn, Regions II and V. 200 farmers grew wheat. Therefore, the sum of the numbers in Regions I, II, IV, V must equal 200. 125 + 60 + number in Region IV = 200. Thus, the number in Region IV is 15.

Exercise Set 2.6

1. An **infinite set** is a set that can be placed in a one-to-one correspondence with a proper subset of itself.

2. If the set can be placed in a one-to-one correspondence with the set of counting numbers it has cardinality aleph-null and is countable.

3. $\{4, 5, 6, 7, 8, \ldots, n+3, \ldots\}$
   $\downarrow\downarrow\downarrow\downarrow\downarrow \quad\quad \downarrow$
   $\{5, 6, 7, 8, 9, \ldots, n+4, \ldots\}$

4. $\{3, 4, 5, 6, 7, \ldots, n+2, \ldots\}$
   $\downarrow\downarrow\downarrow\downarrow\downarrow \quad\quad \downarrow$
   $\{4, 5, 6, 7, 8, \ldots, n+3, \ldots\}$

5. $\{6, 8, 10, 12, 14, \ldots, 2n+4, \ldots\}$
   $\downarrow\downarrow\downarrow\downarrow\downarrow \quad\quad \downarrow$
   $\{8, 10, 12, 14, 16, \ldots, 2n+6, \ldots\}$

6. $\{3, 5, 7, 9, 11, \ldots, 2n+1, \ldots\}$
   $\downarrow\downarrow\downarrow\downarrow\downarrow \quad\quad \downarrow$
   $\{5, 7, 9, 11, 13, \ldots, 2n+3, \ldots\}$

7. $\{4, 7, 10, 13, 16, \ldots, 3n+1, \ldots\}$
   $\downarrow\downarrow\downarrow\downarrow\downarrow \quad\quad \downarrow$
   $\{7, 10, 13, 16, 19, \ldots, 3n+4, \ldots\}$

8. $\{4, 8, 12, 16, 20, \ldots, 4n, \ldots\}$
   $\downarrow\downarrow\downarrow\downarrow\downarrow \quad\quad \downarrow$
   $\{8, 12, 16, 20, 24, \ldots, 4n+4, \ldots\}$

9. $\{6, 11, 16, 21, 26, \ldots, 5n+1, \ldots\}$
   $\downarrow\downarrow\downarrow\downarrow\downarrow \quad\quad \downarrow$
   $\{11, 16, 21, 26, 31, \ldots, 5n+6, \ldots\}$

10. $\{1, \dfrac{1}{2}, \dfrac{1}{3}, \dfrac{1}{4}, \dfrac{1}{5}, \ldots, \dfrac{1}{n}, \ldots\}$
    $\downarrow\downarrow\downarrow\downarrow\downarrow \quad\quad \downarrow$
    $\{\dfrac{1}{2}, \dfrac{1}{3}, \dfrac{1}{4}, \dfrac{1}{5}, \dfrac{1}{6}, \ldots, \dfrac{1}{n+1}, \ldots\}$

11. $\{1, \dfrac{1}{3}, \dfrac{1}{5}, \dfrac{1}{7}, \dfrac{1}{9}, \ldots, \dfrac{1}{2n-1}, \ldots\}$
$\downarrow \quad \downarrow \quad \downarrow \quad \downarrow \quad \downarrow \qquad \downarrow$
$\{\dfrac{1}{3}, \dfrac{1}{5}, \dfrac{1}{7}, \dfrac{1}{9}, \dfrac{1}{11}, \ldots, \dfrac{1}{2n+1}, \ldots\}$

12. $\{\dfrac{5}{8}, \dfrac{6}{8}, \dfrac{7}{8}, \dfrac{8}{8}, \dfrac{9}{8}, \ldots, \dfrac{n+4}{8}, \ldots\}$
$\downarrow \quad \downarrow \quad \downarrow \quad \downarrow \quad \downarrow \qquad \downarrow$
$\{\dfrac{6}{8}, \dfrac{7}{8}, \dfrac{8}{8}, \dfrac{9}{8}, \dfrac{10}{8}, \ldots, \dfrac{n+5}{8}, \ldots\}$

13. $\{1, 2, 3, 4, 5, \ldots, n, \ldots\}$
$\downarrow \downarrow \downarrow \downarrow \downarrow \quad \downarrow$
$\{3, 6, 9, 12, 15, \ldots, 3n, \ldots\}$

14. $\{1, \quad 2, \quad 3, \quad 4, \quad 5, \ldots, \quad n, \ldots\}$
$\downarrow \quad \downarrow \quad \downarrow \quad \downarrow \quad \downarrow \qquad \downarrow$
$\{100, 101, 102, 103, 104, \ldots, n+99, \ldots\}$

15. $\{1, 2, 3, 4, 5, \ldots, \quad n, \ldots\}$
$\downarrow \downarrow \downarrow \downarrow \downarrow \qquad \downarrow$
$\{4, 6, 8, 10, 12, \ldots, 2n+2, \ldots\}$

16. $\{1, 2, 3, 4, 5, \ldots, \quad n, \ldots\}$
$\downarrow \downarrow \downarrow \downarrow \downarrow \qquad \downarrow$
$\{0, 2, 4, 6, 8, \ldots, 2n-2, \ldots\}$

17. $\{1, 2, 3, 4, \quad 5, \ldots, \quad n, \ldots\}$
$\downarrow \downarrow \downarrow \downarrow \quad \downarrow \qquad \downarrow$
$\{2, 5, 8, 11, 14, \ldots, 3n-1, \ldots\}$

18. $\{1, 2, 3, \quad 4, \quad 5, \ldots, \quad n, \ldots\}$
$\downarrow \downarrow \downarrow \quad \downarrow \quad \downarrow \qquad \downarrow$
$\{4, 9, 14, 19, 24, \ldots, 5n-1, \ldots\}$

19. $\{1, \quad 2, \quad 3, \quad 4, \quad 5, \ldots, \quad n, \ldots\}$
$\downarrow \quad \downarrow \quad \downarrow \quad \downarrow \quad \downarrow \qquad \downarrow$
$\{5, 8, 11, 14, 17, \ldots, 3n+2, \ldots\}$

20. $\{1, \quad 2, \quad 3, \quad 4, \quad 5, \ldots, \quad n, \ldots\}$
$\downarrow \quad \downarrow \quad \downarrow \quad \downarrow \quad \downarrow \qquad \downarrow$
$\{\dfrac{1}{2}, \dfrac{1}{4}, \dfrac{1}{6}, \dfrac{1}{8}, \dfrac{1}{10}, \ldots, \dfrac{1}{2n}, \ldots\}$

21. $\{1, \quad 2, \quad 3, \quad 4, \quad 5, \ldots, \quad n, \ldots\}$
$\downarrow \quad \downarrow \quad \downarrow \quad \downarrow \quad \downarrow \qquad \downarrow$
$\{\dfrac{1}{3}, \dfrac{1}{4}, \dfrac{1}{5}, \dfrac{1}{6}, \dfrac{1}{7}, \ldots, \dfrac{1}{n+2}, \ldots\}$

22. $\{1, \quad 2, \quad 3, \quad 4, \quad 5, \ldots, \quad n, \ldots\}$
$\downarrow \quad \downarrow \quad \downarrow \quad \downarrow \quad \downarrow \qquad \downarrow$
$\{\dfrac{1}{2}, \dfrac{2}{3}, \dfrac{3}{4}, \dfrac{4}{5}, \dfrac{5}{6}, \ldots, \dfrac{n}{n+1}, \ldots\}$

23. $\{1, 2, 3, 4, 5, \ldots, n, \ldots\}$
$\downarrow \quad \downarrow \quad \downarrow \quad \downarrow \quad \downarrow \qquad \downarrow$
$\{1, 4, 9, 16, 25, \ldots, n^2, \ldots\}$

24. $\{1, 2, 3, 4, 5, \ldots, n, \ldots\}$
$\downarrow \downarrow \downarrow \downarrow \downarrow \qquad \downarrow$
$\{2, 4, 8, 16, 32, \ldots, 2^n, \ldots\}$

25. $\{1, 2, 3, 4, 5, \ldots, \quad n, \ldots\}$
$\downarrow \downarrow \downarrow \downarrow \downarrow \qquad \downarrow$
$\{3, 9, 27, 81, 243, \ldots, 3^n, \ldots\}$

26. $\{1, \quad 2, \quad 3, \quad 4, \quad 5, \ldots, \quad n, \ldots\}$
$\downarrow \quad \downarrow \quad \downarrow \quad \downarrow \quad \downarrow \qquad \downarrow$
$\{\dfrac{1}{3}, \dfrac{1}{6}, \dfrac{1}{12}, \dfrac{1}{24}, \dfrac{1}{48}, \ldots, \dfrac{1}{3 \times 2^{n-1}}, \ldots\}$

Review Exercises

1. True

2. False, the word best makes the statement not well defined.

3. True

4. False, no set is a proper subset of itself.

5. False, 6, 12, 18, 24, ... are members of both sets.

6. True

7. False, both sets do not contain exactly the same elements.

8. True

9. True

10. True

11. True

12. True

13. True

14. True

15. A = {7, 9, 11, 13, 15}

16. B = {TX, NM, CO, KS, MO, AR}

17. C = {1, 2, 3, 4, ..., 296}

18. D = {9, 10, 11, 12, ..., 96}

19. A = {x | x ∈ N and 72 < x < 100}

20. B = {x | x ∈ N and x > 85}

21. C = {x | x ∈ N and x < 3}

22. D = {x | x ∈ N and 23 ≤ x ≤ 41}

23. A is the set of capital letters in the English alphabet from E through M, inclusive.

24. B is the set of U.S. coins with a value of less than one dollar.

25. C is the set of the last three lowercase letters in the English alphabet.

26. D is the set of numbers greater than or equal to 3 and less than 9.

27. $A \cap B = \{1, 3, 5, 7\} \cap \{5, 7, 9, 13\} = \{5, 7\}$

28. $A \cup B' = \{1, 3, 5, 7\} \cup \{5, 7, 9, 13\}' = \{1, 3, 5, 7\} \cup \{1, 3, 11, 15\} = \{1, 3, 5, 7, 11, 15\}$

29. $A' \cap B = \{1, 3, 5, 7\}' \cap \{5, 7, 9, 13\} = \{9, 11, 13, 15\} \cap \{5, 7, 9, 13\} = \{9, 13\}$

30. $(A \cup B)' \cup C = (\{1, 3, 5, 7\} \cup \{5, 7, 9, 13\})' \cup \{1, 7, 13\} = \{1, 3, 5, 7, 9, 13\}' \cup \{1, 7, 13\}$
    $= \{11, 15\} \cup \{1, 7, 13\} = \{1, 7, 11, 13, 15\}$

31. $2^4 = 2 \times 2 \times 2 \times 2 = 16$

32. $2^4 - 1 = (2 \times 2 \times 2 \times 2) - 1 = 16 - 1 = 15$

33.

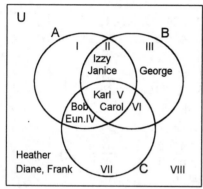

34. $A \cup B = \{a, c, d, e, f, g, i, k\}$

35. $A \cap B' = \{d, i\}$

36. $A \cup B \cup C = \{a, b, c, d, e, f, g, i, k\}$

37. $A \cap B \cap C = \{e\}$

38. $(A \cup B) \cap C = \{a, c, d, e, f, g, i, k\} \cap \{a, b, d, e\} = \{a, d, e\}$

39. $(A \cap B) \cup C = \{e, f, g\} \cup \{a, b, d, e\} = \{a, b, d, e, f, g\}$

40. $(A' \cup B')'$ $A \cap B$

Set	Regions	Set	Regions
A	I, II	A	I, II
A'	III, IV	B	II, III
B	II, III	$A \cap B$	II
B'	I, IV		
A' ∪ B'	I, III, IV		
(A' ∪ B')'	II		

The two statements are represented by the same region, II, of the Venn diagram. Therefore,

$(A' \cup B')' = A \cap B$ for all sets A and B.

41. $(A \cup B') \cup (A \cup C')$ $A \cup (B \cap C)'$

Set	Regions	Set	Regions
A	I, II, IV, V	B	II, III, V, VI
B	II, III, V, VI	C	IV, V, VI, VII
B'	I, IV, VII, VIII	B ∩ C	V, VI
A ∪ B'	I, II, IV, V, VII, VIII	(B ∩ C)'	I, II, III, IV, VII, VIII
C	IV, V, VI, VII	A	I, II, IV, V
C'	I, II, III, VIII	A ∪ (B ∩ C)'	I, II, III, IV, V, VII, VIII
A ∪ C'	I, II, III, IV, V, VIII		
(A ∪ B') ∪ (A ∪ C')	I, II, III, IV, V, VII, VIII		

The two statements are represented by the same regions, I, II, III, IV, V, VII, VIII, of the Venn diagram. Therefore, $(A \cup B') \cup (A \cup C') = A \cup (B \cap C)'$ for all sets A, B, and C.

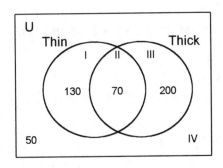

42.   The company paid $450 since the sum of the numbers in Regions I through IV is **450**.

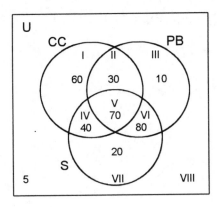

43. a) 315, the sum of the numbers in Regions I through VIII
b) 10, Region III
c) 30, Region II
d) 110, the sum of the numbers in Regions III, VI, VII

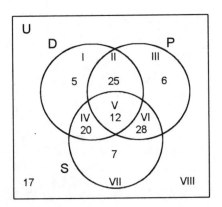

44. a) 5, Region I
b) 18, the sum of the numbers in Regions I, III, VII
c) 73, the sum of the numbers in Regions II, IV, VI
d) 28, Region VI
e) 41, the sum of the numbers in Regions III, VI, VII

45. {2, 4, 6, 8, 10, ..., 2n, ...}
↓ ↓ ↓ ↓ ↓   ↓
{4, 6, 8, 10, 12, ..., 2n + 2, ...}

46. {3, 5, 7, 9, 11, ..., 2n + 1, ...}
↓ ↓ ↓ ↓ ↓   ↓
{5, 7, 9, 11, 13, ..., 2n + 3, ...}

47. {1, 2, 3, 4, 5, ..., n, ...}
↓ ↓ ↓ ↓ ↓   ↓
{5, 8, 11, 14, 17, ..., 3n + 2, ...}

48. {1, 2, 3 , 4, 5, ..., n, ...}
↓ ↓ ↓ ↓ ↓   ↓
{4, 9, 14, 19, 24, ..., 5n - 1, ...}

Chapter Test

1. True

2. False, the sets do not contain exactly the same elements.

3. True

4. False, the second set has no subset that contains the element 7.

5. False, the empty set is a proper subset of every set except itself.

6. False, the set has 2^3 = 2 x 2 x 2 = 8 subsets.

7. True

8. False, $A \cup A' = U$.

9. True

10. A = {1, 2, 3, 4, 5, 6, 7}

11. Set A is the set of natural numbers less than 8.

12. $A \cap B$ = {3, 5, 7, 9} ∩ {7, 9, 11, 13} = {7, 9}

13. $A \cup C'$ = {3, 5, 7, 9} ∪ {3, 11, 15}' = {3, 5, 7, 9} ∪ {5, 7, 9, 13} = {3, 5, 7, 9, 13}

14. $A \cap (B \cap C)'$ = {3, 5, 7, 9} ∩ ({7, 9, 11, 13} ∩ {3, 11, 15})'

    = {3, 5, 7, 9} ∩ {11}' = {3, 5, 7, 9} ∩ {3, 5, 7, 9, 13, 15} = {3, 5, 7, 9} = A

15. $n(A \cap B')$ = n({3, 5, 7, 9} ∩ {7, 9, 11, 13}') = n({3, 5, 7, 9} ∩ {3, 5, 15}) = n({3, 5}) = 2

16.

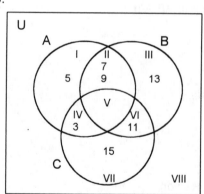

17.   A ∩ (B ∪ C')   (A ∩ B) ∪ (A ∩ C')

Set	Regions
B	II, III, V, VI
C	IV, V, VI, VII
C'	I, II, III, VIII
B ∪ C'	I, II, III, V, VI, VIII
A	I, II, IV, V
A ∩ (B ∩ C')	I, II, V

Set	Regions
A	I, II, IV, V
B	II, III, V, VI
A ∩ B	II, V
C	IV, V, VI, VII
C'	I, II, III, VIII
A ∩ C'	I, II
(A ∩ B) ∪ (A ∩ C')	I, II, V

The two statements are represented by the same regions, I, II, V, of the Venn diagram.

Therefore, A ∩ (B ∪ C') = (A ∩ B) ∪ (A ∩ C')for all sets A, B, and C.

18. a)

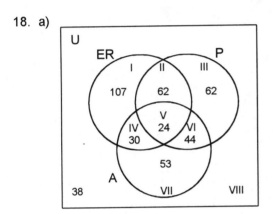

b) 222, the sum of the numbers in
Regions I, III, VII.

c) 38, Region VIII

d) 136, the sum of the numbers in
Regions II, IV, VI

e) 160, the sum of the numbers in
Regions II, IV, V, VI

f) 231, the sum of the numbers in
Regions I, II, III

g) 62, Region II

19. {7, 8, 9, 10, 11, ..., n + 6, ...}
    ↓ ↓ ↓ ↓ ↓   ↓
    {8, 9, 10, 11, 12, ..., n + 7, ...}

20. {1, 2, 3, 4, 5, ..., n, ...}
    ↓ ↓ ↓ ↓ ↓   ↓
    {1, 3, 5, 7, 9, ..., 2n - 1, ...}

Group Projects

1. a)   A: Does not shed, B: Less than 16 in. tall, C: Good with kids

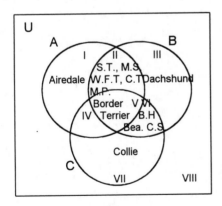

b) Border terrier, Region V

2.   a) Animal   b) Chordate   c) Mammalia   d) Carnivore
      e) Felidae   f) Felis   g) Catus

3.

	First	Second	Third	Fourth	Fifth
a) Color	yellow	blue	red	ivory	green
b) Nationality	Norwegian	Afghan.	Senegalese	Spanish	Japanese
c) Food	apple	cheese	banana	peach	fish
d) Drink	vodka	tea	milk	whiskey	ale
e) Pet	fox	horse	snail	dog	zebra
f) ale					

CHAPTER THREE

LOGIC

Exercise Set 3.1

1. A simple statement is a sentence that conveys one idea and can be identified as either true or false.

2. All, none (no), some

3. a) Some are   b) All are
   c) Some are not   d) None are

4. Statements consisting of two or more simple statements.

5. Let p: The ink is purple.
   The symbolic form is ~ p. The negation symbol, ~ , represents the word <u>not</u>.

6. a) →   b) ∨   c) ∧
   d) ~   e) ↔

7. When a compound statement contains more than one connective a comma can be used to indicate which simple statements are to be grouped together. When writing a statement symbolically, the simple statements on the same side of the comma are to be grouped together within parentheses.

8. 1st Biconditional ↔, 2nd Conditional →, 3rd Conjunction ∧ /Disjunction ∨, 4th Negation ~

9. compound; conjunction, ∧

10. compound; negation, ~

11. compound; biconditional, ↔

12. compound; conditional, →

13. compound; disjunction, ∨

14. compound; conjunction, ∧

15. simple statement

16. compound; biconditional, ↔

17. compound; negation, ~

18. compound; conditional, →

19. compound; conjunction, ∧

20. compound; conjunction, ∧

21. compound; negation, ~

22. compound; conditional, →

23. No flowers are yellow.

24. Some money grows on trees.

25. Some fish do not swim.

26. Some bowling balls are not round.

27. All dogs have fleas.

28. Some doctors make house calls.

29. Some books are round.

30. Some cows do not give milk.

31. All rain forests are being destroyed.

32. Someone likes a bully.

33. No students maintain an A average.

34. All people who earn money pay taxes.

35. ~ p

36. p ∧ q

37. ~ q ∨ ~ p

38. ~ q ↔ ~ p

39. ~ p → ~ q

40. ~ q ∧ p

41. ~ q ↔ ~ p

42. ~ q → ~ p

43. ~ p ∧ ~ q

44. ~ p ∧ q

45. ~ (q → ~ p)

46. ~ (p ∧ q)

47. Firemen do not wear red suspenders.

48. Firemen do not work hard.

49. Firemen wear red suspenders or firemen work hard.

50. Firemen work hard and firemen wear red suspenders.

51. If firemen do not work hard, then firemen wear red suspenders.

52. Firemen do not work hard if and only if firemen do not wear red suspenders.

53. It is false that firemen wear red suspenders or firemen work hard.

54. Firemen do not work hard or firemen do not wear red suspenders.

55. Firemen do not work hard and firemen do not wear red suspenders.

56. It is false that firemen work hard and firemen wear red suspenders.

57. $(p \wedge q) \vee r$

58. $(p \vee \sim q) \rightarrow r$

59. $(r \leftrightarrow \sim p) \vee \sim q$

60. $p \rightarrow (q \vee \sim r)$

61. $(r \wedge q) \rightarrow p$

62. $(\sim p \leftrightarrow \sim q) \vee \sim r$

63. $(r \leftrightarrow q) \wedge p$

64. $\sim (r \rightarrow \sim q)$

65. $q \rightarrow (p \leftrightarrow r)$

66. $(r \vee \sim q) \leftrightarrow p$

67. The water is 70^0 and the sun is shinning, or we will go swimming.

68. The water is 70^0 or the sun is shinning, and we do not go swimming.

69. If the sun is shinning then the water is 70^0, or we will go swimming.

70. The water is not 70^0, and the sun is shinning or we will go swimming.

71. If we do not go swimming, then the sun is shinning and the water is 70^0.

72. If the sun is shinning and we go swimming, then the water is 70^0.

73. If the sun is shinning then we go swimming, and the water is 70^0.

74. If the water is not 70^0, then the sun is shinning or we will go swimming.

75. The sun is shinning if and only if the water is 70^0, and we go swimming.

76. If the sun is shinning, then the water is 70^0 if and only if we go swimming.

77. Not permissible. In the list of choices, the connective "or" is the exclusive or, thus one can order either the soup or the salad but not both items.

78. Permissible.

79. Not permissible. Potatoes and pasta cannot be ordered together.

80. Not permissible. Potatoes and pasta cannot be ordered together.

81. a) $(\sim p) \rightarrow q$ b) conditional

82. a) $(\sim p \wedge r) \leftrightarrow (\sim q)$ b) biconditional

83. a) $(\sim q) \wedge (\sim r)$ b) conjunction

84. a) $(\sim p) \vee q$ b) disjunction

85. a) $(p \vee q) \rightarrow r$ b) conditional

86. a) $q \rightarrow (p \wedge \sim r)$ b) conditional

87. a) $r \rightarrow (p \vee q)$ b) conditional

88. a) $(q \rightarrow p) \leftrightarrow (p \rightarrow q)$ b) biconditional

89. a) $(\sim p) \leftrightarrow (\sim q \rightarrow r)$ b) biconditional

90. a) $(\sim q) \rightarrow (r \wedge p)$ b) conditional

91. a) $(r \wedge \sim q) \rightarrow (q \wedge \sim p)$ b) conditional

92. a) $\sim [p \rightarrow (q \vee r)]$ b) negation

93. a) $\sim [(p \wedge q) \leftrightarrow (p \vee r)]$ b) negation

94. a) $\sim [r \wedge \sim q) \rightarrow (q \wedge r)]$ b) negation

95. c: Carol Britz visited Nancy Hart.
    d: Carol Britz did drive to Maine.
    a) $c \vee \sim d$ b) disjunction

96. m: The moon is out.
    e: It is evening.
    s: The sun is shinning.
    a) $m \rightarrow (e \vee \sim s)$ b) conditional

97. p: You pay your taxes.
    a: You will get audited.
    s: The sun is shinning.
    a) $\sim (p \rightarrow \sim a)$ b) negation

98. m: The moon is out.
    e: It is evening.
    s: The sun is shinning.
    a) $(m \rightarrow e) \vee \sim s$ b) disjunction

99. f: The fruit is red.
    v: The vegetables are carrots.
    e: You will eat well.
    a) $(f \vee v) \rightarrow e$ b) conditional

100. t: Today is Tuesday.
    w: Tomorrow is Wednesday.
    a) $(t \rightarrow w) \leftrightarrow \sim t$ b) biconditional

101. o: The store is open.
      s: Today is Sunday.
      f: It is before 5 PM.
      a) o ↔ (~ s ∨ f)   b) biconditional

102. d: The number is divisible by 2.
      t : The number is divisible by 3.
      s: The number is divisible by 6.
      a) (d ∧ t) → s   b) conditional

103. e: The store is empty.
      s: Today is Sunday.
      f: It is after 5 PM.
      a) (e ↔ s) ∨ f   b) disjunction

104. This statement/question is a paradox. Therefore it is false.

105. [(~ q) → (r ∨ p)] ↔ [(~ r) ∧ q], biconditional

106. ~[[(~r) → (p ∧ q)] ↔[(~p) ∨ r]], negation

107. a) The conjunction and disjunction have the same dominance.
      c) If we evaluate the truth table for p ∨ q ∧ r using the order (p ∨ q) ∧ r we get a different solution than if
          we used the order p ∨ (q ∧ r). Therefore, unless we are told where the parentheses belong, we do
          not know which solution is correct.

Exercise Set 3.2

1. a) 2^2 = 2 × 2 = 4 distinct cases
   b)

	p	q
case 1:	T	T
case 2	T	F
case 3:	F	T
case 4:	F	F

2. a) 2^3 = 2 × 2 × 2 = 8 distinct cases
   b)

	p	q	r
case 1:	T	T	T
case 2:	T	T	F
case 3:	T	F	T
case 4:	T	F	F
case 5:	F	T	T
case 6:	F	T	F
case 7:	F	F	T
case 8:	F	F	F

3. a)

p	q	p ∧ q
T	T	T T T
T	F	T F F
F	T	F F T
F	F	F F F
		1 3 2

   b) Only in case 1, when both simple
      statements are true.

4. a)

p	Q	p ∨ q
T	T	T T T
T	F	T T F
F	T	F T T
F	F	F F F
		1 3 2

   b) Only in case 4, when both simple
      statements are false.

5.

p	p ∧ ~ p
T	T F F
F	F F T
	1 3 2

6.

p	p ∨ ~ p
T	T T F
F	F T T
	1 3 2

7.

p	q	q ∨ ~ p
T	T	T T F
T	F	F F F
F	T	T T T
F	F	F T T
		1 3 2

8.

p	q	p ∧ ~ q
T	T	T F F
T	F	T T T
F	T	F F F
F	F	F F T
		1 3 2

9.

p	q	~p ∨ ~q
T	T	F F F
T	F	F T T
F	T	T T F
F	F	T T T
		1 3 2

10.

p	q	~ (p ∨ ~ q)
T	T	F T T F
T	F	F T T T
F	T	T F F F
F	F	F F T T
		4 1 3 2

11.

p	q	~ (p ∧ ~q)
T	T	T T F F
T	F	F T T T
F	T	T F F F
F	F	T F F T
		4 1 3 2

12.

p	q	~(~p ∧ ~q)
T	T	T F F F
T	F	T F F T
F	T	T T F F
F	F	F T T T
		4 1 3 2

13.

p	q	r	(p ∧ r) ∨ ~q)
T	T	T	T T F
T	T	F	F F F
T	F	T	T T T
T	F	F	F T T
F	T	T	F F F
F	T	F	F F F
F	F	T	F T T
F	F	F	F T T
			1 3 2

14.

p	q	r	(p ∨ ~q) ∧ r
T	T	T	T T F T T
T	T	F	T T F F F
T	F	T	T T T T T
T	F	F	T T T F F
F	T	T	F F F F T
F	T	F	F F F F F
F	F	T	F T T T T
F	F	F	F T T F F
			1 3 2 5 4

15.

p	q	R	r ∨ (p ∧ ~q)
T	T	T	T T T F F
T	T	F	F F T F F
T	F	T	T T T T T
T	F	F	F T T T T
F	T	T	T T F F F
F	T	F	F F F F F
F	F	T	T T F F T
F	F	F	F F F F T
			1 5 2 4 2

16.

p	q	r	(r ∧ q) ∧ ~p
T	T	T	T F F
T	T	F	F F F
T	F	T	F F F
T	F	F	F F F
F	T	T	T T T
F	T	F	F F T
F	F	T	F F T
F	F	F	F F T
			1 3 2

17.

p	q	r	~q ∧ (r ∨ ~p)
T	T	T	F F T T F
T	T	F	F F F F F
T	F	T	T T T T F
T	F	F	T F F F F
F	T	T	F F T T T
F	T	F	F F T T T
F	F	T	T T T T T
F	F	F	T T F T T
			1 5 2 4 3

18.

p	q	r	~p ∧ (q ∨ r)
T	T	T	F F T T T
T	T	F	F F T T F
T	F	T	F F F T T
T	F	F	F F F F F
F	T	T	T T T T T
F	T	F	T T T T F
F	F	T	T T F T T
F	F	F	T F F F F
			1 5 2 4 3

19.

p	q	r	(~q ∧ r) ∨ p
T	T	T	F F T T T
T	T	F	F F F T T
T	F	T	T T T T T
T	F	F	T F F T T
F	T	T	F F T F F
F	T	F	F F F F F
F	F	T	T T T T F
F	F	F	T F F F F
			1 3 2 5 4

20.

p	q	r	~r	∨	(~p	∧	q)
T	T	T	F	F	F	F	T
T	T	F	T	T	F	F	T
T	F	T	F	F	F	F	F
T	F	F	T	T	F	F	F
F	T	T	F	T	T	T	T
F	T	F	T	T	T	T	T
F	F	T	F	F	T	F	F
F	F	F	T	T	T	F	F
			4	5	1	3	2

21. p: Driving is fun.
q: Walking is good exercise.
In symbolic form the statement is p ∧ q.

p	q	p ∧ q
T	T	T
T	F	F
F	T	F
F	F	F
		1

22. p: The calculator is solar powered.
q: The sun is out.
In symbolic form the statement is p ∧ ~q.

p	q	p	∧	~q
T	T	T	F	F
T	F	T	T	T
F	T	F	F	F
F	F	F	F	T
		1	3	2

23. p: The sock fits.
q: The shoe fits.
In symbolic form the statement is p ∧ ~q.

p	q	p	∧	~q
T	T	T	F	F
T	F	T	T	T
F	T	F	F	F
F	F	F	F	T
		1	3	2

24. p: At least 200 tickets must be sold.
q: The concert will be canceled.
In symbolic form the statement is ~ (p ∨ q).

p	q	~	(p	∨	q)
T	T	F	T	T	T
T	F	F	T	T	F
F	T	F	F	T	T
F	F	T	F	F	F
		4	1	3	2

25. p: Ricardo will take mathematics.
q: Ricardo will take history.
r : Ricardo will take psychology.
In symbolic form the statement is (p ∨ q) ∧ ~r.

p	q	r	(p ∨ q)	∧	~r
T	T	T	T	F	F
T	T	F	T	T	T
T	F	T	T	F	F
T	F	F	T	T	T
F	T	T	T	F	F
F	T	F	T	T	T
F	F	T	F	F	F
F	F	F	F	F	T
			1	3	2

26. p: The shirt is green.
q: The suit is blue.
r : They go well together.
In symbolic form the statement is (p ∧ q) ∧ r.

p	q	r	(p ∧ q)	∧	r
T	T	T	T	T	T
T	T	F	T	F	F
T	F	T	F	F	T
T	F	F	F	F	F
F	T	T	F	F	T
F	T	F	F	F	F
F	F	T	F	F	T
F	F	F	F	F	F
			1	3	2

27. p: Karen uses American Online.
q: Karen uses Yahoo.
r : Karen uses Microsoft Explorer.
In symbolic form the statement is (p ∧ q) ∧ ~ r).

p	q	r	(p ∧ q)	∧	~r
T	T	T	T	F	F
T	T	F	T	T	T
T	F	T	F	F	F
T	F	F	F	F	T
F	T	T	F	F	F
F	T	F	F	F	T
F	F	T	F	F	F
F	F	F	F	F	T
			1	3	2

28. p: The dog sheds.
q: I wanted a collie.
r : I wanted a large dog.
In symbolic form the statement is $p \wedge (q \wedge r)$.

p	q	r	p	$\wedge$	(q	$\wedge$	r)
T	T	T	T	T			T
T	T	F	T	F			F
T	F	T	T	F			F
T	F	F	T	F			F
F	T	T	F	F			T
F	T	F	F	F			F
F	F	T	F	F			F
F	F	F	F	F			F
			2	3			1

29. p: The password is pistachio.
q: The gate is open.
In symbolic form the statement is $p \wedge (q \vee \sim q)$.

p	q	p	$\wedge$	(q	$\vee$	$\sim$q)
T	T	T	T	T	T	F
T	F	T	T	F	T	T
F	T	F	F	T	T	F
F	F	F	F	F	T	T
		1	5	2	4	3

30. p: The pen is out of ink.
q: The ink is white.
r : I am sleepy.
In symbolic form the statement is $p \vee (q \vee r)$.

p	q	r	p	$\vee$	(q	$\vee$	r)
T	T	T	T	T			T
T	T	F	T	T			T
T	F	T	T	T			T
T	F	F	T	T			F
F	T	T	F	T			T
F	T	F	F	T			T
F	F	T	F	T			T
F	F	F	F	F			F
			2	3			1

31. $\sim p \vee (q \wedge r)$
    $F \vee (F \wedge T)$
    $F \vee \quad F$
    $\quad\quad F$
    Therefore the statement is false.

32. $(\sim p \wedge r) \wedge q$
    $(F \wedge T) \wedge F$
    $\quad F \wedge F$
    $\quad\quad F$
    Therefore the statement is false.

33. $(\sim q \wedge \sim p) \vee \sim r$
    $(T \wedge F) \vee F$
    $\quad F \quad\quad \vee F$
    $\quad\quad\quad F$
    Therefore the statement is false.

34. $(\sim p \vee \sim q) \vee \sim r$
    $(F \vee T) \vee F$
    $\quad T \quad\quad \vee F$
    $\quad\quad\quad T$
    Therefore the statement is true.

35. (p ∧ ~q) ∨ r
     (T ∧ T) ∨ T
          T   ∨ T
                 T
Therefore the statement is true.

37. (~r ∧ p) ∨ q
     (T   ∧ F) ∨ T
           F   ∨ T
                 T
Therefore the statement is true.

39. (~q ∨ ~p) ∧ r
     (F   ∨ T) ∧ F
           T   ∧ F
                  F
Therefore the statement is false.

41. (~p ∨ ~q) ∨ (~r ∨ q)
     (T   ∨ F) ∨ (T   ∨ T)
           T   ∨   T
                  T
Therefore the statement is true.

43.   4 + 3 = 7 or 6 + 4 = 12
            T   ∨   F
                  T
Therefore the statement is true.

36. (p ∨ ~q) ∧ ~(p ∧ ~r)
     (T ∨ T) ∧ ~(T ∧ F)
          T   ∧ ~   F
          T   ∧ T
                 T
Therefore the statement is true.

38. ~q ∨ (r ∧ p)
     F   ∨ (F
     F
Therefore the statement is false.

40. (~r ∨ ~p) ∨ ~q
     (T   ∨ T) ∨ F
           T   ∨ F
                  T
Therefore the statement is true.

42. (~r ∧ ~q) ∧ (~r ∨ ~p)
     (T   ∧ F) ∧ (T   ∨ T)
           F   ∧   T
                  F
Therefore the statement is false.

44. 9 – 6 = 15 and 7 – 4 = 3
         F   ∧   T
                  F
Therefore the statement is false.

45. p: Elvis Presley was born in Tupelo Mississippi.
     q: The giraffe has only two legs.

                              p ∨ q
                              T ∨ F
                              True

46. p: The capital of Texas is San Antonio.
     q: Kentucky is east of the Mississippi River.
     r: Los Angeles is the capital of California.

                              (p ∨ q) ∧ ~ r
                              (F ∨ T) ∧ T
                                 T   ∧ T
                                 True

47. p: Algebra is a mathematics course.
     q: Geometry is a mathematics course.
     r: Shakespearean literature is a mathematics course.

                              (p ∧ q) ∧ ~ r
                              (T ∧ T) ∧ T
                                 T   ∧ T
                                 True

48. p: Rome is in France.
     q: Paris is in Germany.
     r: London is in England.

                              (p ∨ ~ q) ∧ r
                              (F ∨ T) ∧ T
                                 T   ∧ T
                                 True

49. p: Marco Polo played football.
    q: John Glenn built houses.
    r: George Washington is on a US one dollar bill.

$$(p \lor q) \land r$$
$$(F \lor F) \land T$$
$$F \qquad \land T$$
False

50. p: Mars is a planet.
    q: The sun is a star.
    r: The moon is a star.

$$(p \land q) \lor \sim r$$
$$(T \land T) \lor T$$
$$T \qquad \lor T$$
True

51. p: 28 pounds of cheese was consumed by the average American in 1909.
    q: The average American consumed 154 pounds sweeteners in 1997.

$$p \land \sim q$$
$$F \land \sim T$$
$$F \land F$$
False

52. p: The per capita consumption of red meat was less for the average American in 1997 than in 1909.
    q: The per capita consumption of poultry was greater for the average American in 1997 than it was in 1909.

$$p \lor q$$
$$F \lor T$$
True

53. p: 30% of Americans get 6 hours of sleep each night.
    q: 9% of Americans get 5 hours of sleep each night.

$$\sim (p \land q)$$
$$\sim (F \land T)$$
$$\sim \qquad F$$
True

54. p: 25% of Americans get 6 hours of sleep each night.
    q: 30% of Americans get 7 hours of sleep each night.
    r: 9% of Americans get 5 hours of sleep each night.

$$p \land (q \lor \sim r)$$
$$T \land (T \lor \sim T)$$
$$T \land (T \lor F)$$
$$T \land \qquad T$$
True

55. In symbolic form the statement is $\sim p \land q$.

p	q	$\sim p$	$\land$	q
T	T	F	F	T
T	F	F	F	F
F	T	T	T	T
F	F	T	F	F
		1	3	2

The statement is true in case 3.

56. In symbolic form the statement is $p \land \sim q$.

p	q	p	$\land$	$\sim q$
T	T	T	F	F
T	F	T	T	T
F	T	F	F	F
F	F	F	F	T
		1	3	2

The statement is true in case 2.

57. In symbolic form the statement is $p \lor \sim q$.

p	q	p	$\lor$	$\sim q$
T	T	T	T	F
T	F	T	T	T
F	T	F	F	F
F	F	F	T	T
		1	3	2

The statement is true in cases 1, 2, & 4.

58. In symbolic form the statement is $\sim p \lor \sim q$.

p	q	$\sim p$	$\lor$	$\sim q$
T	T	F	F	F
T	F	F	T	T
F	T	T	T	F
F	F	T	T	T
		1	3	2

The statement is true in cases 2, 3, & 4.

59. In symbolic form the statement is
$(p \wedge q) \vee r$.

p	q	r	(p	∧	q)	∨	r
T	T	T		T		T	T
T	T	F		T		T	F
T	F	T		F		T	T
T	F	F		F		F	F
F	T	T		F		T	T
F	T	F		F		F	F
F	F	T		F		T	T
F	F	F		F		F	F
				1		3	2

The statement is true in cases 1, 2, 3, 5, and 7.

60. In symbolic form the statement is
$(r \vee q) \wedge p$.

p	q	r	(r	∨	q)	∧	p
T	T	T		T		T	T
T	T	F		T		T	T
T	F	T		T		T	T
T	F	F		F		F	T
F	T	T		T		F	F
F	T	F		T		F	F
F	F	T		T		F	F
F	F	F		F		F	F
				1		3	2

The statement is true in cases 1, 2, and 3.

61. In symbolic form the statement is
$q \vee (p \wedge \sim r)$.

p	q	r	q	∨	(p	∧	~r)
T	T	T	T	T	T	F	F
T	T	F	T	T	T	T	T
T	F	T	F	F	T	F	F
T	F	F	F	T	T	T	T
F	T	T	T	T	F	F	F
F	T	F	T	T	F	F	T
F	F	T	F	F	F	F	F
F	F	F	F	F	F	F	T
			4	5	1	3	2

The statement is true in cases 1, 2, 4, 5, and 6.

62. In symbolic form the statement is
$\sim p \wedge (\sim r \wedge q)$.

p	q	r	~p	∧	(~r	∧	q)
T	T	T	F	F	F	F	T
T	T	F	F	F	T	T	T
T	F	T	F	F	F	F	F
T	F	F	F	F	T	F	F
F	T	T	T	F	F	F	T
F	T	F	T	T	T	T	T
F	F	T	T	F	F	F	F
F	F	F	T	F	T	F	F
			4	5	1	3	2

The statement is true in case 6.

63.a) Ms. Duncan qualifies for the loan. Mrs. Tuttle qualifies for the loan.

b) The Furmans do not qualify since they are married and do not have a combined income of $46,000 or more.

64.a) Mr. Argento qualifies for the loan.

b) Tina McVey does not qualify since she is single and her income is less than $30,000. Mr. Henke does not qualify since his assets are less than $10,000

65.a) Mike Bolinder qualifies for the special fare.

b) Gina Vela does not qualify since she will return after April 1st. Laura Griffin Heller does not qualify since she is not returning on a Tuesday Wednesday, or Thursday. Christos G. does not qualify since he will not be staying over at least one Saturday. Alex Chang does not qualify since he is not returning on a Tuesday, Wednesday, or Thursdayz

66.

p	q	r	~[(~	(p	∨	q))	∨	(q	∧	r)]
T	T	T	F		F		T		T	T
T	T	F	T		F		T		F	F
T	F	T	T		F		T		F	F
T	F	F	T		F		T		F	F
F	T	T	F		F		T		T	T
F	T	F	T		F		T		F	F
F	F	T	F		T		F		T	F
F	F	F	F		T		F		T	F
			5		2		1		4	3

67.

p	q	r	q	∧	~r	∧	~p	∨	~q]	∨	p	∨	~r
T	T	T	T	F	F	F	F	F	F	T	T	T	F
T	T	F	T	T	T	F	F	F	F	T	T	T	T
T	F	T	F	F	F	F	F	T	T	T	T	T	F
T	F	F	F	F	T	F	F	T	T	T	T	T	T
F	T	T	T	F	F	F	T	T	F	F	F	F	F
F	T	F	T	T	T	T	T	T	F	T	F	T	T
F	F	T	F	F	F	F	T	T	T	F	F	F	F
F	F	F	F	F	T	F	T	T	T	T	F	T	T
			1	3	2	7	4	6	5	11	8	10	9

The main statement: [(q ∧ ~r) ∧ (~p ∨ ~q)] ∨ (p ∨ ~r)

68.a) n = 4, $2^4 = 2 \times 2 \times 2 \times 2 = 16$ distinct cases

b) c) (q ∧ p) ∨ (~r ∧ s)   **d)** (~r ∧ ~s) ∧ (~p ∨ q)

p	q	r	s	(q∧p)	∨	~r	∧	s	~r	∧	~s	∧	~p	∨	q
T	T	T	T	T	T	F	F	T	F	F	F	F	F	T	T
T	T	T	F	T	T	F	F	F	F	F	T	F	F	T	T
T	T	F	T	T	T	T	T	T	T	F	F	F	F	T	T
T	T	F	F	T	T	T	F	F	T	T	T	T	F	T	T
T	F	T	T	F	F	F	F	T	F	F	F	F	F	F	F
T	F	T	F	F	F	F	F	F	F	F	T	F	F	F	F
T	F	F	T	F	T	T	T	T	T	F	F	F	F	F	F
T	F	F	F	F	F	T	F	F	T	T	T	F	F	F	F
F	T	T	T	F	F	F	F	T	F	F	F	F	T	T	T
F	T	T	F	F	F	F	F	F	F	F	T	F	T	T	T
F	T	F	T	F	T	T	T	T	T	F	F	F	T	T	T
F	T	F	F	F	F	T	F	F	T	T	T	T	T	T	T
F	F	T	T	F	F	F	F	T	F	F	F	F	T	T	F
F	F	T	F	F	F	F	F	F	F	F	T	F	T	T	F
F	F	F	T	F	T	T	T	T	T	F	F	F	T	T	F
F	F	F	F	F	F	T	F	F	T	T	T	T	T	T	F
				1	5	2	4	3	1	3	2	7	4	6	5

69.   Yes. Each statement uses the exact same arrangement of connectives

Exercise Set 3.3

1.a)

p	q	p	→	q
T	T	T	T	T
T	F	T	F	F
F	T	F	T	T
F	F	F	T	F
		1	3	2

b) The conditional statement is false only in the case when antecedent is true and the consequent is false, otherwise it is true.

3.a) Substitute the truth values for the simple statement. Then evaluate the compound statement for that specific case.

b)
[(p → q) ∨ (~q → r)] → ~r
[(T → F) ∨ (~F → T)] → ~T
[F   ∨ (T → T)] → F
[F   ∨   T] → F
         T   → F
              F

In this specific case the statement is false.

2.a)

p	q	P	↔	q
T	T	T	T	T
T	F	T	F	F
F	T	F	F	T
F	F	F	T	F
		1	3	2

b) The biconditional statement is true when the statements to the left and right of the biconditional symbol match, otherwise it is false.

4. A self-contradiction is a compound statement that is false in every case.

5. A tautology is a compound statement that is true in every case.

6. An implication is a <u>conditional</u> statement that is a tautology.

7.

p	q	p	→	~q
T	T	T	F	F
T	F	T	T	T
F	T	F	T	F
F	F	F	T	T
		1	3	2

8.

p	q	~q	→	~p
T	T	F	T	F
T	F	T	F	F
F	T	F	T	T
F	F	T	T	T
		1	3	2

9.

p	q	~	(p ↔ q)
T	T	F	T
T	F	T	F
F	T	T	F
F	F	F	T
		2	1

10.

p	q	~	(q → p)
T	T	F	T
T	F	F	T
F	T	T	F
F	F	F	T
		2	1

11.

p	q	~q	↔	p
T	T	F	F	T
T	F	T	T	T
F	T	F	F	F
F	F	T	F	F
		1	3	2

12.

p	q	(p	↔	q)	→	p
T	T		T		T	T
T	F		F		T	T
F	T		F		T	F
F	F		T		F	F
			1		3	2

13.

p	q	p	↔	(q ∨ p)
T	T	T	T	T
T	F	T	T	T
F	T	F	F	T
F	F	F	T	F
		1	3	2

14.

p	q	(~ q	∧	p)	→	~ q
T	T	F	F	T	T	F
T	F	T	T	T	T	T
F	T	F	F	T	F	F
F	F	T	F	T	T	T
		1	3	2	5	4

15.

p	q	q	→	(p	→	~ q)
T	T	T	F	T	F	F
T	F	F	T	T	T	T
F	T	T	T	F	T	F
F	F	F	T	F	T	T
		4	5	1	3	2

16.

p	q	(p ∨ q)	↔	(p ∧ q)
T	T	T	T	T
T	F	T	F	F
F	T	T	F	F
F	F	F	T	F
		1	3	2

17.

p	q	r	p	→	(q ∨ r)
T	T	T	T	T	T
T	T	F	T	T	T
T	F	T	T	T	T
T	F	F	T	F	F
F	T	T	F	T	T
F	T	F	F	T	T
F	F	T	F	T	T
F	F	F	F	T	F
			2	3	1

18.

p	q	r	r	∧	(~ q	→	p)
T	T	T	T	T	F	T	T
T	T	F	F	F	F	T	T
T	F	T	T	T	T	T	T
T	F	F	F	F	T	T	T
F	T	T	T	T	F	T	F
F	T	F	F	F	F	T	F
F	F	T	T	T	T	F	F
F	F	F	F	F	T	F	F
			4	5	1	3	2

19.

p	q	r	q	↔	(r ∧ p)
T	T	T	T	T	T
T	T	F	T	F	F
T	F	T	F	F	T
T	F	F	F	T	F
F	T	T	T	F	F
F	T	F	T	F	F
F	F	T	F	T	F
F	F	F	F	T	F
			2	3	1

20.

p	q	r	(q ↔ p)	∧	~r
T	T	T	T	F	F
T	T	F	T	T	T
T	F	T	F	F	F
T	F	F	F	F	T
F	T	T	F	F	F
F	T	F	F	F	T
F	F	T	T	F	F
F	F	F	T	T	T
			1	3	2

21.

p	q	r	(q	∨	~ r)	↔	~p
T	T	T	T	T	F	F	F
T	T	F	T	T	T	F	F
T	F	T	F	F	F	T	F
T	F	F	F	T	T	F	F
F	T	T	T	T	F	T	T
F	T	F	T	T	T	T	T
F	F	T	F	F	F	F	T
F	F	F	F	T	T	T	T
			1	3	2	5	4

22.

p	q	r	(p ∧ r)	→	(q ∨ r)
T	T	T	T	T	T
T	T	F	F	T	T
T	F	T	T	T	T
T	F	F	F	T	F
F	T	T	F	T	T
F	T	F	F	T	T
F	F	T	F	T	T
F	F	F	F	T	F
			1	3	2

23.

p	q	r	(~r	∨	~ q)	→	p
T	T	T	F	F	F	T	T
T	T	F	T	T	F	T	T
T	F	T	F	T	T	T	T
T	F	F	T	T	T	T	T
F	T	T	F	F	F	T	F
F	T	F	T	T	F	F	F
F	F	T	F	T	T	F	F
F	F	F	T	T	T	F	F
			1	3	2	5	4

24.

p	q	r	[r	∧	(q	∨	~p)]	↔	~p
T	T	T	T	T	T	T	F	F	F
T	T	F	F	F	T	T	F	T	F
T	F	T	T	F	F	F	F	T	F
T	F	F	F	F	F	F	F	T	F
F	T	T	T	T	T	T	T	T	T
F	T	F	F	F	T	T	T	F	T
F	F	T	T	T	F	T	T	T	T
F	F	F	F	F	F	T	T	F	T
			4	5	1	3	2	7	6

25.

p	q	r	(p → q)	↔	(~q	→	~r)
T	T	T	T	T	F	T	F
T	T	F	T	T	F	T	T
T	F	T	F	T	T	F	F
T	F	F	F	F	T	T	T
F	T	T	T	T	F	T	F
F	T	F	T	T	F	T	T
F	F	T	T	F	T	F	F
F	F	F	T	T	T	T	T
			1	5	2	4	3

26.   In symbolic form the statement is p → (q ∧ r).

p	q	r	p	→	(q ∧ r)
T	T	T	T	T	T
T	T	F	T	F	F
T	F	T	T	F	F
T	F	F	T	F	F
F	T	T	F	T	T
F	T	F	F	T	F
F	F	T	F	T	F
F	F	F	F	T	F
			2	3	1

27.
p: I cut the grass.
q: I will need to rake.
r: I will need to bag the clippings

p → (q ∧ r)

p	q	r	p	→	(q∧r)
T	T	T	T	T	T
T	T	F	T	F	F
T	F	T	T	F	F
T	F	F	T	F	F
F	T	T	F	T	T
F	T	F	F	T	F
F	F	T	F	T	F
F	F	F	F	T	F
			2	3	1

28.
p: The pizza will be delivered.
q: The driver finds the house.
r: The pizza will be hot.

(p ↔ q) ∨ ~r

p	q	r	(p↔q)	∨	~r
T	T	T	T	T	F
T	T	F	T	T	T
T	F	T	F	F	F
T	F	F	F	T	T
F	T	T	F	F	F
F	T	F	F	T	T
F	F	T	T	T	F
F	F	F	T	T	T
			1	3	2

29.
p: The cable is out.
q: We can watch T.V.
r: We will use the antenna.
In symbolic form the statement is
(p ↔ ~q) ∨ r.

p	q	r	p	↔	~q	∨	r
T	T	T	T	F	F	T	T
T	T	F	T	F	F	F	F
T	F	T	T	T	T	T	T
T	F	F	T	T	T	T	F
F	T	T	F	T	F	T	T
F	T	F	F	T	F	T	F
F	F	T	F	F	T	T	T
F	F	F	F	F	T	F	F
			2	3	1	5	4

30.
p: It rains.
q: The roof will leak.
r: The sun shines.
In symbolic form the statement is
(p → q) ∧ (r → ~q).

p	q	r	(p→q)	∧	r	(r→~q)	~q
T	T	T	T	F	T	F	F
T	T	F	T	T	F	T	F
T	F	T	F	F	T	T	T
T	F	F	F	F	F	T	T
F	T	T	T	F	T	F	F
F	T	F	T	T	F	T	F
F	F	T	T	T	T	T	T
F	F	F	T	T	F	T	T
			1	5	2	4	3

31.
p: The computer is being used.
q: We can use the telephone.
r: We can use the fax machine.
In symbolic form the statement is
(~p → q) ∨ r.

p	q	r	~p	→	q	∨	r
T	T	T	F	T	T	T	T
T	T	F	F	T	T	T	F
T	F	T	F	T	F	T	T
T	F	F	F	T	F	T	F
F	T	T	T	T	T	T	T
F	T	F	T	T	T	T	F
F	F	T	T	F	F	T	T
F	F	F	T	F	F	F	F
			1	3	2	5	4

32.
p: Paige Dunbar went to the movie.
q: She did go to the party.
r: She went to school.
In symbolic form the statement is
~ [p → (~ q ∧ r)].

p	q	r	~	p	→	~q	∧	r
T	T	T	T	T	F	F	F	T
T	T	F	T	T	F	F	F	F
T	F	T	F	T	T	T	T	T
T	F	F	T	T	F	T	F	F
F	T	T	F	F	T	F	F	T
F	T	F	F	F	T	F	F	F
F	F	T	F	F	T	T	T	T
F	F	F	F	F	T	T	F	F
			6	4	5	1	3	2

33.

p	q	~q	→	p
T	T	F	T	T
T	F	T	T	T
F	T	F	T	F
F	F	T	F	F
		1	3	2

Neither

34.

p	q	(p∧q)	↔	p
T	T	T	T	T
T	F	F	F	T
F	T	F	T	F
F	F	F	T	F
		1	3	2

Neither

35.

p	q	~q	∧	(q∧p)
T	T	F	F	T
T	F	T	F	F
F	T	F	F	F
F	F	T	F	F
		1	3	2

Self-contradiction

36.

p	q	~p	∨	~q	→	p
T	T	F	F	F	T	T
T	F	F	T	T	T	T
F	T	T	T	F	F	F
F	F	T	T	T	F	F
		1	3	2	5	4

Neither

37.

p	q	~p	→	q	∨	~p
T	T	F	T	T	T	F
T	F	F	T	F	T	F
F	T	T	T	T	T	T
F	F	T	F	F	T	T
		1	3	2	5	4

Tautology

38.

p	q	r	[(p ∧ q) ∧ ~r] ↔ [(p ∨ q) ∧ r]
T	T	T	T F F F T T T
T	T	F	T T T F T F F
T	F	T	F F F F T T T
T	F	F	F F T T T F F
F	T	T	F F F F T T T
F	T	F	F F T T T F F
F	F	T	F F F F F F T
F	F	F	F F T T F F F
			1 3 2 7 4 6 5

Neither

39.

p	q	(p ∨ q) → (q ∧ p)
T	T	T T T
T	F	T F F
F	T	T F F
F	F	F T F
		1 3 2

Not an implication

40.

p	q	q → (p ∨ q)
T	T	T T T
T	F	F T T
F	T	T T T
F	F	F T F
		2 3 1

Implication

41.

p	q	(q ∧ p) → (p ∧ q)
T	T	T T T
T	F	F T F
F	T	F T F
F	F	F T F
		1 3 2

Implication

42.

p	q	r	(p ∨ q) → (p ∨ ~ r)
T	T	T	T T T T F
T	T	F	T T T T T
T	F	T	T T T T F
T	F	F	T T T T T
F	T	T	T F F F F
F	T	F	T T F T T
F	F	T	F T F F F
F	F	F	F T F T T
			1 5 2 4 3

Not an implication

43.

p	q	[(p → q) ∧ (q → p)] → (p ↔ q)
T	T	T T T T T
T	F	F F T T F
F	T	T F F T F
F	F	T T T T T
		1 3 2 5 4

Implication

44.

p	q	r	[(p ∨ q) ∧ r] → (p ∨ q)
T	T	T	T T T T T
T	T	F	T F F T T
T	F	T	T T T T T
T	F	F	T F F T T
F	T	T	T T T T T
F	T	F	T F F T T
F	F	T	F F T T F
F	F	F	F F T T F
			1 3 2 5 4

Implication

45.

~p → (q ∧ ~r)
F → (F ∧ F)
F → F
T

46.

~p → (q ∨ ~r)
F → (F ∨ F)
F → F
T

47.

(q ∧ ~ p) ↔ ~ r
(F ∧ F) ↔ F
F ↔ F
T

48.

p ↔ (~ q ∧ r)
T ↔ (T ∧ T)
T ↔ T
T

49.

(~ p ∧ ~ q) ∨ ~ r
(F ∧ T) ∨ F
F ∨ F
F

50.

~[p → (q ∧ r)]
~[T → F]
~ F
T

51. $(p \wedge r) \leftrightarrow (p \vee \sim q)$
      T $\leftrightarrow$ (T $\vee$ T)
      T $\leftrightarrow$ T
          T

52. $(\sim p \vee q) \rightarrow \sim r$
   (F $\vee$ F) $\rightarrow$ F
      F $\rightarrow$ F
        T

53. $(\sim p \leftrightarrow r) \vee (\sim q \leftrightarrow r)$
  (F $\leftrightarrow$ T) $\vee$ (T $\leftrightarrow$ T)
     F $\vee$ T
          T

54. $(r \rightarrow \sim p) \wedge (q \rightarrow \sim r)$
  (T $\rightarrow$ F) $\wedge$ (F $\rightarrow$ F)
     F $\wedge$ T
         F

55. $\sim [(p \vee q) \leftrightarrow (p \rightarrow \sim r)]$
 $\sim [(T \vee F) \leftrightarrow (T \rightarrow F)]$
 $\sim [$ T $\leftrightarrow$ F $]$
 $\sim [$ F $]$
 T

56. $[(\sim r \rightarrow \sim q) \vee (p \wedge \sim r)] \rightarrow q$
 $[(\,F \rightarrow T) \vee (T \wedge F)] \rightarrow F$
 $[$ T $\vee$ F $] \rightarrow$ F
      T $\rightarrow$ F
         F

57. p: 2 + 3 = 5. (T) $p \rightarrow q$
   q: 4 + 2 = 6. (T)   T $\rightarrow$ T
                        T

58. p: 1 + 1 = 2 (T) $(p \wedge q) \rightarrow r$
   q: 2 = 2 + 3 (F)   F $\rightarrow$ F
   r: 5 − 1 =3 (F)   T

59. p: 2 + 3 = 6. (F) $(p \vee q) \wedge r$
   q: 4 + 5 = 8. (F)   F $\wedge$ T
   r : 2 = 1 + 1. (T)   F

60. p: The Verazano Bridge is in New York. (T) $(p \wedge q) \vee r$
   q: The Golden Gate Bridge is in San Francisco. (T)   (T $\wedge$ T) $\vee$ F
    r: The Sears Tower is in Cincinnati. (F)   T $\vee$ F
                                         True

61. p: A pound contains 16 ounces. (T) $p \leftrightarrow (q \vee r)$
   q: A foot is equal to 15 inches. (F)   T $\leftrightarrow$ T
   r : A yard is equal to 3 feet. (T)   True

62. p: Steven Speilberg is a motion picture director. (T) $p \vee (\sim q \rightarrow r)$
   q: Julia Roberts is an actress. (T)   T $\vee$ (F $\rightarrow$ T)
   r : Tom Cruise is an actor. (T)   T $\vee$ T
                                         True

63. p: July 4ᵗʰ is Independence Day. (T) $(p \vee q) \wedge r$
   q: Two dimes have the same value as 1 quarter. (F)   T $\wedge$ T
   r : One dollar has the same value as 100 pennies. (T)   True

64. p: Wednesday follows Sunday. (F) $(p \vee q) \leftrightarrow r$
   q: Wednesday follows Tuesday. (T)   T $\leftrightarrow$ F
   r : Monday follows Wednesday. (F)   False

65. d: Io has a diameter of 1000-3161 miles. (T) $(d \vee w) \wedge a$
   w: Thebe may have water. (F)   (T $\vee$ F) $\wedge$ T
   a: Io may have atmosphere. (T)   T $\wedge$ T
                                    True

66. w: Titan may have water. (T) $(w \wedge a) \leftrightarrow j$
   a: Titan may have atmosphere. (T)   (T $\wedge$ T) $\leftrightarrow$ F
   j: Janus may have water. (F)   T $\leftrightarrow$ F
                             False

67. d: Phoebe has a larger diameter than Rhea. (F) $(d \leftrightarrow w) \wedge c$
   w: Callisto may have water. (T)   (F $\leftrightarrow$ T) $\wedge$ T
   c: Calypso has a diameter of 6 − 49 miles. (T)   F $\wedge$ T
                                    False

68. p: Jupiter has 16 moons. (T)
    q: Saturn has 18 moons. (T)
    r: Saturn has 7 moons that may have water. (T)

$$(p \vee \sim q) \to r$$
$$(T \vee \sim T) \to T$$
$$(T \vee F) \quad \to T$$
$$T \quad \to T$$
True

69. f: The most common cosmetic surgery for females is liposuction. (T)
    m: The most common procedure for males is eyelid surgery. (F)
    n: 20% of male cosmetic surgery is nose reshaping. (F)

$$(f \vee m) \wedge n$$
$$(T \vee F) \wedge F$$
$$T \quad \wedge F$$
False

70. p: 7% of female cosmetic surgeries are for facelifts. (T)
    q: 10% of male cosmetic surgeries are for facelifts. (F)
    r: Males have a higher percent of eyelid surgeries than females. (T)

$$(p \wedge q) \leftrightarrow r$$
$$(T \wedge F) \leftrightarrow T$$
$$F \quad \leftrightarrow T$$
False

71. $p \to q$
     $T \to T$
     $\quad T$

72. $\sim p \to \sim q$
     $F \quad \to F$
     $\quad T$

73. $\sim p \to q$
     $F \quad \to T$
     $\quad T$

74. $\sim q \leftrightarrow p$
     $F \quad \leftrightarrow T$
     $\quad F$

75. $q \leftrightarrow p$
     $T \leftrightarrow T$
     $\quad T$

76. $\sim q \to \sim p$
     $F \quad \to F$
     $\quad T$

77. No. Your father does not say what he will do if he does not get the raise. He may decide to buy the car even if he does not get the raise.

78. No. The statement only states what will occur if the interview goes well. If the interview does not go well, you may or may not get the job.

79.

p	q	r	[(p ∨ q)	→	~ r]	↔	(p	∧	~ q)
T	T	T	T	F	F	T	T	F	F
T	T	F	T	T	T	F	T	F	F
T	F	T	T	F	F	F	T	T	T
T	F	F	T	T	T	T	T	T	T
F	T	T	T	F	F	T	F	F	F
F	T	F	T	T	T	F	F	F	F
F	F	T	F	T	F	F	F	F	T
F	F	F	F	T	T	F	F	F	T
			1	3	2	7	4	6	5

80.

p	q	r	[(r → ~ q)	→	~ p]	∨	(q	↔	~ r)
T	T	T	T F F	T	F	T	F	T	F
T	T	F	F T F	F	F	F	F	F	T
T	F	T	T T T	F	F	F	T	F	F
T	F	F	F T T	F	F	T	T	T	T
F	T	T	T F F	T	T	T	F	T	F
F	T	F	F T F	T	T	T	F	F	T
F	F	T	T T T	T	T	T	T	F	F
F	F	F	F T T	T	T	T	T	T	T
			1 3 2	5	4	9	6	8	7

81. Let p: Heads I win. If we assume that you losing means that I win, then this statement is of the form p ∨ ~ p which is a tautology.

82. Katie was born last. All three triplets were asked the same question and we know that two will tell the truth and one will lie, thus, the two that agree must be telling the truth. Since Mary and Katie agree, they must be telling the truth and therefore Katie was born last.

83.

	Tiger	Boots	Sam	Sue
bowl:	blue	yellow	red	green
food:	Nine Lives	Whiskas	Friskies	Meow Mix

84.

p	q	r	s	a) (p ∨ q) → (r ∧ s)			b) (q → ~ p) ∨ (r ↔ s)				
T	T	T	T	T	T	T	T	F	F	T	T
T	T	T	F	T	F	F	T	F	F	F	F
T	T	F	T	T	F	F	T	F	F	F	F
T	T	F	F	T	F	F	T	F	F	T	T
T	F	T	T	T	T	T	F	T	F	T	T
T	F	T	F	T	F	F	F	T	F	T	F
T	F	F	T	T	F	F	F	T	F	T	F
T	F	F	F	T	F	F	F	T	F	T	T
F	T	T	T	T	T	T	T	T	T	T	T
F	T	T	F	T	F	F	T	T	T	T	F
F	T	F	T	T	F	F	T	T	T	T	F
F	T	F	F	T	F	F	T	T	T	T	T
F	F	T	T	F	T	T	F	T	T	T	T
F	F	T	F	F	T	F	F	T	T	T	F
F	F	F	T	F	T	F	F	T	T	T	F
F	F	F	F	F	T	F	F	T	T	T	T
				1	3	2	1	3	2	5	4

Exercise Set 3.4

1. ⇔

2. Two statements are equivalent if both statements have exactly the same truth values in the answer column of the truth table.

3. Construct a truth table for each statement and then compare the answer columns. If they are identical, then the statements are equivalent. If the answer columns are not identical, then the statements are not equivalent.

4. The two statements must be equivalent. A biconditional is a tautology only when the statements on each side of the biconditional are equivalent.

5. ~ (p ∧ q) ⇔ ~ p ∨ ~ q
   ~ (p ∨ q) ⇔ ~ p ∧ ~ q

6. a) q → p   b) ~ p → ~ q   c) ~ q → ~ p

7. converse ⇔ inverse;   conditional ⇔ contrapositive

8. ~ p ∨ q

9. Using DeMorgan's Laws on the statement ~ (p ∨ q), we get the following: (1) p ∨ q, (2) ~ p ∨ ~ q, (3) ~ p ∧ ~ q. Therefore ~ (p ∨ q) ⇔ ~ p ∧ ~ q.

10. Using DeMorgan's Laws on the statement ~ p ∨ ~ q, we get the following: (1) ~(~ p ∨ ~ q) (2) ~ (p ∨ q), (3) ~ (p ∧ q). Therefore ~ p ∨ ~ q ⇔ ~ (p ∧ q).

11. Using DeMorgan's Laws on the statement ~ (p ∧ q), we get the following: (1) p ∧ q, (2) ~ p ∧ ~ q, (3) ~ p ∨ ~ q. Therefore ~ (p ∧ q) is not equivalent to ~ p ∧ q.

12. Using DeMorgan's Laws on the statement ~ (p ∧ q), we get the following: (1) (p ∧ q), (2) ~ p ∧ ~ q, (3) ~ p ∨ ~ q. Therefore ~ (p ∧ q) is not equivalent to p ∨ ~ q.

13. Using DeMorgan's Laws on the statement p ∧ q, we get the following: (1) ~ (p ∧ q), (2) ~ (~ p ∧ ~ q), (3) ~ (~ p ∨ ~ q). Therefore p ∧ q ⇔ ~ (~ p ∨ ~ q).

14. Using DeMorgan's Laws on the statement ~ (p ∧ q), we get the following: (1) p ∧ q, (2) ~ p ∧ ~ q, (3) ~ p ∨ ~ q. Therefore ~ (p ∧ q) not equivalent to ~ (q ∨ ~ p)

15. Using DeMorgan's Laws on the statement ~ (p ∧ ~ q), we get the following: (1) p ∧ ~ q, (2) ~ p ∧ q, (3) ~ p ∨ q. Therefore ~ (p ∧ ~ q) ⇔ ~ p ∨ q.

16. Using DeMorgan's Laws on the statement ~ (p ∧ ~ r), we get the following: (1) p ∧ ~ r, (2) ~ p ∧ r, (3) ~ p ∨ r. Therefore q → ~ (p ∧ ~ r) ⇔ q → ~ p ∨ r.

17. Using DeMorgan's Laws on the statement (~ p ∨ ~ q) → r, we get the following: (1) ~ (~ p ∨ q) → r, (2) ~ (p∨ q)→ r, (3) ~ (p ∧ q)→ r. Therefore (~ p ∨ ~ q) → r ⇔ ~ (p ∧ q)→ r

18. Using DeMorgan's Laws on the statement q ∨ ~ r, we get the following: (1) ~ (q ∨ ~ r), (2) ~ (~ q ∨ r), (3) ~ (~ q ∧ r). Therefore p ↔ (q ∨ ~ r) ⇔ p ↔ ~ (~ q ∧ r)

19.

p	q	~p → q	p ∧ q
T	T	F T T	T
T	F	F T F	F
F	T	T T T	F
F	F	T F F	F
		1 3 2	1

The statements are not equivalent.

20.

p	q	p → q	~p ∨ q
T	T	T	F T T
T	F	F	F F F
F	T	T	T T T
F	F	T	T T F
		1	1 3 2

The statements are equivalent.

21.

p	q	p → q	~q → ~p
T	T	T	F T F
T	F	F	T F F
F	T	T	F T T
F	F	T	T T T
		1	1 3 2

The statements are equivalent.

22.

p	q	r	(p ∧ q) ∧ r	p ∧ (q ∧ r)
T	T	T	T T T	T T T
T	T	F	T F F	T F F
T	F	T	F F T	T F F
T	F	F	F F F	T F F
F	T	T	F F T	F F T
F	T	F	F F F	F F F
F	F	T	F F T	F F F
F	F	F	F F F	F F F
			1 3 2	2 3 1

The statements are equivalent.

23.

p	q	r	(p ∨ q) ∨ r	p ∨ (q ∨ r)
T	T	T	T T T	T T T
T	T	F	T T F	T T T
T	F	T	T T T	T T T
T	F	F	T T F	T T F
F	T	T	T T T	F T T
F	T	F	T T F	F T T
F	F	T	F T T	F T T
F	F	F	F F F	F F F
			1 3 2	2 3 1

The statements are equivalent.

24.

p	q	r	~p → (q ∧ r)	p ∨ (q ∧ r)
T	T	T	F T T	T T T
T	T	F	F T F	T T F
T	F	T	F T F	T T F
T	F	F	F T F	T T F
F	T	T	T T T	F T T
F	T	F	T F F	F F F
F	F	T	T F F	F F F
F	F	F	T F F	F F F
			1 3 2	2 3 1

The statements are equivalent.

25.

p	q	r	q ↔ (p ∧ ~r)	q → (p ∨ r)
T	T	T	T F T F F	T T T
T	T	F	T T T T T	T T T
T	F	T	F T T F F	F T T
T	F	F	F F T T T	F T T
F	T	T	T F F F F	T T T
F	T	F	T F F F T	T F F
F	F	T	F T F F F	F T T
F	F	F	F T F F T	F T F
			1 5 3 4 2	1 3 2

The statements are not equivalent.

26.

p	q	r	~(q → p) ∨ r	(p ∨ q) ∧ ~r
T	T	T	F T T T	T F F
T	T	F	F T F F	T T T
T	F	T	F T T T	T F F
T	F	F	F T F F	T T T
F	T	T	T F T T	T F F
F	T	F	T F T F	T T T
F	F	T	F T T T	F F F
F	F	F	F T F F	F F T
			2 1 4 3	1 3 2

The statements are not equivalent.

27.

p	q	r	(p → q) ∧ (q → r)			(p → q) → r		
T	T	T	T	T	T	T	T	T
T	T	F	T	F	F	T	F	F
T	F	T	F	F	T	F	T	T
T	F	F	F	F	T	F	T	F
F	T	T	T	T	T	T	T	T
F	T	F	T	F	F	T	F	F
F	F	T	T	T	T	T	T	T
F	F	F	T	T	T	T	F	F
			1	3	2	1	3	2

The statements are not equivalent.

28.

p	q	r	~q → (p ∧ r)			~(p ∨ r) → q			
T	T	T	F	T	T	F	T	T	T
T	T	F	F	T	F	F	T	T	T
T	F	T	T	T	T	F	T	T	F
T	F	F	T	F	F	F	T	T	F
F	T	T	F	T	F	F	T	T	T
F	T	F	F	T	F	T	F	T	T
F	F	T	T	F	F	F	T	T	T
F	F	F	T	F	F	T	F	F	F
			2	3	1	2	1	4	3

The statements are not equivalent.

29.

p	q	(p → q) ∧ (q → p)			p ↔ q
T	T	T	T	T	T
T	F	F	F	T	F
F	T	T	F	F	F
F	F	T	T	T	T
		1	3	2	1

The statements are equivalent.

30.

p	q	[~ (p → q)] ∧ [~(q → p)]					~ (p ↔ q)	
T	T	F	T	F	F	T	F	T
T	F	T	F	F	F	T	T	F
F	T	F	T	F	T	F	T	F
F	F	F	T	F	F	T	F	T
		2	1	5	4	3	2	1

The statements are not equivalent.

31. p: The boat is at the dock.

q: The boat will depart.

In symbolic form the statement is ~ (p ∨ q). Applying DeMorgan's Laws we get:

(1) p ∨ q, (2) ~ p ∨ ~ q, (3) ~ p ∧ ~ q. The boat is not at the dock and the boat will not depart.

32. p: The ink is red.

q: The pen has a ball point.

In symbolic form the statement is ~ (p ∧ q). Applying DeMorgan's Laws we get:

(1) p ∧ q, (2) ~ p ∧ ~ q, (3) ~ p ∨ ~ q. The ink is not red or the pen does not have a ball point.

33. p: The house has one phone line.

q: The house has two phone lines.

In symbolic form the statement is ~ p ∨ ~ q. Applying DeMorgan's Laws we get: (1) ~ (~ p ∨ ~ q),

(2) ~ (p ∨ q), (3) ~ (p ∧ q). It is false that the house has one phone line and the house has two phone lines.

34. p: David teaches English.

q: David teaches Chemistry.

In symbolic form the statement is p ∧ ~ q. Applying DeMorgan's Laws we get: (1) ~ (p ∧ ~ q),

(2) ~ (~ p ∧ q), (3) ~ (~ p ∨ q). It is false that David does not teach English or he teaches Chemistry.

35. p: The novel is written by Dinya Floyd.

q: It is well illustrated.

In symbolic form the statement is ~ p ∧ ~ q. Applying DeMorgan's Laws we get: (1) ~ (~ p ∧ ~ q),

(2) ~ (p ∧ q), (3) ~ (p ∨ q). It is false that the novel is written by Dinya Floyd or it is well illustrated.

36. p: Felicia ate the ice cream.

q: Felicia ate the yogurt.

In symbolic form the statement is p ∨ ~ q. Applying DeMorgan's Laws we get: (1) ~ (p ∨ ~ q),

(2) ~ (~ p ∨ q), (3) ~ (~ p ∧ q). It is false that Felicia did not eat the ice cream and she ate the yogurt.

37. p: We go to Cozemel.
    q: We will go snorkeling.
    r : We will go to Senior Frogs.
    In symbolic form the statement is p → (q ∨ ~ r). Applying DeMorgan's Laws we get: (1) p → ~ (q ∨ ~ r), (2) p → ~ (~ q ∨ r), (3) p → ~ (~ q ∧ r). If we go to Cozemel, then it is false that we will not go snorkeling and we will go to Senior Frogs.

38. p: We will visit Aunt Lilly.
    q: She will go on vacation.
    r: She will make her famous pancakes.
    In symbolic form the statement is p → (~ q ∧ r). Applying DeMorgan's Laws we get: (1) p → ~ (~ q ∧ r), (2) p → ~ (q ∧ ~ r), (3) p → ~ (q ∨ ~ r). If we visit Aunt Lilly, then it is false that she will go on vacation or she will not make her famous pancakes.

39. p: You drink milk.
    q: Your bones will be strong.
    In symbolic form the statement is p → q. p → q ⇔ ~ p ∨ q. You do not drink milk or your bones will be strong.

40. p: The rollercoaster ride was exciting.
    q: The rollercoaster was out of service.
    In symbolic form the statement is p ∨ q. p ∨ q ⇔ ~ p → q. If the rollercoaster ride was not exciting, then the rollercoaster was out of service.

41. p: John painted the picture.
    q: Ada purchased the picture.
    In symbolic form the statement is p ∨ ~ q. p ∨ ~ q ⇔ ~ p → ~ q. If John did not paint the picture, then Ada did not purchase the picture.

42. p: We will renew the subscription.
    q: The magazine will stop coming.
    In symbolic form the statement is ~ p → q. ~ p → q ⇔ p ∨ q. We will renew the subscription or the magazine will stop coming.

43. p: The noise is too loud.
    q: The police will come.
    In symbolic form the statement is ~ p → ~ q. ~ p → ~ q ⇔ p ∨ ~ q. The noise is too loud or the police will not come.

44. p: Stone Mt. is in Georgia.
    q: The Empire State Building is in Austin, Texas.
    In symbolic form the statement is p ∨ ~ q. p ∨ ~ q ⇔ ~ p → ~ q. If Stone Mt. is not in Georgia, then The Empire State Building is not in Austin, Texas.

45. p: You are 18 years old.
    q: You are eligible to vote.
    In symbolic form the statement is (p → q) ∧ (q → p).
    (p → q) ∧ (q → p) ⇔ p ↔ q. You are 18 years old if and only if you are eligible to vote.

46. p: The number is even.
    q: The number is divisible by 2.
    In symbolic form the statement is (p → q) ∧ (q → p).
    (p → q) ∧ (q → p) ⇔ p ↔ q. A number is even if and only if the number is divisible by 2.

47. p: An animal is a mammal.
   q: An animal is warm blooded.
   In symbolic form the statement is $p \leftrightarrow q$.
   $p \leftrightarrow q \Leftrightarrow (p \rightarrow q) \wedge (q \rightarrow p)$. If an animal is a mammal then it is warm blooded, and if an animal is warm blooded then it is a mammal.

48. p: You need to pay taxes.
   q: You receive income.
   In symbolic form the statement is $p \leftrightarrow q$.
   $p \leftrightarrow q \Leftrightarrow (p \rightarrow q) \wedge (q \rightarrow p)$. If you need to pay taxes, then you receive income, and if you receive income, then you need to pay taxes.

49. p: The fish are biting.
   q: We will go fishing.
   In symbolic form the statement is $p \rightarrow q$.
   converse: $q \rightarrow p$; If we go fishing, then the fish are biting.
   inverse: $\sim p \rightarrow \sim q$; If the fish are not biting, then we will not go fishing.
   contrapositive: $\sim q \rightarrow \sim p$; If we do not go fishing, then the fish are not biting.

50. p: The computer goes on sale.
   q: We will buy the computer.
   In symbolic form the statement is $p \rightarrow q$.
   converse: $q \rightarrow p$; If we buy the computer, then it is on sale.
   inverse: $\sim p \rightarrow \sim q$; If the computer is not on sale, then we will not buy the computer.
   contrapositive: $\sim q \rightarrow \sim p$; If we do not buy the computer, then it is not on sale

51. p: The phone bill is large.
   q: You will have to give up your phone.
   In symbolic form the statement is $p \rightarrow q$.
   converse: $q \rightarrow p$; If you have to give up your phone, then the phone bill is large.
   inverse: $\sim p \rightarrow \sim q$; If the phone bill is not large, then you will not have to give up your phone.
   contrapositive: $\sim q \rightarrow \sim p$; If you do not have to give up your phone, then the phone bill is not large

52. p: There are clothes on the floor.
   q: You have cleaned your room.
   In symbolic form the statement is $p \rightarrow \sim q$.
   converse: $\sim q \rightarrow p$; If you did not clean your room, then there are clothes on the floor.
   inverse: $\sim p \rightarrow q$; If there are no clothes on the floor, then you cleaned your room.
   contrapositive: $q \rightarrow \sim p$; If you cleaned your room, then there are no clothes on the floor.

53. p: The dog is friendly.
   q: I will get out of the car.
   In symbolic form the statement is $\sim p \rightarrow \sim q$.
   converse: $\sim q \rightarrow \sim p$; If I do not get out of the car, then the dog is not friendly.
   inverse: $p \rightarrow q$; If the dog is friendly, then I will get out of the car.
   contrapositive: $q \rightarrow p$; If I get out of the car, then the dog is friendly.

54. p: The nut will turn.
   q: Sean needs to use liquid wrench.
   In symbolic form the statement is $\sim p \rightarrow q$.
   converse: $q \rightarrow \sim p$; If Sean needs to use liquid wrench, then the nut will not turn.
   inverse: $p \rightarrow \sim q$; If the nut will turn, then Sean does not need to use liquid wrench.
   contrapositive: $\sim q \rightarrow p$; If Sean does not need to use liquid wrench, then the nut will turn.

55. p: The sun is shining.
q: We will go down to the marina.
r: We will take out the sailboat.
In symbolic form the statement is p → (q ∧ r).
converse: (q ∧ r) → p; If we go down to the marina and we take out the sail boat, then the sun is shining.
inverse: ~ p → ~ (q ∧ r); Applying DeMorgan's Laws the statement becomes ~ p → (~ q ∨ ~ r). If the sun is not shining, then we will not go down to the marina or we will not take out the sail boat.
contrapositive: ~ (q ∧ r) → ~ p; Applying DeMorgan's Laws the statement becomes (~ q ∨ ~ r) → p. If we do not go down to the marina or we do not take out the sail boat, then the sun is not shining.

56. p: The apple pie is baked.
q: .We will eat a piece of pie.
r : We will save some pie for later.
In symbolic form the statement is p → (q ∧ r).
converse: (q ∧ r) → p; If we eat a piece of pie and we save some pie for later, then the apple pie is baked.
inverse: ~ p → ~ (q ∧ r); after applying DeMorgan's Laws we get ~ p → (~ q ∨ ~ r); If the apple pie is not baked, then we will not eat a piece of pie or we will not save some pie for later.
contrapositive: ~ (q ∧ r) ~ p; after applying DeMorgan's Laws we get (~ q ∨ ~ r) → ~ p.
If we will not eat a piece of pie or we will not save some pie for later, then the apple pie is not baked.

57. If two angles of the triangle are equal, then the triangle is isosceles. The statement is true.

58. If the sum of the digits is divisible by 3, then the number is divisible by 3. The statement is true.

59. If 2 divides the units digit of the counting number, then 2 divides the counting number. The statement is true.

60. If n is a natural number, then 1/n is a natural number. The statement is false.

61. If two lines are not parallel, then the two lines intersect in at least one point. The statement is true.

62. If m is a counting number, then $\dfrac{ma}{mb} = \dfrac{a}{b}$. The statement is true.

63. If the polygon is a quadrilateral, then the sum of the interior angles of the polygon measure 360^{0}. The statement is true.

64. If the product of a and b is an even counting number, then a and b are both even counting numbers. The statement is false.

65. p: Maria has retired.
q: Maria is still working.

In symbolic form the statements are: a) ~ p ∨ q, b) q → ~ p, c) p → ~ q

Statement (c) is the contrapositive of statement (b). Therefore, statements (b) and (c) are equivalent.

p	q	a) ~p ∨ q	b) q →~ p
T	T	F T T	T F F
T	F	F F F	F T F
F	T	T T T	T T T
F	F	T T F	F T T
		1 3 2	1 3 2

Since the truth tables for (a) and (b) are different we conclude that only statements (b) and (c) are equivalent.

66. p: Today is Monday.

q: Tomorrow is Wednesday.

In symbolic form the statements are: a) p → ~ q, b) ~ (p ∧ ~ q), c) ~ p ∨ q.

If we use DeMorgan's Laws on statement (b) we get statement (c). Therefore, statements (b) and (c) are equivalent. If we look at the truth tables for all three statements we can see that only statements (b) and (c) are equivalent.

		a)	b)	c)
p	q	p → ~q	~ (p ∧ ~ q)	~p ∨ q
T	T	T F F	T T F F	F T T
T	F	T T T	F T T T	F F F
F	T	F T F	T F F F	T T T
F	F	F T T	T F F T	T T F
		1 3 2	4 1 3 2	1 3 2

67. p: The car is reliable.

q: The car is noisy.

In symbolic form the statements are: a) ~ p ∧ q, b) ~ p → ~ q, c) ~ (p ∨ ~ q.

If we use DeMorgan's Laws on statement (a), we get statement (c). Therefore, statements (a) and (c) are equivalent. If we look at the truth tables for statements (a), (b), and (c) we see that only statements (a) and (c) are equivalent.

		a)	b)	c)
p	q	~ p ∧ q	~ p → ~ q	~ (p ∨ ~ q)
T	T	F F T	F T F	F T T F
T	F	F F F	F T T	F T T T
F	T	T T T	T F F	T F F F
F	F	T F F	T T T	F F T T
		1 3 2	1 3 2	4 1 3 2

68. p: The sales tax is 6%.

q: You live in Kings County.

In symbolic form the statements are: a) p ↔ q, b) (q → p) ∧ (p → q), c) ~ q ∧ ~ p.

In sec. 3.3 we learned that p ↔ q ⇔ (p → q) ∧ (q → p). Therefore, statements (a) and (c) are equivalent. If we look at the truth tables for statements (a) and (c) we can conclude that only statements (a) and (b) are equivalent.

		a)	c)
p	q	p ↔ q	~ q ∧ ~ p
T	T	T	F F F
T	F	F	T F F
F	T	F	F F T
F	F	T	T T T
		1	1 3 2

69. p: The house is made of wood.

q: The shed is made of wood.

In symbolic form the statements are: a) ~ p ∨ ~ q, b) p → ~ q, c) ~ (q ∧ ~ p).

Using the fact that p → q ⇔ ~ p ∨ q to rewrite statement (b), we get ~ p ∨ ~ q. Therefore, statements (a) and (b) are equivalent. Looking at the truth tables for all three, it can be determined that only statements (a) and (b) are equivalent.

p	q	a) ~ p ∨ ~ q			b) p → ~ q			c) ~ (q ∧ ~ p)			
T	T	F	F	F	T	F	F	T	T	F	F
T	F	F	T	T	T	T	T	T	F	F	F
F	T	T	T	F	F	T	F	F	T	T	T
F	F	T	T	T	F	T	T	T	F	F	T
		1	3	2	1	3	2	4	1	3	2

70. p: You leave your lights on.

q: Your electric bill will be higher.

In symbolic form the statements are: a) ~ (~ p → q), b) q ↔ p, c) ~ (p → q).

Looking at the truth tables for statements (a), (b), and (c), it can be determined that none of these statements are equivalent.

p	q	a) ~ (~ p → q)				b) q ↔ p	c) ~ (p → q)	
T	T	F	F	T	T	T	F	T
T	F	F	F	T	F	F	T	F
F	T	F	T	T	T	F	F	T
F	F	T	T	F	F	T	F	T
		4	1	3	2	1	2	1

71. p: You will get a speeding ticket.

q: You speed.

In symbolic form the statements are: a) ~ p ↔ ~ q, b) ~ (p ↔ ~ q), c) p → q.

Looking at the truth tables for statements (a), (b), and (c) it can be determined that only statements (a) and (b) are equivalent.

p	q	a) ~ p ↔ ~ q			b) ~ (p ↔ ~ q)				c) p → q
T	T	F	T	F	T	T	F	F	T
T	F	F	F	T	F	T	T	T	F
F	T	T	F	F	F	F	T	F	T
F	F	T	T	T	T	F	F	T	T
		1	3	2	4	1	3	2	1

72. p: Today is Sunday.

q: The library is open.

In symbolic form the statements are: a) ~ p ∨ q,   b) p → ~ q,   c) q → ~ p.

Looking at the truth table for all three statements, we can determine that only statements (b) and (c) are equivalent.

p	q	a) ~ p ∨ q	b) p → ~ q	c) q → ~ p
T	T	F T T	T F F	T F F
T	F	F F F	T T T	F T F
F	T	T T T	F T F	T T T
F	F	T T F	F T T	F T T
		1 3 2	1 3 2	1 3 2

73. p: You are fishing at 1 PM.

q: You are driving a car at 1 PM.

In symbolic form the statements are: a) p → q,   b) ~ p ∨ q,   c) ~ (p ∧ ~ q).

Using the fact that p → q ⇔ ~ p ∨ q, we see that (a) and (b) are equivalent statements.

If we use DeMorgan's Laws on statement (b) we get statement (c). Therefore all three statements are equivalent.

74. p: The grass grows.

q: The trees are blooming.

In symbolic form the statements are: a) p ∧ q,   b) q → ~ p,   c) ~ q ∨ ~ p.

Using the fact that p → q ⇔ ~ p ∨ q, on statement (b) we get ~ q ∨ ~ p. Therefore, statements (b) and (c) are equivalent. Looking at the truth table for statements (a) and (b) we can conclude that only statements (b) and (c) are equivalent.

p	q	p ∧ q	q → ~ p
T	T	T	T F F
T	F	F	F T F
F	T	F	T T T
F	F	F	F T T
		1	1 3 2

75. p: The pay is good.

q: Today is Monday.

r : I will take the job.

Looking at the truth tables for statements (a), (b), and (c), we can determine that none of these statements are equivalent.

p	q	r	a) (p ∧ q) → r	b) ~r → ~(p ∨ q)	c) (p ∧ q) ∨ r
T	T	T	T T T	F T F T	T T T
T	T	F	T F F	T F F T	T T F
T	F	T	F T T	F T F T	F T T
T	F	F	F T F	T F F T	F F F
F	T	T	F T T	F T F T	F T T
F	T	F	F T F	T F F T	F F F
F	F	T	F T T	F T T F	F T T
F	F	F	F T F	T T T F	F F F
			1 3 2	1 4 3 2	1 3 2

76. p: You are 18 years old.
    q: You are a citizen of the United States.
    r : You can vote in a presidential election.
    Looking at the truth tables for statements (a), (b), and (c), we can determine that none of these statements are equivalent.

a)

p	q	r	(p	∧	q)	→	r
T	T	T		T		T	T
T	T	F		T		F	F
T	F	T		F		T	T
T	F	F		F		T	F
F	T	T		F		T	T
F	T	F		F		T	F
F	F	T		F		T	T
F	F	F		F		T	F
				1		3	2

b)

p	q	r	r	↔	(q	∧	p)
T	T	T	T	T		T	
T	T	F	F	F		T	
T	F	T	T	F		F	
T	F	F	F	T		F	
F	T	T	T	F		F	
F	T	F	F	T		F	
F	F	T	T	F		F	
F	F	F	F	T		F	
			1	3		2	

c)

p	q	r	~r	∨	(p	∧	~q)
T	T	T	F	F	T	F	F
T	T	F	T	T	T	F	F
T	F	T	F	T	T	T	T
T	F	F	T	T	T	T	T
F	T	T	F	F	F	F	F
F	T	F	T	T	F	F	F
F	F	T	F	F	F	F	T
F	F	F	T	T	F	F	T
			1	5	2	4	3

77. p: The package was sent by Federal Express.
    q: The package was sent by United Parcel Service.
    r : The package arrived on time.
    Using the fact that p → q ⇔ ~ p ∨ q, to rewrite statement (c) we get p ∨ (~ q ∧ r). Therefore, statements (a) and (c) are equivalent. Looking at the truth table for statements (a) and (b), we can conclude that only statements (a) and (c) are equivalent.

a)

p	q	r	p	∨	(~q	∧	r)
T	T	T	T	T	F	F	T
T	T	F	T	T	F	F	F
T	F	T	T	T	T	T	T
T	F	F	T	T	T	F	F
F	T	T	F	F	F	F	T
F	T	F	F	F	F	F	F
F	F	T	F	T	T	T	T
F	F	F	F	F	T	F	F
			1	5	2	4	3

b)

p	q	r	r	↔	(p	∨	~q)
T	T	T	T	T	T	T	F
T	T	F	F	F	T	T	F
T	F	T	T	T	T	T	T
T	F	F	F	F	T	T	T
F	T	T	T	F	F	F	F
F	T	F	F	T	F	F	F
F	F	T	T	T	F	T	T
F	F	F	F	F	F	T	T
			1	5	2	4	3

78. p: We will put the dog outside.
    q: We feed the dog.
    r : The dog will bark.
    In symbolic form the statements are: a) (p ∨ q) → ~ r, b) r → (~ p ∧ ~ q), c) r → ~ (p ∨ q). Statement (c) is the contrapositive of statement (b) and if we use DeMorgan's Laws on statement (b) we obtain statement (c). Therefore, statements (a), (b), and (c) are equivalent.

79. p: The car needs oil.
q: The car needs gas.
r : The car is new.
In symbolic form the statements are: a) p ∧ (q ∨ r), b) p ∧ ~ (~ q ∧ ~ r), c) p → (q ∨ ~ r). If we use DeMorgan's Laws on the disjunction in statement (a), we obtain p ∧ ~ (~ q ∧ ~ r). Therefore, statements (a) and (b) are equivalent. If we compare the truth tables for (a) and (c) we see that they are not equivalent. Therefore, only statements (a) and (b) are equivalent.

```
p  q  r | p ∧ (q ∨ r) | p → (q ∨ ~ r)
T  T  T | T T    T     | T  T   T T F
T  T  F | T T    T     | T  T   T T T
T  F  T | T T    T     | T  F   F F F
T  F  F | T F    F     | T  T   F T T
F  T  T | F F    T     | F  T   T T F
F  T  F | F F    T     | F  T   T T T
F  F  T | F F    T     | F  T   F F F
F  F  F | F F    F     | F  T   F T T
          1 3    2       1  5   2 4 3
```

80. p: The mortgage rate went down.
q: Tim purchased the house.
r : The down payment was 10%.
Looking at the truth tables for statements (a), (b), and (c), we can determine that none of these statements are equivalent.

```
          a)              b)              c)
p  q  r | p ↔ (q ∧ r) | r ∧ (q → p) | q → (p ∧ ~ r)
T  T  T | T T    T     | T T    T     | T  F T  F F
T  T  F | T F    F     | F F    T     | T  T T  T T
T  F  T | T F    F     | T T    T     | F  T T  F F
T  F  F | T F    F     | F F    T     | F  T T  T T
F  T  T | F F    T     | T F    F     | T  F F  F F
F  T  F | F T    F     | F F    F     | T  F F  F T
F  F  T | F T    F     | T T    T     | F  T F  F F
F  F  F | F T    F     | F F    T     | F  T F  F T
          1 3    2       1 3    2       1  5 2  4 3
```

81. Yes.   conditional: If it is a bird, then it can fly. (False)
            converse: If it can fly, then it is a bird. (False)

82. Yes.   conditional: If 5 + 1 = 9, then 2 + 5 = 7. (True)
            converse: If 2 + 5 = 7, then 5 + 1 = 9. (False)

83. Yes.   conditional: If 2 + 5 = 7, then 5 + 1 = 4. (False)
            contrapositive: If 5 + 1 ≠ 4, then 2 + 5 ≠ 7. (False)

84. No. A conditional statement and its contrapositive are equivalent statements.

85. If we use DeMorgan's Laws to rewrite ~ p ∨ q we get ~ (p ∧ ~ q). Since ~ p ∨ q ⇔ ~ (p ∧ ~ q) and
p → q ⇔ ~ p ∨ q, we can conclude that p → q ⇔ ~ (p ∧ ~ q). Other answers are possible.

86. ~ [~ (p ∨ ~ q)] ⇔ p ∨ ~ q. Make use of the fact that ~ (~ p) ⇔ p.

87. Research problem.

88. a) ~ p = 1 − p = 1 − 0.25 = 0.75
b) ~ q = 1 − q = 1 − 0.20 = 0.80
c) p ∧ q has a truth value equal to the lesser of p = 0.75 and q = 0.20. Thus p ∧ q = 0.20
d) p ∨ q has truth value equal to the greater of p = 0.25 and q = 0.20. Thus p ∨ q = 0.25
e) p → q has truth value equal to the lesser of 1 and 1 − p + q = 1 − 0.25 + 0.20 = 0.95. Thus p → q = 0.95
f) p ↔ q has a truth value equal to 1 − |p − q| = 1 − |0.25 − 0.20| = 1 − 0.05 = 0.95. Thus p ↔ q = 0.95

Exercise Set 3.5

1. An argument is valid when its conclusion necessarily follows from the given set of premises.

2. Yes. It is not necessary for the premises or the conclusion to be true statements for the argument to be valid.

3. Yes. If the conclusion does not follow from the set of premises, then the argument is invalid.

4. Yes. If the conclusion necessarily follows from the set of premises, then the argument is valid, even if the premises are false.

5. (1) Write the argument in symbolic form.

(2) Compare the form of the argument with forms that are known to be valid or invalid. If there are no known form to compare then go on to step 3.

(3) Write a conditional statement of the form. $(p_1 \wedge p_2) \to c$.

(4) Construct a truth table for the statement in step 3.

(5) If the truth table is a tautology, then the argument is valid. If the truth table is not a tautology, then the argument is invalid.

6. A fallacy

7. a)
$$p \to q$$
$$\underline{p}$$
$$\therefore q$$

b) If the sky is clear, then I will go to the game.
The sky is clear.
∴ I will go to the game.

8. a)
$$p \to q$$
$$\underline{q \to r}$$
$$\therefore p \to r$$

b) If the sky is clear, then it will be hot.
If it is hot, then we will wear shorts.
∴ If the sky is clear, then we will wear shorts.

9. a)
$$p \to q$$
$$\underline{\sim q}$$
$$\therefore \sim p$$

b) If the soil is dry, then the grass needs water.
The grass does not need water.
∴ The soil is not dry.

10. a)
$$p \vee q$$
$$\underline{\sim p}$$
$$\therefore q$$

b) The pizza is served on time or it is free.
The pizza was not served on time.
∴ The pizza is free.

11. a)
$$p \to q$$
$$\underline{q}$$
$$\therefore p$$

b) If you wash my car, then I will give you $5.
I will give you $5.
∴ You washed my car.

12. a)
$$p \to q$$
$$\underline{\sim p}$$
$$\therefore \sim q$$

b) If you wash my car, then I will give you $5.
You did not wash my car.
∴ I will not give you $5.

13.

p	q	[(p → q)	∧	~p]	→	q
T	T	T	F	F	T	T
T	F	F	F	F	T	F
F	T	T	T	T	T	T
F	F	T	T	T	F	F
		1	3	2	5	4

The argument is invalid.

14.

p	q	[(p ∧ ~q)	∧	q]	→	~p
T	T	T F F	F	T	T	F
T	F	T T T	F	F	T	F
F	T	F F F	F	T	T	T
F	F	F F T	F	F	T	T
		1 3 2	5	4	7	6

The argument is valid.

15. This argument is the law of detachment and therefore it is valid.

16.

p	q	[(~p ∨ q)	∧	q]	→	p
T	T	F T T T	T	T	T	T
T	F	F F F F	F	F	T	T
F	T	T T T T	T	T	F	F
F	F	T T F F	F	F	T	F
		1 3 2 5		4	7	6

The argument is not valid.

17.

p	q	[~p ∧ (p ∨ q)]	→	~q
T	T	F F T	T	F
T	F	F F T	T	T
F	T	T T T	F	F
F	F	T F F	T	T
		1 3 2	5	4

The argument is a fallacy.

18. This argument is the law of contraposition and therefore it is valid.
19. This argument is the fallacy of the inverse. Therefore it is not valid.

20.

p	q	[(p	∨	q)	∧	~q]	→	p
T	T	T	F	F		T	T	
T	F	T	T	T		T	T	
F	T	T	F	F		T	F	
F	F	F	F	T		T	F	
		1	3	2		5	4	

The argument is valid.

21.

p	q	[(~p	→	q)	∧	~q]	→	~p
T	T	F	T	T	F	F	T	F
T	F	F	T	F	T	T	F	F
F	T	T	T	T	F	F	T	T
F	F	T	F	F	F	T	T	T
		1	3	2	5	4	7	6

The argument is invalid.

22.

p	q	[(q	∧	~p)	∧	~p]	→	q
T	T	T	F	F	F	F	T	T
T	F	F	F	F	F	F	T	F
F	T	T	T	T	T	T	T	T
F	F	F	F	T	F	T	T	F
		1	3	2	5	4	7	6

The argument is valid.

23. This argument is the law of syllogism and therefore it is valid.

24.

p	q	[(q	∧	p)	∧	q]	→	~p
T	T	T	T	T		F	F	
T	F	F	F	F		T	F	
F	T	F	F	T		T	T	
F	F	F	F	T		T	T	
		1	3	2		5	4	

The argument is invalid.

25.

p	q	r	[(p ↔ q)	∧	(q ∧ r)]	→	(p ∨ r)
T	T	T	T	T	T	T	T
T	T	F	T	F	F	T	T
T	F	T	F	F	F	T	T
T	F	F	F	F	F	T	T
F	T	T	F	F	T	T	T
F	T	F	F	F	F	T	F
F	F	T	T	F	F	T	T
F	F	F	T	F	F	T	F
			1	3	2	5	4

The argument is valid.

26.

p	q	r	[(p ↔ q)	∧	(q → r)]	→	(~r	→	~p)
T	T	T	T	T	T	T	F	T	F
T	T	F	T	F	F	T	T	F	F
T	F	T	F	F	T	T	F	T	F
T	F	F	F	F	T	T	T	F	F
F	T	T	F	F	T	T	F	T	T
F	T	F	F	F	F	T	T	T	T
F	F	T	T	T	T	T	F	T	T
F	F	F	T	T	T	T	T	T	T
			1	3	2	7	4	6	5

The argument is valid.

27.

p	q	r	[(r ↔ p)	∧	(~p	∧	q)]	→	(p ∧ r)
T	T	T	T	F	F	F	T	T	T
T	T	F	F	F	F	F	T	T	F
T	F	T	T	F	F	F	T	T	T
T	F	F	F	F	F	F	T	T	F
F	T	T	F	F	T	T	T	F	F
F	T	F	T	T	T	T	T	F	F
F	F	T	F	F	T	F	F	T	F
F	F	F	T	F	T	F	F	T	F
			1	5	2	4	3	7	6

The argument is invalid.

28. [(p ∨ q) ∧ (r ∧ p)] → q

p	q	r	(p ∨ q)	∧	(r ∧ p)	→	q
T	T	T	T	T	T	T	T
T	T	F	T	F	F	T	T
T	F	T	T	T	T	F	F
T	F	F	T	F	F	T	F
F	T	T	T	F	F	T	T
F	T	F	T	F	F	T	T
F	F	T	F	F	F	T	F
F	F	F	F	F	F	T	F
			1	3	2	5	4

The argument is invalid

29. [(p → q) ∧ (q ∨ r) ∧ (r ∨ p)] → p

p	q	r	(p → q)	∧	(q ∨ r)	∧	(r ∨ p)	→	p
T	T	T	T	T	T	T	T	T	T
T	T	F	T	T	T	T	T	T	T
T	F	T	F	F	T	F	T	T	T
T	F	F	F	F	F	F	T	T	T
F	T	T	T	T	T	T	T	F	F
F	T	F	T	T	T	F	F	T	F
F	F	T	T	T	T	T	T	F	F
F	F	F	T	F	F	F	F	T	F
			1	3	2	5	4	7	6

The argument is invalid.

30. This argument is the law of syllogism and therefore it is valid.

31. [(p → q) ∧ (r → ~ p) ∧ (p ∨ r)] → (q ∨ ~ p)

p	q	r											
T	T	T	T	F	T	F	F	F	T	T	T	T	F
T	T	F	T	T	F	T	F	T	T	T	T	T	F
T	F	T	F	F	T	F	F	F	T	T	F	F	F
T	F	F	F	F	F	T	F	F	T	T	F	F	F
F	T	T	T	T	T	T	T	T	T	T	T	T	T
F	T	F	T	T	F	T	T	F	F	T	T	T	T
F	F	T	T	T	T	T	T	T	T	T	F	T	T
F	F	F	T	T	F	T	T	F	F	T	F	T	T
			1	5	2	4	3	7	6	11	9	10	8

The argument is valid.

32. [(p ↔ q) ∧ (p ∨ q) ∧ (q → r)] → (q ∨ r)

p	q	r	(p ↔ q)	∧	(p ∨ q)	∧	(q → r)	→	(q ∨ r)
T	T	T	T	T	T	T	T	T	T
T	T	F	T	T	T	F	F	T	T
T	F	T	F	F	T	F	T	T	T
T	F	F	F	F	T	F	T	T	F
F	T	T	F	F	T	F	T	T	T
F	T	F	F	F	T	F	F	T	T
F	F	T	T	F	F	F	T	T	T
F	F	F	T	F	F	F	T	T	F
			1	4	2	5	3	7	6

The argument is valid.

33. t: Today is Tuesday.
b: We will play bingo.

$$t \to b$$
$$\underline{t\hphantom{\to b}}$$
$$\therefore b$$

This argument is the law of detachment and therefore it is valid.

34. t: The game is televised.
w: People will watch the game.

$$t \to w$$
$$\underline{w\hphantom{\to w}}$$
$$\therefore t$$

This argument is the fallacy of the converse, and therefore not valid.

35. w: The sweater is white.   w ∨ r
    r: The sweater is red.   ~ r
                                   ∴ w

w	r	[(w ∨ r) ∧ ~ r] → w
T	T	T F F T T
T	F	T T T T T
F	T	T F F T F
F	F	F F T T F
		1 3 2 5 4

The argument is valid.

36. f: The canteen is full.   f → w
    w: We can go for a walk.   w ∧ ~ t
    t: We will get thirsty.   ∴ w → ~ f

f	w	t	[(f → w) ∧ (w ∧ ~ t)] → (w → ~ f)
T	T	T	T F TF F T T F F
T	T	F	T T TT T F T F F
T	F	T	F F FF F T F T F
T	F	F	F F FF T T F T F
F	T	T	T F TF F T T T T
F	T	F	T T TT T T T T T
F	F	T	T F FF F T F T T
F	F	F	T F FF T T F T T
			1 5 24 3 9 6 8 7

The argument is not valid.

37. r: The painting is a Rembrandt.
     p: The painting is a Picasso.

r ∨ p

p → ~ r

∴ ~ p

r	p	[(r ∨ p) ∧ (p → ~ r)] → ~ p
T	T	T F T F F T F
T	F	T T F T F T T
F	T	T T T T T F F
F	F	F F F T T T T
		1 5 2 4 3 7 6

The argument is invalid.

38. c: You can cook the meal.
     v: I will vacuum the rug.

c → v

~ v

∴ ~ c

This argument is the law of contraposition and therefore it is valid.

39. t: The package is more than 2 pounds.
     m: We can mail the package.

~ t

t → m

∴ m

t	m	[~ t ∧ (t → m)] → m
T	T	F F T T T
T	F	F F F T F
F	T	T T T T T
F	F	T T T F F
		2 3 1 5 4

The argument is invalid.

40. s: It is snowing.   s ∧ g
     g: I am going skiing.   g → c
     c: I will wear a coat.   ∴ s → c

s	g	c	[(s ∧ g) ∧ (g → c)] → (s → c)
T	T	T	T T T T T
T	T	F	T F F T F
T	F	T	F F T T T
T	F	F	F F T T F
F	T	T	F F T T T
F	T	F	F F F T T
F	F	T	F F T T T
F	F	F	F F T T T
			1 3 2 5 4

The argument is valid.

41. g: The garden has vegetables.
f: The garden has flowers.

g ∨ f
~f → g
∴ f ∨ g

g	f	[(g ∨ f)	∧	(~f	→	g)]	→	(f ∨ g)
T	T	T	T	F	T	T	T	T
T	F	T	T	T	T	T	T	T
F	T	T	T	F	T	F	T	T
F	F	F	F	T	F	F	T	F
		1	5	2	4	3	7	6

The argument is valid.

42. h: The house has electric heat.
b: The Flynns will buy the house.
p: The price is less than $100,000.

h → b
~p → ~b
∴ h → p

h	b	p	[(h → b)	∧	(~p	→	~b)]	→	(h→p)
T	T	T	T	T	F	T	F	T	T
T	T	F	T	F	T	F	F	T	F
T	F	T	F	F	F	T	T	T	T
T	F	F	F	F	T	T	T	T	F
F	T	T	T	T	F	T	F	T	T
F	T	F	T	F	T	F	F	T	T
F	F	T	T	T	F	T	T	T	T
F	F	F	T	T	T	T	T	T	T
			1	5	2	4	3	7	6

The argument is valid.

43. c: The children are young.
d: We will get a dog.
w: We will get a white carpet.

c → d
d ↔ ~ w
∴ c → ~ w

c	d	w	[(c → d)	∧	(d	↔	~ w)]	→	(c	→	~ w)
T	T	T	T	F	T	F	F	T	T	F	F
T	T	F	T	T	T	T	T	T	T	T	T
T	F	T	F	F	F	T	F	T	T	F	F
T	F	F	F	F	F	F	T	T	T	T	T
F	T	T	T	F	T	F	F	T	F	T	F
F	T	F	T	T	T	T	T	T	F	T	T
F	F	T	T	T	F	T	F	T	F	T	F
F	F	F	T	F	F	F	T	T	F	T	T
			1	5	2	4	3	9	6	8	7

The argument is valid.

44. a: There is an atmosphere.
g: There is gravity.
w: An object has weight.

a → g
w → g
∴ a → w

a	g	w	[(a → g)	∧	(w → g)]	→	(a → w)
T	T	T	T	T	T	T	T
T	T	F	T	T	T	F	F
T	F	T	F	F	F	T	T
T	F	F	F	F	T	T	F
F	T	T	T	T	T	T	T
F	T	F	T	T	T	T	T
F	F	T	T	F	F	T	T
F	F	F	T	T	T	T	T
			1	3	2	5	4

The argument is invalid.

45. c: The cat is in the room.
m: The mice are hiding.

c → m
~ m
∴ ~ c

This argument is the law of contraposition and therefore it is valid.

46. t: The television is on.
p: The plug is plugged in.

t ∨ ~ p
p
∴ t

t	p	[(t ∨ ~ p)	∧	(p)]	→	t
T	T	TT F	T	T	T	T
T	F	TT T	F	F	T	T
F	T	FF F	F	T	T	F
F	F	FT T	F	F	T	F
		1 3 2	5	4	7	6

The argument is valid

47. b: Bonnie passed the bar exam.   b → p
        p: Bonnie will practice law.   ~ p

                                         ∴ ~ b

This argument is the law of contraposition and therefore it is valid

48.   t: The test was easy.   t ∧ g
         g: I received a good grade.   ~ t ∨ ~ g

                                       ∴ ~ t

t	g	[(t ∧ g)	∧	(~ t	∨	~ g)]	→	~ t
T	T	T	F	F	F	F	T	F
T	F	F	F	F	T	T	T	F
F	T	F	F	T	T	F	T	T
F	F	F	F	T	T	T	T	T
		1	5	2	4	3	7	6

The argument is invalid.

49.   c: The baby is crying.   c ∧ ~ h
         h: The baby is hungry.   h → c

                                  ∴ h

c	h	[(c ∧ ~ h)	∧	(h → c)]	→	h
T	T	T F F	F	T	T	T
T	F	T T T	T	T	F	F
F	T	F F F	F	F	T	T
F	F	F F T	F	T	T	F
		1 3 2	5	4	7	6

The argument is invalid

50.   n: The car is new.   n → a
         a: The car has air conditioning. ~ n ∧ a

                                           ∴ ~ n

n	a	[(n → a)	∧	(~ n	∧	a)]	→	~ n
T	T	T	F	F	F	T	T	F
T	F	F	F	F	F	F	T	F
F	T	T	T	T	T	T	T	T
F	F	T	F	T	F	F	T	T
		1	5	2	4	3	7	6

The argument is valid.

51.   f: The football team wins the game.
         d: Dave played quarterback.
         s: The team is in second place.

         f → d

         d → ~ s

         ∴ f → s

Using the law of syllogism, this argument is invalid.

52.   e: The engineering courses are difficult.
         c: The chemistry labs are long.
         a: The art tests are easy.

         e ∧ c

         c → a

         ∴ e ∧ ~ a

e	c	a	[(e ∧ c)	∧	(c → a)]	→	(e ∧ ~ a)
T	T	T	T	T	T	F	T F F
T	T	F	T	F	F	T	T T T
T	F	T	F	F	T	T	T T F
T	F	F	F	F	T	T	T T T
F	T	T	F	F	T	T	F F F
F	T	F	F	F	F	T	F F T
F	F	T	F	F	T	T	F F F
F	F	F	F	F	T	T	F F T
			1	3	2	7	4 6 5

The argument is invalid.

53.   l: The lights are on.
         p: We can play ball.
         u: The umpires are present.

         l → p

         u → p

         ∴ l → u

l	p	u	[(l → p)	∧	(u → p)]	→	(l → u)
T	T	T	T	T	T	T	T
T	T	F	T	T	T	F	F
T	F	T	F	F	F	T	T
T	F	F	F	F	T	T	F
F	T	T	T	T	T	T	T
F	T	F	T	T	T	T	T
F	F	T	T	F	F	T	T
F	F	F	T	T	T	T	T
			1	3	2	5	4

The argument is invalid

54. f: You fertilize the shrubs. $f \vee \sim g$
    g: The shrubs will grow. $\sim g \to \sim p$
    p: You will have privacy. $\underline{p}$
    $\therefore f$

```
f  g  p | [(f ∨ ~g) ∧ (~g → ~p) ∧  p]  →  f
T  T  T |  TT  F  T  F  T  F  TT     T  T
T  T  F |  TT  F  T  F  T  T  FF     T  T
T  F  T |  TT  T  F  T  F  F  FT     T  T
T  F  F |  TT  T  T  T  T  T  FF     T  T
F  T  T |  FF  F  F  F  T  F  FT     T  F
F  T  F |  FF  F  F  F  T  T  FF     T  F
F  F  T |  FT  T  F  T  F  F  FT     T  F
F  F  F |  FT  T  T  T  T  T  FF     T  F
           1 3  2  7  4  6  5  9 8  11 10
```
The argument is valid.

55. h: You do your homework everyday.
    a: You will get an A.
    $h \to a$
    $\underline{h}$
    $\therefore a$ (the law of detachment)
    Therefore, you will get an A.

56. p: You had lunch.
    q: You paid the bill.
    $p \to q$
    $\underline{\sim q}$
    $\therefore \sim p$ (the law of contraposition)
    Therefore, you did not have lunch.

57. p: John reads the history assignment.
    q: John fixes the car.
    $p \vee q$
    $\underline{\sim p}$
    $\therefore p$ (the law of disjunctive syllogism)
    Therefore, John fixes the car.

58. p: The electric bill is too high.
    q: I am able to pay the bill.
    r: My electric will be shut off.
    $p \to \sim q$
    $\underline{\sim q \to r}$
    $\therefore p \to r$ (the law of syllogism)
    Therefore, if the electric bill is too high, then my electricity will be shut off.

59. d: You close the deal.
    c: You will get a commission.
    $d \to c$
    $\underline{\sim c}$
    $\therefore \sim d$ (the law of contraposition)
    Therefore, you did not close the deal.

60. Use the law of detachment.
    Therefore, you will not gain knowledge.

61. c: You pay off your credit card bill. $\sim c \to p$
    p: You will have to pay interest. $\underline{p \to m}$
    m: The bank makes money. $\therefore \sim c \to m$ (the law of syllogism)
    Therefore, if you do not pay off your credit card bill, then the bank makes money.

62. p: Lynn wins the contest.
    q: Lynn strikes oil.
    r : Lynn will be rich.
    s: Lynn will stop working.

$(p \vee q) \rightarrow r$
$\underline{r \rightarrow s}$
$\therefore \sim s \rightarrow \sim p$

p	q	r	s	[((p ∨ q) → r) ∧ (r → s)] → (~s → ~p)
T	T	T	T	T T T T T T F T F
T	T	T	F	T T T F F T T F F
T	T	F	T	T F F F T T F T F
T	T	F	F	T F F F T T T F F
T	F	T	T	T T T T T T F T F
T	F	T	F	T T T F F T T F F
T	F	F	T	T F F F T T F T F
T	F	F	F	T F F F T T T F F
F	T	T	T	T T T T T T F T T
F	T	T	F	T T T F F T T T T
F	T	F	T	T F F F T T F T T
F	T	F	F	T F F F T T T T T
F	F	T	T	F T T T T T F T T
F	F	T	F	F T T F T T T T T
F	F	F	T	F T F T T T F T T
F	F	F	F	F T F T T T T T T
				1 3 2 5 4 9 6 8 7

The argument is valid.

63. No. An argument is <u>invalid</u> only when the conjunction of the premises are true and the conclusion is false.

Exercise Set 3.6
1. A syllogism
2. All are, none are, some are, some are not.
3. The conclusion necessarily follows from the given set of premises.
4. Symbolic arguments use the connectives "and," "or," "not," "but," "if-then," and "if and only if." Syllogistic arguments use the quantifiers "all," "some," and "none."
5. Yes. If the conjunction of the premises is false in all cases, then the argument is valid regardless of the truth value of the conclusion.
6. Yes. An argument in which the conclusion does not necessarily follow from the given set of premises is invalid, even if the conclusion is a true statement.

7.

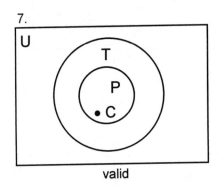

valid

8.

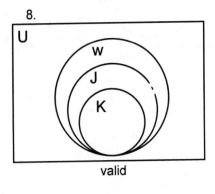

valid

9.

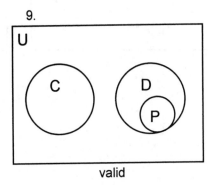

valid

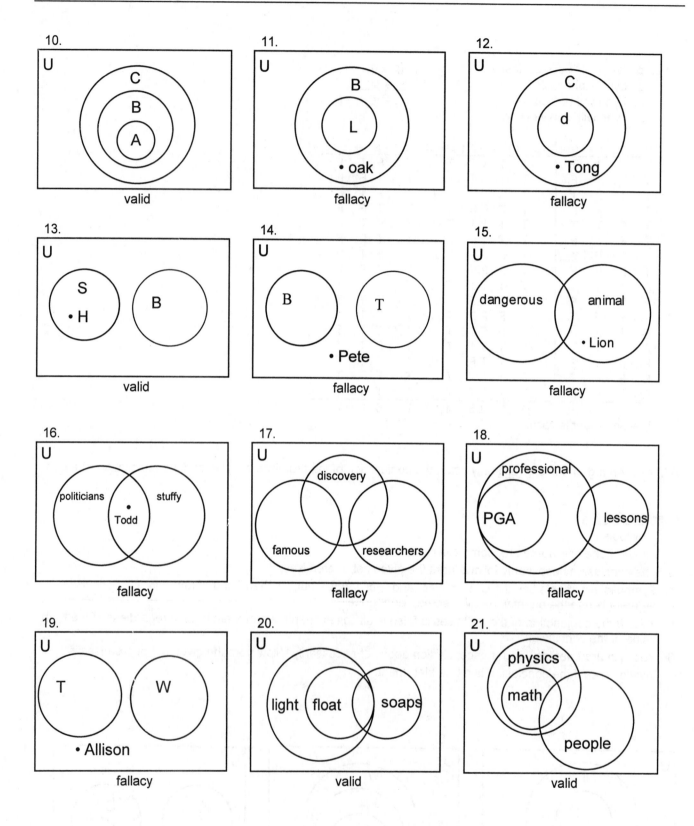

10.

U

C
B
A

valid

11.

U

B
L
• oak

fallacy

12.

U

C
d
• Tong

fallacy

13.

U

S
•H

B

valid

14.

U

B

T

• Pete

fallacy

15.

U

dangerous   animal
• Lion

fallacy

16.

U

politicians   stuffy
•
Todd

fallacy

17.

U

discovery
famous   researchers

fallacy

18.

U

professional
PGA   lessons

fallacy

19.

U

T   W

• Allison

fallacy

20.

U

light float soaps

valid

21.

U

physics
math
people

valid

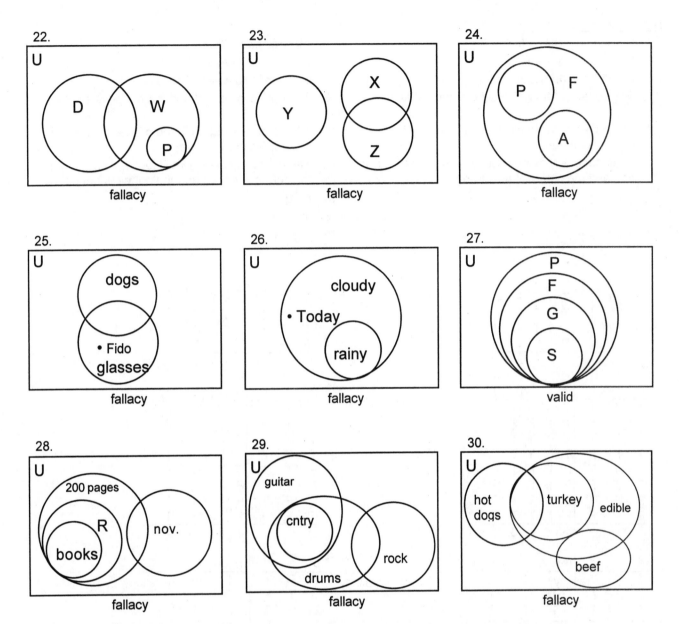

22.

U

D   W   P

fallacy

23.

U

Y   X   Z

fallacy

24.

U

P   F   A

fallacy

25.

U

dogs

• Fido
glasses

fallacy

26.

U

cloudy

• Today   rainy

fallacy

27.

U

P   F   G   S

valid

28.

U

200 pages
R
books   nov.

fallacy

29.

U

guitar
cntry
drums   rock

fallacy

30.

U

hot dogs   turkey   edible   beef

fallacy

31. $[(P \rightarrow Q) \wedge (P \vee Q)] \rightarrow \sim P$ can be expressed as a set statement by $[(P' \cup Q) \cap (P \cup Q)] \subseteq P'$. If this statement is true, then the argument is valid; otherwise, the argument is invalid.

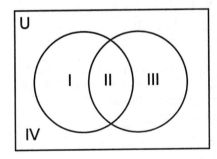

U

I   II   III

IV

Set	Regions
$P' \cup Q$	II, III, IV
$P \cup Q$	I, II, III
$(P' \cup Q) \cap (P \cup Q)$	II, III
P'	III, IV

Since $(P' \cup Q) \cap (P \cup Q)$ is not a subset of P', the argument is invalid.

Review Exercises

1. No people drink milk.
2. All dogs have fleas.
3. Some butterflies bite.
4. No locks are keyless.
5. Some pens do not use ink.
6. Some rabbits wear glasses.
7. The coffee is Maxwell House or the coffee is hot.
8. The coffee is not hot and the coffee is strong.
9. The coffee is Maxwell House if and only if the coffee is not strong.
10. If the coffee is hot, then the coffee is strong and it is not Maxwell House.
11. The coffee is Maxwell House or the coffee is not hot, and the coffee is not strong.
12. The coffee is not Maxwell House, if and only if the coffee is strong and the coffee is not hot.
13. $p \rightarrow r$
14. $r \wedge q$
15. $(r \rightarrow q) \vee \sim p$
16. $(q \leftrightarrow p) \wedge \sim r$
17. $(r \wedge q) \vee \sim p$
18. $\sim (r \wedge q)$

19.

p	q	(p	$\vee$	q)	$\wedge$	$\sim$	p
T	T		T		F	F	
T	F		T		F	F	
F	T		T		T	T	
F	F		F		F	T	
			1		3	2	

20.

p	q	q	$\leftrightarrow$	(p	$\vee$	$\sim$	q)
T	T	T	T	T	T	F	
T	F	F	F	T	T	T	
F	T	T	F	F	F	F	
F	F	F	F	F	T	T	
		1	5		2	4	3

21.

p	q	r	p	$\wedge$	($\sim$	q	$\vee$	r)
T	T	T	T	T	F	T	T	
T	T	F	T	F	F	F	F	
T	F	T	T	T	T	T	T	
T	F	F	T	T	T	T	F	
F	T	T	F	F	F	T	T	
F	T	F	F	F	F	F	F	
F	F	T	F	F	T	T	T	
F	F	F	F	F	T	T	F	
			4	5	1	3	2	

22.

p	q	r	p	$\rightarrow$	(q	$\wedge$	$\sim$	r)
T	T	T	T	F	T	F	F	
T	T	F	T	T	T	T	T	
T	F	T	T	F	F	F	F	
T	F	F	T	F	F	F	T	
F	T	T	F	T	T	F	F	
F	T	F	F	T	T	T	T	
F	F	T	F	T	F	F	F	
F	F	F	F	T	F	F	T	
			4	5	1	3	2	

23.

p	q	r	(p	$\vee$	q)	$\leftrightarrow$	(p	$\vee$	r)
T	T	T		T		T		T	
T	T	F		T		T		T	
T	F	T		T		T		T	
T	F	F		T		T		T	
F	T	T		T		T		T	
F	T	F		T		F		F	
F	F	T		F		F		T	
F	F	F		F		T		F	
				1		3		2	

24.

p	q	r	(p	$\wedge$	q)	$\rightarrow$	$\sim$	r
T	T	T		T		F	F	
T	T	F		T		T	T	
T	F	T		F		T	F	
T	F	F		F		T	T	
F	T	T		F		T	F	
F	T	F		F		T	T	
F	F	T		F		T	F	
F	F	F		F		T	T	
				1		3	2	

25. p: $4 - 1 = 3$ $p \rightarrow q$
    q: $2 + 2 = 3$ $T \rightarrow F$
                       F

26. p: The St. Louis arch is in St. Louis. $p \vee q$
    q: Abraham Lincoln is buried in Grant's Tomb. $T \vee F$
                       T

27. p: George Washington was the first president of the U.S.
    q: All mushrooms are edible.
    r: Florida is south of Central America.

    $(p \vee q) \rightarrow r$
    $(T \vee F) \rightarrow F$
    $\quad T \quad \rightarrow F$
    $\qquad\qquad F$

28. p: $3 + 7 = 11$ $(p \lor q) \land r$
   q: $6 + 5 = 11$ $(F \lor T) \land T$
   r: $7 \times 6 = 42$ $T \quad \land T$
                           T

29. p: Michael Jordan averaged 33.4 points per game. $(p \leftrightarrow q) \lor r$
   q: Jerry West averaged 29.1 points per game. $(T \leftrightarrow T) \lor F$
   r: Wilt Chamberlain played for 10 years. $T \quad \lor F$
                                               T

30. p: Magic Johnson played for 15 years. $p \lor (q \to r)$
   q: Kareem Abdul-Jabbar scored 6000 points. $F \lor (F \to T)$
   r: Elgin Baylor played for 12 years. $F \lor \quad T$
                                         T

31. $(p \lor q) \leftrightarrow (\sim r \land p)$
   $(T \lor F) \leftrightarrow (T \land T)$
      $T \quad \leftrightarrow \quad T$
             T

32. $(p \to \sim r) \lor (p \land q)$
   $(T \to T) \lor (T \land F)$
      $T \quad \lor \quad F$
             T

33. $\sim r \leftrightarrow [(p \lor q) \leftrightarrow \sim p]$
   $T \leftrightarrow [(T \lor F) \leftrightarrow F]$
   $T \leftrightarrow [\quad T \quad \leftrightarrow F]$
   $T \leftrightarrow \quad\quad\quad F$
         F

34. $\sim [(q \land r) \to (\sim p \lor r)]$
   $\sim [(F \land F) \to (F \lor F)]$
   $\sim [\quad F \quad \to \quad\quad F]$
   $\sim \quad\quad\quad\quad T$
   F

35. Using the fact that $(p \to q) \Leftrightarrow (\sim p \lor q)$, we can conclude that $\sim p \to \sim q \Leftrightarrow p \lor \sim q$.

36.

p	q	$\sim p$	$\lor$	$\sim q$	$\sim p$	$\leftrightarrow$	q
T	T	F	F	F	F	F	T
T	F	F	T	T	F	T	F
F	T	T	T	F	T	T	T
F	F	T	T	T	T	F	F
		1	3	2	1	3	2

The statements are not equivalent.

37.

p	q	r	$\sim p$	$\lor$	(q	$\land$	r)	($\sim p$	$\lor$	q)	$\land$	($\sim p$	$\lor$	r)
T	T	T	F	T	T	T	T	F	T	T	T	F	T	T
T	T	F	F	F	T	F	F	F	T	T	F	F	F	F
T	F	T	F	F	F	F	T	F	F	F	F	F	T	T
T	F	F	F	F	F	F	F	F	F	F	F	F	F	F
F	T	T	T	T	T	T	T	T	T	T	T	T	T	T
F	T	F	T	T	T	F	F	T	T	T	T	T	T	F
F	F	T	T	T	F	F	T	T	F	T	T	T	T	T
F	F	F	T	T	F	F	F	T	F	T	T	T	T	F
			2	3		1		1	3	2	7	4	6	5

The statements are equivalent.

38.

p	q	($\sim q$	$\to$	p)	$\land$	p	$\sim$	($\sim p$	$\leftrightarrow$	q)	$\lor$	p
T	T	F	T	T	T	T	T	F	F	T	T	T
T	F	T	T	T	T	T	F	F	T	F	T	T
F	T	F	T	F	F	F	F	T	T	T	F	F
F	F	T	F	F	F	F	T	T	F	F	T	F
		1	3	2	5	4	4	1	3	2	6	5

The statements are not equivalent.

39. p: The stapler is empty.

    q: The stapler is jammed.

    In symbolic form the statement is p ∨ q. Using the fact that p → q ⇔ ~ p ∨ q, we can rewrite the given statement as ~ p → q. If the stapler is not empty, then the stapler is jammed.

40. p: The boy sang bass.

    q: The girl sang alto.

    In symbolic form the statement is p ∧ q. Using DeMorgan's Laws we get p ∧ q ⇔ ~ (~ p ∨ ~ q). It is false that the boy did not sing bass or the girl did not sing alto.

41. p: Newsweek is a comic book.

    q: Time is an almanac.

    The symbolic form is ~ (p ∨ ~ q). Using DeMorgan's Laws we get

    ~ (p ∨ ~ q) ⇔ ~ p ∧ q. Newsweek is not a comic book and Time is an almanac.

42. p: There is water in the vase.

    q: The flowers will wilt.

    In symbolic form the statement is ~ p→ q

    Using the fact that p → q ⇔ ~ p ∨ q, we get ~ p → q ⇔ p ∨ q. There is water is in the vase or the flowers will wilt.

43. p: I went to the party.

    q: I finished my special report.

    Using DeMorgan's Laws we get ~ p ∧ ~ q ⇔ ~ (p ∨ q). It is not true that I went to the party or I finished my special report.

44. If you do not have to stop, then the railroad crossing light is not flashing red.

45. If John's eyes do not need to be checked, then John is not having difficulty seeing.

46. If I am not at work, then today is a holiday.

47. If the carpet stains, then it is not Scotch-guarded or it is not properly cared for.

48. Converse: If I get a passing grade, then I studied.

    Inverse: If I don't study, then I will not get a passing grade.

    Contrapositive: If I don't get a passing grade, then I didn't study.

49. p: The temperature is over 80^0.

    q: The air conditioner will come on.

    In symbolic form the statements are: a) p → q, b) ~ p ∨ q, c) ~ (p ∧ ~ q).

    Using the fact that p → q ⇔ ~ p ∨ q, statements (a) and (b) are equivalent. Using DeMorgan's Laws on statement (b) we get ~ (p ∧ ~ q). Therefore all three statements are equivalent.

50. p: The screwdriver is on the workbench.

    q: The screwdriver is on the counter.

    In symbolic form the statements are: a) p ↔ ~ q, b) ~ q → ~ p, c) ~ (q ∧ ~ p). Looking at the truth tables for statements (a), (b), and (c) we can conclude that none of the statements are equivalent.

p	q	p ↔ ~ q	~ q → ~ p	~ (q ∧ ~ p)
T	T	T F F	F T F	T T F F
T	F	T T T	T F F	T F F F
F	T	F T F	F T T	F T T T
F	F	F F T	T T T	T F F T
		1 3 2	1 3 2	4 1 3 2

51. p: 2 + 3 = 6.

q: 3 + 1 = 5.

In symbolic form the statements are: a) p → q, b) p ↔ ~ q, c) ~ q → ~ p. Statement (c) is the contrapositive of statement (a). Therefore statements (a) and (c) are equivalent. Since the truth tables for statements (a) and (b) are different we can conclude that only statements (a) and (c) are equivalent.

p	q	p → q	p ↔ ~ q		
T	T	T	T	F	F
T	F	F	T	T	T
F	T	T	F	T	F
F	F	T	F	F	T
		1	1	3	2

52. p: The sale is on Tuesday.

q: I have money.

r : I will go to the sale.

In symbolic form the statements are: a) (p ∧ q) → r, b) r → (p ∧ q), c) r ∨ (p ∧ q).

The truth table for statements (a), (b), and (c) shows that none of the statements are equivalent.

p	q	r	(p ∧ q) → r			r → (p ∧ q)			r ∨ (p ∧ q)		
T	T	T	T	T	T	T	T	T	T	T	T
T	T	F	T	F	F	F	T	T	F	T	T
T	F	T	F	T	T	T	F	F	T	T	F
T	F	F	F	T	F	F	T	F	F	F	F
F	T	T	F	T	T	T	F	F	T	T	F
F	T	F	F	T	F	F	T	F	F	F	F
F	F	T	F	T	T	T	F	F	T	T	F
F	F	F	F	T	F	F	T	F	F	F	F
			1	3	2	1	3	2	1	3	2

53.

p	q	[(p → q) ∧ ~ p] → q				
T	T	T	F	F	T	T
T	F	F	F	F	T	F
F	T	T	T	T	T	T
F	F	T	T	T	F	F
		1	3	2	5	4

The argument is invalid.

54.

p	q	r	[(p ∧ q) ∧ (q → r)] → (p → r)				
T	T	T	T	T	T	T	T
T	T	F	T	F	F	T	F
T	F	T	F	F	T	T	T
T	F	F	F	F	T	T	F
F	T	T	F	F	T	T	T
F	T	F	F	F	F	T	T
F	F	T	F	F	T	T	T
F	F	F	F	F	T	T	T
			1	3	2	5	4

The argument is valid.

55. p: Nicole is in the hot tub.
    q: Nicole is in the shower.

    $p \lor q$

    $\underline{p}$

    $\therefore \sim q$

p	q	[(p ∨ q)	∧	p]	→	∼ q
T	T	T	T	T	F	F
T	F	T	T	T	T	T
F	T	T	F	F	T	F
F	F	F	F	F	T	T
		1	3	2	5	4

The argument is invalid.

56. p: The car has a sound system.
    p: Rick will buy the car.
    r: The price is less than $18,000.

    $p \rightarrow q$

    $\underline{\sim r \rightarrow \sim q}$

    $\therefore p \rightarrow r$

p	q	r	[(p → q)	∧	(∼ r	→	∼q)]	→	(p → r)
T	T	T	T	T	F	T	F	T	T
T	T	F	T	F	T	F	F	T	F
T	F	T	F	F	F	T	T	T	F
T	F	F	F	F	T	T	T	T	F
F	T	T	T	T	F	T	F	T	T
F	T	F	T	F	T	F	F	T	T
F	F	T	T	T	F	T	T	T	T
F	F	F	T	T	T	T	T	T	T
			1	5	2	4	3	7	6

The argument is valid.

57.

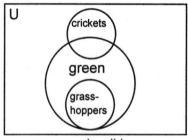

invalid

58.

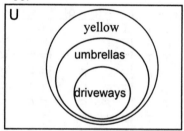

invalid

Chapter Test

1. $(p \land r) \lor \sim q$

2. $(r \rightarrow q) \lor \sim p$

3. $\sim (r \leftrightarrow \sim q)$

4. It is false that if Celion is the president, then Ron is not the secretary.

5. Celion is the president, if and only if Sheldon is the vice president and Ron is the secretary.

6.

p	q	r	[∼ (p → r)]	∧	q
T	T	T	F	T	F	T
T	T	F	T	F	T	T
T	F	T	F	T	F	F
T	F	F	T	F	F	F
F	T	T	F	T	F	T
F	T	F	F	T	F	T
F	F	T	F	T	F	F
F	F	F	F	T	F	F
			2	1	4	3

7.

p	q	r	(q ↔ ∼ r)	∨	p
T	T	T	T	F	F	T	T
T	T	F	T	T	T	T	T
T	F	T	F	T	F	T	T
T	F	F	F	F	T	T	T
F	T	T	T	F	F	F	F
F	T	F	T	T	T	T	F
F	F	T	F	T	F	T	F
F	F	F	F	F	T	F	F
			1	3	2	5	4

8. p: $2 + 6 = 8$

    q: $7 - 12 = 5$

    $p \lor q$

    $T \lor F$

    $\quad T$

9. p: A scissors can cut paper.

    q: A dime has the same value as 2 nickels.

    r : Louisville is a city in Kentucky.

    $(p \lor q) \leftrightarrow r$

    $(T \lor T) \leftrightarrow T$

    $\quad T \quad \leftrightarrow T$

    $\quad\quad\quad T$

10. $[\sim(r \rightarrow \sim p)] \land (q \rightarrow p)$

    $[\sim(T \rightarrow F\;)] \land (F \rightarrow T)$

    $[\sim \quad F \quad] \land \quad T$

    $\;T \quad\quad\quad \land \quad T$

    $\quad\quad\quad\quad T$

11. $(r \lor q) \leftrightarrow (p \land \sim q)$

    $(T \lor F) \leftrightarrow (T \land T\;)$

    $\quad T \quad \leftrightarrow \quad T$

    $\quad\quad\quad T$

12. Applying DeMorgan's Law to statement (a), we get: (1) $\sim(\sim p \lor q)$, (2) $\sim(p \lor \sim q)$, and (3) $\sim(p \land \sim q)$. Therefore, $\sim p \lor q \Leftrightarrow \sim(p \land \sim q)$.

13. p: The bird is red.

    q: It is a cardinal.

    In symbolic form the statements are: a) $p \rightarrow q$, b) $\sim p \lor q$, c) $\sim p \rightarrow \sim q$. Statement (c) is the inverse of statement (a) and thus they cannot be equivalent. Using the fact that $p \rightarrow q \Leftrightarrow \sim p \lor q$, to rewrite statement (a) we get $\sim p \lor q$. Therefore statements (a) and (b) are equivalent.

14. p: The test is today.

    q: The concert is tonight.

    In symbolic form the statements are: a) $\sim(p \lor q)$, b) $\sim p \land \sim q$, c) $\sim p \rightarrow \sim q$. Applying DeMorgan's Law to statement (a) we get: $\sim p \land \sim q$. Therefore statements (a) and (b) are equivalent. When we compare the truth tables for statements (a), (b), and (c) we see that only statements (a) and (b) are equivalent.

p	q	a) ~ (p ∨ q)		b) ~ p ∧ ~ q			c) ~ p → ~ q		
T	T	F	T	F	F	F	F	T	F
T	F	F	T	F	F	T	F	T	T
F	T	F	T	T	F	F	T	F	F
F	F	T	F	T	T	T	T	T	T
		2	1	1	3	2	1	3	2

15. s: The soccer team won the game.

    f: Sue played fullback.

    p: The team is in second place.

    This argument is the law of syllogism and therefore it is valid.

    $s \rightarrow f$

    $\underline{f \rightarrow p}$

    $\therefore s \rightarrow p$

16.

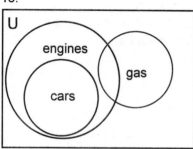

Fallacy

17. Some leopards are not spotted.

18. No people are funny.

19. Inverse: If the apple is not red, then it is not a delicious apple.
    Converse: If it is a delicious apple, then the apple is red.
    Contrapositive: If it is not a delicious apple, then the apple is not red.

20. Yes. An argument is valid when its conclusion necessarily follows from the given set of premises. It doesn't matter whether the conclusion is a true or false statement.

Group Projects

1. a) 4,   p closed, q closed
             p closed, q open
             p open, q closed
             p open, q open

   b)

p	q	p∧q
1	1	1
1	0	0
0	1	0
0	0	0

   c) If a closed switch is represented as T and an open switch is represented as F, and the bulb lighting as T, and the bulb not lighting as F, then the table would be identical to the truth table for p ∧q.

   d)

p	q	p∨q
1	1	1
1	0	1
0	1	1
0	0	0

   e) If a closed switch is represented as T and an open switch is represented as F, and the bulb lighting as T, and the bulb not lighting as F, then the table would be identical to the truth table for p ∨ q.

   f) (p ∧ q) ∨ r

   g)

   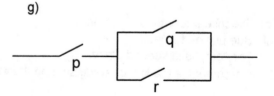

2.a) The tables have the same truth values as the
      not, *and* and *or* tables respectively.

    b) 0

    c) 1

    d) 0

    e) $I_a = 0$, $I_b = 1$ or $I_a = 1$, $I_b = 0$

f)

I_a	I_b	0
1	1	1
1	0	1
0	1	1
0	0	0

3. a) 1, 2 or 3, 4, 5, 8, 11 or 12

CHAPTER FOUR

SYSTEMS OF NUMERATION

Exercise Set 4.1

1. A **number** is a quantity, and it answers the question "How many?". A **numeral** is a symbol used to represent a number.

2. X, ι, ∩, ◀

3. C, ρ, ϟ, 百

4. A **system of numeration** consists of a set of numerals and a scheme or rule for combining the numerals to represent numbers.

5. Hindu-Arabic numeration system

6. An **additive system** is one in which the number represented by a particular set of numerals is the sum of the values of the numerals.

7. In a **multiplicative system** there are numerals for each number less than the base and for powers of the base. Each numeral less than the base is multiplied by a numeral for the power of the base and these products are added to obtain the number.

8. A **ciphered system** is one in which the number represented by a particular set of numerals is the sum of the values of the numerals.

9. $100 + 100 + 10 + 10 + 10 + 1 + 1 = 232$

10. $10 + 100 + 10 + 1 + 1 = 122$

11. $1000 + 1000 + 100 + 100 + 100 + 100 + 10 + 10 + 1 + 1 + 1 = 2423$

12. $10,000 + 10,000 + 10,000 + 10,000 + 1000 + 100 + 100 + 10 = 41,210$

13. $100,000 + 100,000 + 100,000 + 10,000 + 10,000 + 10,000 + 1000 + 1000 + 1000 + 1000 + 100 + 100 + 10 + 1 + 1 + 1 + 1 = 334,214$

14. $1,000,000 + 1,000,000 + 1,000,000 + 100,000 + 100,000 + 100,000 + 100 + 100 + 100 + 100 + 10 + 10 + 10 + 1 = 3,300,431$

15. 9999 ∩∩∩ ⅼⅼⅼⅼⅼⅼ

16. 9999999 ∩∩∩∩∩ ⅼⅼ

17. 𐦠𐦠 ∩∩∩∩ ⅼⅼⅼⅼ

18. 𐦠 99999999 ∩ ⅼⅼ

19. ⌒𝖎 𝖎𝖎𝖎𝖎𝖎𝖎 𐦠𐦠𐦠 99999999 ∩∩∩ ⅼⅼⅼⅼⅼ

20. 𓏢𓏢 ⌒⌒⌒ 𐦠 𐦠𐦠𐦠𐦠𐦠 9 ∩∩ ⅼⅼ

21. $10 + (5 - 1) = 10 + 4 = 14$

22. $10 + 5 + 1 = 16$

23. $500 + (50 - 10) + 5 + 1 + 1 = 547$

24. $100 + 50 + 10 + 1 + 1 = 162$

25. $1000 + (500 - 100) + (100 - 10) + 1 + 1 = 1492$

26. $1000 + (1000 - 100) + 10 + 5 + 1 + 1 + 1 = 1918$

27. $1000 + (1000 - 100) + (50 - 10) + 5 = 1945$

28. $1000 + 500 + 100 + 100 + (50 - 10) + 5 + 1 = 1746$

29. $10(1000) + 1000 + 1000 + 500 + 100 + 50 + 10 + 5 + 1 = 12,666$

30. $50(1000) + 1000 + (1000 - 100) + (50 - 10) + (5 - 1) = 51,944$

31. $9(1000) + (500 - 100) + 50 + 10 + (5 - 1) = 9464$

32. $5(1000) + 1000 + 100 + 100 + 100 + 10 + 10 + 10 + 1 + 1 + 1 = 6333$

33. XLVII

34. XCIV

35. CLXIV

36. CCLXIX

37. MM

38. MMMDLXIV

39. MMMMDCCXCIII

40. MMMMMCCLXXIV

41. $\overline{\text{I}}$XCMXCIX

42. $\overline{\text{X}}$MMMMCCCXV

43. $\overline{\text{XX}}$DCXLIV

44. $\overline{\text{XCIX}}$CMXCIX

45. 9(10) + 4 = 94

46. 6(10) + 2 = 62

47. 4(1000) + 8(10) + 1 = 4081

48. 3(1000) + 2(10) + 9 = 3029

49. 7(1000) + 6(100) + 5(10) = 7650

50. 3(1000) + 4(100) + 8(10) + 7 = 3487

51.
四
十
七

52.
一
百
七
十
八

53.
三
百
七
十
八

54.
二
千
一

55.
三
千
五
百
七
十

56.
六
千
九
百
五

57. 200 + 60 + 4 = 264

58. 600 + 70 + 8 = 678

59. 20(1000) + 2(1000) + 500 + 5 = 22,505

60. 100(1000) + 50(1000) + 800 + 10 + 3 = 150,813

61. 9(1000) + 600 + 7 = 9607

62. 1(1000) + 900 + 90 + 9 + 1 = 1999

63. $\mu\zeta$

64. $\rho o \eta$

65. $\psi\kappa\lambda$

66. $\beta'\,\alpha$

67. $\lambda'\,\varepsilon'\,\psi\,\delta$

68. $\chi'\,\varrho'\phi\mu$

69. Advantage: Numbers can be written in a compact form.
Disadvantage: A ciphered system has many symbols to be memorized.

70. Advantage: Numbers can be written in a compact form.
Disadvantage: A ciphered system has many symbols to be memorized.

71. Advantage: Numbers can be written in a compact form.
Disadvantage: A ciphered system has many symbols to be memorized.
The Hindu-Arabic system has fewer symbols, more compact notation, the inclusion of zero, and the capability of expressing decimal numbers and fractions.

72. 1000 + 10 + 10 + 1 = 1021, MXXI,
    $\alpha'\kappa\alpha$

73. 1000 + (1000 - 100) + 10 + 10 + 10 + 5 + 1
    = 1936, $\mathcal{S}$ 999999999∩∩∩ IIIII,
    $\alpha'\pi\lambda\zeta$,

74. 5(100) + 2(10) + 7 = 527,
    99999 ∩∩ IIIIIII,
    DXXVII, $\phi\kappa\zeta$

75. 400 + 20 + 2 = 422, 9999 ∩∩ II,
    CDXXII,

76. $\overline{\text{CMXCIX}}\text{CMXCIX}$

77. $\pi'\mathcal{Q}'\theta'\pi\mathcal{Q}\theta$

Exercise Set 4.2

1. A base 10 place-value system
2. 30 → three tens, 300 → three hundreds
3. A true positional-value system requires a base and a set of symbols, including a symbol for zero and one for each counting number less than the base.
4. a) 10
   b) 0, 1, 2, 3, 4, 5, 6, 7, 8, 9
5. Write each numeral times its corresponding positional value.
6. It lacked a symbol for zero.
7. (10 + 1)(1) = 11 and (10 + 1)(60) = 660
8. a) The lack of a symbol for zero led to a great deal of ambiguity and confusion.
   b) ▼▼   ◀▼▼▼   for both numbers; 133 = 2(60) + 13(1) and 7980 = 133(60)
9. 1, 20, 18 × 20, 18 × 20^2, 18 × 20^3
10. The Mayan system has a different base and the numbers are written vertically.

11. (5 × 10) + (7 × 1)
12. (8 × 10) + (6 × 1)
13. (3 × 100) + (5 × 10) + (9 × 1)
14. (5 × 100) + (6 × 10) + (2 × 1)
15. (8 × 100) + (9 × 10) + (7 × 1)
16. (3 × 1000) + (7 × 100) + (6 × 10) + (9 × 1)
17. (5 × 1000) + (2 × 100) + (6 × 10) + (2 × 1)
18. (2 × 10,000) + (3 × 1000) + (4 × 100) + (6 × 10) + (8 × 1)

19. (1 × 10,000) + (0 × 1000) + (7 × 100) + (3 × 10) + (2 × 1)
20. (1 × 100,000) + (2 × 10,000) + (5 × 1000) + (6 × 100) + (7 × 10) + (8 × 1)
21. (3 × 100,000) + (4 × 10,000) + (6 × 1000) + (8 × 100) + (6 × 10) + (1 × 1)
22. (3 × 1,000,000) + (7 × 100,000) + (6 × 10,000) + (5 × 1000) + (9 × 100) + (3 × 10) + (4 × 1)
23. (10 + 10 + 1 + 1 + 1 + 1)(1) = 24
24. (10 + 10 + 10)(1) − (1 + 1 + 1 + 1)(1) = 30 − 4 = 26
25. (10 + 1 + 1 + 1)(60) + (1 + 1 + 1 + 1)(1) = 13(60) + 4(1) = 780 + 4 = 784
26. (1 + 10)(60) + ((10 + 10) − (1 + 1))(1) = 11(60) + (20 − 2)(1) = 660 + 18 = 678

27. $1(60^2) + (10 + 10 + 1)(60) + (10 - (1 + 1))(1) = 3600 + 21(60) + (10 - 2)(1) = 3600 + 1260 + 8 = 4868$

28. $10(60^2) + ((10 + 10) - (1 + 1 + 1))(60) + (1 + 1)(1) = 10(3600) + (20 - 3)(60) + 2 = 36,000 + 17(60) + 2$
    $= 36,000 + 1020 + 2 = 37,022$

29. 76 is 1 group of 60 and 16 units remaining

30. 86 is 1 group of 60 and 26 units remaining

31. 121 is 2 groups of 60 and 1 unit remaining

32. 512 is 8 groups of 60 and 32 units remaining

33. 3685 is 1 group of 3600, 1 group of 60, and 25 units remaining

34. 3030 is 50 groups of 60 and 30 units remaining

35. $2(20) + 11(1) = 40 + 11 = 51$

36. $10(20) + 5(1) = 200 + 5 = 205$

37. $12(18 \times 20) + 0(20) + 1(1) = 4320 + 0 + 1 = 4321$

38. $7(18 \times 20) + 9(20) + 7(1) = 2520 + 180 + 7 = 2707$

39. $11(18 \times 20) + 2(20) + 0(1) = 3960 + 40 + 0 = 4000$

40. $4(18 \times 20) + 10(20) + 5(1) = 1440 + 200 + 5 = 1645$

41.

42.
$$20 \overline{)257}$$
$$\underline{20}$$
$$57$$
$$\underline{40}$$
$$17$$
$257 = 12(20) + 17(1)$

43.
$$20 \overline{)300}$$
$$\underline{20}$$
$$100$$
$$\underline{100}$$
$$0$$
$300 = 15(20) + 0(1)$

44.
$$360 \overline{)406} \qquad 20 \overline{)46}$$
$$\underline{360} \qquad\qquad \underline{40}$$
$$46 \qquad\qquad 6$$
$406 = 1(18 \times 20) + 2(20) + 6(1)$

45.
$$360 \overline{)3181} \qquad 20 \overline{)301}$$
$$\underline{2880} \qquad\qquad \underline{300}$$
$$301 \qquad\qquad 1$$
$3181 = 8(18 \times 20) + 15(20) + 1(1)$

46.
$$360 \overline{)1978} \qquad 20 \overline{)178}$$
$$\underline{1800} \qquad\qquad \underline{160}$$
$$178 \qquad\qquad 18$$
$1978 = 5(18 \times 20) + 8(20) + 18(1)$

47. Advantages: In general, a place-value system is more compact than an additive or multiplicative system, there are fewer symbols to memorize in a place-value system compared to a ciphered system, large and small numbers can be written more easily.

Disadvantage: If many of the place values are zero, then a place-value system may be less compact.

48. Answers will vary.

49. Hindu-Arabic: $10 + 10 + 10 + 1 + 1 + 1 = 33$
    Mayan: $33 = 1(20) + 13(1)$

50. Hindu-Arabic: $5(18 \times 20) + 7(20) + 4(1)$
    $= 1800 + 140 + 4 = 1944$
    Babylonian: $1944 = 32(60) + 24(1)$

51. $(\bigcirc \times \ominus^2) + (\square \times \ominus) + (\Delta \times 1)$

52. $(\bigcirc \times \ominus^3) + (\Delta \times \ominus^2) + (\bigcirc \times \ominus) + (\square \times 1)$

53. a) No largest number. The positional values are ..., $(60)^3$, $(60)^2$, 60, 1
    b) $999,999 = 4(60)^3 + 37(60)^2 + 46(60) + 39(1)$

54. a) No largest number. The positional values above 18×20 are 18×20^2, 18×20^3, ...
    b) $999,999 = 6(18 \times 20^3) + 18(18 \times 20^2) + 17(18 \times 20) + 13(20) + 19(1)$

55. $2(60) + 23(1) = 120 + 23 = 143$
    23
    $143 + 23 = 166$
    $166 = 2(60) + 46(1)$

56. $3(60) + 33(1) = 180 + 33 = 213$
    32
    $213 - 32 = 181$
    $181 = 3(60) + 1(1)$

57. $7(18 \times 20) + 6(20) + 15(1) = 2520 + 120 + 15 = 2655$
    $6(18 \times 20) + 7(20) + 13(1) = 2160 + 140 + 13 = 2313$
    $2655 + 2313 = 4968$
    $4968 = 13(18 \times 20) + 14(20) + 8(1)$

58. $7(18 \times 20) + 6(20) + 15(1) = 2520 + 120 + 15 = 2655$
   $6(18 \times 20) + 7(20) + 13(1) = 2160 + 140 + 13 = 2313$
   $2655 - 2313 = 342$
   $342 = 17(20) + 2(1)$

Exercise Set 4.3

1. Answers will vary.
2. Answers will vary.
3. $7_8 = 7(1) = 7$
4. $50_7 = 5(7) + 0(1) = 35$
5. $23_5 = 2(5) + 3(1) = 13$
6. $101_2 = 1(2^2) + 0(2) + 1(1) = 5$
7. $1011_2 = 1(2^3) + 0(2^2) + 1(2) + 1(1) = 11$
8. $1101_2 = 1(2^3) + 1(2^2) + 0(2) + 1(1) = 13$

9. $84_{12} = 8(12) + 4(1) = 100$
10. $21021_3 = 2(3^4) + 1(3^3) + 0(3^2) + 2(3) + 1(1) = 2(81) + 27 + 0(9) + 6 + 1 = 196$
11. $465_7 = 4(7^2) + 6(7) + 5(1) = 4(49) + 42 + 5 = 243$
12. $654_7 = 6(7^2) + 5(7) + 4(1) = 6(49) + 35 + 4 = 333$
13. $20432_5 = 2(5^4) + 0(5^3) + 4(5^2) + 3(5) + 2(1) = 2(625) + 0 + 4(25) + 15 + 2 = 1367$
14. $101111_2 = 1(2^5) + 0(2^4) + 1(2^3) + 1(2^2) + 1(2) + 1(1) = 32 + 0 + 8 + 4 + 2 + 1 = 47$
15. $4003_6 = 4(6^3) + 0(6^2) + 0(6) + 3(1) = 4(216) + 0 + 0 + 3 = 867$
16. $123E_{12} = 1(12^3) + 2(12^2) + 3(12) + 11(1) = 1728 + 2(144) + 36 + 11 = 2063$
17. $123_8 = 1(8^2) + 2(8) + 3(1) = 64 + 16 + 3 = 83$
18. $1043_8 = 1(8^3) + 0(8^2) + 4(8) + 3(1) = 512 + 0 + 32 + 3 = 547$
19. $14705_8 = 1(8^4) + 4(8^3) + 7(8^2) + 0(8) + 5(1) = 4096 + 4(512) + 7(64) + 0 + 5 = 6597$
20. $67342_9 = 6(9^4) + 7(9^3) + 3(9^2) + 4(9) + 2(1) = 6(6561) + 7(729) + 3(81) + 36 + 2 = 44,750$

21. To convert 8 to base 2   ... 16 8 4 2 1

```
     1        0       0       0
   8⌐8      4⌐0     2⌐0     1⌐0
    8        0       0       0
    0        0       0       0        8 = 1000₂
```
   $8 = 1000_2$

22. To convert 16 to base 2   ... 32 16 8 4 2 1

```
      1       0       0       0       0
  16⌐16     8⌐0     4⌐0     2⌐0     1⌐0
     16       0       0       0       0
      0       0       0       0       0      16 = 10000₂
```
   $16 = 10000_2$

23. To convert 22 to base 2   ... 32 16 8 4 2 1

```
      1       0       1       1       0
  16⌐22     8⌐6     4⌐6     2⌐2     1⌐0
     16       0       4       2       0
      6       6       2       0       0      22 = 10110₂
```
   $22 = 10110_2$

24. To convert 243 to base 6   ... 1296 216 36 6 1

```
       1         0        4        3
  216⌐243    36⌐27     6⌐27     1⌐3
     216         0       24        3
      27        27        3        0      243 = 1043₆
```
   $243 = 1043_6$

25. To convert 435 to base 7   ... 2401 343 49 7 1

$$
\begin{array}{cccc}
& 1 & 1 & 6 & 1 \\
343\,\overline{)\,435} & 49\,\overline{)\,92} & 7\,\overline{)\,43} & 1\,\overline{)\,1} \\
\underline{343} & \underline{49} & \underline{42} & \underline{1} \\
92 & 43 & 1 & 0
\end{array}
$$

$435 = 1161_7$

26. To convert 908 to base 4   ... 1024 256 64 16 4 1

$$
\begin{array}{ccccc}
& 3 & 2 & 0 & 3 & 0 \\
256\,\overline{)\,908} & 64\,\overline{)\,140} & 16\,\overline{)\,12} & 4\,\overline{)\,12} & 1\,\overline{)\,0} \\
\underline{768} & \underline{128} & \underline{0} & \underline{12} & \underline{0} \\
140 & 12 & 12 & 0 & 0
\end{array}
$$

$908 = 32030_4$

27. To convert 2061 to base 12   ... 20,736 1728 144 12 1

$$
\begin{array}{cccc}
& 1 & 2 & 3 & 9 \\
1728\,\overline{)\,2061} & 144\,\overline{)\,333} & 12\,\overline{)\,45} & 1\,\overline{)\,9} \\
\underline{1728} & \underline{288} & \underline{36} & \underline{9} \\
333 & 45 & 9 & 0
\end{array}
$$

$2061 = 1239_{12}$

28. To convert 100 to base 3   ... 243 81 27 9 3 1

$$
\begin{array}{ccccc}
& 1 & 0 & 2 & 0 & 1 \\
81\,\overline{)\,100} & 27\,\overline{)\,19} & 9\,\overline{)\,19} & 3\,\overline{)\,1} & 1\,\overline{)\,1} \\
\underline{81} & \underline{0} & \underline{18} & \underline{0} & \underline{1} \\
19 & 19 & 1 & 1 & 0
\end{array}
$$

$100 = 10201_3$

29. To convert 529 to base 8   ... 4096 512 64 8 1

$$
\begin{array}{cccc}
& 1 & 0 & 2 & 1 \\
512\,\overline{)\,529} & 64\,\overline{)\,17} & 8\,\overline{)\,17} & 1\,\overline{)\,1} \\
\underline{512} & \underline{0} & \underline{16} & \underline{1} \\
17 & 17 & 1 & 0
\end{array}
$$

$529 = 1021_8$

30. To convert 64 to base 2   ... 128 64 32 16 8 4 2 1

$$
\begin{array}{ccccccc}
& 1 & 0 & 0 & 0 & 0 & 0 & 0 \\
64\,\overline{)\,64} & 32\,\overline{)\,0} & 16\,\overline{)\,0} & 8\,\overline{)\,0} & 4\,\overline{)\,0} & 2\,\overline{)\,0} & 1\,\overline{)\,0} \\
\underline{64} & \underline{0} & \underline{0} & \underline{0} & \underline{0} & \underline{0} & \underline{0} \\
0 & 0 & 0 & 0 & 0 & 0 & 0
\end{array}
$$

$64 = 1000000_2$

31. To convert 2867 to base 12   ... 20,736 1728 144 12 1

$$
\begin{array}{cccc}
& 1 & 7 & 10 & 11 \\
1728\,\overline{)\,2867} & 144\,\overline{)\,1139} & 12\,\overline{)\,131} & 1\,\overline{)\,11} \\
\underline{1728} & \underline{1008} & \underline{120} & \underline{11} \\
1139 & 131 & 11 & 0
\end{array}
$$

$2867 = 17TE_{12}$

32. To convert 4312 to base 6   ... 7776 1296 216 36 6 1

$$
\begin{array}{ccccc}
& 3 & 1 & 5 & 4 & 4 \\
1296\,\overline{)\,4312} & 216\,\overline{)\,424} & 36\,\overline{)\,208} & 6\,\overline{)\,28} & 1\,\overline{)\,4} \\
\underline{3888} & \underline{216} & \underline{180} & \underline{24} & \underline{4} \\
424 & 208 & 28 & 4 & 0
\end{array}
$$

$4312 = 31544_6$

33. To convert 1011 to base 2   ... 1024 512 256 128 64 32 16 8 4 2 1

$$\begin{array}{r}1\\512\overline{)1011}\\\underline{512}\\499\end{array}\quad\begin{array}{r}1\\256\overline{)499}\\\underline{256}\\243\end{array}\quad\begin{array}{r}1\\128\overline{)243}\\\underline{128}\\115\end{array}\quad\begin{array}{r}1\\64\overline{)115}\\\underline{64}\\51\end{array}\quad\begin{array}{r}1\\32\overline{)51}\\\underline{32}\\19\end{array}$$

$$\begin{array}{r}1\\16\overline{)19}\\\underline{16}\\3\end{array}\quad\begin{array}{r}0\\8\overline{)3}\\\underline{0}\\3\end{array}\quad\begin{array}{r}0\\4\overline{)3}\\\underline{0}\\3\end{array}\quad\begin{array}{r}1\\2\overline{)3}\\\underline{2}\\1\end{array}\quad\begin{array}{r}1\\1\overline{)1}\\\underline{1}\\0\end{array}\quad 1011 = 1111110011_2$$

34. To convert 1589 to base 7   ... 2401 343 49 7 1

$$\begin{array}{r}4\\343\overline{)1589}\\\underline{1372}\\217\end{array}\quad\begin{array}{r}4\\49\overline{)217}\\\underline{196}\\21\end{array}\quad\begin{array}{r}3\\7\overline{)21}\\\underline{21}\\0\end{array}\quad\begin{array}{r}0\\1\overline{)0}\\\underline{0}\\0\end{array}\quad 1589 = 4430_7$$

35. To convert 2307 to base 8   ... 4096 512 64 8 1

$$\begin{array}{r}4\\512\overline{)2307}\\\underline{2048}\\259\end{array}\quad\begin{array}{r}4\\64\overline{)259}\\\underline{256}\\3\end{array}\quad\begin{array}{r}0\\8\overline{)3}\\\underline{0}\\3\end{array}\quad\begin{array}{r}3\\1\overline{)3}\\\underline{3}\\0\end{array}\quad 2307 = 4403_8$$

36. To convert 13,469 to base 8   ... 32,768 4096 512 64 8 1

$$\begin{array}{r}3\\4096\overline{)13,469}\\\underline{12,288}\\1181\end{array}\quad\begin{array}{r}2\\512\overline{)1181}\\\underline{1024}\\157\end{array}\quad\begin{array}{r}2\\64\overline{)157}\\\underline{128}\\29\end{array}\quad\begin{array}{r}3\\8\overline{)29}\\\underline{24}\\5\end{array}\quad\begin{array}{r}5\\1\overline{)5}\\\underline{5}\\0\end{array}\quad 13,469 = 32235_8$$

37. $826_{16} = 8(16^2) + 2(16) + 6(1) = 8(256) + 32 + 6 = 2086$
38. $581_{16} = 5(16^2) + 8(16) + 1(1) = 5(256) + 128 + 1 = 1409$
39. $6D3B7_{16} = 6(16^4) + 13(16^3) + 3(16^2) + 11(16) + 7(1) = 6(65,536) + 13(4096) + 3(256) + 176 + 7 = 447,415$
40. $24FEA_{16} = 2(16^4) + 4(16^3) + 15(16^2) + 14(16) + 10(1) = 2(65,536) + 4(4096) + 15(256) + 224 + 10 = 151,530$

41. To convert 412 to base 16   ... 4096 256 16 1

$$\begin{array}{r}1\\256\overline{)412}\\\underline{256}\\156\end{array}\quad\begin{array}{r}9\\16\overline{)156}\\\underline{144}\\12\end{array}\quad\begin{array}{r}12 = C\\1\overline{)12}\\\underline{12}\\0\end{array}\quad 412 = 19C_{16}$$

42. To convert 349 to base 16   ... 4096 256 16 1

$$\begin{array}{r}1\\256\overline{)349}\\\underline{256}\\93\end{array}\quad\begin{array}{r}5\\16\overline{)93}\\\underline{80}\\13\end{array}\quad\begin{array}{r}13 = D\\1\overline{)13}\\\underline{13}\\0\end{array}\quad 349 = 15D_{16}$$

43. To convert 5478 to base 16   ... 65,536 4096 256 16 1

$$\begin{array}{r}1\\4096\overline{)5478}\\\underline{4096}\\1382\end{array}\quad\begin{array}{r}5\\256\overline{)1382}\\\underline{1280}\\102\end{array}\quad\begin{array}{r}6\\16\overline{)102}\\\underline{96}\\6\end{array}\quad\begin{array}{r}6\\1\overline{)6}\\\underline{6}\\0\end{array}\quad 5478 = 1566_{16}$$

44. To convert 34,721 to base 16   ... 65,536 4096 256 16 1

$$
\begin{array}{ccccc}
 & 8 & 7 & 10 = A & 1 \\
4096\overline{)34{,}721} & 256\overline{)1953} & 16\overline{)161} & & 1\overline{)1} \\
\underline{32{,}768} & \underline{1792} & \underline{160} & & \underline{1} \\
1953 & 161 & 1 & & 0
\end{array}
$$

$34{,}721 = 87A1_{16}$

45. To convert 2001 to base 2   ... 2048 1024 512 256 128 64 32 16 8 4 2 1

$$
\begin{array}{ccccc}
 & 1 & 1 & 1 & 1 & 1 \\
1024\overline{)2001} & 512\overline{)977} & 256\overline{)465} & 128\overline{)209} & 64\overline{)81} \\
\underline{1024} & \underline{512} & \underline{256} & \underline{128} & \underline{64} \\
977 & 465 & 209 & 81 & 17
\end{array}
$$

$$
\begin{array}{cccccc}
 & 0 & 1 & 0 & 0 & 0 & 1 \\
32\overline{)17} & 16\overline{)17} & 8\overline{)1} & 4\overline{)1} & 2\overline{)1} & 1\overline{)1} \\
\underline{0} & \underline{16} & \underline{0} & \underline{0} & \underline{0} & \underline{1} \\
17 & 1 & 1 & 1 & 1 & 0
\end{array}
$$

$2001 = 11111010001_2$

46. To convert 2001 to base 3   ... 2187 729 243 81 27 9 3 1

$$
\begin{array}{ccccccc}
 & 2 & 2 & 0 & 2 & 0 & 1 & 0 \\
729\overline{)2001} & 243\overline{)543} & 81\overline{)57} & 27\overline{)57} & 9\overline{)3} & 3\overline{)3} & 1\overline{)0} \\
\underline{1458} & \underline{486} & \underline{0} & \underline{54} & \underline{0} & \underline{3} & \underline{0} \\
543 & 57 & 57 & 3 & 3 & 0 & 0
\end{array}
$$

$2001 = 2202010_3$

47. To convert 2001 to base 5   ... 3125 625 125 25 5 1

$$
\begin{array}{ccccc}
 & 3 & 1 & 0 & 0 & 1 \\
625\overline{)2001} & 125\overline{)126} & 25\overline{)1} & 5\overline{)1} & 1\overline{)1} \\
\underline{1875} & \underline{125} & \underline{0} & \underline{0} & \underline{1} \\
126 & 1 & 1 & 1 & 0
\end{array}
$$

$2001 = 31001_5$

48. To convert 2001 to base 7   ... 2401 343 49 7 1

$$
\begin{array}{cccc}
 & 5 & 5 & 5 & 6 \\
343\overline{)2001} & 49\overline{)286} & 7\overline{)41} & 1\overline{)6} \\
\underline{1715} & \underline{245} & \underline{35} & \underline{6} \\
286 & 41 & 6 & 0
\end{array}
$$

$2001 = 5556_7$

49. To convert 2001 to base 12   ... 20,736 1728 144 12 1

$$
\begin{array}{cccc}
 & 1 & 1 & 10 = T & 9 \\
1728\overline{)2001} & 144\overline{)273} & 12\overline{)129} & 1\overline{)9} \\
\underline{1728} & \underline{144} & \underline{120} & \underline{9} \\
273 & 129 & 9 & 0
\end{array}
$$

$2001 = 11T9_{12}$

50. To convert 2001 to base 16   ... 4096 256 16 1

$$
\begin{array}{ccc}
 & 7 & 13 = D & 1 \\
256\overline{)2001} & 16\overline{)209} & 1\overline{)1} \\
\underline{1792} & \underline{208} & \underline{1} \\
209 & 1 & 0
\end{array}
$$

$2001 = 7D1_{16}$

51. Incorrect, there is no 5 in base 5.   52. Incorrect, there is no 3 in base 3.
53. Correct   54. Correct
55. $2(5) + 3(1) = 13$ 56. $3(5) + 3(1) = 18$
57. $2(5^2) + 4(5) + 3(1) = 2(25) + 20 + 3 = 73$ 58. $3(5^2) + 0(5) + 3(1) = 3(25) + 0 + 3 = 78$

59. To convert   ... 25 5 1

$$\begin{array}{r} 3 = \ominus \\ 5\overline{\smash{)}17} \\ \underline{15} \\ 2 \end{array} \qquad \begin{array}{r} 2 = \oslash \\ 1\overline{\smash{)}2} \\ \underline{2} \\ 0 \end{array}$$

$17 = \ominus\,\oslash_5$

60. To convert   ... 25 5 1

$$\begin{array}{r} 4 = \oslash \\ 5\overline{\smash{)}23} \\ \underline{20} \\ 3 \end{array} \qquad \begin{array}{r} 3 = \ominus \\ 1\overline{\smash{)}3} \\ \underline{3} \\ 0 \end{array}$$

$23 = \oslash\,\ominus_5$

61. To convert   ... 125 25 5 1

$$\begin{array}{r} 2 = \oslash \\ 25\overline{\smash{)}74} \\ \underline{50} \\ 24 \end{array} \qquad \begin{array}{r} 4 = \oslash \\ 5\overline{\smash{)}24} \\ \underline{20} \\ 4 \end{array} \qquad \begin{array}{r} 4 = \oslash \\ 1\overline{\smash{)}4} \\ \underline{4} \\ 0 \end{array}$$

$74 = \oslash\,\oslash\,\oslash_5$

62. To convert   ... 125 25 5 1

$$\begin{array}{r} 3 = \ominus \\ 25\overline{\smash{)}87} \\ \underline{75} \\ 12 \end{array} \qquad \begin{array}{r} 2 = \oslash \\ 5\overline{\smash{)}12} \\ \underline{10} \\ 2 \end{array} \qquad \begin{array}{r} 2 = \oslash \\ 1\overline{\smash{)}2} \\ \underline{2} \\ 0 \end{array}$$

$87 = \ominus\,\oslash\,\oslash_5$

63. $1(4) + 3(1) = 7$

64. $3(4) + 2(1) = 14$

65. $2(4^2) + 1(4) + 0(1) = 2(16) + 4 + 0 = 36$

66. $3(4^2) + 2(4) + 1(1) = 3(16) + 8 + 1 = 57$

For #67-70, blue = 0 = b, red = 1 = r, gold = 2 = go, green = 3 = gr

67. To convert   ... 16 4 1

$$\begin{array}{r} 2 = \text{go} \\ 4\overline{\smash{)}11} \\ \underline{8} \\ 3 \end{array} \qquad \begin{array}{r} 3 = \text{gr} \\ 1\overline{\smash{)}3} \\ \underline{3} \\ 0 \end{array}$$

$11 = \text{(go)(gr)}_4$

68. To convert   ... 16 4 1

$$\begin{array}{r} 3 = \text{gr} \\ 4\overline{\smash{)}15} \\ \underline{12} \\ 3 \end{array} \qquad \begin{array}{r} 3 = \text{gr} \\ 1\overline{\smash{)}3} \\ \underline{3} \\ 0 \end{array}$$

$15 = \text{(gr)(gr)}_4$

69. To convert   ... 64 16 4 1

$$\begin{array}{r} 3 = \text{gr} \\ 16\overline{\smash{)}60} \\ \underline{48} \\ 12 \end{array} \qquad \begin{array}{r} 3 = \text{gr} \\ 4\overline{\smash{)}12} \\ \underline{12} \\ 0 \end{array} \qquad \begin{array}{r} 0 = \text{b} \\ 1\overline{\smash{)}0} \\ \underline{0} \\ 0 \end{array}$$

$60 = \text{(gr)(gr)(b)}_4$

70. To convert   ... 64 16 4 1

$$\begin{array}{r} 3 = \text{gr} \\ 16\overline{\smash{)}56} \\ \underline{48} \\ 8 \end{array} \qquad \begin{array}{r} 2 = \text{go} \\ 4\overline{\smash{)}8} \\ \underline{8} \\ 0 \end{array} \qquad \begin{array}{r} 0 = \text{b} \\ 1\overline{\smash{)}0} \\ \underline{0} \\ 0 \end{array}$$

$56 = \text{(gr)(go)(b)}_4$

71. a) Each remainder is multiplied by the proper power of 5.

b)

5	683		
5	136	3	↑
5	27	1	↑
5	5	2	↑
5	1	0	↑
	0	1	↑

$683 = 10213_5$

c)

8	763		
8	95	3	↑
8	11	7	↑
8	1	3	↑
	0	1	↑

$763 = 1373_8$

72. a) 1_3, 2_3, 10_3, 11_3, 12_3, 20_3, 21_3, 22_3, 100_3, 101_3, 102_3, 110_3, 111_3, 112_3, 120_3, 121_3, 122_3, 200_3, 201_3, 202_3

b) 1000_3

73. Answers will vary.

74. $2^7 = 2 \times 2 \times 2 \times 2 \times 2 \times 2 \times 2 = 128$

75. $1(b^2) + 1(b) + 1 = 43$

$b^2 + b + 1 = 43$

$b^2 + b - 42 = 0$

$(b + 7)(b - 6) = 0$

$b + 7 = 0$ or $b - 6 = 0$

$b = -7$ or $b = 6$

Since the base cannot be negative, $b = 6$.

Exercise Set 4.4

1. a) b^0, b^1, b^2, b^3, b^4

   b) 6^0, 6^1, 6^2, 6^3, 6^4

2. 7^0, 7^1, 7^2, or 1, 7, 49 using base 7.

3. Answers will vary.

4. Answers will vary.

5.
$$\begin{array}{r} 32_5 \\ \underline{41_5} \\ 123_5 \end{array}$$

6.
$$\begin{array}{r} 33_7 \\ \underline{65_7} \\ 131_7 \end{array}$$

7.
$$\begin{array}{r} 3031_4 \\ \underline{232_4} \\ 3323_4 \end{array}$$

8.
$$\begin{array}{r} 101_2 \\ \underline{11_2} \\ 1000_2 \end{array}$$

9.
$$\begin{array}{r} 799_{12} \\ \underline{218_{12}} \\ 9E5_{12} \end{array}$$

10.
$$\begin{array}{r} 222_3 \\ \underline{22_3} \\ 1021_3 \end{array}$$

11.
$$\begin{array}{r} 1112_3 \\ \underline{1011_3} \\ 2200_3 \end{array}$$

12.
$$\begin{array}{r} 470_{12} \\ \underline{347_{12}} \\ 7E7_{12} \end{array}$$

13.
$$\begin{array}{r} 14631_7 \\ \underline{6040_7} \\ 24001_7 \end{array}$$

14.
$$\begin{array}{r} 1341_8 \\ \underline{341_8} \\ 1702_8 \end{array}$$

15.
$$\begin{array}{r} 1011_2 \\ \underline{110_2} \\ 10001_2 \end{array}$$

16.
$$\begin{array}{r} 43A_{16} \\ \underline{496_{16}} \\ 8D0_{16} \end{array}$$

17.
$$\begin{array}{r} 312_4 \\ -103_4 \\ \hline 203_4 \end{array}$$

18.
$$\begin{array}{r} 426_7 \\ -134_7 \\ \hline 262_7 \end{array}$$

19.
$$\begin{array}{r} 2432_5 \\ -1243_5 \\ \hline 1134_5 \end{array}$$

20.
$$\begin{array}{r} 1011_2 \\ -101_2 \\ \hline 110_2 \end{array}$$

21.
$$\begin{array}{r} 782_{12} \\ -13T_{12} \\ \hline 644_{12} \end{array}$$

22.
$$\begin{array}{r} 1221_3 \\ -202_3 \\ \hline 1012_3 \end{array}$$

23.
$$\begin{array}{r} 1001_2 \\ -110_2 \\ \hline 11_2 \end{array}$$

24.
$$\begin{array}{r} 1E41_{12} \\ -345_{12} \\ \hline 17E8_{12} \end{array}$$

25.
$$\begin{array}{r} 4223_7 \\ -304_7 \\ \hline 3616_7 \end{array}$$

26.
$$\begin{array}{r} 4232_5 \\ -2341_5 \\ \hline 1341_5 \end{array}$$

27.
$$\begin{array}{r} 2100_3 \\ -1012_3 \\ \hline 1011_3 \end{array}$$

28.
$$\begin{array}{r} 4E7_{16} \\ -189_{16} \\ \hline 35E_{16} \end{array}$$

29.
$$
\begin{array}{r}
34_5 \\
\times\ 2_5 \\
\hline
123_5
\end{array}
$$

30.
$$
\begin{array}{r}
123_5 \\
\times\ \ 4_5 \\
\hline
1102_5
\end{array}
$$

31.
$$
\begin{array}{r}
342_7 \\
\times\ \ 5_7 \\
\hline
2403_7
\end{array}
$$

32.
$$
\begin{array}{r}
101_2 \\
\times\ 11_2 \\
\hline
101 \\
101 \\
\hline
1111_2
\end{array}
$$

33.
$$
\begin{array}{r}
512_6 \\
\times\ 23_6 \\
\hline
2340 \\
1424 \\
\hline
21020_6
\end{array}
$$

34.
$$
\begin{array}{r}
124_{12} \\
\times\ \ 6_{12} \\
\hline
720_{12}
\end{array}
$$

35.
$$
\begin{array}{r}
234_9 \\
\times\ 25_9 \\
\hline
1282 \\
468 \\
\hline
6072_9
\end{array}
$$

36.
$$
\begin{array}{r}
6T3_{12} \\
\times\ 24_{12} \\
\hline
2350 \\
1186 \\
\hline
13EE0_{12}
\end{array}
$$

37.
$$
\begin{array}{r}
111_2 \\
\times\ 101_2 \\
\hline
111 \\
000 \\
111 \\
\hline
100011_2
\end{array}
$$

38.
$$
\begin{array}{r}
584_9 \\
\times\ 24_9 \\
\hline
2567 \\
1278 \\
\hline
15457_9
\end{array}
$$

39.
$$
\begin{array}{r}
316_7 \\
\times\ 16_7 \\
\hline
2541 \\
316 \\
\hline
6031_7
\end{array}
$$

40.
$$
\begin{array}{r}
8T_{12} \\
\times\ 2T_{12} \\
\hline
744 \\
158 \\
\hline
2104_{12}
\end{array}
$$

41. $1_2 \times 1_2 = 1_2$

$$
\begin{array}{r}
110_2 \\
1_2\overline{)\,110_2} \\
\underline{1}\ \ \ \ \\
01\ \ \\
\underline{1}\ \ \\
0 \\
\underline{0} \\
0
\end{array}
$$

42.
$4_6 \times 1_6 = 4_6$
$4_6 \times 2_6 = 12_6$
$4_6 \times 3_6 = 20_6$
$4_6 \times 4_6 = 24_6$
$4_6 \times 5_6 = 32_6$

$$
\begin{array}{r}
34_6\ \ \text{R3} \\
4_6\overline{)\,231_6} \\
\underline{20}\ \ \ \\
31\ \\
\underline{24}\ \\
3
\end{array}
$$

43.
$4_5 \times 1_5 = 4_5$
$4_5 \times 2_5 = 13_5$
$4_5 \times 3_5 = 22_5$
$4_5 \times 4_5 = 31_5$

$$
\begin{array}{r}
22_5 \\
4_5\overline{)\,143_5} \\
\underline{13}\ \ \\
13\ \\
\underline{13}\ \\
0
\end{array}
$$

44.
$7_8 \times 1_8 = 7_8$
$7_8 \times 2_8 = 16_8$
$7_8 \times 3_8 = 25_8$
$7_8 \times 4_8 = 34_8$
$7_8 \times 5_8 = 43_8$
$7_8 \times 6_8 = 52_8$
$7_8 \times 7_8 = 61_8$

$$
\begin{array}{r}
54_8\ \ \text{R2} \\
7_8\overline{)\,466_8} \\
\underline{43}\ \ \ \\
36\ \\
\underline{34}\ \\
2
\end{array}
$$

45.
$2_4 \times 1_4 = 2_4$
$2_4 \times 2_4 = 10_4$
$2_4 \times 3_4 = 12_4$

$$
\begin{array}{r}
123_4 \\
2_4\overline{)\,312_4} \\
\underline{2}\ \ \ \ \\
11\ \\
\underline{10}\ \\
12 \\
\underline{12} \\
0
\end{array}
$$

46.
$6_{12} \times 1_{12} = 6_{12}$
$6_{12} \times 2_{12} = 10_{12}$
$6_{12} \times 3_{12} = 16_{12}$
$6_{12} \times 4_{12} = 20_{12}$
$6_{12} \times 5_{12} = 26_{12}$
$6_{12} \times 6_{12} = 30_{12}$
$6_{12} \times 7_{12} = 36_{12}$
$6_{12} \times 8_{12} = 40_{12}$

$$
\begin{array}{r}
86_{12}\ \ \text{R1} \\
6_{12}\overline{)\,431_{12}} \\
\underline{40}\ \ \ \\
31\ \\
\underline{30}\ \\
1
\end{array}
$$

47.
$3_4 \times 1_4 = 3_4$
$3_4 \times 2_4 = 12_4$
$3_4 \times 3_4 = 21_4$

$$
\begin{array}{r}
33_4\ \ \text{R1} \\
3_4\overline{)\,232_4} \\
\underline{21}\ \ \ \\
22\ \\
\underline{21}\ \\
1
\end{array}
$$

48.
$5_6 \times 1_6 = 5_6$
$5_6 \times 2_6 = 14_6$
$5_6 \times 3_6 = 23_6$
$5_6 \times 4_6 = 32_6$
$5_6 \times 5_6 = 41_6$

$$5_6 \overline{)214_6} \quad 24_6 \text{ R2}$$
14
34
32
2

49.
$3_5 \times 1_5 = 3_5$
$3_5 \times 2_5 = 11_5$
$3_5 \times 3_5 = 14_5$
$3_5 \times 4_5 = 22_5$

$$3_5 \overline{)224_5} \quad 41_5 \text{ R1}$$
22
04
3
1

50.
$4_6 \times 1_6 = 4_6$
$4_6 \times 2_6 = 12_6$
$4_6 \times 3_6 = 20_6$
$4_6 \times 4_6 = 24_6$
$4_6 \times 5_6 = 32_6$

$$4_6 \overline{)210_6} \quad 31_6 \text{ R2}$$
20
10
4
2

51.
$6_7 \times 1_7 = 6_7$
$6_7 \times 2_7 = 15_7$
$6_7 \times 3_7 = 24_7$
$6_7 \times 4_7 = 33_7$
$6_7 \times 5_7 = 42_7$
$6_7 \times 6_7 = 51_7$

$$6_7 \overline{)404_7} \quad 45_7 \text{ R2}$$
33
44
42
2

52.
$3_7 \times 1_7 = 3_7$
$3_7 \times 2_7 = 6_7$
$3_7 \times 3_7 = 12_7$
$3_7 \times 4_7 = 15_7$
$3_7 \times 5_7 = 21_7$
$3_7 \times 6_7 = 24_7$

$$3_7 \overline{)2101_7} \quad 500_7 \text{ R1}$$
21
00
00
01
00
1

53.
2_5
$+ \ 3_5$
$10_5 = \ominus\bigcirc_5$

54.
3_5
$+ \ 3_5$
$11_5 = \ominus\ominus_5$

55.
21_5
$+ \ 43_5$
$114_5 = \ominus\ominus\textcircled{1}_5$

56.
23_5
$+ \ 13_5$
$41_5 = \textcircled{1}\ominus_5$

For #57-64, blue = 0 = b, red = 1 = r, gold = 2 = go, green = 3 = gr

57.
3_4
$+ \ 3_4$
$12_4 = (r)(go)_4$

58.
21_4
$+ \ 30_4$
$111_4 = (r)(r)(r)_4$

59.
32_4
$+ \ 11_4$
$103_4 = (r)(b)(gr)_4$

60.
130_4
$+ \ 221_4$
$1011_4 = (r)(b)(r)(r)_4$

61.
33_4
$- \ 12_4$
$21_4 = (go)(r)_4$

62.
31_4
$- \ 13_4$
$12_4 = (r)(go)_4$

63.
231_4
$- \ 103_4$
$122_4 = (r)(go)(go)_4$

64.
301_4
$- \ 120_4$
$121_4 = (r)(go)(r)_4$

65. $2302_5 = 2(5^3) + 3(5^2) + 0(5) + 2(1) = 2(125) + 3(25) + 0 + 2 = 327$

66.
To convert 327 to base 9

$$\begin{array}{r} 4 \\ 81\overline{\smash)327} \\ \underline{324} \\ 3 \end{array} \qquad \begin{array}{r} 0 \\ 9\overline{\smash)3} \\ \underline{0} \\ 3 \end{array} \qquad \begin{array}{r} 3 \\ 1\overline{\smash)3} \\ \underline{3} \\ 0 \end{array}$$

... 729 81 9 1

$327 = 403_9$

$9^2 = \cdots \bullet$
$9^1 =$
$9^0 = \cdots$

67.
$14_5 \times 1_5 = 14_5$
$14_5 \times 2_5 = 33_5$
$14_5 \times 3_5 = 102_5$
$14_5 \times 4_5 = 121_5$

$$\begin{array}{r} 13_5 \\ 14_5\overline{\smash)242_5} \\ \underline{14} \\ 102 \\ \underline{102} \\ 0 \end{array}$$

68.
$20_4 \times 1_4 = 20_4$
$20_4 \times 2_4 = 100_4$
$20_4 \times 3_4 = 120_4$

$$\begin{array}{r} 11_4 \ \text{R3} \\ 20_4\overline{\smash)223_4} \\ \underline{20} \\ 23 \\ \underline{20} \\ 3 \end{array}$$

69. a)
$$\begin{array}{r} 462_8 \\ \times\ 35_8 \\ \hline 2772 \\ 1626 \\ \hline 21252_8 \end{array}$$

b) $462_8 = 4(8^2) + 6(8) + 2(1) = 4(64) + 48 + 2 = 306$

$35_8 = 3(8) + 5(1) = 24 + 5 = 29$

c) $306 \times 29 = 8874$

d) $21252_8 = 2(8^4) + 1(8^3) + 2(8^2) + 5(8) + 2(1)$
$= 2(4096) + 512 + 2(64) + 40 + 2$
$= 8874$

e) Yes, in part a), the numbers were multiplied in base 8 and then converted to base 10 in part d). In part b), the numbers were converted to base 10 first, then multiplied in part c).

70. If $1304_b = 204$, then b = 5 since $1(5^3) + 3(5^2) + 0(5) + 4(1) = 125 + 3(25) + 0 + 4 = 204$

Exercise Set 4.5

1. Duplation and mediation, the galley method and Napier rods

2. a) Answers will vary.
    b)
267	–	193
133	–	386
~~66~~	~~–~~	~~772~~
33	–	1544
~~16~~		~~3088~~
8		~~6176~~
~~4~~		~~12,352~~
~~2~~		~~24,704~~
1	–	49,408
		51,531

3. a) Answers will vary.
    b)

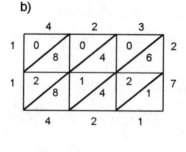

$423 \times 27 = 11,421$

4. a) Answers will vary.
    b)

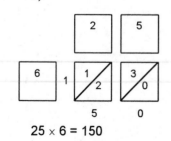

$25 \times 6 = 150$

5. | 17 – 29
    | 8 – 58
    | 4 – 116
    | 2 – 232
    | 1 – 464
    | 493

6. | 35 – 23
    | 17 – 46
    | 8 – 92
    | 4 – 184
    | 2 – 368
    | 1 – 736
    | 805

7. | 9 – 162
    | 4 – 324
    | 2 – 648
    | 1 – 1296
    | 1458

8. | 182 – 93
    | 91 – 186
    | 45 – 372
    | 22 – 744
    | 11 – 1488
    | 5 – 2976
    | 2 – 5952
    | 1 – 11,904
    | 16,926

9. | 35 – 236
    | 17 – 472
    | 8 – 944
    | 4 – 1888
    | 2 – 3776
    | 1 – 7552
    | 8260

10. | 96 – 53
    | 48 – 106
    | 24 – 212
    | 12 – 424
    | 6 – 848
    | 3 – 1696
    | 1 – 3392
    | 5088

11. | 85 – 85
    | 42 – 170
    | 21 – 340
    | 10 – 680
    | 5 – 1360
    | 2 – 2720
    | 1 – 5440
    | 7225

12. | 49 – 124
    | 24 – 248
    | 12 – 496
    | 6 – 992
    | 3 – 1984
    | 1 – 3968
    | 6076

13.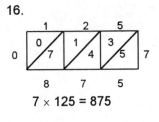

$7 \times 365 = 2555$

14.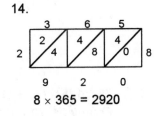

$8 \times 365 = 2920$

15.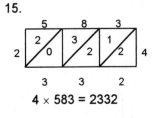

$4 \times 583 = 2332$

16.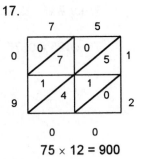

$7 \times 125 = 875$

17.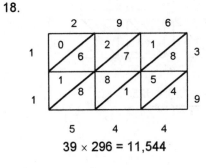

$75 \times 12 = 900$

18.

$39 \times 296 = 11,544$

19.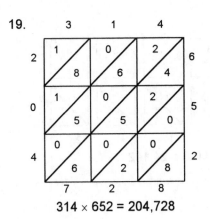

$314 \times 652 = 204,728$

20.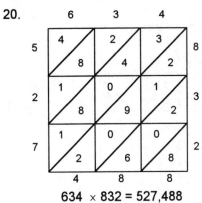

$634 \times 832 = 527,488$

21.

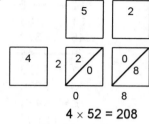

$4 \times 52 = 208$

22.

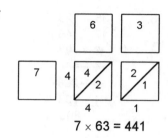

$7 \times 63 = 441$

23.

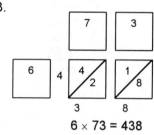

$6 \times 73 = 438$

24.

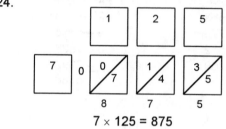

$7 \times 125 = 875$

25.

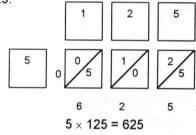

$5 \times 125 = 625$

26. $75 \times 125 = (70 + 5)125 = 70(125) + 5(125)$
From # 24, $70 \times 125 = 8750$
From # 25, $\quad 5 \times 125 = \underline{\quad 625}$
$\qquad\qquad\qquad\qquad 9375$

$75 \times 125 = 9375$

27.

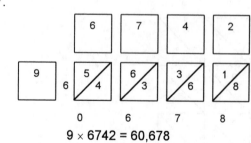

$9 \times 6742 = 60,678$

28.

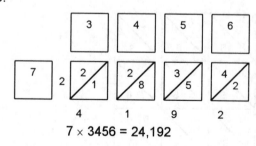

$7 \times 3456 = 24,192$

29. a) 253 × 46; Place the factors of 8 until the
        correct factors and placements are found
        so the rest of the rectangle can be completed.

    b)

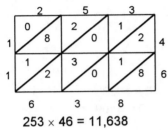

$$253 \times 46 = 11,638$$

30. a) 475 × 263; Place the factors of 8 until the
        correct factors and placements are found
        so the rest of the rectangle can be
        completed.

    b)

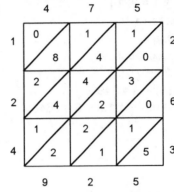

$$475 \times 263 = 124,925$$

31. a) 4 × 382; Place the factors of 12 until the correct
       factors and placements are found so the rest
       can be completed.

    b)

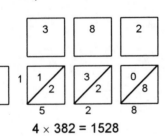

$$4 \times 382 = 1528$$

32. a) 7 × 685; Place the factors of 42 until the
        correct factors and placements are found
        so the rest can be completed.

    b)

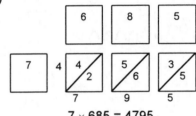

$$7 \times 685 = 4795$$

33. 13 – 22
     ~~6~~ – ~~44~~
      3 – 88
      1 – 176
         286 = 99 ∩∩∩∩∩∩∩∩ |||||

34. ~~26~~ – ~~67~~
     13 – 134
     ~~6~~ – ~~268~~
      3 – 536
      1 – 1072
         1742 = MDCCXLII

35. $12_3 \times 121_3 = 5 \times 16$

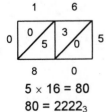

$$5 \times 16 = 80$$
$$80 = 2222_3$$

36. $24_5 \times 234_5 = 14 \times 69$

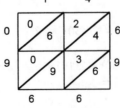

$$14 \times 69 = 966$$
$$966 = 12331_5$$

Review Exercises

1. $1000 + 1000 + 100 + 1 + 1 = 2102$
2. $1 + 10 + 100 + 1000 + 1 = 1112$
3. $10 + 100 + 100 + 100 + 1 + 1000 = 1311$
4. $100 + 10 + 1000 + 1 + 1000 + 1 + 1 + 1 = 2114$
5. $1000 + 1000 + 1000 + 100 + 100 + 10 + 1 + 1 + 1 + 1 = 3214$
6. $100 + 100 + 10 + 1 + 1000 + 1000 + 1 + 100 = 2312$
7. bbbbbbaaaaaaa
8. cbbaaaaa
9. ccbbbbbbbbbaaa
10. dda
11. dddddcccccccccbbbbba
12. ddcccbaaaa
13. $3(10) + 5 = 35$
14. $2(10) + 7 = 27$
15. $7(100) + 4(10) + 9 = 749$
16. $4(1000) + 6(10) + 8 = 4068$
17. $5(1000) + 6(100) + 4(10) + 8 = 5648$
18. $4(1000) + 8(100) + 9 = 4809$
19. gxd
20. byixe
21. hyfxb
22. bzbx
23. fzd
24. bza
25. $7(10) + 6(1) = 76$
26. $3(100) + 8(1) = 308$
27. $5(100) + 6(10) + 8(1) = 568$
28. $4(10,000) + 6(1000) + 8(100) + 8(10) + 3(1) = 46,883$
29. $4(10,000) + 8(10) + 2(1) = 40,082$
30. $6(10,000) + 5(100) + 2(10) + 9(1) = 60,529$
31. mb
32. xpe
33. vrc
34. BArg
35. ODvog
36. QFvrf

37.

38. MCDLXII

39.

40. $\alpha'\upsilon\xi\beta$

41.

$$1462 = 24(60) + 22$$

42.

$$1462 = 4(18 \times 20) + 1(20) + 2(1)$$

43. $100,000 + 2(10,000) + 2(1000) + 2(10) + 5 = 122,025$
44. $8(1000) + 2(100) + 5(10) + 4 = 8254$

45. $500 + 80 + 5 = 585$
46. $1000 + (1000 - 100) + (100 - 10) + 1 = 1991$
47. $21(60) + (20 - 3) = 1277$
48. $5(18 \times 20) + 8(20) + 11(1) = 1971$
49. $54_9 = 5(9) + 4(1) = 49$
50. $101_2 = 1(2^2) + 0(2) + 1(1) = 4 + 0 + 1 = 5$
51. $130_4 = 1(4^2) + 3(4) + 0(1) = 16 + 12 + 0 = 28$
52. $2746_8 = 2(8^3) + 7(8^2) + 4(8) + 6(1) = 2(512) + 7(64) + 32 + 6 = 1510$

53. $TOE_{12} = 10(12^2) + 0(12) + 11(1) = 10(144)$
$+ 0 + 11 = 1451$

54. $20220_3 = 2(3^4) + 0(3^3) + 2(3^2) + 2(3) + 0(1)$
$= 2(81) + 0 + 2(9) + 6 + 0 = 186$

55. To convert 463 to base 4 ... 1024 256 64 16 4 1

$$
\begin{array}{r} 1 \\ \hline 256 \,|\, 463 \\ \underline{256} \\ 207 \end{array} \quad
\begin{array}{r} 3 \\ \hline 64 \,|\, 207 \\ \underline{192} \\ 15 \end{array} \quad
\begin{array}{r} 0 \\ \hline 16 \,|\, 15 \\ \underline{0} \\ 15 \end{array} \quad
\begin{array}{r} 3 \\ \hline 4 \,|\, 15 \\ \underline{12} \\ 3 \end{array} \quad
\begin{array}{r} 3 \\ \hline 1 \,|\, 3 \\ \underline{3} \\ 0 \end{array}
$$

$463 = 13033_4$

56. To convert 463 to base 3 ... 729 243 81 27 9 3 1

$$
\begin{array}{r} 1 \\ \hline 243 \,|\, 463 \\ \underline{243} \\ 220 \end{array} \quad
\begin{array}{r} 2 \\ \hline 81 \,|\, 220 \\ \underline{162} \\ 58 \end{array} \quad
\begin{array}{r} 2 \\ \hline 27 \,|\, 58 \\ \underline{54} \\ 4 \end{array} \quad
\begin{array}{r} 0 \\ \hline 9 \,|\, 4 \\ \underline{0} \\ 4 \end{array} \quad
\begin{array}{r} 1 \\ \hline 3 \,|\, 4 \\ \underline{3} \\ 1 \end{array} \quad
\begin{array}{r} 1 \\ \hline 1 \,|\, 1 \\ \underline{1} \\ 0 \end{array}
$$

$463 = 122011_3$

57. To convert 463 to base 2 ... 512 256 128 64 32 16 8 4 2 1

$$
\begin{array}{r} 1 \\ \hline 256 \,|\, 463 \\ \underline{256} \\ 207 \end{array} \quad
\begin{array}{r} 1 \\ \hline 128 \,|\, 207 \\ \underline{128} \\ 79 \end{array} \quad
\begin{array}{r} 1 \\ \hline 64 \,|\, 79 \\ \underline{64} \\ 15 \end{array} \quad
\begin{array}{r} 0 \\ \hline 32 \,|\, 15 \\ \underline{0} \\ 15 \end{array} \quad
\begin{array}{r} 0 \\ \hline 16 \,|\, 15 \\ \underline{0} \\ 15 \end{array} \quad
\begin{array}{r} 1 \\ \hline 8 \,|\, 15 \\ \underline{8} \\ 7 \end{array} \quad
\begin{array}{r} 1 \\ \hline 4 \,|\, 7 \\ \underline{4} \\ 3 \end{array} \quad
\begin{array}{r} 1 \\ \hline 2 \,|\, 3 \\ \underline{2} \\ 1 \end{array} \quad
\begin{array}{r} 1 \\ \hline 1 \,|\, 1 \\ \underline{1} \\ 0 \end{array}
$$

$463 = 111001111_2$

58. To convert 463 to base 5 ... 625 125 25 5 1

$$
\begin{array}{r} 3 \\ \hline 125 \,|\, 463 \\ \underline{375} \\ 88 \end{array} \quad
\begin{array}{r} 3 \\ \hline 25 \,|\, 88 \\ \underline{75} \\ 13 \end{array} \quad
\begin{array}{r} 2 \\ \hline 5 \,|\, 13 \\ \underline{10} \\ 3 \end{array} \quad
\begin{array}{r} 3 \\ \hline 1 \,|\, 3 \\ \underline{3} \\ 0 \end{array}
$$

$463 = 3323_5$

59. To convert 463 to base 12 ... 1728 144 12 1

$$
\begin{array}{r} 3 \\ \hline 144 \,|\, 463 \\ \underline{432} \\ 31 \end{array} \quad
\begin{array}{r} 2 \\ \hline 12 \,|\, 31 \\ \underline{24} \\ 7 \end{array} \quad
\begin{array}{r} 7 \\ \hline 1 \,|\, 7 \\ \underline{7} \\ 0 \end{array}
$$

$463 = 327_{12}$

60. To convert 463 to base 8 ... 512 64 8 1

$$
\begin{array}{r} 7 \\ \hline 64 \,|\, 463 \\ \underline{448} \\ 15 \end{array} \quad
\begin{array}{r} 1 \\ \hline 8 \,|\, 15 \\ \underline{8} \\ 7 \end{array} \quad
\begin{array}{r} 7 \\ \hline 1 \,|\, 7 \\ \underline{7} \\ 0 \end{array}
$$

$463 = 717_8$

61.
$$
\begin{array}{r} 42_6 \\ \underline{55_6} \\ 141_6 \end{array}
$$

62.
$$
\begin{array}{r} 10110_2 \\ \underline{11001_2} \\ 101111_2 \end{array}
$$

63.
$$
\begin{array}{r} TE_{12} \\ \underline{87_{12}} \\ 176_{12} \end{array}
$$

64.
$$
\begin{array}{r} 234_7 \\ \underline{456_7} \\ 1023_7 \end{array}
$$

65.
$$
\begin{array}{r} 3024_5 \\ \underline{4023_5} \\ 12102_5 \end{array}
$$

66.
$$
\begin{array}{r} 1407_8 \\ \underline{7014_8} \\ 10423_8 \end{array}
$$

67.
$$
\begin{array}{r} 4032_7 \\ \underline{-\ 321_7} \\ 3411_7 \end{array}
$$

68.
$$
\begin{array}{r} 1001_2 \\ \underline{-\ 101_2} \\ 100_2 \end{array}
$$

69.
$$
\begin{array}{r} 4TE_{12} \\ \underline{-\ E7_{12}} \\ 3E4_{12} \end{array}
$$

70.
$$
\begin{array}{r} 4321_5 \\ \underline{-\ 442_5} \\ 3324_5 \end{array}
$$

71.
$$
\begin{array}{r} 1713_8 \\ \underline{-\ 1243_8} \\ 450_8 \end{array}
$$

72.
$$
\begin{array}{r} 2021_3 \\ \underline{-\ 212_3} \\ 1102_3 \end{array}
$$

73.
$$\begin{array}{r} 22_5 \\ \times\ 4_5 \\ \hline 143_5 \end{array}$$

74.
$$\begin{array}{r} 23_4 \\ \times\ 21_4 \\ \hline 23 \\ 112 \\ \hline 1203_4 \end{array}$$

75.
$$\begin{array}{r} 126_{12} \\ \times\ 47_{12} \\ \hline 856 \\ 4T0 \\ \hline 5656_{12} \end{array}$$

76.
$$\begin{array}{r} 221_3 \\ \times\ 22_3 \\ \hline 1212 \\ 1212 \\ \hline 21102_3 \end{array}$$

77.
$$\begin{array}{r} 1011_2 \\ \times\ 101_2 \\ \hline 1011 \\ 0000 \\ 1011 \\ \hline 110111_2 \end{array}$$

78.
$$\begin{array}{r} 476_8 \\ \times\ 23_8 \\ \hline 1672 \\ 1174 \\ \hline 13632_8 \end{array}$$

79. $1_2 \times 1_2 = 1_2$

$$\begin{array}{r} 1011_2 \\ 1_2\ \overline{)\ 1011_2} \\ \underline{1} \\ 00 \\ \underline{00} \\ 01 \\ \underline{1} \\ 01 \\ \underline{1} \\ 0 \end{array}$$

80. $2_4 \times 1_4 = 2_4$
$2_4 \times 2_4 = 10_4$
$2_4 \times 3_4 = 12_4$

$$\begin{array}{r} 130_4 \\ 2_4\ \overline{)\ 320_4} \\ \underline{2} \\ 12 \\ \underline{12} \\ 0 \\ \underline{0} \\ 0 \end{array}$$

81. $3_5 \times 1_5 = 3_5$
$3_5 \times 2_5 = 11_5$
$3_5 \times 3_5 = 14_5$
$3_5 \times 4_5 = 22_5$

$$\begin{array}{r} 30_5 \\ 3_5\ \overline{)\ 140_5} \\ \underline{14} \\ 00 \\ \underline{00} \\ 0 \end{array}$$

82. $4_6 \times 1_6 = 4_6$
$4_6 \times 2_6 = 12_6$
$4_6 \times 3_6 = 20_6$
$4_6 \times 4_6 = 24_6$
$4_6 \times 5_6 = 32_6$

$$\begin{array}{r} 433_6 \\ 4_6\ \overline{)\ 3020_6} \\ \underline{24} \\ 22 \\ \underline{20} \\ 20 \\ \underline{20} \\ 0 \end{array}$$

83. $3_6 \times 1_6 = 3_6$
$3_6 \times 2_6 = 10_6$
$3_6 \times 3_6 = 13_6$
$3_6 \times 4_6 = 20_6$
$3_6 \times 5_6 = 23_6$

$$\begin{array}{r} 411_6 \quad \text{R1} \\ 3_6\ \overline{)\ 2034_6} \\ \underline{20} \\ 03 \\ \underline{3} \\ 04 \\ \underline{3} \\ 1 \end{array}$$

84. $6_8 \times 1_8 = 6_8$
$6_8 \times 2_8 = 14_8$
$6_8 \times 3_8 = 22_8$
$6_8 \times 4_8 = 30_8$
$6_8 \times 5_8 = 36_8$
$6_8 \times 6_8 = 44_8$
$6_8 \times 7_8 = 52_8$

$$\begin{array}{r} 664_8 \quad \text{R2} \\ 6_8\ \overline{)\ 5072_8} \\ \underline{44} \\ 47 \\ \underline{44} \\ 32 \\ \underline{30} \\ 2 \end{array}$$

85.
$$\begin{array}{rcl} \cancel{142} & - & \cancel{24} \\ 71 & - & 48 \\ 35 & - & 96 \\ 17 & - & 192 \\ \cancel{8} & - & \cancel{384} \\ \cancel{4} & - & \cancel{768} \\ \cancel{2} & - & \cancel{1536} \\ 1 & - & \underline{3072} \\ & & 3408 \end{array}$$

86.

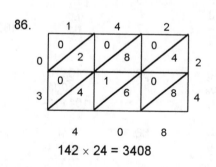

$142 \times 24 = 3408$

87.

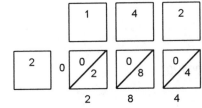

$2 \times 142 = 284$

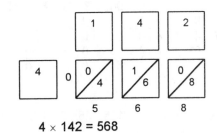

$4 \times 142 = 568$

$2 \times 142 = 284$, therefore $20 \times 142 = 2840$

Therefore, $142 \times 24 = 2840 + 568 = 3408$.

Chapter Test

1. A **number** is a quantity and answers the question "How many?". A **numeral** is the symbol used to represent the number.

2. $1000 + 1000 + 500 + 100 + (50 - 10) + 5 + 2$
    $= 2647$

3. $21(60) + 15(1) = 1275$

4. $8(1000) + 9(10) = 8090$

5. $2(18 \times 20) + 11(20) + 4(1) = 944$

6. $10,000 + 10,000 + 1000 + 1000 + 100 + 10 + 10 + 10 + 10 + 1 + 1 = 22,142$

7. $9(1000) + 900 + 90 + 9 = 9999$

8. ꝯꝯꝯ∩∩∩∩∩ıı

9. β'ʋο2

10.

$$\begin{array}{r} 4 \\ 360 \overline{)1512} \\ 1440 \\ \hline 72 \end{array} \quad \begin{array}{r} 3 \\ 20 \overline{)72} \\ 60 \\ \hline 12 \end{array} \quad \begin{array}{c} \bullet\bullet\bullet\bullet \\ \bullet\bullet\bullet \\ \overset{\bullet\bullet}{\equiv} \end{array}$$

$1512 = 4(18 \times 20) + 3(20) + 12(1)$

11.

$$\begin{array}{r} 26 \\ 60 \overline{)1596} \\ 1560 \\ \hline 36 \end{array} \quad \text{《《ıııÿ} \quad \text{《《《ıııÿı}$$

$1596 = 26(60) + 36(1)$

12. MMCCCLXXVIII

13. In an additive system, the number represented by a particular set of numerals is the sum of the values of the numerals.

14. In a multiplicative system, there are numerals for each number less than the base and for powers of the base. Each numeral less than the base is multiplied by a numeral for the power of the base, and these products are added to obtain the number.

15. In a ciphered system, the number represented by a particular set of numerals is the sum of the values of the numerals. There are numerals for each number up to and including the base and multiples of the base.

16. In a place-value system, each number is multiplied by a power of the base. The position of the numeral indicates the power of the base by which it is multiplied.

17. $37_8 = 3(8) + 7(1) = 31$

18 $403_5 = 4(5^2) + 0(5) + 3(1) = 4(25) + 0 + 3 = 103$

19. $101101_2 = 1(2^5) + 0(2^4) + 1(2^3) + 1(2^2) + 0(2) + 1(1) = 32 + 0 + 8 + 4 + 0 + 1 = 45$

20. $368_9 = 3(9^2) + 6(9) + 8(1) = 3(81) + 54 + 8 = 305$

21. To convert 36 to base 2   ... 64 32 16 8 4 2 1

$$32 \overline{)36} \quad 16 \overline{)4} \quad 8 \overline{)4} \quad 4 \overline{)4} \quad 2 \overline{)0} \quad 1 \overline{)0}$$

	1	0	0	1	0	0
	$32\overline{)36}$	$16\overline{)4}$	$8\overline{)4}$	$4\overline{)4}$	$2\overline{)0}$	$1\overline{)0}$
	32	0	0	4	0	0
	4	4	4	0	0	0

$$36 = 100100_2$$

22. To convert 84 to base 5   ... 125 25 5 1

	3	1	4
	$25\overline{)84}$	$5\overline{)9}$	$1\overline{)4}$
	75	5	4
	9	4	0

$$84 = 314_5$$

23. To convert 2356 to base 12   ... 20,736 1728 144 12 1

	1		4		4	4
	$1728\overline{)2356}$		$144\overline{)628}$		$12\overline{)52}$	$1\overline{)4}$
	1728		576		48	4
	628		52		4	0

$$2356 = 1444_{12}$$

24. To convert 2938 to base 7   ... 16,807 2401 343 49 7 1

	1		1		3		6		5
	$2401\overline{)2938}$		$343\overline{)537}$		$49\overline{)194}$		$7\overline{)47}$		$1\overline{)5}$
	2401		343		147		42		5
	537		194		47		5		0

$$2938 = 11365_7$$

25.
$$\begin{array}{r} 133_5 \\ \underline{434_5} \\ 1122_5 \end{array}$$

26.
$$\begin{array}{r} 425_7 \\ \underline{-154_7} \\ 241_7 \end{array}$$

27.
$$\begin{array}{r} 45_6 \\ \underline{\times 23_6} \\ 223 \\ \underline{134} \\ 2003_6 \end{array}$$

28.
$3_5 \times 1_5 = 3_5$
$3_5 \times 2_5 = 11_5$
$3_5 \times 3_5 = 14_5$
$3_5 \times 4_5 = 22_5$

$$\begin{array}{r} 220_5 \\ 3_5 \overline{)1210_5} \\ \underline{11} \\ 11 \\ \underline{11} \\ 00 \\ \underline{00} \\ 0 \end{array}$$

29.
$$\begin{array}{r} \cancel{14 - 28} \\ 7 - 56 \\ 3 - 112 \\ \underline{1 - 224} \\ 392 \end{array}$$

30.

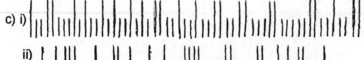

$$43 \times 196 = 8428$$

Group Projects

1.   a) 06470-9869-1
   b) i) 51593-4837-7   ii) 14527-8924-75-6

   c) i)

       ii)

CHAPTER FIVE

NUMBER THEORY AND THE REAL NUMBER SYSTEM

Exercise Set 5.1

1. Number theory is the study of numbers and their properties.
2. If a and b are factors of c, then c ÷ a is an integer and c ÷ b is an integer.
3. a) *a divides b* means that *b* divided by *a* has a remainder of zero.
   b) *a is divisible by b* means that *a* divided by *b* has a remainder of zero.
4. A prime number is natural number greater than 1 that has exactly two factors (or divisors), itself and 1.
5. A composite number is a natural number that is divisible by a number other than itself
   and 1. Any natural number that is not prime is composite.
6. Every composite number can be expressed as a unique product of prime numbers.
7. a) The greatest common divisor (GCD) of a set of natural numbers is the largest natural number that divides (without remainder) every number in that set.

   b) Determine the prime factorization of each number. Then find the product of the prime factors with the smallest exponent that appears in each of the prime factorizations.

   c)

   $$\begin{array}{c|c} 2 & 16 \\ 2 & 8 \\ 2 & 4 \\ & 2 \end{array}$$
   $$16 = 2^4$$

   $$\begin{array}{c|c} 5 & 40 \\ 2 & 8 \\ 2 & 4 \\ & 2 \end{array}$$
   $$40 = 2^3 \cdot 5$$

   The prime factors with the smallest exponents that appear in each of the factorizations are 2^3.
   The GCD of 16 and 40 is $2^3 = 8$.

8. a) The least common multiple (LCM) of a set of natural numbers is the smallest natural number that is divisible (without remainder) by each element of the set.

   b) Determine the prime factorization of each number. Then find the product of the prime factors with the largest exponent in each of the prime factorizations.

   c)

   $$\begin{array}{c|c} 2 & 16 \\ 2 & 8 \\ 2 & 4 \\ & 2 \end{array}$$
   $$16 = 2^4$$

   $$\begin{array}{c|c} 5 & 40 \\ 2 & 8 \\ 2 & 4 \\ & 2 \end{array}$$
   $$40 = 2^3 \cdot 5$$

   The prime factors that appear in any of the factorizations are 2^4 and 5. The LCM of 16 and 40 is
   $2^4 \cdot 5 = 16 \cdot 5 = 80$.

9. Mersenne Primes are prime numbers of the form 2^n-1 where n is a prime number.

10. A conjecture is a supposition that has not been proved nor disproved.

11. Goldbach's conjecture states that every even number greater than or equal to 4 can be represented as the sum of two (not necessarily distinct) prime numbers.

12. Twin primes are of the form p, p+2, where p is a prime number. An example is 5 & 7.

13.

1̶	2	3	4̶	5	6̶	7	8̶	9̶	1̶0̶
11	1̶2̶	13	1̶4̶	1̶5̶	1̶6̶	17	1̶8̶	19	2̶0̶
2̶1̶	2̶2̶	23	2̶4̶	2̶5̶	2̶6̶	2̶7̶	2̶8̶	29	3̶0̶
31	3̶2̶	3̶3̶	3̶4̶	3̶5̶	3̶6̶	37	3̶8̶	3̶9̶	4̶0̶
41	4̶2̶	43	4̶4̶	4̶5̶	4̶6̶	47	4̶8̶	4̶9̶	5̶0̶
5̶1̶	5̶2̶	53	5̶4̶	5̶5̶	5̶6̶	5̶7̶	5̶8̶	59	6̶0̶
61	6̶2̶	6̶3̶	6̶4̶	6̶5̶	6̶6̶	67	6̶8̶	6̶9̶	7̶0̶
71	7̶2̶	73	7̶4̶	7̶5̶					

The prime numbers between 1 and 75 are: 2, 3, 5, 7, 11, 13, 17, 19, 23, 29, 31, 37, 41, 43, 47, 53, 59, 61, 67, 71, 73.

14. The prime numbers between 1 and 100 are: 2, 3, 5, 7, 11, 13, 17, 19, 23, 29, 31, 37, 41, 43, 47, 53, 59, 61, 67, 71, 73, 79, 83, 89, 97.

15. True; since $42 \div 7 = 6$

16. True; since $56 \div 7 = 8$

17. True; since $6 \times 7 = 42$

18. True; since $42 \div 7 = 6$

19. False; 42 is divisible by 7.

20. False; 42 is a multiple of 7.

21. True; If a number is divisible by 10, then it is also divisible by 5.

22. False; If a number is divisible by 10, then it is also divisible by 5.

23. False; If a number is divisible by 3, then the sum of the number's digits is divisible by 3.

24. True.

25. True; since $2 \times 3 = 6$.

26. True; since $3 \times 4 = 12$.

27. Divisible by 2, 3, 4, and 6.

28. Divisible by 2, 3, 4, 5, 6, 7, 8, 9, and 10.

29. Divisible by 3 and 5.

30. Divisible by 2, 3, 4, 5, 6, 8, and 10.

31. Divisible by 2, 3, 4, 5, 6, 8, and 10.

32. Divisible by none of the numbers.

33. $2 \cdot 3 \cdot 4 \cdot 5 \cdot 6 = 720$. (other answers are possible)

34. $3 \cdot 4 \cdot 5 \cdot 9 \cdot 10 = 5400$. (other answers are possible)

35.
```
2 | 44
2 | 22
    11
```
$44 = 2^2 \cdot 11$

36.
```
3 | 51
    17
```
$51 = 3 \cdot 17$

37.
```
2 | 72
2 | 36
2 | 18
3 | 9
    3
```
$72 = 2^3 \cdot 3^2$

38.
```
2 | 150
3 | 75
5 | 25
    5
```
$150 = 2 \cdot 3 \cdot 5^2$

39.
```
3 | 303
    101
```
$303 = 3 \cdot 101$

40.
```
2 | 400
2 | 200
2 | 100
2 | 50
5 | 25
    5
```
$400 = 2^4 \cdot 5^2$

41.
```
3 | 513
3 | 171
3 | 57
    19
```
$513 = 3^3 \cdot 19$

42.
```
3 | 663
13 | 221
    17
```
$663 = 3 \cdot 13 \cdot 17$

43.
$$\begin{array}{r|r} 2 & 1336 \\ 2 & 668 \\ 2 & 334 \\ & 167 \end{array}$$
$1336 = 2^3 \cdot 167$

44.
$$\begin{array}{r|r} 13 & 1313 \\ & 101 \end{array}$$
$1313 = 13 \cdot 101$

45.
$$\begin{array}{r|r} 3 & 2001 \\ 23 & 667 \\ & 29 \end{array}$$
$2001 = 3 \cdot 23 \cdot 29$

46.
$$\begin{array}{r|r} 2 & 3190 \\ 5 & 1595 \\ 11 & 319 \\ & 29 \end{array}$$
$3190 = 2 \cdot 5 \cdot 11 \cdot 29$

47. The prime factors of 15 and 18 are:
$15 = 3 \cdot 5, \ 18 = 2 \cdot 3^2$
a) The common factors are: 3;
thus, the GCD = 3.
b) The factors with the greatest exponent that appear in either are: $2, 3^2, 5$;
thus, the LCM = $2 \cdot 3^2 \cdot 5 = 90$

48. The prime factors of 15 and 44 are:
$15 = 3 \cdot 5, \ 44 = 2^2 \cdot 11$
a) The common factors are: none;
thus, the GCD = 1.
b) The factors with the greatest exponent that appear in either are: $2^2, 3, 5, 11$;
thus, the LCM = $2^2 \cdot 3 \cdot 5 \cdot 11 = 660$

49. The prime factors of 42 and 56 are:
$42 = 2 \cdot 3 \cdot 7, \ 56 = 2^3 \cdot 7$
a) The common factors are: 2, 7;
thus, the GCD = $2 \cdot 7 = 14$.
b) The factors with the greatest exponent that appear in either are: $2^3, 3, 7$;
thus, the LCM = $2^3 \cdot 3 \cdot 7 = 168$

50. The prime factors of 52 and 65 are:
$52 = 2^2 \cdot 13, \ 65 = 5 \cdot 13$
a) The common factors are: 13;
thus, the GCD = 13.
b) The factors with the greatest exponent that appear in either are: $2^2, 5, 13$;
thus, the LCM = $2^2 \cdot 5 \cdot 13 = 260$

51. The prime factors of 40 and 900 are:
$40 = 2^3 \cdot 5, \ 900 = 2^2 \cdot 3^2 \cdot 5^2$
a) The common factors are: $2^2, 5$;
thus, the GCD = $2^2 \cdot 5 = 20$.
b) The factors with the greatest exponent that appear in either are: $2^3, 3^2, 5^2$;
thus, the LCM = $2^2 \cdot 3^2 \cdot 5^2 = 1800$

52. The prime factors of 120 and 240 are:
$120 = 2^3 \cdot 3 \cdot 5, \ 240 = 2^4 \cdot 3 \cdot 5$
a) The common factors are: $2^3, 3, 5$;
thus, the GCD = $2^3 \cdot 3 \cdot 5 = 120$.
b) The factors with the greatest exponent that appear in either are: $2^4, 3, 5$;
thus, the LCM = $2^4 \cdot 3 \cdot 5 = 240$

53. The prime factors of 96 and 212 are:
$96 = 2^5 \cdot 3, \ 212 = 2^2 \cdot 53$
a) The common factors are: 2^2;
thus, the GCD = $2^2 = 4$.
b) The factors with the greatest exponent that appear in either are: $2^5, 3, 53$;
thus, the LCM = $2^5 \cdot 3 \cdot 53 = 5088$

54. The prime factors of 240 and 285 are:
$240 = 2^4 \cdot 3 \cdot 5, \ 285 = 3 \cdot 5 \cdot 19$
a) The common factors are: 3, 5;
thus, the GCD = $3 \cdot 5 = 15$.
b) The factors with the greatest exponent that appear in either are: $2^4, 3, 5, 19$;
thus, the LCM = $2^4 \cdot 3 \cdot 5 \cdot 19 = 4560$

55. The prime factors of 24, 48, and 128 are:
$24 = 2^3 \cdot 3, \ 48 = 2^4 \cdot 3, \ 128 = 2^7$
a) The common factors are: 2^3;
thus, the GCD = $2^3 = 8$.
b) The factors with the greatest exponent that appear in either are: $2^7, 3$;
thus, the LCM = $2^7 \cdot 3 = 384$

56. The prime factors of 18, 78, and 198 are:
$18 = 2 \cdot 3^2, \ 78 = 2 \cdot 3 \cdot 13, \ 198 = 2 \cdot 3^2 \cdot 11$
a) The common factors are: 2, 3;
thus, the GCD = $2 \cdot 3 = 6$.
b) The factors with the greatest exponent that appear in either are: $2, 3^2, 11, 13$;
thus, the LCM = $2 \cdot 3^2 \cdot 11 \cdot 13 = 2574$

57. Use the list of primes generated in exercise 13. The next two sets of twin primes are: 17, 19 and 29, 31.

58. No. Any other two consecutive natural numbers will include an even number, and even numbers greater than two are composite.

59. $4 = 2 + 2, 6 = 3 + 3, 8 = 3 + 5, 10 = 3 + 7, 12 = 5 + 7, 14 = 7 + 7, 16 = 3 + 13, 18 = 5 + 13, 20 = 3 + 17$.

60. Use the formula $2^n - 1$, where n is a prime number. $2^2 - 1 = 3, 2^3 - 1 = 7, 2^5 - 1 = 31, 2^7 - 1 = 127, 2^{13} - 1 = 8191$.

61. Fermat number = $2^{2^n} + 1$, where n is a natural number. $2^{2^1} + 1 = 5, \ 2^{2^2} + 1 = 2^4 + 1 = 17, \ 2^{2^3} + 1 = 2^8 + 1 = 257$. These numbers are prime.

62. The least common multiple of 45 and 60 is 180. Thus, it will be 180 minutes before the planes leave at the same time again.

63. The lcm of 40 and 60 is 120. Thus, it will be 120 days before they are on sale at the same time again.
64. The least common multiple of 5 and 6 is 30. Thus, it will be 30 days before they both have the same night off again.
65. The least common multiple of 15 and 18 is 90. Thus, it will be 90 days before he visits both on the same day again.
66. To solve this problem we must find the greatest common divisor of 432 and 360.

2	432
2	216
2	108
2	54
3	27
3	9
	3

$432 = 2^4 \cdot 3^3$

2	360
2	180
2	90
3	45
3	15
	5

$360 = 2^3 \cdot 3^2 \cdot 5$

The GCD is $2^3 \cdot 3^2 = 8 \cdot 9 = 72$. That is, 72 is the largest number that divides (without remainder) both 432 and 360. $432 = 72 \cdot 6$ and $360 = 72 \cdot 5$. Therefore, John can make 6 stacks of 72 each from the baseball cards and 5 stacks of 72 each from the football cards.

67. The GCD of 288 and 192 is 96. Thus, each group should have 96 cars.

68. a) The possible committee sizes are: 4, 5, 10, 20, or 25.
    b) The number of committees possible are: 25 committees of 4, 20 committees of 5, 10 committees of 10, 5 committees of 20, or 4 committees of 25.

69. a)
5 = 6 − 1	7 = 6 + 1
11 = 12 − 1	13 = 12 + 1
17 = 18 − 1	19 = 18 + 1
23 = 24 − 1	29 = 30 − 1

b) Conjecture: Every prime number greater than 3 differs by 1 from a multiple of the number 6.

c) This conjecture appears to be correct.

70. A number is divisible by 15 if both 3 and 5 divide the number.

71. $75 \div 35 = 2$ with remainder 5.
    $35 \div 5 = 7$ with remainder 0.
    Thus, the gcd of 35 and 75 is 5.

72. $160 \div 20 = 8$ with remainder 0.
    Thus, the gcd of 20 and 160 is 20.

73. $112 \div 18 = 6$ with remainder 4.
    $18 \div 4 = 4$ with remainder 2.
    $4 \div 2 = 2$ with remainder 0.
    Thus, the gcd of 18 and 112 is 2.

74. $115 \div 96 = 1$ with remainder 19.
    $96 \div 19 = 5$ with remainder 1.
    $19 \div 1 = 19$ with remainder 0.
    Thus, the gcd of 96 and 115 is 1.

75. $180 \div 150 = 1$ with remainder 30.
    $150 \div 30 = 5$ with remainder 0.
    Thus, the gcd of 150 and 180 is 30.

76. $560 \div 210 = 2$ with remainder 140.
    $210 \div 140 = 1$ with remainder 70.
    $140 \div 70 = 2$ with remainder 0.
    Thus, the gcd of 210 and 560 is 70.

77. The proper factors of 12 are:
    1, 2, 3, 4, and 6.
    $1 + 2 + 3 + 4 + 6 = 16 \neq 12$
    Thus, 12 is not a perfect number.

78. The proper factors of 28 are:
    1, 2, 4, 7, and 14.
    $1 + 2 + 4 + 7 + 14 = 28$
    Thus, 28 is a perfect number.

79. The proper factors of 496 are:
    1, 2, 4, 8, 16, 31, 62, 124, and 248.
    $1+2+4+8+16+31+62+124+248 = 496$
    Thus, 496 is a perfect number.

80. The proper factors of 48 are:
    1, 2, 3, 4, 6, 8, 12, 16, and 24.
    $1+2+3+4+6+8+12+16+24 = 76 \neq 48$
    Thus, 48 is not a perfect number.

81. a) $60 = 2^2 \cdot 3^1 \cdot 5^1$ Adding 1 to each exponent and then multiplying these numbers, we get $(2+1)(1+1)(1+1) = 3 \cdot 2 \cdot 2 = 12$ divisors of 60.
    b) The divisors of 60 are: 1, 2, 3, 4, 5, 6, 10, 12, 15, 20, 30, and 60. Counting these we get 12, the same answer as in part (a).

82. No, 2 and 4 are not unique prime factors since $4 = 2 \cdot 2$. Any number that 4 divides, 2 will also divide, but 8 does not divide all numbers that are divisible by 4. Some examples are: 4, 12, and 20.

83. The sum of the digits will be a number divisible by 3, thus the number is divisible by 6.

84. The sum of the groups which have the same three digits will always be divisible by three.
    (i.e. $d + d + d = 3d$ and $3|3d$)

85. $36,018 = (36,000 + 18)$; $36,000 \div 18 = 2,000$ and $18 \div 18 = 1$
    Thus, since $18 \mid 36000$ and $18 \mid 18$, $18 \mid 36018$.

86. $2^2 - 1 = 3, 2^3 - 1 = 7, 2^5 - 1 = 31, 2^7 - 1 = 127$ are prime numbers, but
    $2^{11} - 1 = 2,048 - 1 = 2,047$; and since $23 \times 89 = 2,047$, 2047 is not prime.

87. $8 = 2+3+3$, $9 = 3+3+3$, $10 = 2+3+5$, $11 = 2+2+7$, $12 = 2+5+5$, $13 = 3+3+7$, $14 = 2+5+7$,
    $15 = 3+5+7$, $16 = 2+7+7$, $17 = 5+5+7$, $18 = 2+5+11$, $19 = 3+5+11$, $20 = 2+7+11$.

Exercise Set 5.2

1. Begin at zero, draw an arrow to the value of the first number. From the tip of that arrow draw another arrow by moving a number of spaces equal to the value of the second number. Be sure to move left if the number is negative and move right if the number is positive. The sum of the two numbers is at the tip of the second arrow.

2. To rewrite a subtraction problem as an addition problem, rewrite the subtraction sign as an addition sign and change the second number to its additive inverse.

3. The product of two numbers with like signs is a positive number, and the product of two numbers with unlike signs is a negative number.

4. The quotient of two numbers with like signs is a positive number, and the quotient of two numbers with unlike signs is a negative number.

5. 0 times any real number is zero.

6. $3 \div 0$ is undefined. Division by 0 is not allowed.

7. $-4 + 7 = 3$

8. $6 + (-11) = -5$

9. $(-3) + 9 = 6$

10. $(-7) + (-7) = -14$

11. $[6 + (-11)] + 0 = -5 + 0 = -5$

12. $(2 + 5) + (-4) = 7 + (-4) = 3$

13. $[(-3) + (-4)] + 9 = -7 + 9 = 2$

14. $[8 + (-3)] + (-2) = [5] + (-2) = 3$

15. $[(-23) + (-9)] + 11 = [-32] + 11 = -21$

16. $[5 + (-13)] + 18 = [-8] + 18 = 10$

17. $5 - 8 = 5 + (-8) = -3$

18. $-6 - 3 = -6 + (-3) = -9$

19. $-7 - 6 = (-7) + (-6) = -13$

20. $4 - (-6) = 4 + 6 = 10$

21. $-5 - (-3) = -5 + 3 = -2$

22. $-4 - 4 = -4 + (-4) = -8$

23. $14 - 20 = 14 + (-20) = -6$

24. $8 - (-3) = 8 + 3 = 11$

25. $[5 + (-3)] - 4 = 2 - 4 = 2 + (-4) = -2$

26. $6 - (8 + 6) = 6 - 14 += 6 + (-14) = -8$

27. $-3 \cdot 6 = -18$

28. $6(-8) = -48$

29. $(-7)(-7) = 49$

30. $(8)(-8) = -64$

31. $[(-8)(-2)] \cdot 6 = 16 \cdot 6 = 96$

32. $(4)(-5)(-6) = (-20)(-6) = 120$

33. $(5 \cdot 6)(-2) = (30)(-2) = -60$

34. $(-9)(-1)(-2) = (9)(-2) = -18$

35. $[(-3)(-6)] \cdot [(-5)(8)] = (18)(-40) = -720$

36. $[-8 \cdot 4) \cdot 5](-2) = [(-32)(5)](-2)$
    $= [-160](-2) = 320$

37. $-27 \div (-9) = 3$

38. $-24 \div 6 = -4$

39. $13 \div (-13) = -1$

40. $-48 \div 3 = -16$

41. $\dfrac{56}{-8} = -7$

42. $\dfrac{-75}{15} = -5$

43. $\dfrac{-210}{14} = -15$

44. $\dfrac{186}{-6} = -31$

45. $144 \div (-3) = -48$

46. $(-900) \div (-4) = 225$

47. False; every integer is not a natural number.
48. True; the natural numbers are a subset of the integers.
49. False; the difference of two negative integers may be positive, negative, or zero.
50. True.
51. True; the product of two integers with like signs is a positive integer.
52. False; the difference of a positive integer and a negative integer may be positive, negative, or zero.
53. True; the quotient of two integers with unlike signs is a negative number.
54. False; the quotient of any two integers with like signs is a positive number.
55. False; the sum of a positive integer and a negative integer could be positive, negative, or zero.
56. False; the product of two integers with unlike signs is always a negative integer.

57. $(6 + 8) \div 2 = 14 \div 2 = 7$
58. $[(-6)5] + 7 = -30 + 7 = -23$
59. $[6(-2)] - 5 = -12 + (-5) = -17$
60. $[(-5)(-6)] - 3 = 30 + (-3) = 27$
61. $(4 - 8)(3) = (-4)(3) = -12$
62. $[18 \div (-2)](-3) = (-9)(-3) = 27$
63. $\{2 + (-17)] \div 3 = [-15] \div 3 = -5$
64. $(5 - 9) \div (-4) = (-4) \div (-4) = 1$
65. $[(-22)(-3)] \div (2 -13) = 66 \div (2 + (-13))$
$= 66 \div (-11) = -6$
66. $[15(-4)] \div (-6) = (-60) \div (-6) = 10$
67. $-9, -5, -3, -1, 0, 7$
68. $-10, -6, -2, 0, 4, 8$
69. $-6, -5, -4, -3, -2, -1$
70. $-108, -76, -47, 33, 72, 106$
71. $15^\circ - (-11^\circ) = 15^\circ + 11^\circ = 26^\circ F$
72. $14,495 - (-282) = 14,495 + 282$
$= 14,777.$ 14,777 feet
73. $842 - (-927) = 842 + 927 = 1,769$
1,769 feet
74. $8 - 5 + 3 + 4 = 3 + 3 + 4 = 6 + 4 = 10.$ The Eagles did make a first down.
75. $7 - 2 - 3 - 2 + 1 = 5 - 3 - 2 + 1$
$= 2 - 2 + 1 = 0 + 1 = 1.$
Her net gain was 1 point.
76. $(2540 + 26) - 91 = 2566 - 91 = 2475$
NASDAQ ave. = 2475 points

77. a) $+ 1 - (-8) = + 1 + 8 = 9.$ There is a 9 hour time difference.
b) $- 5 - (-7) = -5 + 7 = 2.$ There is a 2 hour time difference.

78. $\dfrac{-a}{-b} = \dfrac{-1}{-1} \cdot \dfrac{a}{b} = \dfrac{a}{b}$

79. $\dfrac{1 + 23 + 45 + \ldots 99 + 100}{12 + 34 + 5 \ldots + 99100} = \dfrac{50}{50} = -1$

80. a) The next 3 pentagonal numbers are 35, 51, and 70.

b) The nth pentagonal number is obtained by adding the nth triangular number (see section 1.1) to the nth square number (see section 1.1) and subtracting n. For example, if n = 4, the 4th triangular number is 10 and the 4th square number is 16. The sum of 10 and 16 is 26 and 26 − n = 26 − 4 = 22, which is the 4th pentagonal number. The next five pentagonal numbers are 92, 117, 145, 176, and 210.

c) Since 70 is the 7th pentagonal number and 92 is the 8th pentagonal number, 72 cannot be a pentagonal number.

81. $0 + 1 - 2 + 3 + 4 - 5 + 6 - 7 - 8 + 9 = 1$ (other answers are possible)

Exercise Set 5.3

1. The set of rational numbers is the set of all numbers of the form p/q, where p and q are integers, and $q \neq 0$.

2. a) Multiply and divide the number by the position value of the last nonzero digit to the right of the decimal point.

   b) $0.013 = \dfrac{1000(0.013)}{1000} = \dfrac{13}{1000}$

3. a) Divide both the numerator and the denominator by their greatest common divisor.

   b) $\dfrac{12}{45} = \dfrac{12 \div 3}{45 \div 3} = \dfrac{4}{15}$

4. For positive mixed numbers, multiply the denominator of the fraction by the integer preceding it. Add this product to the numerator. This sum is the numerator of the improper fraction; the denominator is the same as the denomiator of the mixed number. For negative mixed numbers, you can temporarily ignore the negative sign, perform the conversion described above, and then reattach the negative sign.

5. Divide the numerator by the denominator. The quotient is the the integer part of the mixed number. The fraction part of the mixed number is the remainder divided by the divisor.

6. a) The product of two fractions is found by multiplying the numerators and multiplying the denominators.

   b) $\dfrac{24}{15} \cdot \dfrac{7}{36} = \dfrac{24 \cdot 7}{15 \cdot 36} = \dfrac{168}{540} = \dfrac{168 \div 12}{540 \div 12} = \dfrac{14}{45}$

7. a) The reciprocal of a number is 1 divided by the number.

   b) The reciprocal of -5 is $\dfrac{1}{-5} = -\dfrac{1}{5}$

8. a) To divide two fractions, multiply the first fraction by the reciprocal of the second fraction.

   b) $\dfrac{12}{19} \div \dfrac{3}{8} = \dfrac{12}{19} \cdot \dfrac{8}{3} = \dfrac{96}{57} = \dfrac{96 \div 3}{57 \div 3} = \dfrac{32}{19}$

9. a) To add or subtract two fractions with a common denominator, we add or subtract their numerators and keep the common denominator.

   b) $\dfrac{13}{27} + \dfrac{8}{27} = \dfrac{21}{27} = \dfrac{7}{9}$

10. a) First rewrite each fraction with a common denominator. Then add or subtract the fractions.

    b) The LCM for the denominators 12 and 9 is 36.

11. We can multiply a fraction by the number one in the form of c/c (where c is a nonzero integer) and the number will maintain the same value.

12. Yes. $\dfrac{20}{35} = \dfrac{20 \div 5}{35 \div 5} = \dfrac{4}{7}$

13. The GCD of 14 and 21 is 7.

    $\dfrac{14}{21} = \dfrac{14 \div 7}{21 \div 7} = \dfrac{2}{3}$

14. The GCD of 22 and 55 is 11.

    $\dfrac{22}{55} = \dfrac{22 \div 11}{55 \div 11} = \dfrac{2}{5}$

15. The GCD of 63 and 98 is 7.

    $\dfrac{63}{98} = \dfrac{63 \div 7}{98 \div 7} = \dfrac{9}{14}$

16. The GCD of 36 and 56 is 4.

    $\dfrac{36}{56} = \dfrac{36 \div 4}{56 \div 4} = \dfrac{9}{14}$

17. The GCD of 525 and 800 is 25.

    $\dfrac{525}{800} = \dfrac{525 \div 25}{800 \div 25} = \dfrac{21}{32}$

18. The GCD of 13 and 221 is 13.

    $\dfrac{13}{221} = \dfrac{13 \div 13}{221 \div 13} = \dfrac{1}{17}$

19. The GCD of 112 and 176 is 16.

    $\dfrac{112}{176} = \dfrac{112 \div 16}{176 \div 16} = \dfrac{7}{11}$

20. The GCD of 120 and 135 is 15.

    $\dfrac{120}{135} = \dfrac{120 \div 15}{135 \div 15} = \dfrac{8}{9}$

21. The GCD of 45 and 495 is 45.

$$\frac{45}{495} = \frac{45 \div 45}{495 \div 45} = \frac{1}{11}$$

22. The GCD of 124 and 148 is 4.

$$\frac{124}{148} = \frac{124 \div 4}{148 \div 4} = \frac{31}{37}$$

23. $2\frac{5}{8} = \frac{2 \cdot 8 + 5}{8} = \frac{16 + 5}{8} = \frac{21}{8}$

24. $3\frac{7}{9} = \frac{3 \cdot 9 + 7}{9} = \frac{27 + 7}{9} = \frac{34}{9}$

25. $-2\frac{3}{4} = -\frac{2 \cdot 4 + 3}{4} = -\frac{8 + 3}{4} = -\frac{11}{4}$

26. $-7\frac{1}{5} = -\frac{7 \cdot 5 + 1}{5} = -\frac{35 + 1}{5} = -\frac{36}{5}$

27. $-4\frac{15}{16} = -\frac{4 \cdot 16 + 15}{16} = -\frac{64 + 15}{16} = -\frac{79}{16}$

28. $11\frac{9}{16} = \frac{11 \cdot 16 + 9}{16} = \frac{176 + 9}{16} = \frac{185}{16}$

29. $2\frac{1}{8} = \frac{2 \cdot 8 + 1}{8} = \frac{16 + 1}{8} = \frac{17}{8}$

30. $2\frac{3}{4} = \frac{2 \cdot 4 + 3}{4} = \frac{8 + 3}{4} = \frac{11}{4}$

31. $1\frac{7}{8} = \frac{1 \cdot 8 + 7}{8} = \frac{8 + 7}{8} = \frac{15}{8}$

32. $1\frac{1}{2} = \frac{1 \cdot 2 + 1}{2} = \frac{2 + 1}{2} = \frac{3}{2}$

33. $\frac{31}{16} = \frac{16 + 15}{16} = \frac{1 \cdot 16 + 15}{16} = 1\frac{15}{16}$

34. $\frac{45}{14} = \frac{42 + 3}{14} = \frac{3 \cdot 14 + 3}{14} = 3\frac{3}{14}$

35. $-\frac{213}{5} = -\frac{210 + 3}{5} = -\frac{42 \cdot 5 + 3}{5} = -42\frac{3}{5}$

36. $-\frac{457}{11} = -\frac{451 + 6}{11} = -\frac{41 \cdot 11 + 6}{11} = -41\frac{6}{11}$

37. $-\frac{878}{15} = -\frac{870 + 8}{15} = -\frac{58 \cdot 15 + 8}{15} = -58\frac{8}{15}$

38. $\frac{1028}{21} = \frac{1008 + 20}{21} = \frac{48 \cdot 21 + 20}{21} = 48\frac{20}{21}$

39. $1 \div 4 = 0.25$

40. $3 \div 7 = 0.\overline{428571}$

41. $4 \div 7 = 0.\overline{571428}$

42. $5 \div 6 = 0.8\overline{3}$

43. $3 \div 8 = 0.375$

44. $23 \div 7 = 0.\overline{285714}$

45. $13 \div 3 = 4.\overline{3}$

46. $115 \div 15 = 7.\overline{6}$

47. $85 \div 15 = 5.\overline{6}$

48. $1002 \div 11 = 91.\overline{09}$

49. $0.6 = \frac{6}{10} = \frac{3}{5}$

50. $0.88 = \frac{88}{100} = \frac{22}{25}$

51. $0.052 = \frac{52}{1000} = \frac{13}{250}$

52. $0.0125 = \frac{125}{10000} = \frac{1}{80}$

53. $6.2 = \frac{62}{10} = \frac{31}{5}$

54. $7.25 = \frac{725}{100} = \frac{29}{4}$

55. $1.452 = \frac{1452}{1000} = \frac{363}{250}$

56. $1.2345 = \frac{12345}{10000} = \frac{2469}{2000}$

57. $3.0001 = \frac{30001}{10000}$

58. $4.2535 = \frac{42535}{10000} = \frac{8507}{2000}$

59. Let $n = 0.\overline{3}$, then

$$10n = 3.\overline{3}$$
$$- \quad n = 0.\overline{3}$$
$$9n = 3$$
$$\frac{9n}{9} = \frac{3}{9}$$
$$n = \frac{3}{9} = \frac{1}{3}$$

60. Let $n = 0.\overline{4}$, then

$$10n = 4.\overline{4}$$
$$- \quad n = 0.\overline{4}$$
$$9n = 4$$
$$\frac{9n}{9} = \frac{4}{9}$$
$$n = \frac{4}{9}$$

61. Let $n = 2.\overline{9}$, then

$$10n = 29.\overline{9}$$
$$- \quad n = 2.\overline{9}$$
$$9n = 27$$
$$\frac{9n}{9} = \frac{27}{9}$$
$$n = \frac{27}{9} = 3$$

62. Let n = $0.\overline{51}$, then

$100n = 51.\overline{51}$
$\underline{- \quad n = \quad 0.\overline{51}}$
$99n = 51$

$\dfrac{99n}{99} = \dfrac{51}{99}$

$n = \dfrac{51}{99} = \dfrac{17}{33}$

63. Let n = $1.\overline{36}$, then

$100n = 136.\overline{36}$
$\underline{- \quad n = \quad 1.\overline{36}}$
$99n = 135$

$\dfrac{99n}{99} = \dfrac{135}{99}$

$n = \dfrac{135}{99} = \dfrac{15}{11}$

64. Let n = $0.\overline{135}$, then

$1000n = 135.\overline{135}$
$\underline{- \quad n = \quad 0.\overline{135}}$
$999n = 135$

$\dfrac{999n}{999} = \dfrac{135}{999}$

$n = \dfrac{135}{999} = \dfrac{5}{37}$

65. Let n = $1.0\overline{2}$, then

$100n = 102.\overline{2}$
$\underline{- \quad 10n = \quad 10.\overline{2}}$
$90n = 92$

$\dfrac{90n}{90} = \dfrac{92}{90}$

$n = \dfrac{92}{90} = \dfrac{46}{45}$

66. Let n = $2.4\overline{9}$, then

$100n = 249.\overline{9}$
$\underline{- \quad 10n = \quad 24.\overline{9}}$
$90n = 225$

$\dfrac{90n}{90} = \dfrac{225}{90}$

$n = \dfrac{225}{90} = \dfrac{5}{2}$

67. Let n = $3.4\overline{78}$, then

$1000n = 3478.\overline{78}$
$\underline{- \quad 10n = \quad 34.\overline{78}}$
$990n = 3444$

$\dfrac{990n}{990} = \dfrac{3444}{990}$

$n = \dfrac{3444}{990} = \dfrac{574}{165}$

68. Let n = $5.2\overline{39}$, then

$1000n = 5239.\overline{39}$
$\underline{- \quad 10n = \quad 52.\overline{39}}$
$990n = 5187$

$\dfrac{990n}{990} = \dfrac{5187}{990}$

$n = \dfrac{5187}{990} = \dfrac{1729}{330}$

69. $\dfrac{2}{7} \div \dfrac{5}{3} = \dfrac{2}{7} \times \dfrac{3}{5} = \dfrac{6}{35}$

70. $\dfrac{5}{7} \times \dfrac{6}{11} = \dfrac{30}{77}$

71. $\dfrac{-3}{8} \times \dfrac{-16}{15} = \dfrac{48}{120} = \dfrac{2}{5}$

72. $\left(-\dfrac{3}{5}\right) \div \dfrac{10}{21} = \left(-\dfrac{3}{5}\right) \times \dfrac{21}{10} = -\dfrac{63}{50}$

73. $\dfrac{7}{8} \div \dfrac{8}{7} = \dfrac{7}{8} \times \dfrac{7}{8} = \dfrac{49}{64}$

74. $\dfrac{3}{7} \div \dfrac{3}{7} = \dfrac{3}{7} \times \dfrac{7}{3} = \dfrac{21}{21} = 1$

75. $\left(\dfrac{3}{5} \times \dfrac{4}{7}\right) \div \dfrac{1}{3} = \dfrac{12}{35} \div \dfrac{1}{3} = \dfrac{12}{35} \times \dfrac{3}{1} = \dfrac{36}{35}$

76. $\left(\dfrac{4}{7} \div \dfrac{4}{5}\right) \times \dfrac{1}{7} = \left(\dfrac{4}{7} \times \dfrac{5}{4}\right) \times \dfrac{1}{7} = \dfrac{5}{7} \times \dfrac{1}{7} = \dfrac{5}{49}$

77. $\left[\left(\dfrac{-3}{4}\right)\left(\dfrac{-2}{7}\right)\right] \div \dfrac{3}{5} = \left(\dfrac{6}{28}\right) \div \dfrac{3}{5} = \dfrac{3}{14} \times \dfrac{5}{3} = \dfrac{15}{42} = \dfrac{5}{14}$

78. $\left(\dfrac{3}{8} \times \dfrac{5}{9}\right) \times \left(\dfrac{4}{7} \div \dfrac{5}{8}\right) = \left(\dfrac{15}{72}\right) \times \left(\dfrac{4}{7} \times \dfrac{8}{5}\right) = \dfrac{5}{24} \times \dfrac{32}{35} = \dfrac{160}{840} = \dfrac{4}{21}$

79. The lcm of 5 and 6 is 30.

$\dfrac{1}{5} + \dfrac{1}{6} = \left(\dfrac{1}{5} \cdot \dfrac{6}{6}\right) + \left(\dfrac{1}{6} \cdot \dfrac{5}{5}\right) = \dfrac{6}{30} + \dfrac{5}{30} = \dfrac{11}{30}$

80. The lcm of 3 and 15 is 15.

$$\frac{1}{3} - \frac{2}{15} = \left(\frac{1}{3} \cdot \frac{5}{5}\right) - \frac{2}{15} = \frac{5}{15} - \frac{2}{15} = \frac{3}{15} = \frac{1}{5}$$

81. The lcm of 11 and 110 is 110.

$$\frac{2}{11} + \frac{3}{110} = \left(\frac{2}{11} \cdot \frac{10}{10}\right) + \frac{3}{110} = \frac{20}{110} + \frac{3}{110} = \frac{23}{110}$$

82. The lcm of 12 and 36 is 36.

$$\frac{5}{12} + \frac{7}{36} = \left(\frac{5}{12} \cdot \frac{3}{3}\right) + \frac{7}{36} = \frac{15}{36} + \frac{7}{36} = \frac{22}{36} = \frac{22 \div 2}{36 \div 2} = \frac{11}{18}$$

83. The lcm of 9 and 54 is 54.

$$\frac{5}{9} - \frac{7}{54} = \left(\frac{5}{9} \cdot \frac{6}{6}\right) - \frac{7}{54} = \frac{30}{54} - \frac{7}{54} = \frac{23}{54}$$

84. The lcm of 30 and 120 is 120.

$$\frac{13}{30} - \frac{17}{120} = \left(\frac{13}{30} \cdot \frac{4}{4}\right) - \frac{17}{120} = \frac{52}{120} - \frac{17}{120} = \frac{35}{120} = \frac{35 \div 5}{120 \div 5} = \frac{7}{24}$$

85. The lcm of 12, 48, and 72 is 144.

$$\frac{1}{12} + \frac{1}{48} + \frac{1}{72} = \left(\frac{1}{12} \cdot \frac{12}{12}\right) + \left(\frac{1}{48} \cdot \frac{3}{3}\right) + \left(\frac{1}{72} \cdot \frac{2}{2}\right) = \frac{12}{144} + \frac{3}{144} + \frac{2}{144} = \frac{17}{144}$$

86. The lcm of 5, 15, and 75 is 75.

$$\frac{3}{5} + \frac{7}{15} + \frac{9}{75} = \left(\frac{3}{5} \cdot \frac{15}{15}\right) + \left(\frac{7}{15} \cdot \frac{5}{5}\right) + \frac{9}{75} = \frac{45}{75} + \frac{35}{75} + \frac{9}{75} = \frac{89}{75}$$

87. The lcm of 30, 40, and 50 is 600.

$$\frac{1}{30} - \frac{3}{40} - \frac{7}{50} = \left(\frac{1}{30} \cdot \frac{20}{20}\right) \left(\frac{3}{40} \cdot \frac{15}{15}\right) \left(\frac{7}{50} \cdot \frac{12}{12}\right) = \frac{20}{600} - \frac{45}{600} - \frac{84}{600} = -\frac{109}{600}$$

88. The lcm of 25, 100, and 40 is 200.

$$\frac{4}{25} - \frac{9}{100} - \frac{7}{40} = \left(\frac{4}{25} \cdot \frac{8}{8}\right) \left(\frac{9}{100} \cdot \frac{2}{2}\right) \left(\frac{7}{40} \cdot \frac{5}{5}\right) = \frac{32}{200} - \frac{18}{200} - \frac{35}{200} = -\frac{21}{200}$$

89. $\dfrac{2}{3} + \dfrac{3}{4} = \dfrac{2 \cdot 4 + 3 \cdot 3}{3 \cdot 4} = \dfrac{8 + 9}{12} = \dfrac{17}{12}$

90. $\dfrac{5}{7} - \dfrac{1}{12} = \dfrac{5 \cdot 12 - 7 \cdot 1}{7 \cdot 12} = \dfrac{60 - 7}{84} = \dfrac{53}{84}$

91. $\dfrac{5}{7} + \dfrac{3}{4} = \dfrac{5 \cdot 4 + 7 \cdot 3}{7 \cdot 4} = \dfrac{20 + 21}{28} = \dfrac{41}{28}$

92. $\dfrac{7}{3} - \dfrac{5}{12} = \dfrac{7 \cdot 12 - 3 \cdot 5}{3 \cdot 12} = \dfrac{84 - 15}{36} = \dfrac{69}{36} = \dfrac{23}{12}$

93. $\dfrac{3}{8} + \dfrac{5}{12} = \dfrac{3 \cdot 12 + 8 \cdot 5}{8 \cdot 12} = \dfrac{36 + 40}{96} = \dfrac{76}{96} = \dfrac{19}{24}$

94. $\left(\dfrac{2}{3} + \dfrac{1}{4}\right) - \dfrac{3}{5} = \left(\dfrac{2 \cdot 4 + 3 \cdot 1}{3 \cdot 4}\right) - \dfrac{3}{5} = \dfrac{8 + 3}{12} - \dfrac{3}{5} = \dfrac{11}{12} - \dfrac{3}{5} = \dfrac{11 \cdot 5 - 12 \cdot 3}{12 \cdot 5} = \dfrac{55 - 36}{60} = \dfrac{19}{60}$

95. $\left(\dfrac{1}{5} \cdot \dfrac{1}{4}\right) + \dfrac{1}{3} = \dfrac{1}{20} + \dfrac{1}{3} = \left(\dfrac{1}{20} \cdot \dfrac{3}{3}\right) + \left(\dfrac{1}{3} \cdot \dfrac{20}{20}\right) = \dfrac{3}{60} + \dfrac{20}{60} = \dfrac{23}{60}$

96. $\left(\dfrac{3}{5} \div \dfrac{2}{10}\right) - \dfrac{1}{3} = \left(\dfrac{3}{5} \cdot \dfrac{10}{2}\right) - \dfrac{1}{3} = \dfrac{30}{10} - \dfrac{1}{3} = \dfrac{3}{1} - \dfrac{1}{3} = \dfrac{3 \cdot 3}{1 \cdot 3} - \dfrac{1}{3} = \dfrac{9}{3} - \dfrac{1}{3} = \dfrac{8}{3}$

97. $\left(\dfrac{1}{2}+\dfrac{3}{10}\right)\div\left(\dfrac{1}{5}+2\right)=\left(\dfrac{1}{2}\cdot\dfrac{5}{5}+\dfrac{3}{10}\right)\div\left(\dfrac{1}{5}+\dfrac{2}{1}\cdot\dfrac{5}{5}\right)=\left(\dfrac{5}{10}+\dfrac{3}{10}\right)\div\left(\dfrac{1}{5}+\dfrac{10}{5}\right)=\dfrac{8}{10}\div\dfrac{11}{5}=\dfrac{4}{5}\cdot\dfrac{5}{11}=\dfrac{20}{55}=\dfrac{4}{11}$

98. $\left(\dfrac{1}{9}\cdot\dfrac{3}{5}\right)+\left(\dfrac{2}{3}\cdot\dfrac{1}{5}\right)=\dfrac{3}{45}+\dfrac{2}{15}=\dfrac{1}{15}+\dfrac{2}{15}=\dfrac{3}{15}=\dfrac{1}{5}$

99. $\left(3\dfrac{4}{9}\right)\div\left(4+\dfrac{2}{3}\right)=\left(\dfrac{3}{1}\cdot\dfrac{9}{9}-\dfrac{4}{9}\right)\div\left(\dfrac{4}{1}\cdot\dfrac{3}{3}+\dfrac{2}{3}\right)=\left(\dfrac{27}{9}-\dfrac{4}{9}\right)\div\left(\dfrac{12}{3}+\dfrac{2}{3}\right)=\dfrac{23}{9}\div\dfrac{14}{3}=\dfrac{23}{9}\cdot\dfrac{3}{14}=\dfrac{69}{126}=\dfrac{23}{42}$

100. $\left(\dfrac{2}{5}\div\dfrac{4}{9}\right)\left(\dfrac{3}{5}\cdot 6\right)=\left(\dfrac{2}{5}\cdot\dfrac{9}{4}\right)\left(\dfrac{3}{5}\cdot\dfrac{6}{1}\right)=\dfrac{18}{20}\cdot\dfrac{18}{5}=\dfrac{9}{10}\cdot\dfrac{18}{5}=\dfrac{162}{50}=\dfrac{81}{25}$

101. The LCM of 4, 5, 3 is 60. $\dfrac{1}{4}+\dfrac{2}{5}+\dfrac{1}{3}=\left(\dfrac{1}{4}\cdot\dfrac{15}{15}\right)+\left(\dfrac{2}{5}\cdot\dfrac{12}{12}\right)+\left(\dfrac{1}{3}\cdot\dfrac{20}{20}\right)=\dfrac{15}{60}+\dfrac{24}{60}+\dfrac{20}{60}=\dfrac{59}{60}$

102. $1-\left(\dfrac{2}{5}+\dfrac{1}{4}+\dfrac{1}{10}\right)=1-\left(\dfrac{8}{20}+\dfrac{5}{20}+\dfrac{2}{20}\right)=1-\dfrac{15}{20}=1-\dfrac{3}{4}=\dfrac{4}{4}-\dfrac{3}{4}=\dfrac{1}{4}$. The class is 1/4 art majors.

103. $1-\left(\dfrac{1}{2}+\dfrac{2}{5}\right)=1-\left(\dfrac{5}{10}+\dfrac{4}{10}\right)=1-\dfrac{9}{10}=\dfrac{10}{10}-\dfrac{9}{10}=\dfrac{1}{10}$. Student tutors is $\dfrac{1}{10}$ of the budget.

104. $(12)\left(10\dfrac{3}{4}\right)=\left(\dfrac{12}{1}\right)\left(\dfrac{43}{4}\right)=\dfrac{516}{4}=129$. The vertical height of the stairway is 129 inches or 10 ft. 9 in.

105. $1-\left(\dfrac{1}{4}+\dfrac{1}{5}+\dfrac{1}{2}\right)=1-\left(\dfrac{5}{20}+\dfrac{4}{20}+\dfrac{10}{20}\right)=1-\dfrac{19}{20}=\dfrac{20}{20}-\dfrac{19}{20}=\dfrac{1}{20}$

She must proofread 1/20 of the book or (1/20) • 540 = 27 pages.

106. $8-3\left(2\dfrac{5}{16}\right)=8-\left(\dfrac{3}{1}\right)\left(\dfrac{37}{16}\right)=\dfrac{8}{1}-\dfrac{111}{16}=\dfrac{128}{16}-\dfrac{111}{16}=\dfrac{17}{16}=1\dfrac{1}{16}$. $1\dfrac{1}{16}$ feet of pipe remains.

107. $27\dfrac{7}{8}-25\dfrac{1}{2}=\dfrac{223}{8}-\dfrac{204}{8}=\dfrac{19}{8}=2\dfrac{3}{8}$. The stock decreased by $2\dfrac{3}{8}$ points.

108. $1\dfrac{1}{4}\times\dfrac{8}{6}=\dfrac{5}{4}\times\dfrac{8}{6}=\dfrac{40}{24}=\dfrac{5}{3}=1\dfrac{2}{3}$ teaspoons

109. $\left(1\dfrac{1}{4}\right)(15)=\dfrac{5}{4}\cdot\dfrac{15}{1}=\dfrac{75}{4}=18\dfrac{3}{4}$ cups of flour

110. $30\dfrac{1}{4}+24\dfrac{1}{8}+4\dfrac{1}{2}=\dfrac{121}{4}+\dfrac{193}{8}+\dfrac{9}{2}=\dfrac{242}{8}+\dfrac{193}{8}+\dfrac{36}{8}=\dfrac{471}{8}=58\dfrac{7}{8}$ in.

111. $46\dfrac{3}{4}+3\dfrac{5}{16}=46+3+\dfrac{3}{4}+\dfrac{5}{16}=49+\dfrac{17}{16}=49+1\dfrac{1}{16}=50\dfrac{1}{16}$ in.

112. a) $15\dfrac{3}{8}\div 2=\dfrac{123}{8}\cdot\dfrac{1}{2}=\dfrac{123}{16}=7\dfrac{11}{16}$ in.

  b) $\left(15\dfrac{3}{8}-\dfrac{1}{8}\right)\div 2=15\dfrac{2}{8}\div 2=7\dfrac{5}{8}$ in.

113. $\left(24\dfrac{7}{8}\right)\div 2=\dfrac{199}{8}\times\dfrac{1}{2}=\dfrac{199}{16}=12\dfrac{7}{16}$ in.

114. $26\dfrac{1}{2}+105\dfrac{1}{4}+53\dfrac{1}{4}+106\dfrac{5}{16}=290+\dfrac{21}{16}=291\dfrac{5}{16}$ in.

115. $8\frac{3}{4}$ ft = $\left(\frac{35}{4}\cdot\frac{12}{1}\right)$ in. = 105 in.

$\left[105-(3)\left(\frac{1}{8}\right)\right]\div 4 = \left[\frac{840}{8}-\frac{3}{8}\right]\div 4 = \frac{837}{8}\cdot\frac{1}{4} = \frac{837}{32} = 26\frac{5}{32}$. The length of each piece is $26\frac{5}{32}$ in.

116. original area $= 8\frac{1}{2}\times 9\frac{1}{4} = \frac{17}{2}\times\frac{37}{4} = \frac{629}{8} = 78\frac{5}{8}$ sq.in.; new area $= 8\frac{1}{2}\times 10\frac{1}{4} = \frac{17}{2}\times\frac{41}{4} = \frac{697}{8} = 87\frac{1}{8}$ sq.in.

area increase $= 87\frac{1}{8}-78\frac{5}{8} = 8\frac{1}{2}$ sq. in.

117. width = 8 ft. 3 in. = 96 in. + 3 in. = 99 in.; length = 10 ft. 8 in. = 120 in. + 8 in. = 128 in.
    a) perimeter = 2L + 2W = 2(128) + 2(99) = 454 in.=454/12 ft. =$37\frac{10}{12}$ ft. or 37 ft. 10 in.

    b) width = 8ft. 3in. = $8\frac{3}{12}$ ft. = $8\frac{1}{4}$ ft. = $\frac{33}{4}$ ft .; length = 10ft. 8in. = $10\frac{8}{12}$ ft. = $10\frac{2}{3}$ ft. = $\frac{32}{3}$ ft

    Area $= L\times w = \frac{32}{3}\times\frac{33}{4} = \frac{1056}{12} = 88$ sq.ft

    c) Volume $= L\cdot W\cdot H = \frac{32}{3}\times\frac{33}{4}\times\frac{55}{6} = \frac{58080}{72} = 806.7$ cu. ft.

118. a) $20+18\frac{3}{8}\div 2 = 20+9\frac{3}{16} = 29\frac{3}{16}$ in.
    b) $26\frac{1}{4}+6\frac{3}{4} = 33$ in.
    c) $26\frac{1}{4}+\left(6\frac{3}{4}-\frac{1}{4}\right) = 26\frac{1}{4}+6\frac{2}{4} = 32\frac{3}{4}$ in.

In Exercises 119 -126 other answers are possible.

119. $\frac{0.25+0.26}{2} = \frac{0.51}{2} = 0.255$

120. $\frac{4.3+4.003}{2} = \frac{8.303}{2} = 4.1515$

121. $\frac{-2.176+(-2.175)}{2} = \frac{-4.351}{2} = -2.1755$

122. $\frac{1.3457+1.34571}{2} = \frac{2.69141}{2} = 1.345705$

123. $\frac{3.12345+3.123451}{2} = \frac{6.246901}{2} = 3.1234505$

124. $\frac{0.4105+0.4106}{2} = \frac{0.8211}{2} = 0.41055$

125. $\frac{4.872+4.873}{2} = \frac{9.745}{2} = 4.8725$

126. $\frac{3.7896+(3.7895)}{2} = \frac{7.5791}{2} = -3.78955$

127. $\left(\frac{3}{5}+\frac{4}{5}\right)\div 2 = \frac{7}{5}\times\frac{1}{2} = \frac{7}{10}$

128. $\left(\frac{1}{9}+\frac{2}{9}\right)\div 2 = \frac{3}{9}\cdot\frac{1}{2} = \frac{1}{3}\cdot\frac{1}{2} = \frac{1}{6}$

129. $\left(\frac{1}{20}+\frac{1}{10}\right)\div 2 = \left(\frac{1}{20}+\frac{2}{20}\right)\cdot\frac{1}{2} = \frac{3}{20}\cdot\frac{1}{2} = \frac{3}{40}$

130. $\left(\dfrac{7}{13}+\dfrac{8}{13}\right)\div 2 = \dfrac{15}{13}\times\dfrac{1}{2}=\dfrac{15}{26}$

131. $\left(\dfrac{1}{4}+\dfrac{1}{5}\right)\div 2 = \left(\dfrac{5}{20}+\dfrac{4}{20}\right)\cdot\dfrac{1}{2}=\dfrac{9}{20}\cdot\dfrac{1}{2}=\dfrac{9}{40}$

132. $\left(\dfrac{1}{3}+\dfrac{2}{3}\right)\div 2 = \dfrac{3}{3}\cdot\dfrac{1}{2}=\dfrac{1}{1}\cdot\dfrac{1}{2}=\dfrac{1}{2}$

133. $\left(\dfrac{1}{10}+\dfrac{1}{100}\right)\div 2 = \left(\dfrac{10}{100}+\dfrac{1}{100}\right)\cdot\dfrac{1}{2}=\dfrac{11}{100}\cdot\dfrac{1}{2}=\dfrac{11}{200}$

134. $\left(\dfrac{1}{2}+\dfrac{2}{3}\right)\div 2 = \left(\dfrac{3}{6}+\dfrac{4}{6}\right)\cdot\dfrac{1}{2}=\dfrac{7}{6}\cdot\dfrac{1}{2}=\dfrac{7}{12}$

135. a) Water (or milk): $\left(1+1\dfrac{3}{4}\right)\div 2 = \left(\dfrac{4}{4}+\dfrac{7}{4}\right)\cdot\dfrac{1}{2}=\dfrac{11}{4}\cdot\dfrac{1}{2}=\dfrac{11}{8}=1\dfrac{3}{8}$ cup; Oats: $\left(\dfrac{1}{2}+1\right)\div 2 = \dfrac{3}{2}\cdot\dfrac{1}{2}=\dfrac{3}{4}$ cup

   b) Water (or milk): $1+\dfrac{1}{2}=1\dfrac{1}{2}$ cup; Oats: $\dfrac{1}{2}+\dfrac{1}{4}=\dfrac{2}{4}+\dfrac{1}{4}=\dfrac{3}{4}$ cup

136. a) 1   b) $0.\overline{9}$ c) $\dfrac{1}{3}=0.\overline{3},\ \dfrac{2}{3}=0.\overline{6},\ \dfrac{1}{3}+\dfrac{2}{3}=\dfrac{3}{3}=1,\ 0.\overline{3}+0.\overline{6}=1$ d) $0.\overline{9}=1$

Exercise Set 5.4

1. A rational number can be written as a ratio of two integers, p/q, with q not equal to zero. Numbers that cannot be written as the ratio of two integers are called irrational numbers.

2. The principal square root of a number n written $\sqrt{n}$, is the positive number that when multiplied by itself gives n.

3. A perfect square number is any number that is the square of a natural number.

4. The product of two radical numbers is equal to the radical of the product of the two numbers, provided that the two numbers are nonnegative.

5. a) To add or subtract two or more square roots with the same radicand, add or subtract their coefficients and then multiply by the common radical.

   b) $7\sqrt{3}-2\sqrt{3}+3\sqrt{3}=5\sqrt{3}+3\sqrt{3}=8\sqrt{3}$

6. The quotient of two radical numbers is equal to the radical of the quotient of the two numbers, provided that the numbers are nonnegative.

7. A rationalized denominator contains no radical expressions.

8. a) Multiply both the numerator and denominator by the same number that will result in the radicand in the denominator becoming a perfect square.

   b) $\dfrac{3}{\sqrt{5}}=\dfrac{3}{\sqrt{5}}\times\dfrac{\sqrt{5}}{\sqrt{5}}=\dfrac{3\sqrt{5}}{\sqrt{25}}=\dfrac{3\sqrt{5}}{5}$

9. Rational; $\sqrt{49}=7$ is an integer.

10. Irrational; 10 is not a perfect square.

11. Rational; quotient of two integers is rational.

12. Irrational; nonterminating, nonrepeating decimal.

13. Irrational; nonterminating, nonrepeating decimal.

14. Irrational; π is a nonterminating, nonrepeating decimal.

15. Rational; quotient of two integers.

16. Rational; terminating decimal.

17. Irrational; nonterminating, nonrepeating decimal.

18. Rational; $\dfrac{\sqrt{5}}{\sqrt{5}}=1$ is an integer.

19. $\sqrt{81} = 9$

20. $\sqrt{121} = 11$

21. $\sqrt{49} = 7$

22. $-\sqrt{144} = -12$

23. $-\sqrt{169} = -13$

24. $\sqrt{25} = 5$

25. $-\sqrt{225} = -15$

26. $-\sqrt{36} = -6$

27. $-\sqrt{100} = -10$

28. $\sqrt{256} = 16$

29. rational, integer, natural

30. rational, integer

31. rational, integer, natural

32. rational

33. rational

34. rational

35. rational

36. rational

37. rational

38. irrational

39. $\sqrt{12} = \sqrt{4}\sqrt{3} = 2\sqrt{3}$

40. $\sqrt{27} = \sqrt{9}\sqrt{3} = 3\sqrt{3}$

41. $\sqrt{52} = \sqrt{4}\sqrt{13} = 2\sqrt{13}$

42. $\sqrt{60} = \sqrt{4}\sqrt{15} = 2\sqrt{15}$

43. $\sqrt{63} = \sqrt{9}\sqrt{7} = 3\sqrt{7}$

44. $\sqrt{75} = \sqrt{25}\sqrt{3} = 5\sqrt{3}$

45. $\sqrt{80} = \sqrt{16}\sqrt{5} = 4\sqrt{5}$

46. $\sqrt{90} = \sqrt{9}\sqrt{10} = 3\sqrt{10}$

47. $\sqrt{162} = \sqrt{81}\sqrt{2} = 9\sqrt{2}$

48. $\sqrt{300} = \sqrt{100}\sqrt{3} = 10\sqrt{3}$

49. $3\sqrt{5} + 4\sqrt{5} = (3+4)\sqrt{5} = 7\sqrt{5}$

50. $\sqrt{11} + 5\sqrt{11} = (1+5)\sqrt{11} = 6\sqrt{11}$

51. $3\sqrt{7} - 5\sqrt{7} = (3-5)\sqrt{7} = -2\sqrt{7}$

52. $2\sqrt{5} + 3\sqrt{20} = 2\sqrt{5} + 3 \cdot 2\sqrt{5}$
$= 2\sqrt{5} + 6\sqrt{5} = (2+6)\sqrt{5} = 8\sqrt{5}$

53. $4\sqrt{12} - 7\sqrt{27} = 4 \cdot 2\sqrt{3} - 7 \cdot 3\sqrt{3} = 8\sqrt{3} - 21\sqrt{3} = (8-21)\sqrt{3} = -13\sqrt{3}$

54. $2\sqrt{7} + 5\sqrt{28} = 2\sqrt{7} + 5 \cdot 2\sqrt{7} = 2\sqrt{7} + 10\sqrt{7} = (2+10)\sqrt{7} = 12\sqrt{7}$

55. $5\sqrt{3} + 7\sqrt{12} - 3\sqrt{75} = 5\sqrt{3} + 7 \cdot 2\sqrt{3} - 3 \cdot 5\sqrt{3} = 5\sqrt{3} + 14\sqrt{3} - 15\sqrt{3} = (5+14-15)\sqrt{3} = 4\sqrt{3}$

56. $13\sqrt{2} + 2\sqrt{18} - 5\sqrt{32} = 13\sqrt{2} + 2 \cdot 3\sqrt{2} - 5 \cdot 4\sqrt{2} = 13\sqrt{2} + 6\sqrt{2} - 20\sqrt{2} = (13+6-20)\sqrt{2} = -\sqrt{2}$

57. $\sqrt{8} - 3\sqrt{50} + 9\sqrt{32} = 2\sqrt{2} - 3 \cdot 5\sqrt{2} + 9 \cdot 4\sqrt{2} = 2\sqrt{2} - 15\sqrt{2} + 36\sqrt{2} = (2-15+36)\sqrt{2} = 23\sqrt{2}$

58. $\sqrt{63} + 13\sqrt{98} - 5\sqrt{112} = 3\sqrt{7} + 13 \cdot 7\sqrt{2} - 5 \cdot 4\sqrt{7} = 3\sqrt{7} + 91\sqrt{2} - 20\sqrt{7} = (3-20)\sqrt{7} + 91\sqrt{2} = -17\sqrt{7} + 91\sqrt{2}$

59. $\sqrt{3} \cdot \sqrt{2} = \sqrt{6}$

60. $\sqrt{8} \cdot \sqrt{10} = \sqrt{80} = \sqrt{16} \cdot \sqrt{5} = 4\sqrt{5}$

61. $\sqrt{9} \cdot \sqrt{15} = \sqrt{135} = \sqrt{9} \cdot \sqrt{15} = 3\sqrt{15}$

62. $\sqrt{3} \cdot \sqrt{6} = \sqrt{18} = \sqrt{9} \cdot \sqrt{2} = 3\sqrt{2}$

63. $\sqrt{10} \cdot \sqrt{20} = \sqrt{200} = \sqrt{100} \cdot \sqrt{2} = 10\sqrt{2}$

64. $\sqrt{11} \cdot \sqrt{33} = \sqrt{11} \cdot \sqrt{11} \cdot \sqrt{3} = 11\sqrt{3}$

65. $\dfrac{\sqrt{8}}{\sqrt{4}} = \sqrt{2}$

66. $\dfrac{\sqrt{125}}{\sqrt{5}} = \sqrt{25} = 5$

67. $\dfrac{\sqrt{72}}{\sqrt{8}} = \sqrt{9} = 3$

68. $\dfrac{\sqrt{136}}{\sqrt{8}} = \sqrt{17}$

69. $\dfrac{7}{\sqrt{2}} = \dfrac{7}{\sqrt{2}} \dfrac{\sqrt{2}}{\sqrt{2}} = \dfrac{7\sqrt{2}}{\sqrt{4}} = \dfrac{7\sqrt{2}}{2}$

70. $\dfrac{5}{\sqrt{11}} = \dfrac{5}{\sqrt{11}} \dfrac{\sqrt{11}}{\sqrt{11}} = \dfrac{5\sqrt{11}}{\sqrt{121}} = \dfrac{5\sqrt{11}}{11}$

71. $\dfrac{\sqrt{5}}{\sqrt{13}} = \dfrac{\sqrt{5}}{\sqrt{13}} \cdot \dfrac{\sqrt{13}}{\sqrt{13}} = \dfrac{\sqrt{65}}{13}$

72. $\dfrac{\sqrt{3}}{\sqrt{10}} = \dfrac{\sqrt{3}}{\sqrt{10}} \cdot \dfrac{\sqrt{10}}{\sqrt{10}} = \dfrac{\sqrt{30}}{\sqrt{100}} = \dfrac{\sqrt{30}}{10}$

73. $\dfrac{\sqrt{20}}{\sqrt{3}} = \dfrac{\sqrt{20}}{\sqrt{3}} \dfrac{\sqrt{3}}{\sqrt{3}} = \dfrac{\sqrt{60}}{\sqrt{9}} = \dfrac{\sqrt{4}\sqrt{15}}{3} = \dfrac{2\sqrt{15}}{3}$

74. $\dfrac{\sqrt{50}}{\sqrt{14}} = \sqrt{\dfrac{50}{14}} = \sqrt{\dfrac{25}{7}} = \dfrac{\sqrt{25}}{\sqrt{7}} \dfrac{\sqrt{7}}{\sqrt{7}} = \dfrac{5\sqrt{7}}{7}$

75. $\dfrac{\sqrt{9}}{\sqrt{2}} \cdot \dfrac{\sqrt{2}}{\sqrt{2}} = \dfrac{3\sqrt{2}}{2}$

76. $\dfrac{\sqrt{15}}{\sqrt{3}} = \sqrt{5}$

77. $\dfrac{\sqrt{10}}{\sqrt{6}} \cdot \dfrac{\sqrt{6}}{\sqrt{6}} = \dfrac{\sqrt{60}}{6} = \dfrac{2\sqrt{15}}{6} = \dfrac{\sqrt{15}}{3}$

78. $\dfrac{8}{\sqrt{8}} = \dfrac{8}{\sqrt{8}} \cdot \dfrac{\sqrt{2}}{\sqrt{2}} = \dfrac{8\sqrt{2}}{\sqrt{16}} = \dfrac{8\sqrt{2}}{4} = 2\sqrt{2}$

79. $\sqrt{15}$ is between 3 and 4 since $\sqrt{15}$ is between $\sqrt{9} = 3$ and $\sqrt{16} = 4$. $\sqrt{15}$ is between 3.5 and 4 since 15 is closer to 16 than to 9. Using a calculator $\sqrt{15} \approx 3.9$.

80. $\sqrt{43}$ is between 6 and 7 since $\sqrt{43}$ is between $\sqrt{36} = 6$ and $\sqrt{49} = 7$. $\sqrt{43}$ is between 6.5 and 7 since 43 is closer to 49 than to 36. Using a calculator $\sqrt{43} \approx 6.6$.

81. $\sqrt{107}$ is between 10 and 11 since $\sqrt{107}$ is between $\sqrt{100} = 10$ and $\sqrt{121} = 11$. $\sqrt{107}$ is between 10 and 10.5 since 107 is closer to 100 than to 121. Using a calculator $\sqrt{107} \approx 10.3$.

82. $\sqrt{135}$ is between 11 and 12 since $\sqrt{135}$ is between $\sqrt{121} = 11$ and $\sqrt{144} = 12$. $\sqrt{135}$ is between 11.5 and 12 since 135 is closer to 144 than to 121. Using a calculator $\sqrt{135} \approx 11.6$.

83. $\sqrt{170}$ is between 13 and 14 since $\sqrt{170}$ is between $\sqrt{169} = 13$ and $\sqrt{196} = 14$. $\sqrt{170}$ is between 13 and 13.5 since 170 is closer to 169 than to 196. Using a calculator $\sqrt{170} \approx 13.04$.

84. $\sqrt{200}$ is between 14 and 15 since $\sqrt{200}$ is between $\sqrt{196} = 14$ and $\sqrt{225} = 15$. $\sqrt{200}$ is between 14 and 14.5 since 200 is closer to 196 than to 225. Using a calculator $\sqrt{200} \approx 14.1$.

85. True. Prime numbers are not perfect square numbers.

86. False. The result may be a rational number or an irrational number.

87. False. The result may be a rational number or an irrational number.

88. True.

89. False. The result may be a rational number or an irrational number.

90. False. The result may be a rational number or an irrational number.

91. $\sqrt{3} + 5\sqrt{3} = 6\sqrt{3}$

92. $\sqrt{2} + (-\sqrt{2}) = 0$

93. $\sqrt{2} \cdot \sqrt{3} = \sqrt{6}$

94. $\sqrt{3} \cdot \sqrt{3} = \sqrt{9} = 3$

95. No. $\sqrt{3} \ne 1.732$ since $\sqrt{3}$ is an irrational number and 1.732 is a rational number.

96. No. $\sqrt{11}$ is an irrational number and $3.31\overline{6}$ is a rational number.

97.
$\sqrt{9+16} \ne \sqrt{9} + \sqrt{16}$
$\sqrt{25} \ne 3 + 4$
$5 \ne 7$

98. No, 3.14 and $\dfrac{22}{7}$ are rational numbers, π is an irrational number.

99. $T = 2\pi \sqrt{\dfrac{35}{980}} = 2\pi \sqrt{\dfrac{7}{196}} = 2\pi \cdot \dfrac{\sqrt{7}}{14} = \dfrac{\pi\sqrt{7}}{7} \approx 1.2$ sec.

100. a) $s = \sqrt{\dfrac{4}{0.04}} = \sqrt{100} = 10$ mph

b) $s = \sqrt{\dfrac{16}{0.04}} = \sqrt{400} = 20$ mph

c) $s = \sqrt{\dfrac{64}{0.04}} = \sqrt{1600} = 40$ mph

d) $s = \sqrt{\dfrac{256}{0.04}} = \sqrt{6400} = 80$ mph

101. a) $t = \dfrac{\sqrt{100}}{4} = \dfrac{10}{4} = 2.5 \text{ sec}$ b) $t = \dfrac{\sqrt{400}}{4} = \dfrac{20}{4} = 5 \text{ sec}$

  c) $t = \dfrac{\sqrt{900}}{4} = \dfrac{30}{4} = 7.5 \text{ sec}$ d) $t = \dfrac{\sqrt{1600}}{4} = \dfrac{40}{4} = 10 \text{ sec}$

102. a) The number is rational if the result on the calculator is a terminating or repeating decimal number. Otherwise, the number is irrational.

  b) Using a calculator, $\sqrt{0.04} = 0.2$ a terminating decimal and thus it is rational.

  c) Using a calculator, $\sqrt{0.07} = 0.264575131\ldots$, thus it is irrational.

103. No. The sum of two irrational numbers may not be irrational. (i.e. $-\sqrt{3}+\sqrt{3} = 0$)

Exercise Set 5.5

1. The set of real numbers is the union of the rational numbers and the irrational numbers.
2. $\mathbb{R}$
3. If the given operation is preformed on any two elements of the set and the result is an element of the set, then the set is <u>closed</u> under the given operation.
4. The order in which two numbers are added does not make a difference in the result.
    a+b = b+a
5. The order in which two numbers are multiplied does not make a difference in the result.
    Ex. $2\times 3 = 3\times 2$
6. The associative property of addition states that when adding three real numbers, parentheses may be placed around any two adjacent numbers. (a+b)+c = a+(b+c)
7. The associative property of multiplication states that when multiplying three real numbers, parentheses may be placed around any two adjacent numbers.
    One example is $(2\times 3)\times 4 = 2\times(3\times 4)$.
8. The distributive property of multiplication over addition allows you to either add first and then multiply, or multiply first and then add. a(b+c) = ab + ac
9. Not closed. (i.e. $3 - 5 = -2$ is not a natural number).
10. Closed. The sum of two natural numbers is a natural number.
11. Closed. The product of two natural numbers is a natural number.
12. Not closed. (i.e. $3 \div 5 = \dfrac{3}{5} = 0.6$ is not a natural number).
13. Closed. The sum of two integers is an integer.
14. Closed. The difference of two integers is an integer.
15. Closed. The product of two integers is an integer.
16. Not closed. (i.e. $2 \div 5 = \dfrac{2}{5} = 0.4$ is not an integer).

17. Closed   18. Closed   19. Not closed
20. Closed   21. Not closed   22. Not closed
23. Not closed   24. Not closed   25. Closed
26. Closed   27. Closed   28. Not closed

29. Commutative property. The order is changed from 7 + 8 to 8 + 7.
30. Commutative property. The order is changed from (1 + 2) + 3 to 3 + (1 + 2).

31. $(-4)\cdot(-5) = 20 = (-5)\cdot(-4)$ 32. $(-2)+(-3) = -5 = (-3)+(-2)$

33. No. $6 \div 3 = 2$, but $3 \div 6 = 1/2$
34. No. $5 - 3 = 2$, but $3 - 5 = -2$.
35. $[-3 \cdot (-5)] \cdot (-7) = (15) \cdot (-7) = -105$
    $(-3) \cdot [-5 \cdot (-7)] = (-3) \cdot (35) = -105$
36. $[-3 + (-5)] + (-7) = -8 + (-7) = -15$
    $-3 + [-5 + (-7)] = -3 + (-12) = -15$
37. No. $(8 \div 4) \div 2 = 2 \div 2 = 1$,
    but $8 \div (4 \div 2) = 8 \div 2 = 4$
38. No. $(8 - 7) - 12 = 1 - 12 = -11$,
    but $8 - (7 - 12) = 8 - (-5) = 13$
39. No. $(8 \div 4) \div 2 = 2 \div 2 = 1$,
    but $8 \div (4 \div 2) = 8 \div 2 = 4$
40. No. $2 + (3 \cdot 4) = 2 + 12 = 14$,
    but $(2 + 3) \cdot (2 + 4) = 5 \cdot 8 = 40$
41. Associative property of addition
42. Commutative property of addition
43. Commutative property of multiplication
44. Commutative property of multiplication
45. Associative property of addition
46. Distributive property
47. Associative property of addition
48. Commutative property of addition
49. Commutative property of addition
50. Distributive property
51. Commutative property of addition
52. Commutative property of addition
53. Distributive property
54. Commutative property of multiplication
55. Commutative property of addition
56. Commutative property of multiplication
57. $3(y + 4) = 3y + 12$
58. $7(x + 4) = 7x + 28$
59. $\sqrt{2}(3+\sqrt{6})=3\sqrt{2}+\sqrt{12}=3\sqrt{2}+2\sqrt{3}$
60. $\sqrt{3}(\sqrt{8}+4)=\sqrt{24}+4\sqrt{3}=2\sqrt{6}+4\sqrt{3}$
61. $\sqrt{5}(x+\sqrt{5})=x\sqrt{5}+\sqrt{25}=x\sqrt{5}+5$
62. $x(y + z) = xy + xz$
63. $\sqrt{3}(\sqrt{3}-\sqrt{6})=\sqrt{9}-\sqrt{18}=3-3\sqrt{2}$
64. $x(\sqrt{3}-\sqrt{5})=x\sqrt{3}-x\sqrt{5}$
65. Distributive property
66. Associative property of addition
67. Distributive property
68. Associative property of addition
69. Commutative property of addition
70. Associative property of addition
71. Distributive property
72. Commutative property of addition
73. Associative property of addition
74. Commutative property of addition

75. No. The computer would not work if it were not turned on first.
76. No. One normally does not put socks on over shoes.
77. Yes. The order of placing sugar and cream in coffee is not important.
78. No. Assuming the blackboard is clean, it must be written on before it is erased.
79. No. The book cannot be read before the lamp is turned on.
80. No. Your clothes would not be dry.
81. Yes. The order of these events does not matter.
82. Yes. These activities can be done in any order.
83. No. The egg cannot be poured before it is cracked.
84. No. The gas cap must be removed before putting the nozzle in the tank.
85. No. The machine must drop the cup before dispensing the coffee.
86. Yes. The final result will be the same regardless of the order of the events.
87. No. The car will not start if it is put into drive first.
88. Yes. The meatloaf will taste the same regardless of the order the items are mixed.
89. Yes. Since it is possible to remove the sweater without removing the coat; the result will be the same whether the coat is removed first and then the sweater or the sweater removed first and then the coat.
90. a) No. (Man eating) tiger is a tiger that eats men, and man (eating tiger) is a man that is eating a tiger.
    b) No. (Horse riding) monkey is a monkey that rides a horse, and horse (riding monkey) is a horse that rides a monkey.
    c) Answers will vary.

91. No. $0 \div a = 0$ and $a \div 0$ is undefined.

Exercise Set 5.6

1. 4 is the base and 6 is the exponent or power.
2. b^n is b multiplied by itself n times. $b^n = \underbrace{b \cdot b \cdot b \cdots b}_{\text{n factors of b}}$
3. a) If m and n are natural numbers and a is any real number, then $a^m a^n = a^{m+n}$
   b) $3^3 \times 3^5 = 3^{3+5} = 3^8$
4. a) If m and n are natural numbers and a is any real number except 0, then $\dfrac{a^m}{a^n} = a^{m-n}$.

   b) $\dfrac{4^5}{4^3} = 4^{5-3} = 4^2 = 16$

5. a) If n is a natural number and a is any real number except 0, then $a^{-n} = \dfrac{1}{a^n}$.

   b) $3^{-5} = \dfrac{1}{3^5}$

6. a) If a is any real number except 0, then $a^0 = 1$.
   b) $5^0 = 1$

7. a) If m and n are natural numbers and a is any real number, then $\left(a^m\right)^n = a^{m \cdot n}$

   b) $\left(4^4\right)^3 = 4^{4 \cdot 3} = 4^{12}$

8. Since 1 raised to any power equals 1, $1^{500} = 1$.
9. a) Move the decimal point in the original number to the right or left until you obtain a number greater or equal to 1 and less than 10. Count the number of places the decimal was moved. If it was moved to the left the count is a positive number and if it was moved to the right the count is a negative number. Multiply the number obtained in the first step by 10 raised to the count number.

   b) $0.000426 = 4.26 \times 10^{-4}$. note: the count number is -4

10. a) If the exponent is positive, move the decimal point in the number to the right the same number of places as the exponent adding zeros where necessary. If the exponent is negative, move the decimal point in the number to the left the same number of places as the exponent adding zeros where necessary.

    b) $5.76 \times 10^{-4} = 0.000576$

11. a) The number is greater than or equal to 10.

    b) The number is greater than or equal 1 but less than 10.

    c) The number is less than 1.

12. a) $10^5 = 1.0 \times 10^5$ b) $10^5 = 100,000$

13. $3^2 = 3 \times 3 = 9$ 14. $4^3 = 4 \times 4 \times 4 = 64$

15. $(-5)^2 = (-5)(-5) = 25$ 16. $(-2)^5 = (-2)(-2)(-2)(-2)(-2) = -32$

17. $-2^5 = -(2 \times 2 \times 2 \times 2 \times 2) = -32$ 18. $\left(\dfrac{1}{3}\right)^2 = \dfrac{1}{3} \times \dfrac{1}{3} = \dfrac{1}{9}$

19. $\left(\dfrac{4}{5}\right)^2 = \dfrac{4}{5} \times \dfrac{4}{5} = \dfrac{16}{25}$ 20. $2^4 = (2 \times 2 \times 2 \times 2) = 16$

21. $(-2)^4 = (-2)(-2)(-2)(-2) = 16$

22. $-2^4 = -(2 \cdot 2 \cdot 2 \cdot 2) = -16$

23. $2^3 \cdot 3^2 = 2 \times 2 \times 2 \times 3 \times 3 = 8 \times 9 = 72$

24. $\dfrac{15^2}{3^2} = \dfrac{15 \cdot 15}{3 \cdot 3} = \dfrac{225}{9} = 25$

25. $\dfrac{5^7}{5^5} = 5^{7-5} = 5^2 = 5 \cdot 5 = 25$

26. $3^3 \cdot 3^4 = 3^{3+4} = 3^7 = 2187$

27. $\dfrac{7}{7^3} = 7^{1-3} = 7^{-2} = \dfrac{1}{7^2} = \dfrac{1}{7 \times 7} = \dfrac{1}{49}$

28. $3^4 \cdot 7^0 = 3 \cdot 3 \cdot 3 \cdot 3 \cdot 1 = 81$

29. $(-13)^0 = 1$

30. $(-3)^4 = (-3)(-3)(-3)(-3) = 81$

31. $3^4 = 3 \times 3 \times 3 \times 3 = 81$

32. $-3^4 = -3 \times 3 \times 3 \times 3 = -81$

33. $3^{-2} = \dfrac{1}{3^2} = \dfrac{1}{9}$

34. $3^{-3} = \dfrac{1}{3^3} = \dfrac{1}{27}$

35. $(2^3)^4 = 2^{(3)(4)} = 2^{12} = 4096$

36. $(1^{12})^{13} = 1^{156} = 1$

37. $\dfrac{11^{25}}{11^{23}} = 11^{25-23} = 11^2 = 121$

38. $5^2 \cdot 5 = 5^{2+1} = 5^3 = 125$

39. $(-4)^2 = (-4)(-4) = 16$

40. $4^{-2} = \dfrac{1}{4^2} = \dfrac{1}{16}$

41. $-4^2 = -4 \cdot 4 = -16$

42. $(4^3)^2 = 4^{(3)(2)} = 4^6 = 4096$

43. $(2^2)^{-3} = 2^{2(-3)} = 2^{-6} = \dfrac{1}{2^6} = \dfrac{1}{64}$

44. $3^{-3} \cdot 3 = 3^{-3+1} = 3^{-2} = \dfrac{1}{3^2} = \dfrac{1}{9}$

45. 1.2×10^5

46. 9.751×10^6

47. 4.5×10^1

48. 4.21×10^{-4}

49. 5.3×10^{-2}

50. 5.61×10^{-5}

51. 1.9×10^4

52. 1.26×10^9

53. 1.86×10^{-4}

54. 3×10^{-4}

55. 4.23×10^{-6}

56. 5.4×10^4

57. 7.11×10^2

58. 2×10^{-2}

59. 1.53×10^{-1}

60. 4.16×10^5

61. 84,000

62. 0.00271

63. 0.012

64. 519,000

65. 0.0000213

66. 0.000000274

67. 0.312

68. 46

69. 9,000,000

70. 73,000

71. 231

72. 0.0104

73. 35,000

74. 0.00000217

75. 10,000

76. 0.001

77. $(4.0 \times 10^2)(3.0 \times 10^5) = 12 \times 10^7 = 120,000,000$

78. $(2.0 \times 10^{-3})(3.0 \times 10^2) = 6 \times 10^{-1} = 0.6$

79. $(5.1 \times 10^1)(3.0 \times 10^{-4}) = 15.3 \times 10^{-3} = 0.0153$

80. $(1.6 \times 10^{-2})(4.0 \times 10^{-3}) = 6.4 \times 10^{-5} = 0.000064$

81. $\dfrac{6.4 \times 10^5}{2 \times 10^3} = 3.2 \times 10^2 = 320$

82. $\dfrac{8 \times 10^{-3}}{2 \times 10^1} = 4.0 \times 10^{-4} = 0.0004$

83. $\dfrac{8.4 \times 10^{-6}}{4 \times 10^{-3}} = 2.1 \times 10^{-3} = 0.0021$

84. $\dfrac{25 \times 10^3}{5 \times 10^{-2}} = 5.0 \times 10^5 = 500,000$

85. $\dfrac{4 \times 10^5}{2 \times 10^4} = 2.0 \times 10^1 = 20$

86. $\dfrac{16 \times 10^3}{8 \times 10^{-3}} = 2.0 \times 10^6 = 2,000,000$

87. $(7 \times 10^5)(6 \times 10^6) = 42 \times 10^{11} = 4.2 \times 10^{12}$

88. $(6 \times 10^{-4})(5 \times 10^6) = 30 \times 10^2 = 3.0 \times 10^3$

89. $(3 \times 10^{-3})(1.5 \times 10^{-4}) = 4.5 \times 10^{-7}$

90. $(2.3 \times 10^5)(3 \times 10^3) = 6.9 \times 10^8$

91. $\dfrac{1.4 \times 10^6}{7 \times 10^2} = 0.2 \times 10^4 = 2.0 \times 10^3$

92. $\dfrac{2 \times 10^4}{5 \times 10^{-4}} = 0.4 \times 10^8 = 4.0 \times 10^7$

93. $\dfrac{4\times10^{-5}}{2\times10^2} = 2.0 \times 10^{-7}$

94. $\dfrac{1.2\times10^{-3}}{6\times10^{-6}} = 0.2 \times 10^3 = 2.0 \times 10^2$

95. $\dfrac{1.5\times10^5}{5\times10^{-4}} = 0.3 \times 10^9 = 3 \times 10^8$

96. $\dfrac{2.4\times10^4}{8.0\times10^6} = 0.3\times10^{-2} = 3.0 \times 10^{-3}$

97. 8.3×10^{-4}, 3.2×10^{-1}, 4.6, 5.8×10^5

98. 8.5×10^{-5}, 1.3×10^{-1}, 8.2×10^3, 6.2×10^4

99. 8.3×10^{-5}; 0.00079; 4.1×10^3; $40{,}000$; Note: $0.00079 = 7.9 \times 10^{-4}$, $40{,}000 = 4 \times 10^4$

100. $1{,}962{,}000$; 4.79×10^6; 3.14×10^7; $267{,}000{,}000$

101. $(6.008 \times 10^9) - (1.256 \times 10^9) = (6.008 - 1.256) \times 10^9 = 4.752 \times 10^9$
   a) $4{,}752{,}000{,}000$ people   b) 4.752×10^9 people

102. $t = \dfrac{d}{r} = \dfrac{4.5\times10^8}{2.5\times10^4} = 1.8\times10^4$ a) $18{,}000$ hrs   b) 1.8×10^4 hrs

103. time $= \dfrac{dist.}{rate} = \dfrac{239000\ mi}{20000\ mph} = 11.95$ a) 11.95 hrs   b) 1.195×10^1 hrs

104. $500{,}000 \times 40{,}000{,}000{,}000 = (5 \times 10^5)(4 \times 10^{10}) = 20 \times 10^{15} = 2 \times 10^{16}$
   a) $20{,}000{,}000{,}000{,}000{,}000$ drops   b) 2×10^{16} drops

105. $50 \times 5{,}800{,}000 = (5 \times 10^1)(5.8 \times 10^6) = 29 \times 10^7 = 2.9 \times 10^8$
   a) $290{,}000{,}000$ cells   b) 2.9×10^8 cells

106. $\dfrac{4.5\times10^9}{2.5\times10^5} = 1.8 \times 10^4$ a) $18{,}000$ times   b) 1.8×10^4 times

107. a) $(100{,}000$ cu.ft./sec$) \times (60$ sec/min$) \times (60$ min/hr$) \times (24$ hr$) = 8{,}640{,}000{,}000$ ft^3
   b) 8.64×10^9 ft^3

108. a) $\dfrac{4{,}650{,}000{,}000{,}000}{257{,}000{,}000} = \dfrac{4.65\times10^{12}}{2.57\times10^8} \approx 1.809339\times10^4 = \$18{,}093.39$ per person
   b) $\$20{,}695.97 - \$18{,}093.39 = \$2{,}602.58$

109. a) 18 billion $= 18{,}000{,}000{,}000 = 1.8 \times 10^{10}$ diapers
   b) $14 \times 2.38 \times 10^5 = 33.32 \times 10^5 = 3.332 \times 10^6$ or $3{,}332{,}000$ miles

110. a) $(0.60) \times (1{,}200{,}000{,}000) = \$720{,}000{,}000$
   b) $(0.25) \times (1{,}200{,}000{,}000) = \$300{,}000{,}000$
   c) $(0.10) \times (1{,}200{,}000{,}000) = \$120{,}000{,}000$
   d) $(0.05) \times (1{,}200{,}000{,}000) = \$60{,}000{,}000$

111. a) $(0.40) \times (3{,}400{,}000{,}000) = \$1{,}360{,}000{,}000$
   b) $(0.40) \times (3{,}400{,}000{,}000) = \$1{,}360{,}000{,}000$
   c) $(0.10) \times (3{,}400{,}000{,}000) = \$340{,}000{,}000$
   d) $(0.10) \times (3{,}400{,}000{,}000) = \$340{,}000{,}000$

112. $1{,}000$ times, since 1 meter $= 10^3$ millimeters $= 1{,}000$ millimeters

113. Since 1 gram $= 10^3$ milligrams and 1 gram $= 10^{-3}$ kilograms,
   10^{-3} kilograms $= 10^3$ milligrams

   $\dfrac{10^{-3}\ \text{Kilograms}}{10^{-3}} = \dfrac{10^3\ \text{milligrams}}{10^{-3}}$,   Thus,   1 kilogram $= 10^6$ milligrams

114. $\dfrac{2\times10^{30}}{6\times10^{24}} = 0.\overline{3}\times10^6 = 333,333$ times

115. a) 2×6 billion $= 12$ billion $= 12,000,000,000$ people

   b) $\dfrac{6,000,000,000}{(35)(365)} = \dfrac{6,000,000,000}{12775} = 469,667$ people per day

116. $\dfrac{897,000,000,000,000,000}{3,900,000,000,000} = \dfrac{8.97\times10^{17}}{3.9\times1012} = 2.3\times10^5 = 230,000$ sec. or about 2.66 days

117. a) $1,000,000 = 1.0 \times 10^6$; $1,000,000,000 = 1.0 \times 10^9$; $1,000,000,000,000 = 1.0 \times 10^{12}$

   b) $\dfrac{1.0\times10^6}{1.0\times10^3} = 1.0\times10^3$ days or $1,000$ days $= 2.74$ years

   c) $\dfrac{1.0\times10^9}{1.0\times10^3} = 1.0\times10^6$ days or $1,000,000$ days $= 2,739.73$ years

   d) $\dfrac{1.0\times10^{12}}{1.0\times10^3} = 1.0\times10^9$ days or $1,000,000,000$ days $= 2,739,726.03$ years

   e) $\dfrac{1\text{ billion}}{1\text{ million}} = \dfrac{1.0\times10^9}{1.0\times10^6} = 1.0\times10^3 = 1,000$ times greater

118. a) $(1.86 \times 10^5 \text{ mi/sec}) \times (60 \text{ sec/min}) \times (60 \text{ min/hr}) \times (24 \text{ hr/day}) \times (365 \text{ days/yr}) \times (1 \text{ yr})$
   $= (1.86 \times 10^5)(6 \times 10^1)(6 \times 10^1)(2.4 \times 10^1)(3.65 \times 10^2) = 586.5696 \times 10^{10}$
   $= 5.865696 \times 10^{12}$ miles

   b) $t = \dfrac{d}{r} = \dfrac{9.3\times10^7}{1.86\times10^5} = 5 \times 10^2 = 500$ seconds or 8 min. 20 sec.

119. a) $E(0) = 2^{10} \cdot 2^0 = 2^{10} \cdot 1 = 1024$ bacteria
   b) $E(1/2) = 2^{10} \cdot 2^{1/2} = 2^{10.5} = 1448.2$ bacteria

Exercise Set 5.7

1. A sequence is a list of numbers that are related to each other by a given rule. One example is 2, 4, 6, 8, ...
2. The terms of the sequence.
3. An arithmetic sequence is a sequence in which each term differs from the preceding term by a constant amount. One example is 1, 4, 7, 10, ...
4. The amount by which each pair of successive terms differs.
5. A geometric sequence is one in which the ratio of any term to the term that directly precedes it is a constant. One example is 1, 3, 9, 27, ...
6. The ratio of any term to the term that directly precedes it.

7. 2, 6, 10, 14, 18
9. $-3, 0, 3, 6, 9$
11. $5, 3, 1, -1, -3$
13. 1/2, 1, 3/2, 2, 5/2
15. $a_5 = a_1 + (5-1)d = 4+(4)(3) = 4+12 = 16$

17. $a_9 = -5 + (9-1)(2) = -5+(8)(2)$
   $= -5 + 16 = 11$
19. $a_{20} = 4/5 + (19)(-1) = 4/5 - 19 = -91/5$
21. $a_{11} = 4 + (10)(1/2) = 4 + 5 = 9$
23. $a_n = 2 + (n-1)2 = 2 + 2n - 2 = 2n$

8. 3, 8, 13, 18, 23
10. $-4, -2, 0, 2, 4$
12. $-3, -7, -11, -15, -19$
14. $5/2, 1, -1/2, -2, -7/2$
16. $a_8 = -4 + (8-1)(-5) = -4+(7)(-5)$
   $= -4 - 35 = -39$
18. $a_{12} = 7 + (12-1)(-3) = 7+(11)(-3)$
   $= 7 - 33 = -26$
20. $a_{15} = (-1/2) + (14)(-2) = -1/2 - 28 = -57/2$
22. $a_{15} = 4/3 + (14)(1/3) = 4/3 + (14/3) = 18/3 = 6$
24. $a_n = 7 + (n-1)(-4) = -4n + 11$

25. $a_n = 6 + (n-1)10 = 10n - 4$

26. $a_n = -2 + (n-1)(-3) = -3n + 1$

27. $a_n = -5/3 + (n-1)(1/3) = (1/3)n - 2$

28. $a_n = -15 + (n-1)(5) = 5n - 20$

29. $a_n = -3 + (n-1)(3/2) = (3/2)n - (9/2)$

30. $a_n = -5 + (n-1)(3) = 3n - 8$

31. $s_{14} = \dfrac{14(14+1)}{2} = \dfrac{14\cdot 15}{2} = 105$

32. $s_{10} = \dfrac{10(3+30)}{2} = \dfrac{10\cdot 33}{2} = 165$

33. $s_9 = \dfrac{9(45+5)}{2} = \dfrac{9\cdot 50}{2} = 225$

34. $s_9 = \dfrac{9(-4+(-28))}{2} = \dfrac{9\cdot(-32)}{2} = -144$

35. $s_8 = \dfrac{8(11+(-24))}{2} = \dfrac{8\cdot(-13)}{2} = -52$

36. $s_{18} = \dfrac{18(-9+(-\frac{1}{2}))}{2} = \dfrac{18\cdot(-\frac{19}{2})}{2} = -\dfrac{171}{2} = -85.5$

37. $s_8 = \dfrac{8(\frac{1}{2}+\frac{29}{2})}{2} = \dfrac{8\cdot(\frac{30}{2})}{2} = \dfrac{8\cdot 15}{2} = 60$

38. $s_{18} = \dfrac{18(\frac{3}{5}+4)}{2} = \dfrac{18\cdot(\frac{23}{5})}{2} = \dfrac{207}{5} = 41.4$

39. 2, 8, 32, 128, 512

40. 4, 12, 36, 108, 324

41. 4, $-$ 12, 36, $-$ 108, 324

42. 8, 4, 2, 1, 1/2

43. $-$ 3, 3, $-$ 3, 3, $-$ 3

44. $-$ 6, 12, $-$ 24, 48, $-$ 96

45. $-$ 16, 8, $-$ 4, 2, $-$ 1

46. 5, 3, 9/5, 27/25, 81/125

47. $a_6 = 3(4)^5 = 3\cdot 1024 = 3072$

48. $a_5 = 2(2)^4 = 2\cdot 16 = 32$

49. $a_8 = 5(3)^7 = 5\cdot 2187 = 10{,}935$

50. $a_9 = -3(-2)^8 = -3\cdot 256 = -768$

51. $a_7 = 10(-3)^6 = 10(729) = 7290$

52. $a_3 = 3(1/2)^2 = 3\cdot(1/4) = 3/4$

53. $a_7 = -3(-3)^6 = -3(729) = -2187$

54. $a_5 = (1/2)\cdot 2^4 = (1/2)\cdot 16 = 8$

55. $a_n = a_1 r^{n-1} = 3(3)^{n-1} = 3^n$

56. $a_n = a_1 r^{n-1} = 2(3)^{n-1}$

57. $a_n = a_1 r^{n-1} = -5(-1)^{n-1}$

58. $a_n = a_1 r^{n-1} = -16(1/2)^{n-1}$

59. $a_n = a_1 r^{n-1} = (1/4)(2)^{n-1}$

60. $a_n = a_1 r^{n-1} = -3(-2)^{n-1}$

61. $a_n = a_1 r^{n-1} = 9(1/3)^{n-1}$

62. $a_n = a_1 r^{n-1} = -4(2/3)^{n-1}$

63. $s_4 = \dfrac{a_1(1-r^4)}{1-r} = \dfrac{3(1-2^4)}{1-2} = \dfrac{3(-15)}{-1} = 45$

64. $s_5 = \dfrac{a_1(1-r^5)}{1-r} = \dfrac{2(1-3^5)}{1-3} = \dfrac{2(-242)}{-2} = 242$

65. $s_7 = \dfrac{a_1(1-r^7)}{1-r} = \dfrac{5(1-4^7)}{1-4} = \dfrac{5(-16383)}{-3} = 27{,}305$

66. $s_9 = \dfrac{a_1(1-r^9)}{1-r} = \dfrac{-3(1-5^9)}{1-5} = \dfrac{-3(-1953124)}{-4}$
$= -1{,}464{,}843$

67. $s_{11} = \dfrac{a_1(1-r^{11})}{1-r} = \dfrac{-7(1-3^{11})}{1-3} = \dfrac{-7(-177146)}{-2}$
$= -620{,}011$

68. $s_{11} = \dfrac{a_1(1-r^{11})}{1-r} = \dfrac{-5(1-(-2)^{11})}{1-(-2)} = \dfrac{-5(2049)}{3}$
$= -3{,}415$

69. $s_{13} = \dfrac{a_1(1-r^{13})}{1-r} = \dfrac{-8(1-(-3)^{13})}{1-(-3)} = \dfrac{-8(1594324)}{4}$
$= -3{,}188{,}648$

70. $s_{14} = \dfrac{a_1(1-r^{14})}{1-r} = \dfrac{-1(1-2^{14})}{1-2} = \dfrac{-1(-16383)}{-1}$
$= -16{,}383$

71. $\dfrac{50(1+50)}{2} = \dfrac{50\cdot 51}{2} = 1{,}275$

72. $\dfrac{50(2+100)}{2} = \dfrac{50\cdot 102}{2} = 2{,}550$

73. $\dfrac{50(1+99)}{2} = \dfrac{50\cdot 100}{2} = 2{,}500$

74. $\dfrac{20(3+60)}{2} = \dfrac{20\cdot 63}{2} = 630$

75. a) Using the formula $a_n = a_1 + (n-1)d$, we get
$a_8 = 20{,}200 + (8-1) \times 1200 = \$28{,}600$

b) $\dfrac{8(20200+28600)}{2} = \dfrac{8(48800)}{2} = \$195{,}200$

76. a) $a_{12} = 96 + (11)(-3) = 96 - 33 = 63$ in.

b) $[12(96 + 63)]/2 = 6 \times 159 = 954$ in.

77. $a_6 = 200(0.8)^6 = 200(0.262144) = 52.4288$ g

78. $a_{11} = 72 + (10)(-6) = 72 - 60 = 12$ in.

79. $s_{12} = \frac{12(1+12)}{2} = \frac{12 \cdot 13}{2} = 78$ times

80. $a_{15} = 20,000(1.06)^{14} = \$45,218$

81. $a_{15} = a_1 r^{15} = 1(2)^{15} = 32,768$ layers

82. $a_5 = 30(0.8)^4 = 12.288$ ft.

83. The visitors sequence is arithmetic.
Runs scored in the 8th is a_8.
$a_8 = a_1 + (8 - 1)d = 1 + 7(1) = 8$ runs
Visitors total score after 8 is s_8.
$s_8 = \frac{8(a_1 + a_8)}{2} = \frac{8(1+8)}{2} = 36$ runs

The home team scored runs in a geometric sequence.
Runs scored in the 8th is $a_8 = a_1 r^{8-1} = 1(2)^7 = 128$

Home team total score after 8 is s_8.
$s_8 = \frac{a_1(1-2^8)}{1-2} = \frac{1(-255)}{-1} = 255$ runs

84. This is a geometric sequence where $a_1 = 2000$ and $r = 3$. In ten years the stock will triple its value 5 times.
$a_6 = a_1 r^{6-1} = 2000(3)^5 = \$486,000$

85. The sequence of bets during a losing streak is geometric.

a) $a_6 = a_1 r^{n-1} = 1(2)^{6-1} = 1(32) = \$32$ $s_5 = \frac{a_1(1-r^n)}{1-r} = \frac{1(1-2^5)}{1-2} = \frac{-31}{-1} = \$31$

b) $a_6 = a_1 r^{n-1} = 10(2)^{6-1} = 10(32) = \$320$ $s_5 = \frac{a_1(1-r^n)}{1-r} = \frac{10(1-2^5)}{1-2} = \frac{10(-31)}{-1} = \$310$

c) $a_{11} = a_1 r^{n-1} = 1(2)^{11-1} = 1(1024) = \$1,024$ $s_{10} = \frac{a_1(1-r^n)}{1-r} = \frac{1(1-2^{10})}{1-2} = \frac{1(-1023)}{-1} = \$1,023$

d) $a_{11} = a_1 r^{n-1} = 10(2)^{11-1} = 10(1024) = \$10,240$ $s_{10} = \frac{a_1(1-r^n)}{1-r} = \frac{10(1-2^{10})}{1-2} = \frac{10(-1023)}{-1} = \$10,230$

e) If you lose too many times in a row, then you will run out of money.

86. $\frac{82[1-(1/2)^6]}{1-(1/2)} = \frac{82[1-(1/64)]}{1/2} = \frac{82}{1} \cdot \frac{63}{64} \cdot \frac{2}{1} = 161.4375$

87. The arithmetic sequence $180^0, 360^0, 540^0, 720^0, \ldots$ has a common difference of 180. Thus,
$a_n = 180(n-2) = 180n - 360, n \geq 3$

88. 12, 18, 24, ... , 1608 is an arithmetic sequence with $a_1 = 12$ and $d = 6$. Using the expression for the nth term of an arithmetic sequence $a_n = a_1 + (n-1)d$ or $1608 = 12 + (n-1)6$ and dividing both sides by 6 gives $268 = 2 + n - 1$ or $n = 267$

89. Since $a_5 = a_1 r^4$ and $a_2 = a_1 r$, $a_5/a_2 = r^3$. Thus $r^3 = 648/24 = 27$ or $r = 3$.
Then $24 = a_2 = a_1 r = a_1(3)$ or $a_1 = 24/3 = 8$.

90. The total distance is 30 plus twice the sum of the terms of the geometric sequence having
$a_1 = 30 \cdot (0.8) = 24$ and $r = 0.8$. Thus $s_5 = \frac{24[1-(0.8)^5]}{(1-0.8)} = \frac{24[1-0.32768]}{0.2} = \frac{24(0.67232)}{0.2} = 80.6784$.

So the total distance is $30 + 2(80.6784) = 191.3568$ ft.

Exercise Set 5.8

1. Begin with the numbers 1, 1, then add 1 and 1 to get 2 and continue to add the previous two numbers in the sequence to get the next number in the sequence.

2. a) 8th term = 6th term + 7th term = 8 + 13 = 21   b) 34/21 = 1.619

   9th term = 7th term + 8th term = 13 + 21 = 34   c) 55/34 = 1.618

   10th term = 8th term + 9th term = 21 + 34 = 55

   d) The ratio a_{n+1}/a_n of terms from the Fibonacci sequence approaches the number 1.618 (rounded to the nearest thousandth) as n increases.

3. $\dfrac{a_n}{a_{n+1}} \approx \dfrac{1}{1.618} \approx 0.618$ as n increases.

4. The golden number = $\dfrac{\sqrt{5}+1}{2}$.

5. Student research question.

6. The divine proportion is the golden proportion - named divine because of the belief in its relationship to the will of God.

7. a) $\dfrac{\sqrt{5}+1}{2} \approx 1.618$ b) $\dfrac{\sqrt{51}}{2} \approx 0.618$ c) 1.618 – 0.618 = 1.000

8. 1/89 = 0.011235. The decimal displays part of the Fibonacci sequence.

9. 1/1 = 1, 2/1 = 2, 3/2 = 1.5, 5/3 = 1.6, 8/5 = 1.6, 13/8 = 1.625, 21/13 = 1.6154, 34/21 = 1.619, 55/34 = 1.6176, 89/55 = 1.61818. The consecutive ratios alternate increasing then decreasing about the golden ratio.

10. The ratio of the second to the first and the fourth to the third estimates the golden ratio

11.

Fib. No.	prime factors	Fib. No.	prime factors
1	-------	34	2 · 17
1	-------	55	5 · 11
2	prime	89	prime
3	prime	144	$2^4 \cdot 3^2$
5	prime	233	prime
8	2^3	377	13 · 29
13	prime	610	2 · 5 · 61

12. If the first ten are selected; $\dfrac{1+1+2+3+5+8+13+21+34+55}{11} = \dfrac{143}{11} = 13$

13. If 5 is selected the result is 2(5) – 8 = 10 – 8 = 2 which is the second number preceding 5.

14. If 2, 3, 5, and 8 are selected the result is $5^2 - 3^2 = 2 \cdot 8$

$$25 - 9 = 16$$
$$16 = 16$$

15. Answers will vary.

16. 6/4 = 1.5 which is a little less than Φ.

17. Answers will vary.   18. Answers will vary.   19. Answers will vary.
20. Answers will vary.   21. Answers will vary.   22. Answers will vary.

23. Fibonacci type; 19 + 31 = 50; 31 + 50 = 81

24. Not Fibonacci. Each term is not the sum of the two preceding terms.

25. Not Fibonacci. Each term is not the sum of the two preceding terms.

26. Not Fibonacci. Each term is not the sum of the two preceding terms.

27. Fibonacci type; $40 + 65 = 105$; $65 + 105 = 170$.

28. Fibonacci type; $1\frac{1}{4} + 2 = 3\frac{1}{4}$; $2 + 3\frac{1}{4} = 5\frac{1}{4}$

29. Fibonacci type; $-1 + 0 = -1$; $0 + (-1) = -1$

30. Fibonacci type; $7 + 13 = 20$; $13 + 20 = 33$

31. a) If 6 and 10 are selected the sequence is 6, 10, 16, 26, 42, 68, 110, ...

    b) $10/6 = 1.666$, $16/10 = 1.600$, $26/16 = 1.625$, $42/26 = 1.615$, $68/42 = 1.619$, $110/68 = 1.618$, ...

32. a) If 5 and 7 are selected the sequence is 5, 7, 12, 19, 31, 50, 81, ...

    b) $7/5 = 1.4$, $12/7 = 1.714$, $19/12 = 1.583$, $31/19 = 1.623$, $50/31 = 1.613$, $81/50 = 1.62$, ...

33. a) If 5, 8, and 13 are selected the result is $8^2 - (5)(13) = 64 - 65 = -1$.

    b) If 21, 34, and 55 are selected the result is $34^2 - (21)(55) = 1156 - 1155 = 1$.

    c) The square of the middle term of three consecutive terms in a Fibonacci sequence differs from the product of the 1st and 2nd term by 1.

34. The sum of the numbers along the diagonals parallel to the one shown is a Fibonacci number.

35. a) Lucas sequence: 1, 3, 4, 7, 11, 18, 29, 47, ...

    b) $8 + 21 = 29$; $13 + 34 = 47$

    c) The first column is a Fibonacci-type sequence.

36. a) $-10, 4, -6, -2, -8, -10, -18, -28, -46, -74$

    b) $-10, 5, -5, 0, -5, -5, -10, -15, -25, -40$

    c) $-10, 6, -4, 2, -2, 0, -2, -2, -4, -6$

    d) $-10, 7, -3, 4, 1, 5, 6, 11, 17, 28$

    e) $-10, 8, -2, 6, 4, 10, 14, 24, 38, 62$

    f) In order for the Fibonacci-type sequence $-10, x, -10 + x, -10 + 2x, -20 + 3x, ...$ to have all positive terms beyond the 7th term, $10/x$ must be less than Φ.

37.
$$1 + 1/x = x$$
$$x(1 + 1/x) = x(x) \text{ multiply by } x$$
$$x + 1 = x^2$$
$$x^2 - x - 1 = 0 \text{ solve for } x$$
Using the quadratic formula,
$$x = \frac{1 \pm \sqrt{1 - 4(1)(-1)}}{2(1)} = \frac{1 \pm \sqrt{5}}{2}$$

38. |————————————————————————————|——————————————|
    0   3 in.   5 in.

Using the Fibonacci sequence - mark the line at 3 in. to approximate the golden ratio.

39. Answers will vary.

40. a)

    b)

    c) 13 paths - using the Fibonacci sequence.

Review Exercises

1. Use the divisibility rules in section 5.1.
   670,920 is divisible by 2, 3, 4, 5, 6, 8 and 10

2. Use the divisibility rules in section 5.1.
   400,644 is divisible by 2, 3, 4, 6, and 9

3.
$$\begin{array}{r} 2 \,\overline{|328|} \\ 2 \,\overline{|164|} \\ 2 \,\overline{|82|} \\ 41 \end{array}$$
$328 = 2^3 \cdot 41$

4.
$$\begin{array}{r} 2 \,\overline{|350|} \\ 5 \,\overline{|175|} \\ 5 \,\overline{|35|} \\ 7 \end{array}$$
$350 = 2 \cdot 5^2 \cdot 7$

5.
$$\begin{array}{r} 2 \,\overline{|840|} \\ 2 \,\overline{|420|} \\ 2 \,\overline{|210|} \\ 5 \,\overline{|105|} \\ 3 \,\overline{|21|} \\ 7 \end{array}$$
$840 = 2^3 \cdot 3 \cdot 5 \cdot 7$

6.
$$\begin{array}{r} 2 \,\overline{|882|} \\ 3 \,\overline{|441|} \\ 3 \,\overline{|147|} \\ 7 \,\overline{|49|} \\ 7 \end{array}$$
$882 = 2 \cdot 3^2 \cdot 7^2$

7.
$$\begin{array}{r} 2 \,\overline{|1452|} \\ 2 \,\overline{|726|} \\ 3 \,\overline{|363|} \\ 11 \,\overline{|121|} \\ 11 \end{array}$$
$1452 = 2^2 \cdot 3 \cdot 11^2$

8. $12 = 2^2 \cdot 3$, $36 = 2^2 \cdot 3^2$; gcd $= 2^2 \cdot 3 = 12$; lcm $= 2^2 \cdot 3^2 = 36$

9. $72 = 2^3 \cdot 3^2$, $52 = 2^2 \cdot 13$; gcd $= 2^2 = 4$; lcm $= 2^3 \cdot 3^2 \cdot 13 = 936$

10. $45 = 3^2 \cdot 5$, $250 = 2 \cdot 5^3$; gcd $= 5$; lcm $= 2 \cdot 3^2 \cdot 5^3 = 2250$

11. $840 = 2^3 \cdot 3 \cdot 5 \cdot 7$, $320 = 2^6 \cdot 5$; gcd $= 2^3 \cdot 5 = 40$; lcm $= 2^6 \cdot 3 \cdot 5 \cdot 7 = 6720$

12. $60 = 2^2 \cdot 3 \cdot 5$, $40 = 2^3 \cdot 5$, $96 = 2^5 \cdot 3$; gcd $= 2^2 = 4$; lcm $= 2^5 \cdot 3 \cdot 5 = 480$

13. $36 = 2^2 \cdot 3^2$, $108 = 2^2 \cdot 3^3$, $144 = 2^4 \cdot 3^2$; gcd $= 2^2 \cdot 3^2 = 36$; lcm $= 2^4 \cdot 3^3 = 432$

14. $15 = 3 \cdot 5$, $9 = 3^2$; lcm $= 3^2 \cdot 5 = 45$. In 45 days the train will stop in both cities.

15. $-5 + 3 = -2$

16. $7 + (-5) = 2$

17. $4 - 8 = 4 + (-8) = -4$

18. $(-2) + (-4) = -6$

19. $-5 - 4 = -5 + (-4) = -9$

20. $-3 - (-6) = -3 + 6 = 3$

21. $(-3 + 7) - 4 = 4 + (-4) = 0$

22. $-1 + (9 - 4) = -1 + 5 = 4$

23. $(-4)(-6) = 24$

24. $(-3)(7) = -21$

25. $5(-3) = -15$

26. $\dfrac{-35}{-7} = 5$

27. $\dfrac{12}{-6} = -2$

28. $[8 \div (-4)](-3) = (-2)(-3) = 6$

29. $[(-4)(-3)] \div 2 = 12 \div 2 = 6$

30. $[-30 \div (10)] \div (-1) = -3 \div (-1) = 3$

31. $4/5 = 0.8$

32. $7/10 = 0.7$

33. $12/16 = 3/4 = 0.75$

34. $13/4 = 3.25$

35. $3/7 = 0.\overline{428571}$

36. $7/12 = 0.58\overline{3}$

37. $3/8 = 0.375$

38. $7/8 = 0.875$

39. $5/7 = 0.\overline{714285}$

40. $0.175 = \dfrac{175}{1000} = \dfrac{7}{40}$

41. Let $n = 0.\overline{3}$, then
$$\begin{array}{rcl} 10n &=& 3.\overline{3} \\ -\ n &=& -0.\overline{3} \\ \hline 9n &=& 3 \\ \dfrac{9n}{9} &=& \dfrac{3}{9} \\ n &=& \dfrac{3}{9} = \dfrac{1}{3} \end{array}$$

42. $5.31 = \dfrac{531}{100}$

43. Let $n = 2.\overline{37}$, then

$$100n = 237.\overline{37}$$
$$\underline{-\ n = -2.\overline{37}}$$
$$99n = 235$$
$$\frac{99n}{99} = \frac{235}{99}$$
$$n = \frac{235}{99}$$

44. $12.083 = \dfrac{12083}{1000}$

45. $0.0042 = \dfrac{42}{10000} = \dfrac{21}{5000}$

46. Let $n = 2.3\overline{4}$, then

$$100n = 234.\overline{4}$$
$$\underline{-\ 10n = -23.\overline{4}}$$
$$90n = 211$$
$$\frac{90n}{90} = \frac{211}{90}$$
$$n = \frac{211}{90}$$

47. $5\frac{1}{2} = \dfrac{(5\cdot2)+1}{2} = \dfrac{11}{2}$

48. $12\frac{3}{4} = \dfrac{(12\cdot4)+3}{4} = \dfrac{51}{4}$

49. $-3\frac{1}{4} = \dfrac{(-3\cdot4)-1}{4} = \dfrac{-13}{4}$

50. $-35\frac{3}{8} = \dfrac{(-35\cdot8)-3}{8} = \dfrac{-283}{8}$

51. $\dfrac{27}{4} = \dfrac{6\cdot4+3}{4} = 6\frac{3}{4}$

52. $\dfrac{39}{12} = \dfrac{3\cdot12+3}{12} = 3\frac{3}{12} = 3\frac{1}{4}$

53. $\dfrac{-12}{7} = \dfrac{(-1)\cdot7-5}{7} = -1\frac{5}{7}$

54. $\dfrac{-136}{5} = \dfrac{(-27)\cdot5-1}{5} = -27\frac{1}{5}$

55. $\dfrac{1}{3}+\dfrac{1}{7} = \dfrac{7}{7}\cdot\dfrac{1}{3}+\dfrac{3}{3}\cdot\dfrac{1}{7} = \dfrac{7}{21}+\dfrac{3}{21} = \dfrac{10}{21}$

56. $\dfrac{3}{4}-\dfrac{1}{3} = \dfrac{3}{3}\cdot\dfrac{3}{4}-\dfrac{4}{4}\cdot\dfrac{1}{3} = \dfrac{9}{12}-\dfrac{4}{12} = \dfrac{5}{12}$

57. $\dfrac{7}{12}+\dfrac{5}{14} = \dfrac{7}{7}\cdot\dfrac{7}{12}+\dfrac{6}{6}\cdot\dfrac{5}{14} = \dfrac{49}{84}+\dfrac{30}{84} = \dfrac{79}{84}$

58. $\dfrac{2}{3}\cdot\dfrac{3}{11} = \dfrac{2\cdot3}{3\cdot11} = \dfrac{6}{33} = \dfrac{2}{11}$

59. $\dfrac{5}{9}\div\dfrac{6}{7} = \dfrac{5}{9}\cdot\dfrac{7}{6} = \dfrac{35}{54}$

60. $\left(\dfrac{4}{5}+\dfrac{5}{7}\right)\div\dfrac{4}{5} = \dfrac{28+25}{35}\cdot\dfrac{5}{4} = \dfrac{53}{35}\cdot\dfrac{5}{4} = \dfrac{53}{28}$

61. $\left(\dfrac{2}{3}\cdot\dfrac{1}{7}\right)\div\dfrac{4}{7} = \dfrac{2}{21}\cdot\dfrac{7}{4} = \dfrac{1}{6}$

62. $\left(\dfrac{1}{5}+\dfrac{2}{3}\right)\cdot\dfrac{3}{8} = \dfrac{3+10}{15}\cdot\dfrac{3}{8} = \dfrac{13}{15}\cdot\dfrac{3}{8} = \dfrac{13}{40}$

63. $\left(\dfrac{1}{5}\cdot\dfrac{2}{3}\right)+\left(\dfrac{1}{5}\div\dfrac{1}{2}\right) = \dfrac{2}{15}+\left(\dfrac{1}{5}\cdot\dfrac{2}{1}\right) = \dfrac{2}{15}+\dfrac{2}{5} = \dfrac{2}{15}+\dfrac{6}{15} = \dfrac{8}{15}$

64. $\dfrac{1}{8}\cdot17\frac{3}{4} = \dfrac{1}{8}\cdot\dfrac{71}{4} = \dfrac{71}{32} = 2\frac{7}{32}$ teaspoons

65. $\sqrt{20} = \sqrt{4\cdot5} = \sqrt{4}\cdot\sqrt{5} = 2\sqrt{5}$

66. $\sqrt{32} = \sqrt{16\cdot2} = \sqrt{16}\cdot\sqrt{2} = 4\sqrt{2}$

67. $\sqrt{5}+7\sqrt{5} = 8\sqrt{5}$

68. $\sqrt{3}-4\sqrt{3} = -3\sqrt{3}$

69. $\sqrt{8}+6\sqrt{2} = 2\sqrt{2}+6\sqrt{2} = 8\sqrt{2}$

70. $\sqrt{3}-7\sqrt{27} = \sqrt{3}-21\sqrt{3} = -20\sqrt{3}$

71. $\sqrt{75}+\sqrt{27} = 5\sqrt{3}+3\sqrt{3} = 8\sqrt{3}$

72. $\sqrt{3}\cdot\sqrt{6} = \sqrt{18} = \sqrt{9\cdot2} = \sqrt{9}\cdot\sqrt{2} = 3\sqrt{2}$

73. $\sqrt{8}\cdot\sqrt{6} = \sqrt{48} = \sqrt{16\cdot3} = \sqrt{16}\cdot\sqrt{3} = 4\sqrt{3}$

74. $\dfrac{\sqrt{18}}{\sqrt{2}} = \sqrt{\dfrac{18}{2}} = \sqrt{9} = 3$

75. $\dfrac{\sqrt{56}}{\sqrt{2}} = \sqrt{\dfrac{56}{2}} = \sqrt{28} = 2\sqrt{7}$

76. $\dfrac{3}{\sqrt{2}} \cdot \dfrac{\sqrt{2}}{\sqrt{2}} = \dfrac{3\sqrt{2}}{2}$

77. $\dfrac{\sqrt{3}}{\sqrt{5}} \cdot \dfrac{\sqrt{5}}{\sqrt{5}} = \dfrac{\sqrt{15}}{5}$

78. $5(3 + \sqrt{5}) = 15 + 5\sqrt{5}$

79. $\sqrt{3}(4 + \sqrt{6}) = 4\sqrt{3} + \sqrt{18} = 4\sqrt{3} + 3\sqrt{2}$

80. $\sqrt{3}(\sqrt{6} + \sqrt{15}) = \sqrt{18} + \sqrt{45} = 3\sqrt{2} + 3\sqrt{5}$

81. Commutative property of addition
82. Commutative property of multiplication
83. Associative property of addition
84. Distributive property
85. Commutative property of addition
86. Commutative property of addition
87. Associative property of multiplication
88. Commutative property of multiplication
89. Distributive property
90. Commutative property of multiplication
91. Closed
92. Closed
93. Not closed; $1 \div 2$ is not an integer
94. Closed
95. Not closed; $\sqrt{2} \cdot \sqrt{2} = 2$ is not irrational
96. Not closed; $1 \div 0$ is undefined

97. $2^4 = 2 \cdot 2 \cdot 2 \cdot 2 = 16$

98. $2^{-3} = \dfrac{1}{2^3} = \dfrac{1}{2 \cdot 2 \cdot 2} = \dfrac{1}{8}$

99. $\dfrac{7^5}{7^4} = 7^{5-4} = 7^1 = 7$

100. $5^2 \cdot 5^1 = 5^3 = 125$

101. $7^0 = 1$

102. $4^{-3} = \dfrac{1}{4^3} = \dfrac{1}{64}$

103. $(2^3)^2 = 2^{3 \cdot 2} = 2^6 = 64$

104. $(3^2)^2 = 3^{2 \cdot 2} = 3^4 = 81$

105. $230{,}000 = 2.3 \times 10^5$

106. $0.0000158 = 1.58 \times 10^{-5}$

107. $0.00275 = 2.75 \times 10^{-3}$

108. $4{,}950{,}000 = 4.95 \times 10^6$

109. $2.5 \times 10^4 = 25{,}000$

110. $1.39 \times 10^{-4} = 0.000139$

111. $1.75 \times 10^{-4} = 0.000175$

112. $1 \times 10^5 = 100{,}000$

113. a) $(5 \times 10^6)(1.7 \times 10^{-4})$
   $(5)(1.7) \times 10^6 \cdot 10^{-4}$
   8.5×10^2

114. a) $(4 \times 10^2)(2.5 \times 10^2)$
   $(4)(2.5) \times 10^2 \cdot 10^2$
   10×10^4
   1.0×10^5

115. a) $\dfrac{8.4 \times 10^3}{4 \times 10^2} = \dfrac{8.4}{4} \times \dfrac{10^3}{10^2} = 2.1 \times 10^1$

116. a) $\dfrac{1.5 \times 10^{-3}}{5 \times 10^{-4}} = \dfrac{1.5}{5} \times \dfrac{10^{-3}}{10^{-4}} = 0.3 \times 10^1 = 3.0 \times 10^0$

117. a) $(25{,}000)(600{,}000) = (2.5 \times 10^4)(6.0 \times 10^5)$
   $= (2.5)(6) \times 10^4 \cdot 10^5 = 15 \times 10^9$
   $= 1.5 \times 10^{10} = 15{,}000{,}000{,}000$

118. a) $(35{,}000)(0.00002) = (3.5 \times 10^4)(2.0 \times 10^{-5})$
   $= (3.5)(2) \times 10^4 \cdot 10^{-5} = 7 \times 10^{-1} = 0.7$

119. $\dfrac{9600000}{3000} = \dfrac{9.6 \times 10^6}{3 \times 10^3} = 3.2 \times 10^3 = 3{,}200$

120. $\dfrac{0.000002}{0.0000004} = \dfrac{2 \times 10^{-6}}{4 \times 10^{-7}} = 0.5 \times 10^1 = 5.0$

121. $\dfrac{300000}{12000} = \dfrac{3 \times 10^5}{1.2 \times 10^4} = 2.5 \times 10^1 = 25$ times

122. $\dfrac{20{,}000{,}000}{3{,}600} = \dfrac{2.0 \times 10^7}{3.6 \times 10^3} \approx 0.555556 \times 10^4 = \$5{,}555.56$

123. Arithmetic: $d = 5$; 21 and 26
124. Geometric: $r = -3$; -243 and 729
125. Arithmetic: $d = -3$; -15 and -18
126. Geometric: $r = 1/2$; $1/32$ and $1/64$
127. Arithmetic: $d = 3$; 16 and 19
128. Geometric: $r = -1$; -2 and 2

129. $a_6 = -6 + (6-1)3 = -6 + (5)(3) = 9$

130. $a_8 = -6 + (8-1)(-4) = -6 + (7)(-4) = -34$

131. $a_{10} = -20 + (10-1)5 = -20 + (9)(5) = 25$

132. $a_4 = 8(3)^{4-1} = 8(3)^3 = 8(27) = 216$

133. $a_5 = 4(1/2)^{5-1} = 4(1/2)^4 = 4(1/16) = 1/4$

134. $a_4 = -6(2)^{4-1} = -6(2)^3 = -6(8) = -48$

135. $s_{10} = \dfrac{10(2+38)}{2} = \dfrac{(10)(40)}{2} = 200$

136. $s_8 = \dfrac{8(-4+(-2\frac{1}{4}))}{2} = \dfrac{(8)(-6\frac{1}{4})}{2} = -25$

137. $s_8 = \dfrac{8(100+58)}{2} = \dfrac{(8)(158)}{2} = 632$

138. $s_{20} = \dfrac{20(0.5+5.25)}{2} = \dfrac{(20)(5.75)}{2} = 57.5$

139. $s_3 = \dfrac{4(1-2^3)}{1-2} = \dfrac{(4)(1-8)}{-1} = \dfrac{(4)(-7)}{-1} = 28$

140. $s_4 = \dfrac{2(1-3^4)}{1-3} = \dfrac{(2)(1-81)}{-2} = \dfrac{(2)(-80)}{-2} = 80$

141. $s_5 = \dfrac{3(1-(-2)^5)}{1-(-2)} = \dfrac{(3)(1+32)}{3} = \dfrac{(3)(33)}{3} = 33$

142. $s_6 = \dfrac{1(1-(-2)^6)}{1-(-2)} = \dfrac{(1)(1-64)}{3} = \dfrac{(1)(-63)}{3} = -21$

143. Arithmetic: $a_n = -3n + 10$

144. Arithmetic: $a_n = 5n - 5$

145. Arithmetic: $a_n = -(3/2)n + (11/2)$

146. Geometric: $a_n = 3(2)^{n-1}$

147. Geometric: $a_n = 4(-1)^{n-1}$

148. Geometric: $a_n = 5(1/3)^{n-1}$

149. Yes; 13, 21

150. Yes; 17, 28

151. No

152. No

Chapter Test

1. 481,248 is divisible by:
    2, 3, 4, 6, 8, and 9.

2.
$$\begin{array}{r|r} 2 & 420 \\ 2 & 210 \\ 3 & 105 \\ 5 & 35 \\ & 7 \end{array}$$
$420 = 2^2 \cdot 3 \cdot 5 \cdot 7$

3. $[(-6) + (-9)] + 8 = -15 + 8 = -7$

4. $-5 - 15 = -5 + (-15) = -20$

5. $[(-70)(-5)] \div (8 - 10)$
    $= 350 \div [8 + (-10)] = 350 \div (-2) = -175$

6. $4\frac{5}{8} = \dfrac{(8\cdot4)+5}{8} = \dfrac{32+5}{8} = \dfrac{37}{8}$

7. $\dfrac{176}{9} = \dfrac{(19\cdot9)+5}{9} = 19\frac{5}{9}$

8. $\dfrac{5}{8} = 0.625$

9. $6.45 = \dfrac{645}{100} = \dfrac{129}{20}$

10. $\dfrac{5}{16} \div \dfrac{4}{5} \cdot \dfrac{1}{2} = \dfrac{5}{16} \cdot \dfrac{1}{3} + \dfrac{2}{5} = \dfrac{5}{48} + \dfrac{2}{5} = \dfrac{25}{240} + \dfrac{96}{240} = \dfrac{121}{240}$

11. $\dfrac{15}{24} - \dfrac{3}{20} = \dfrac{5}{5}\cdot\dfrac{15}{24} - \dfrac{6}{6}\cdot\dfrac{3}{20} = \dfrac{75}{120} - \dfrac{18}{120} = \dfrac{57}{120} = \dfrac{19}{40}$

12. $\sqrt{75}+\sqrt{48}=\sqrt{25}\sqrt{3}+\sqrt{16}\sqrt{3}= 5\sqrt{3} + 4\sqrt{3} = 9\sqrt{3}$

13. $\dfrac{\sqrt{5}}{\sqrt{6}} = \dfrac{\sqrt{5}}{\sqrt{6}}\cdot\dfrac{\sqrt{6}}{\sqrt{6}} = \dfrac{\sqrt{30}}{\sqrt{36}} = \dfrac{\sqrt{30}}{6}$

14. The integers are closed under multiplication since the product of two integers is always an integer.

15. Associative property of addition

16. Distributive property

17. $\dfrac{6^7}{6^5} = 6^{7-5} = 6^2 = 36$

18. $4^3 \cdot 4^2 = 4^5 = 4 \cdot 4 \cdot 4 \cdot 4 \cdot 4 = 1024$

19. $9^{-2} = \dfrac{1}{9^2} = \dfrac{1}{81}$

20. $\dfrac{64000}{0.008} = \dfrac{5.4 \times 10^4}{8 \times 10^{-3}} = 0.8 \times 10^7 = 8 \times 10^6$

21. $a_n = -4n + 2$

22. $\dfrac{11\left[-2 + (-32)\right]}{2} = \dfrac{11(-34)}{2} = -187$

23. $a_5 = 3(3)^4 = 3^5 = 243$

24. $\dfrac{3\left(1 - 4^5\right)}{1 - 4} = \dfrac{3(1 - 1024)}{-3} = 1023$

25. $a_n = 3 \cdot (2)^{n-1}$

26. 1, 1, 2, 3, 5, 8, 13, 21, 34, 55

Group Projects

In Exercise 1 you may obtain different answers depending upon how you work the problem.

1. a) Rice: 2/3 cup, Salt: 1/4 tsp., Butter: 1 tsp.
   b) Rice: 1/3 cup, Salt: 1/8 tsp., Butter: 1/2 tsp.
   c) Rice: 9 2/3 cup, Salt: 3 5/8 tsp., Butter: 14 1/2 tsp.

2. a) approx. 69.32   b) approx. 69.32

3. a) $197.20   b) $578.80   c) $302.80

4. a&b)

Jan.	Feb.	Mar.	Apr.	May	June

branches: 1   1   2   3   5   8

   c) After 12 months there will be 144 branches. 144 is the 12th Fibonacci number.
   d) The sequence of branches is the Fibonacci sequence.

CHAPTER SIX

ALGEBRA, GRAPHS, AND FUNCTIONS

Exercise Set 6.1

1. **Variables** are letters of the alphabet used to represent numbers.
2. A symbol that represents a specific quantity is called a **constant**.
3. An **algebraic expression** is a collection of variables, numbers, parentheses, and operation symbols. An example is $5x^2y - 11$.
4. The **solution** to an equation is the number or numbers that replace the variable to make the equation a true statement.
5. a) Base: 4, exponent: 5
   b) Multiply 4 by itself 5 times.
6. First: Perform all operations within parentheses or other grouping symbols.
   Next: Perform all exponential operations. Next: Perform all multiplication and division from left to right.
   Finally: Perform all addition and subtraction from left to right.

7. $6 + 12 \div 2 = 6 + 6 = 12$

8. $12 + 8 \cdot 3 = 12 + 24 = 36$

9. $x = -4, x^2 = (-4)^2 = 16$

10. $x = 9, x^2 = (9)^2 = 81$

11. $x = -7, -x^2 = -(-7)^2 = -49$

12. $x = -5, -x^2 = -(-5)^2 = -25$

13. $x = -7, -2x^3 = -2(-7)^3 = -2(-343) = 686$

14. $x = -4, -x^3 = -(-4)^3 = -(-64) = 64$

15. $x = 4, x - 7 = 4 - 7 = -3$

16. $x = \dfrac{5}{2}, 8x - 3 = 8\left(\dfrac{5}{2}\right) - 3 = 20 - 3 = 17$

17. $x = -4, -5x + 8 = -5(-4) + 8 = 20 + 8 = 28$

18. $x = 5, x^2 + 6x - 4 = (5)^2 + 6(5) - 4 = 25 + 30 - 4 = 51$

19. $x = -2, -x^2 - 7x + 5 = -(-2)^2 - 7(-2) + 5$
    $= -4 + 14 + 5 = 15$

20. $x = -1, 5x^2 + 7x - 11 = 5(-1)^2 + 7(-1) - 11$
    $= 5 - 7 - 11 = -13$

22. $x = 3, x^3 + 4x^2 - 3x + 15 = (3)^3 + 4(3)^2 - 3(3) + 15$
    $= 27 + 36 - 9 + 15 = 69$

21. $x = \dfrac{2}{3}, \dfrac{1}{2}x^2 - 5x + 2 = \dfrac{1}{2}\left(\dfrac{2}{3}\right)^2 - 5\left(\dfrac{2}{3}\right) + 2$

$= \dfrac{1}{2}\left(\dfrac{4}{9}\right) - \dfrac{10}{3} + 2$

$= \dfrac{4}{18} - \dfrac{10}{3} + 2$

$= \dfrac{4}{18} - \dfrac{60}{18} + \dfrac{36}{18} = -\dfrac{20}{18} = -\dfrac{10}{9}$

23. $x = \frac{1}{2}, 8x^3 - 4x^2 + 7 = 8\left(\frac{1}{2}\right)^3 - 4\left(\frac{1}{2}\right)^2 + 7$

$$= 8\left(\frac{1}{8}\right) - 4\left(\frac{1}{4}\right) + 7$$

$$= 1 - 1 + 7 = 7$$

24. $x = 2, y = 3, -x^2 + 4xy = -(2)^2 + 4(2)(3)$

$$= -4 + 24 = 20$$

25. $x = 1, y = -2, 3x^2 - xy + 2y^2 = 3(1)^2 - 1(-2) + 2(-2)^2$

$$= 3 + 2 + 8 = 13$$

26. $x = 7, y = -3, 3x^2 + \frac{3}{7}xy - \frac{1}{3}y^2$

$$= 3(7)^2 + \frac{3}{7}(7)(-3) - \frac{1}{3}(-3)^2$$

$$= 147 - 9 - 3 = 135$$

27. $x = 3, y = 2, 4x^2 - 12xy + 9y^2 = 4(3)^2 - 12(3)(2) + 9(2)^2$

$$= 36 - 72 + 36 = 0$$

28. $x = 4, y = -3, (x + 3y)^2 = [4 + 3(-3)]^2$

$$= (-5)^2 = 25$$

29. $6x - 9 = 12, x = 3$

$6(3) - 9 = 18 - 9 = 9$

$9 \neq 12, x = 3$ is not a solution.

30. $4x - 7 = 15, x = -2$

$4(-2) - 7 = -8 - 7 = -15$

$-15 \neq 15, x = -2$ is not a solution.

31. $x + 2y = 0, x = -6, y = 3$

$-6 + 2(3) = -6 + 6 = 0$

$0 = 0, x = -6, y = 3$ is a solution.

32. $3x + 2y = -2, x = -2, y = 2$

$3(-2) + 2(2) = -6 + 4 = -2$

$-2 = -2, x = -2, y = 2$ is a solution.

33. $x^2 + 3x - 4 = 5, x = 2$

$(2)^2 + 3(2) - 4 = 4 + 6 - 4 = 6$

$6 \neq 5, x = 2$ is not a solution.

34. $2x^2 - x - 5 = 0, x = 3$

$2(3)^2 - 3 - 5 = 2(9) - 3 - 5 = 10$

$10 \neq 0, x = 3$ is not a solution.

35. $2x^2 + x = 28, x = -4$

$2(-4)^2 + (-4) = 2(16) - 4 = 32 - 4 = 28$

$28 = 28, x = -4$ is a solution.

36. $y = x^2 + 3x - 5, x = 1, y = -1$

$(1)^2 + 3(1) - 5 = 1 + 3 - 5 = -1$

$-1 = -1, x = 1, y = -1$ is a solution.

37. $y = -x^2 + 4x - 1, x = 3, y = 2$

$-3^2 + 4(3) - 1 = -9 + 12 - 1 = 2$

$2 = 2, x = 3, y = 2$ is a solution.

38. $y = x^3 - 3x^2 + 1, x = 2, y = -3$

$(2)^3 - 3(2)^2 + 1 = 8 - 12 + 1 = -3$

$-3 = -3, x = 2, y = -3$ is a solution.

39. a) $t = 8, 6.55t = 6.55(8) = \$52.40$

   b) $t = 20, 6.55t = 6.55(20) = \$131$

40. $d = \$325, 0.06d = 0.06(\$325) = \$19.50$

41. $x = \$12,500, x + 0.05x = \$12,500 + 0.05(\$12,500)$

$$= \$12,500 + \$625 = \$13,125$$

42. $n = 8,000,000,000,000$

$0.000002n = 0.000002(8,000,000,000,000)$

$$= 16,000,000 \text{ seconds}$$

43. $x = 60, 25x - 0.2x^2 = 25(60) - 0.2(60)^2$
$$= 1500 - 0.2(3600)$$
$$= 1500 - 720$$
$$= 780 \text{ baskets of oranges}$$

44. $h = 0.60, 2h^2 + 80h + 40 = 2(0.60)^2 + 80(0.60) + 40$
$$= 2(0.36) + 48 + 40$$
$$= 0.72 + 48 + 40$$
$$= 88.72 \text{ minutes}$$

45. $R = 2, T = 70, 0.2R^2 + 0.003RT + 0.0001T^2 = 0.2(2)^2 + 0.003(2)(70) + 0.0001(70)^2 = 0.8 + 0.42 + 0.49 = 1.71 \text{ in.}$

46. $(-1)^n = 1$ for any even number n since there will be an even number of factors of (-1), and when these are multiplied, the product will always be 1.

47.

x	y	$(x+y)^2$	$x^2 + y^2$
2	3	$5^2 = 25$	$4 + 9 = 13$
-2	-3	$(-5)^2 = 25$	$4 + 9 = 13$
-2	3	$1^2 = 1$	$4 + 9 = 13$
2	-3	$(-1)^2 = 1$	$4 + 9 = 13$

The two expressions are not equal.

48. $1^n = 1$ for any natural number n since 1 multiplied by itself any number of times will always be 1.

Exercise Set 6.2

1. The parts that are added or subtracted in an algebraic expression are called **terms**.
   In $3x - 2y$, the $3x$ and $-2y$ are terms.

2. **Like terms** are terms that have the same variables with the same exponents on the variables.
   $5x^2$ and $-7x^2$ are like terms.

3. The numerical part of a term is called its **numerical coefficient**.
   For the term $3x$, 3 is the numerical coefficient.

4. To **simplify** an expression means to combine like terms by using the commutative, associative, and distributive properties. Example: $12 + x + 7 - 3x = x - 3x + 12 + 7 = -2x + 19$

5. A **linear equation** is one in which the exponent on the variable is 1. Example: $4x + 6 = 10$

6. If $a = b$, then $a + c = b + c$ for all real numbers a, b, and c. Example: If $x - 5 = 2$, then $x - 5 + 5 = 2 + 5$.

7. If $a = b$, then $a - c = b - c$ for all real numbers a, b, and c. Example: If $2x + 3 = 5$, then $2x + 3 - 3 = 5 - 3$.

8. If $a = b$, then $a \cdot c = b \cdot c$ for all real numbers a, b, and c. Example: If $\dfrac{x}{3} = 2$, then $3\left(\dfrac{x}{3}\right) = 3(2)$.

9. If $a = b$, then $\dfrac{a}{c} = \dfrac{b}{c}$ for all real numbers a, b, and c, where $c \neq 0$. Example: If $4x = 8$ then $\dfrac{4x}{4} = \dfrac{8}{4}$.

10. An **algorithm** is a general procedure for accomplishing a task.

11. A **ratio** is a quotient of two quantities. Example: $\dfrac{7}{9}$

12. A **proportion** is a statement of equality between two ratios. Example: $\dfrac{3}{7} = \dfrac{x}{10}$

13. Yes. They have the same variable and the same exponent on the variable.

14. No. They do not have the same variable.

15. $3x + 8x = 11x$

16. $-9x - 6x = -15x$

17. $8x + 2x - 11 = 10x - 11$

18. $-8x + 2x + 15 = -6x + 15$

19. $7x+3y-4x+8y=3x+11y$

20. $x-4x+3=-3x+3$

21. $-3x+2-5x=-8x+2$

22. $-3x+4x-2+5=x+3$

23. $2-3x-2x+1=-5x+3$

24. $-0.2x+1.7x-4=1.5x-4$

25. $3.7x-5.8+2.6x=6.3x-5.8$

26. $\dfrac{1}{2}x+\dfrac{3}{4}x+5=\dfrac{2}{4}x+\dfrac{3}{4}x+5=\dfrac{5}{4}x+5$

27. $\dfrac{1}{3}x-\dfrac{1}{4}x-2=\dfrac{4}{12}x-\dfrac{3}{12}x-2=\dfrac{1}{12}x-2$

28. $6x+2y+8-4x-9y=2x-7y+8$

29. $5x-4y-3y+8x+3=13x-7y+3$

30. $3(p+2)-4(p+3)=3p+6-4p-12=-p-6$

31. $2(s+3)+6(s-4)+1=2s+6+6s-24+1=8s-17$

32. $6(r-3)-2(r+5)+10=6r-18-2r-10+10$
$=4r-18$

33. $0.2(x-3)-1.6(x+2)$
$=0.2x-0.6-1.6x-3.2$
$=-1.4x-3.8$

34. $\dfrac{1}{4}(x+3)+\dfrac{1}{2}x=\dfrac{1}{4}x+\dfrac{3}{4}+\dfrac{1}{2}x$
$=\dfrac{1}{4}x+\dfrac{2}{4}x+\dfrac{3}{4}=\dfrac{3}{4}x+\dfrac{3}{4}$

35. $\dfrac{3}{4}x+\dfrac{3}{5}-\dfrac{2}{5}x+\dfrac{1}{2}=\dfrac{15}{20}x-\dfrac{8}{20}x+\dfrac{6}{10}+\dfrac{5}{10}$
$=\dfrac{7}{20}x+\dfrac{11}{10}$

36. $n-\dfrac{3}{4}+\dfrac{5}{9}n-\dfrac{1}{6}=\dfrac{9}{9}n+\dfrac{5}{9}n-\dfrac{9}{12}-\dfrac{2}{12}$
$=\dfrac{14}{9}n-\dfrac{11}{12}$

37. $0.5(2.6x-4)+2.3(1.4x-5)=1.3x-2+3.22-11.5$
$=4.52x-13.5$

38. $\dfrac{2}{3}(3x+9)-\dfrac{1}{4}(2x+5)=2x+6-\dfrac{1}{2}x-\dfrac{5}{4}$
$=\dfrac{4}{2}x-\dfrac{1}{2}x+\dfrac{24}{4}-\dfrac{5}{4}=\dfrac{3}{2}x+\dfrac{19}{4}$

39. $y+3=8$

$y+3-3=8-3$ Subtract 3 from both sides of the equation

$y=5$

40. $3y-4=11$

$3y-4+4=11+4$ Add 4 to both sides of the equation

$3y=15$

$\dfrac{3y}{3}=\dfrac{15}{3}$ Divide both sides of the equation by 3

$y=5$

41. $16=2x+6$

$16-6=2x+6-6$ Subtract 6 from both sides of the equation

$10=2x$

$\dfrac{10}{2}=\dfrac{2x}{2}$ Divide both sides of the equation by 2

$5=x$

42. $4 = 7 - 3y$

$4 - 7 = 7 - 7 - 3y$ Subtract 7 from both sides of the equation

$-3 = -3y$

$\dfrac{-3}{-3} = \dfrac{-3y}{-3}$ Divide both sides of the equation by -3

$1 = y$

43. $\dfrac{3}{x} = \dfrac{7}{8}$

$3(8) = 7x$ Cross multiplication

$24 = 7x$

$\dfrac{24}{7} = \dfrac{7x}{7}$ Divide both sides of the equation by 7

$\dfrac{24}{7} = x$

44. $\dfrac{x-1}{5} = \dfrac{x+5}{15}$

$15(x-1) = 5(x+5)$ Cross multiplication

$15x - 15 = 5x + 25$ Distributive Property

$15x - 5x - 15 = 5x - 5x + 25$ Subtract $5x$ from both sides of the equation

$10x - 15 = 25$

$10x - 15 + 15 = 25 + 15$ Add 15 to both sides of the equation

$10x = 40$

$\dfrac{10x}{10} = \dfrac{40}{10}$ Divide both sides of the equation by 10

$x = 4$

45. $\dfrac{1}{2}x + \dfrac{1}{3} = \dfrac{2}{3}$

$6\left(\dfrac{1}{2}x + \dfrac{1}{3}\right) = 6\left(\dfrac{2}{3}\right)$ Multiply both sides of the equation by the LCD

$3x + 2 = 4$ Distributive Property

$3x + 2 - 2 = 4 - 2$ Subtract 2 from both sides of the equation

$3x = 2$

$\dfrac{3x}{3} = \dfrac{2}{3}$ Divide both sides of the equation by 3

$x = \dfrac{2}{3}$

46. $\dfrac{1}{2}y + \dfrac{1}{3} = \dfrac{1}{4}$

$12\left(\dfrac{1}{2}y + \dfrac{1}{3}\right) = 12\left(\dfrac{1}{4}\right)$ Multiply both sides of the equation by the LCD

$6y + 4 = 3$ Distributive Property

$6y + 4 - 4 = 3 - 4$ Subtract 4 from both sides of the equation

$6y = -1$

$\dfrac{6y}{6} = \dfrac{-1}{6}$ Divide both sides of the equation by 6

$y = -\dfrac{1}{6}$

47. $0.7x - 0.3 = 1.8$

$0.7x - 0.3 + 0.3 = 1.8 + 0.3$ Add 0.3 to both sides of the equation

$0.7x = 2.1$

$\dfrac{0.7x}{0.7} = \dfrac{2.1}{0.7}$ Divide both sides of the equation by 0.7

$x = 3$

48. $5x + 0.050 = -0.732$

$5x + 0.050 - 0.050 = -0.732 - 0.050$ Subtract 0.050 from both sides of the equation

$5x = -0.782$

$\dfrac{5x}{5} = \dfrac{-0.782}{5}$ Divide both sides of the equation by 5

$x = -0.1564$

49. $3t - 4 = 2t - 1$

$3t - 2t - 4 = 2t - 2t - 1$ Subtract $2t$ from both sides of the equation

$t - 4 = -1$

$t - 4 + 4 = -1 + 4$ Add 4 to both sides of the equation

$t = 3$

50. $\dfrac{x}{3} + 2x = -\dfrac{2}{5}$

$15\left(\dfrac{x}{3} + 2x\right) = 15\left(-\dfrac{2}{5}\right)$ Multiply both sides of the equation by the LCD

$5x + 30x = -6$ Distributive Property

$35x = -6$

$\dfrac{35x}{35} = \dfrac{-6}{35}$ Divide both sides of the equation by 35

$x = -\dfrac{6}{35}$

51. $\dfrac{x-5}{4} = \dfrac{x-9}{3}$

$3(x-5) = 4(x-9)$ Cross multiplication

$3x - 15 = 4x - 36$ Distributive Property

$3x - 3x - 15 = 4x - 3x - 36$ Subtract $3x$ from both sides of the equation

$-15 = x - 36$

$-15 + 36 = x - 36 + 36$ Add 36 to both sides of the equation

$21 = x$

52. $2r + 8 = 5 + 3r$

$2r - 2r + 8 = 5 + 3r - 2r$ Subtract $2r$ from both sides of the equation

$8 = 5 + r$

$8 - 5 = 5 - 5 + r$ Subtract 5 from both sides of the equation

$3 = r$

53. $\dfrac{x}{15} = 2 + \dfrac{x}{5}$

$15\left(\dfrac{x}{15}\right) = 15\left(2 + \dfrac{x}{5}\right)$ Multiply both sides of the equation by the LCD

$x = 30 + 3x$ Distributive Property

$x - 3x = 30 + 3x - 3x$ Subtract $3x$ from both sides of the equation

$-2x = 30$

$\dfrac{-2x}{-2} = \dfrac{30}{-2}$ Divide both sides of the equation by -2

$x = -15$

54. $12x - 1.2 = 3x + 1.5$

$12x - 3x - 1.2 = 3x - 3x + 1.5$ Subtract $3x$ from both sides of the equation

$9x - 1.2 = 1.5$

$9x - 1.2 + 1.2 = 1.5 + 1.2$ Add 1.2 to both sides of the equation

$9x = 2.7$

$\dfrac{9x}{9} = \dfrac{2.7}{9}$ Divide both sides of the equation by 9

$x = 0.3$

55. $2(x+3)-4=2(x-4)$

$\quad\quad 2x+6-4=2x-8$ Distributive Property

$\quad\quad\quad 2x+2=2x-8$

$\quad 2x-2x+2=2x-2x-8$ Subtract $2x$ from both sides of the equation

$\quad\quad\quad\quad\quad 2=-8$ False

     No solution

56. $6y+3(4+y)=8$

$\quad\quad 6y+12+3y=8$ Distributive Property

$\quad\quad\quad\quad 9y+12=8$

$\quad 9y+12-12=8-12$ Subtract 12 from both sides of the equation

$\quad\quad\quad\quad\quad\quad 9y=-4$

$\quad\quad\quad\quad \dfrac{9y}{9}=\dfrac{-4}{9}$ Divide both sides of the equation by 9

$\quad\quad\quad\quad\quad y=-\dfrac{4}{9}$

57. $6(x+1)=4x+2(x+3)$

$\quad\quad 6x+6=4x+2x+6$ Distributive Property

$\quad\quad 6x+6=6x+6$

This equation is an identity. Therefore, the solution is all real numbers.

58. $\quad\quad \dfrac{x}{3}+4=\dfrac{2x}{5}-6$

$\quad\quad 15\left(\dfrac{x}{3}+4\right)=15\left(\dfrac{2x}{5}-6\right)$ Multiply both sides of the equation by the LCD

$\quad\quad\quad 5x+60=6x-90$ Distributive Property

$\quad 5x-5x+60=6x-5x-90$ Subtract $5x$ from both sides of the equation

$\quad\quad\quad\quad\quad 60=x-90$

$\quad\quad\quad 60+90=x-90+90$ Add 90 to both sides of the equation

$\quad\quad\quad\quad\quad 150=x$

59.　　$\dfrac{1}{4}(x+4)=\dfrac{2}{5}(x+2)$

　　$20\left(\dfrac{1}{4}\right)(x+4)=20\left(\dfrac{2}{5}\right)(x+2)$　　Multiply both sides of the equation by the LCD

　　　　$5(x+4)=8(x+2)$

　　　　$5x+20=8x+16$　　Distributive Property

　　$5x-8x+20=8x-8x+16$　　Subtract $8x$ from both sides of the equation

　　　　$-3x+20=16$

　　$-3x+20-20=16-20$　　Subtract 20 from both sides of the equation

　　　　　$-3x=-4$

　　　　　$\dfrac{-3x}{-3}=\dfrac{-4}{-3}$　　Divide both sides of the equation by -3

　　　　　　$x=\dfrac{4}{3}$

60.　　$\dfrac{2}{3}(x+5)=\dfrac{1}{4}(x+2)$

　　$12\left(\dfrac{2}{3}\right)(x+5)=12\left(\dfrac{1}{4}\right)(x+2)$　　Multiply both sides of the equation by the LCD

　　　　$8(x+5)=3(x+2)$

　　　　$8x+40=3x+6$　　Distributive Property

　　$8x-3x+40=3x-3x+6$　　Subtract $3x$ from both sides of the equation

　　　　$5x+40=6$

　　$5x+40-40=6-40$　　Subtract 40 from both sides of the equation

　　　　　$5x=-34$

　　　　　$\dfrac{5x}{5}=\dfrac{-34}{5}$　　Divide both sides of the equation by 5

　　　　　　$x=-\dfrac{34}{5}$

61.　　$3x+2-6x=-x-15+8-5x$

　　　　$-3x+2=-6x-7$

　　$-3x+6x+2=-6x+6x-7$　　Add $6x$ to both sides of the equation

　　　　$3x+2=-7$

　　$3x+2-2=-7-2$　　Subtract 2 from both sides of the equation

　　　　$3x=-9$

　　　　$\dfrac{3x}{3}=\dfrac{-9}{3}$　　Divide both sides of the equation by 3

　　　　　$x=-3$

62. $6x + 8 - 22x = 28 + 14x - 10 + 12x$

$-16x + 8 = 26x + 18$

$-16x - 26x + 8 = 26x - 26x + 18$ Subtract $26x$ from both sides of the equation

$-42x + 8 = 18$

$-42x + 8 - 8 = 18 - 8$ Subtract 8 from both sides of the equation

$-42x = 10$

$\dfrac{-42x}{-42} = \dfrac{10}{-42}$ Divide both sides of the equation by -42

$x = -\dfrac{10}{42} = -\dfrac{5}{21}$

63. $2(x - 3) + 2 = 2(2x - 6)$

$2x - 6 + 2 = 4x - 12$ Distributive Property

$2x - 4 = 4x - 12$

$2x - 4x - 4 = 4x - 4x - 12$ Subtract $4x$ from both sides of the equation

$-2x - 4 = -12$

$-2x - 4 + 4 = -12 + 4$ Add 4 to both sides of the equation

$-2x = -8$

$\dfrac{-2x}{-2} = \dfrac{-8}{-2}$ Divide both sides of the equation by -2

$x = 4$

64. $5.7x - 3.1(x + 5) = 7.3$

$5.7x - 3.1x - 15.5 = 7.3$ Distributive Property

$2.6x - 15.5 = 7.3$

$2.6x - 15.5 + 15.5 = 7.3 + 15.5$ Add 15.5 to both sides of the equation

$2.6x = 22.8$

$\dfrac{2.6x}{2.6} = \dfrac{22.8}{2.6}$ Divide both sides of the equation by 2.6

$x = \dfrac{22.8}{2.6} = \dfrac{228}{26} = \dfrac{114}{13}$ or $x \approx 8.7692$

65. $\dfrac{1.95}{1000} = \dfrac{x}{35,300}$

$1.95(35,300) = 1000x$

$68,835 = 1000x$

$\dfrac{68,835}{1000} = \dfrac{1000x}{1000}$

$x \approx \$68.84$

66. $\dfrac{1.95}{1000} = \dfrac{40.68}{x}$

$1.95x = 40.68(1000)$

$1.95x = 40,680$

$\dfrac{1.95x}{1.95} = \dfrac{40,680}{1.95}$

$x \approx 20,861$ **gallons**

67.
$$\frac{8.025}{1000} = \frac{x}{132,600}$$

$$8.025(132,600) = 1000x$$

$$1,064,115 = 1000x$$

$$\frac{1,064,115}{1000} = \frac{1000x}{1000}$$

$$x \approx \$1064.12$$

68. a)
$$\frac{30}{2500} = \frac{x}{28,000}$$

$$30(28,000) = 2500x$$

$$840,000 = 2500x$$

$$\frac{840,000}{2500} = \frac{2500x}{2500}$$

$$x = 336 \text{ lbs.}$$

b) $\frac{336}{30} = 11.2$; 12 bags

69. a)
$$\frac{700}{3} = \frac{x}{60}$$

$$700(60) = 3x$$

$$42,000 = 3x$$

$$\frac{42,000}{3} = \frac{3x}{3}$$

$$x = 14,000 \text{ toys}$$

b)
$$\frac{700}{3} = \frac{2800}{x}$$

$$700x = 3(2800)$$

$$700x = 8400$$

$$\frac{700x}{700} = \frac{8400}{700}$$

$$x = 12 \text{ hours}$$

70.
$$\frac{1}{825} = \frac{x}{5775}$$

$$5775 = 825x$$

$$\frac{5775}{825} = \frac{825x}{825}$$

$$x = 7 \text{ gallons}$$

71. a)
$$\frac{50}{80} = \frac{1}{x}$$

$$50x = 80$$

$$\frac{50x}{50} = \frac{80}{50}$$

$$x = 1.6 \text{ kph}$$

b)
$$\frac{50}{80} = \frac{x}{90}$$

$$80x = 50(90)$$

$$80x = 4500$$

$$\frac{80x}{80} = \frac{4500}{80}$$

$$x = 56.25 \text{ mph}$$

72.
$$\frac{40}{0.6} = \frac{250}{x}$$

$$40x = 0.6(250)$$

$$40x = 150$$

$$\frac{40x}{40} = \frac{150}{40}$$

$$x = 3.75 \text{ mm.}$$

73. $\dfrac{40}{1} = \dfrac{12}{x}$

$40x = 12$

$\dfrac{40x}{40} = \dfrac{12}{40}$

$x = 0.3$ cc

74. $\dfrac{40}{1} = \dfrac{35}{x}$

$40x = 35$

$\dfrac{40x}{40} = \dfrac{35}{40}$

$x = 0.875$ cc

75. a) Answers will vary.

b) $2(x+3) = 4x+3-5x$

$2x+6 = -x+3$ Distributive Property

$2x+x+6 = -x+x+3$ Add x to both sides of the equation

$3x+6 = 3$

$3x+6-6 = 3-6$ Subtract 6 from both sides of the equation

$3x = -3$

$\dfrac{3x}{3} = \dfrac{-3}{3}$ Divide both sides of the equation by 3

$x = -1$

76. a) An **identity** is an equation with an infinite number of solutions.
    b) When solving an equation, if you have the same expression on both sides of the equation, the equation is an identity.

77. a) An **inconsistent equation** is an equation with no solution.
    b) When solving an equation, if you obtain a false statement, then the equation is inconsistent.

78. a) $P = 14.70+0.43x$

$148 = 14.70+0.43x$ Given $P = 148$, find x

$148-14.70 = 14.70-14.70+0.43x$ Subtract 14.70 from both sides of the equation

$133.3 = 0.43x$

$\dfrac{133.3}{0.43} = \dfrac{0.43x}{0.43}$ Divide both sides of the equation by 0.43

$x = 310$ ft.

b) $P = 14.70+0.43x$

$128.65 = 14.70+0.43x$ Given $P = 128.65$, find x

$128.65-14.70 = 14.70-14.70+0.43x$ Subtract 14.70 from both sides of the equation

$113.95 = 0.43x$

$\dfrac{113.95}{0.43} = \dfrac{0.43x}{0.43}$ Divide both sides of the equation by 0.43

$x = 265$ ft.

79. a) $2:5$
    b) $m:m+n$

Exercise Set 6.3

1. A **formula** is an equation that typically has a real-life application.
2. To **evaluate a formula**, substitute the given values for their respective variables, then evaluate.
3. **Subscripts** are numbers (or letters) placed below and to the right of variables. They are used to help clarify a formula.
4. $i = prt$

5. An **exponential equation** is of the form $y = a^x, a > 0, a \neq 1$.

6. $a > 0, a \neq 1$

7. $A = bh = 15(4) = 60$

8. $P = a + b + c = 25 + 53 + 32 = 110$

9. $P = 2l + 2w$
   $P = 2(12) + 2(16) = 24 + 32 = 56$

10. $F = MA$
    $40 = M(5)$
    $\dfrac{40}{5} = \dfrac{5M}{5}$
    $8 = M$

11. $E = mc^2$
    $400 = m(4)^2$
    $400 = 16m$
    $\dfrac{400}{16} = \dfrac{16m}{16}$
    $25 = m$

12. $p = i^2 r$
    $62{,}500 = (5)^2 r$
    $62{,}500 = 25r$
    $\dfrac{62{,}500}{25} = \dfrac{25r}{25}$
    $2500 = r$

13. $m = \dfrac{a+b}{2}$
    $\dfrac{55}{1} = \dfrac{27+b}{2}$
    $55(2) = 27 + b$
    $110 = 27 + b$
    $110 - 27 = 27 - 27 + b$
    $83 = b$

14. $z = \dfrac{x - \mu}{\sigma}$
    $z = \dfrac{100 - 110}{5}$
    $z = \dfrac{-10}{5} = -2$

15. $z = \dfrac{x - \mu}{\sigma}$
    $\dfrac{2.5}{1} = \dfrac{42.1 - \mu}{2}$
    $2.5(2) = 42.1 - \mu$
    $5 = 42.1 - \mu$
    $5 - 42.1 = 42.1 - 42.1 - \mu$
    $-37.1 = -\mu$
    $\dfrac{-37.1}{-1} = \dfrac{-\mu}{-1}$
    $37.1 = \mu$

16. $S = B + \dfrac{1}{2} Ps$
    $300 = 100 + \dfrac{1}{2} P(10)$
    $300 = 100 + 5P$
    $300 - 100 = 100 - 100 + 5P$
    $200 = 5P$
    $\dfrac{200}{5} = \dfrac{5P}{5}$
    $40 = P$

17.
$$T = \frac{PV}{k}$$
$$\frac{80}{1} = \frac{P(20)}{0.5}$$
$$80(0.5) = 20P$$
$$40 = 20P$$
$$\frac{40}{20} = \frac{20P}{20}$$
$$2 = P$$

18.
$$m = \frac{a+b+c}{3}$$
$$70 = \frac{a+60+90}{3}$$
$$\frac{70}{1} = \frac{a+150}{3}$$
$$70(3) = a+150$$
$$210 = a+150$$
$$210-150 = a+150-150$$
$$60 = a$$

19.
$$A = P(1+rt)$$
$$3600 = P(1+0.04(5))$$
$$3600 = P(1+0.2)$$
$$3600 = 1.2P$$
$$\frac{3600}{1.2} = \frac{1.2P}{1.2}$$
$$3000 = P$$

20.
$$V = \frac{4}{3}\pi r^2 h$$
$$1846.32 = \frac{4}{3}(3.14)(7)^2 h$$
$$\frac{1846.32}{1} = \frac{615.44h}{3}$$
$$1846.32(3) = 615.44h$$
$$5538.96 = 615.44h$$
$$\frac{5538.96}{615.44} = \frac{615.44h}{615.44}$$
$$9 = h$$

21.
$$V = \frac{1}{2}at^2$$
$$576 = \frac{1}{2}a(12)^2$$
$$\frac{576}{1} = \frac{144a}{2}$$
$$576(2) = 144a$$
$$1152 = 144a$$
$$\frac{1152}{144} = \frac{144a}{144}$$
$$8 = a$$

22.
$$F = \frac{9}{5}C + 32$$
$$F = \frac{9}{5}(7) + 32$$
$$F = \frac{63}{5} + 32 = 12.6 + 32 = 44.6$$

23.
$$C = \frac{5}{9}(F-32)$$
$$C = \frac{5}{9}(77-32)$$
$$C = \frac{5}{9}(45) = 25$$

24.
$$K = \frac{F-32}{1.8} + 273.1$$
$$K = \frac{100-32}{1.8} + 273.1$$
$$K = \frac{68}{1.8} + 273.1$$
$$K = 37.\overline{7} + 273.1 = 310.8\overline{7} \approx 310.88$$

25.
$$z = \frac{\bar{x} - \mu}{\frac{\sigma}{\sqrt{n}}}$$

$$z = \frac{66 - 60}{\frac{15}{\sqrt{25}}}$$

$$z = \frac{6}{\frac{15}{5}} = \frac{6}{3} = 2$$

26.
$$m = \frac{y_2 - y_1}{x_2 - x_1}$$

$$m = \frac{8 - (-4)}{-3 - (-5)}$$

$$m = \frac{8 + 4}{-3 + 5} = \frac{12}{2} = 6$$

27.
$$S = R - rR$$
$$186 = 1R - 0.07R$$
$$186 = 0.93R$$
$$\frac{186}{0.93} = \frac{0.93R}{0.93}$$
$$200 = R$$

28.
$$S = C + rC$$
$$115 = 1C + 0.15C$$
$$115 = 1.15C$$
$$\frac{115}{1.15} = \frac{1.15C}{1.15}$$
$$100 = C$$

29.
$$E = a_1 p_1 + a_2 p_2 + a_3 p_3$$
$$E = 5(0.2) + 7(0.6) + 10(0.2)$$
$$E = 1 + 4.2 + 2 = 7.2$$

30.
$$x = \frac{-b + \sqrt{b^2 - 4ac}}{2a}$$

$$x = \frac{-(-5) + \sqrt{(-5)^2 - 4(2)(-12)}}{2(2)}$$

$$x = \frac{5 + \sqrt{25 + 96}}{4}$$

$$x = \frac{5 + \sqrt{121}}{4} = \frac{5 + 11}{4} = \frac{16}{4} = 4$$

31.
$$x = \frac{-b - \sqrt{b^2 - 4ac}}{2a}$$

$$x = \frac{-(-5) - \sqrt{(-5)^2 - 4(2)(-12)}}{2(2)}$$

$$x = \frac{5 - \sqrt{25 + 96}}{4}$$

$$x = \frac{5 - \sqrt{121}}{4} = \frac{5 - 11}{4} = \frac{-6}{4} = -\frac{3}{2}$$

32.
$$R = O + (V - D)r$$
$$670 = O + (100 - 10)(4)$$
$$670 = O + 360$$
$$670 - 360 = O + 360 - 360$$
$$310 = O$$

33.
$$P = \frac{f}{1 + i}$$

$$3000 = \frac{f}{1 + 0.08}$$

$$\frac{3000}{1} = \frac{f}{1.08}$$

$$3000(1.08) = f$$

$$3240 = f$$

34.
$$V = \sqrt{V_x^2 + V_y^2}$$

$$V = \sqrt{(3)^2 + (4)^2}$$

$$V = \sqrt{9 + 16} = \sqrt{25} = 5$$

35. $F = \dfrac{Gm_1m_2}{r^2}$

$625 = \dfrac{G(100)(200)}{(4)^2}$

$625 = 1250G$

$\dfrac{625}{1250} = \dfrac{1250G}{1250}$

$0.5 = G$

36. $P = \dfrac{nRT}{V}$

$12 = \dfrac{(10)(60)(8)}{V}$

$\dfrac{12}{1} = \dfrac{4800}{V}$

$12V = 4800$

$\dfrac{12V}{12} = \dfrac{4800}{12}$

$V = 400$

37. $S_n = \dfrac{a_1\left(1-r^n\right)}{1-r}$

$S_n = \dfrac{8\left(1-\left(\dfrac{1}{2}\right)^3\right)}{1-\dfrac{1}{2}}$

$S_n = \dfrac{8\left(1-\dfrac{1}{8}\right)}{1-\dfrac{1}{2}}$

$S_n = \dfrac{8\left(\dfrac{7}{8}\right)}{\dfrac{1}{2}} = \dfrac{7}{\dfrac{1}{2}} = 7(2) = 14$

38. $A = P\left(1+\dfrac{r}{n}\right)^{nt}$

$A = 100\left(1+\dfrac{0.06}{1}\right)^{1(3)}$

$A = 100(1+0.06)^3$

$A = 100(1.06)^3$

$A = 100(1.191016)$

$A = 119.1016 \approx 119.10$

39.

$7x - 6y = 15$

$-7x + 7x - 6y = -7x + 15$ Subtract $7x$ from both sides of the equation

$-6y = -7x + 15$

$\dfrac{-6y}{-6} = \dfrac{-7x+15}{-6}$ Divide both sides of the equation by -6

$y = \dfrac{7x-15}{6} = \dfrac{7}{6}x - \dfrac{5}{2}$

40.

$4x - 3y = 21$

$-4x + 4x - 3y = -4x + 21$ Subtract $4x$ from both sides of the equation

$-3y = -4x + 21$

$\dfrac{-3y}{-3} = \dfrac{-4x+21}{-3}$ Divide both sides of the equation by -3

$y = \dfrac{4x-21}{3} = \dfrac{4}{3}x - 7$

41. $\qquad 4x + 7y = 14$

$-4x + 4x + 7y = -4x + 14$ Subtract $4x$ from both sides of the equation

$\qquad 7y = -4x + 14$

$$\frac{7y}{7} = \frac{-4x + 14}{7}$$ Divide both sides of the equation by 7

$$y = \frac{-4x + 14}{7} = -\frac{4}{7}x + 2$$

42. $\qquad -2x + 4y = 9$

$-2x + 2x + 4y = 2x + 9$ Add $2x$ to both sides of the equation

$\qquad 4y = 2x + 9$

$$\frac{4y}{4} = \frac{2x + 9}{4}$$ Divide both sides of the equation by 4

$$y = \frac{2x + 9}{4} = \frac{1}{2}x + \frac{9}{4}$$

43. $\qquad 2x - 3y + 6 = 0$

$2x - 3y + 6 - 6 = 0 - 6$ Subtract 6 from both sides of the equation

$\qquad 2x - 3y = -6$

$-2x + 2x - 3y = -2x - 6$ Subtract $2x$ from both sides of the equation

$\qquad -3y = -2x - 6$

$$\frac{-3y}{-3} = \frac{-2x - 6}{-3}$$ Divide both sides of the equation by -3

$$y = \frac{-2x - 6}{-3} = \frac{2x + 6}{3} = \frac{2}{3}x + 2$$

44. $\qquad 3x + 4y = 0$

$-3x + 3x + 4y = -3x + 0$ Subtract $3x$ from both sides of the equation

$\qquad 4y = -3x$

$$\frac{4y}{4} = \frac{-3x}{4}$$ Divide both sides of the equation by 4

$$y = -\frac{3}{4}x$$

45. $\qquad -3x - 2y = 20$

$-3x + 3x - 2y = 3x + 20$ Add $3x$ to both sides of the equation

$\qquad -2y = 3x + 20$

$$\frac{-2y}{-2} = \frac{3x + 20}{-2}$$ Divide both sides of the equation by -2

$$y = \frac{3x + 20}{-2} = -\frac{3}{2}x - 10$$

46. $3x + 5y - z = 11$

$-3x + 3x + 5y - z = -3x + 11$ Subtract $3x$ from both sides of the equation

$5y - z = -3x + 11$

$5y - z + z = -3x + z + 11$ Add z to both sides of the equation

$5y = -3x + z + 11$

$\dfrac{5y}{5} = \dfrac{-3x + z + 11}{5}$ Divide both sides of the equation by 5

$y = \dfrac{-3x + z + 11}{5} = -\dfrac{3}{5}x + \dfrac{1}{5}z + \dfrac{11}{5}$

47. $9x + 4z = 7 + 8y$

$9x + 4z - 7 = 7 - 7 + 8y$ Subtract 7 from both sides of the equation

$9x + 4z - 7 = 8y$

$\dfrac{9x + 4z - 7}{8} = \dfrac{8y}{8}$ Divide both sides of the equation by 8

$y = \dfrac{9x + 4z - 7}{8} = \dfrac{9}{8}x + \dfrac{1}{2}z - \dfrac{7}{8}$

48. $2x - 3y + 5z = 0$

$2x - 3y + 3y + 5z = 0 + 3y$ Add $3y$ to both sides of the equation

$2x + 5z = 3y$

$\dfrac{2x + 5z}{3} = \dfrac{3y}{3}$ Divide both sides of the equation by 3

$y = \dfrac{2x + 5z}{3} = \dfrac{2}{3}x + \dfrac{5}{3}z$

49. $A = bh$

$\dfrac{A}{h} = \dfrac{bh}{h}$ Divide both sides of the equation by h

$b = \dfrac{A}{h}$

50. $E = IR$

$\dfrac{E}{I} = \dfrac{IR}{I}$ Divide both sides of the equation by I

$R = \dfrac{E}{I}$

51. $p = a + b + c$

$p - b = a + b - b + c$ Subtract b from both sides of the equation

$p - b = a + c$

$p - b - c = a + c - c$ Subtract c from both sides of the equation

$a = p - b - c$

52.

$$p = a + b + s_1 + s_2$$

$$p - a = a - a + b + s_1 + s_2 \qquad \text{Subtract } a \text{ from both sides of the equation}$$

$$p - a = b + s_1 + s_2$$

$$p - a - b = b - b + s_1 + s_2 \qquad \text{Subtract } b \text{ from both sides of the equation}$$

$$p - a - b = s_1 + s_2$$

$$p - a - b - s_2 = s_1 + s_2 - s_2 \qquad \text{Subtract } s_2 \text{ from both sides of the equation}$$

$$s_1 = p - a - b - s_2$$

53. $V = lwh$

$$\frac{V}{l} = \frac{lwh}{l} \qquad \text{Divide both sides of the equation by } l$$

$$\frac{V}{l} = wh$$

$$\frac{V}{lh} = \frac{wh}{h} \qquad \text{Divide both sides of the equation by } h$$

$$w = \frac{V}{lh}$$

54. $p = irt$

$$\frac{p}{i} = \frac{irt}{i} \qquad \text{Divide both sides of the equation by } i$$

$$\frac{p}{i} = rt$$

$$\frac{p}{ir} = \frac{rt}{r} \qquad \text{Divide both sides of the equation by } r$$

$$t = \frac{p}{ir}$$

55. $C = 2\pi r$

$$\frac{C}{2} = \frac{2\pi r}{2} \qquad \text{Divide both sides of the equation by } 2$$

$$\frac{C}{2} = \pi r$$

$$\frac{C}{2\pi} = \frac{\pi r}{\pi} \qquad \text{Divide both sides of the equation by } \pi$$

$$r = \frac{C}{2\pi}$$

56. $PV = KT$

$$\frac{PV}{K} = \frac{KT}{K} \qquad \text{Divide both sides of the equation by } K$$

$$T = \frac{PV}{K}$$

57.

$$y = mx + b$$

$$y - mx = mx - mx + b \qquad \text{Subtract } mx \text{ from both sides of the equation}$$

$$b = y - mx$$

58.
$$y = mx + b$$
$$y - b = mx + b - b \qquad \text{Subtract } b \text{ from both sides of the equation}$$
$$y - b = mx$$
$$\frac{y - b}{x} = \frac{mx}{x} \qquad \text{Divide both sides of the equation by } x$$
$$m = \frac{y - b}{x}$$

59.
$$P = 2l + 2w$$
$$P - 2l = 2l - 2l + 2w \qquad \text{Subtract } 2l \text{ from both sides of the equation}$$
$$P - 2l = 2w$$
$$\frac{P - 2l}{2} = \frac{2w}{2} \qquad \text{Divide both sides of the equation by } 2$$
$$w = \frac{P - 2l}{2}$$

60.
$$A = \frac{d_1 d_2}{2}$$
$$2A = 2\left(\frac{d_1 d_2}{2}\right) \qquad \text{Multiply both sides of the equation by } 2$$
$$2A = d_1 d_2$$
$$\frac{2A}{d_1} = \frac{d_1 d_2}{d_1} \qquad \text{Divide both sides of the equation by } d_1$$
$$d_2 = \frac{2A}{d_1}$$

61.
$$A = \frac{a + b + c}{3}$$
$$3A = 3\left(\frac{a + b + c}{3}\right) \qquad \text{Multiply both sides of the equation by } 3$$
$$3A = a + b + c$$
$$3A - a = a - a + b + c \qquad \text{Subtract } a \text{ from both sides of the equation}$$
$$3A - a = b + c$$
$$3A - a - b = b - b + c \qquad \text{Subtract } b \text{ from both sides of the equation}$$
$$c = 3A - a - b$$

62.
$$A = \frac{1}{2}bh$$
$$2A = 2\left(\frac{1}{2}bh\right) \qquad \text{Multiply both sides of the equation by } 2$$
$$2A = bh$$
$$\frac{2A}{h} = \frac{bh}{h} \qquad \text{Divide both sides of the equation by } h$$
$$b = \frac{2A}{h}$$

63. $P = \dfrac{KT}{V}$

$PV = \left(\dfrac{KT}{V}\right)V$ Multiply both sides of the equation by V

$PV = KT$

$\dfrac{PV}{K} = \dfrac{KT}{K}$ Divide both sides of the equation by K

$T = \dfrac{PV}{K}$

64. $V = \dfrac{1}{3}lwh$

$3V = 3\left(\dfrac{1}{3}lwh\right)$ Multiply both sides of the equation by 3

$3V = lwh$

$\dfrac{3V}{l} = \dfrac{lwh}{l}$ Divide both sides of the equation by l

$\dfrac{3V}{l} = wh$

$\dfrac{3V}{lh} = \dfrac{wh}{h}$ Divide both sides of the equation by h

$w = \dfrac{3V}{lh}$

65. $F = \dfrac{9}{5}C + 32$

$F - 32 = \dfrac{9}{5}C + 32 - 32$ Subtract 32 from both sides of the equation

$F - 32 = \dfrac{9}{5}C$

$\dfrac{5}{9}(F - 32) = \dfrac{5}{9}\left(\dfrac{9}{5}C\right)$ Multiply both sides of the equation by $\dfrac{5}{9}$

$C = \dfrac{5}{9}(F - 32)$

66. $C = \dfrac{5}{9}(F - 32)$

$\dfrac{9}{5}C = \dfrac{9}{5}\left(\dfrac{5}{9}\right)(F - 32)$ Multiply both sides of the equation by $\dfrac{9}{5}$

$\dfrac{9}{5}C = F - 32$

$\dfrac{9}{5}C + 32 = F - 32 + 32$ Add 32 to both sides of the equation

$F = \dfrac{9}{5}C + 32$

67.
$$S = \pi r^2 + \pi rs$$

$$S - \pi r^2 = \pi r^2 - \pi r^2 + \pi rs$$ Subtract πr^2 from both sides of the equation

$$S - \pi r^2 = \pi rs$$

$$\frac{S - \pi r^2}{\pi} = \frac{\pi rs}{\pi}$$ Divide both sides of the equation by π

$$\frac{S - \pi r^2}{\pi} = rs$$

$$\frac{S - \pi r^2}{\pi r} = \frac{rs}{r}$$ Divide both sides of the equation by r

$$s = \frac{S - \pi r^2}{\pi r}$$

68.
$$a_n = a_1 + (n-1)d$$

$$a_n = a_1 + nd - d$$ Distributive Property

$$a_n - a_1 = a_1 - a_1 + nd - d$$ Subtract a_1 from both sides of the equation

$$a_n - a_1 = nd - d$$

$$a_n - a_1 + d = nd - d + d$$ Add d to both sides of the equation

$$a_n - a_1 + d = nd$$

$$\frac{a_n - a_1 + d}{d} = \frac{nd}{d}$$ Divide both sides of the equation by d

$$n = \frac{a_n - a_1 + d}{d}$$

69. a) $i = prt$

        $i = 3500(0.03)(1) = \$105$

    b) $\$3500 + \$105 = \$3605$

70. $i = prt$

        $128 = 800(r)(2)$

        $128 = 1600r$

        $\dfrac{128}{1600} = \dfrac{1600r}{1600}$

        $r = 0.08 = 8\%$

71.   Radius $= \dfrac{2.5}{2} = 1.25 \ in.$

     $V = \pi r^2 h$

     $V = \pi(1.25)^2 (3.75)$

     $V = \pi(1.5625)(3.75)$

     $V = 18.40776945 \ in.^3 \approx 18.41 \ in.^3$

72. $A = P(1+r)^n$

     $A = 10,000(1 + 0.02)^{24}$

     $A = 10,000(1.02)^{24}$

     $A = 10,000(1.608437249)$

     $A = \$16,084.37249 \approx \$16,084.37$

73. $P = P_0 2^{-t/5600}$

$P = (20)2^{-500/5600}$

$P = (20)2^{-0.0892857143}$

$P = (20)(0.9399880269)$

$P = 18.79976054 \ mg. \approx 18.8 \ mg.$

74. $P_n = P(1+r)^n$

$P_n = 8(1+0.03)^{10}$

$P_n = 8(1.03)^{10}$

$P_n = 8(1.343916379)$

$P_n = \$10.75133103 \approx \$10.75$

75. $V = 24e^{0.08t}$

$V = 24e^{0.08(374)}$

$V = 24e^{29.92}$

$V = \$236,756,624,900,000$

76. $S = S_0 e^{-0.028t}$

$S = 1000e^{-0.028(30)}$

$S = 1000e^{-0.84}$

$S = 1000(0.4317105234)$

$S = 431.7105234 \ g. \approx 431.71 \ g.$

77. $V = lwh - \pi r^2 h$

$V = 12(8)(12) - \pi(2)^2(8)$

$V = 1152 - 100.5309649$

$V = 1051.469035 \ in.^3 \approx 1051.47 \ in.^3$

78. $2 \ hrs. \ 9 \ mins. \ 52 \ secs. = 2 \ hrs. + \dfrac{9}{60} \ hrs. + \dfrac{52}{3600} \ hrs.$

$= 2 \ hrs. + 0.15 \ hrs + 0.01\overline{4} \ hrs.$

$= 2.16\overline{4} \ hrs.$

$d = rt$

$26.2 = r(2.16\overline{4})$

$\dfrac{26.2}{2.16\overline{4}} = \dfrac{r(2.16\overline{4})}{2.16\overline{4}}$

$r = 12.1047228 \ mph \approx 12.10 \ mph$

Exercise Set 6.4

1. A **mathematical expression** is a collection of variables, numbers, parentheses and operation symbols. An **equation** is two algebraic expressions joined by an equals sign.

2. Expression: $2x + 3y$; equation: $2x + 3y = 16$

3. $9 - 6x$

4. $3x + 7$

5. $6r + 5$

6. $10s - 13$

7. $15 - 2r$

8. $2m + 9$

9. $x + 6$

10. $8 + 5x$

11. $\dfrac{3+n}{8}$

12. $\dfrac{15-t}{4}$

13. $(5y - 6) + 3$

14. $\dfrac{8}{y} - 3x$

15. Let $x =$ the number
$x + 7 =$ the sum of the number and 7
$x + 7 = 19$
$x + 7 - 7 = 19 - 7$
$x = 12$

16. Let $x =$ the number
$x - 9 =$ the number decreased by 9
$x - 9 = 5$
$x - 9 + 9 = 5 + 9$
$x = 14$

17. Let $x =$ the number
$x - 10 =$ the number decreased by 10
$$x - 10 = 25$$
$$x - 10 + 10 = 25 + 10$$
$$x = 35$$

18. Let $x =$ the number
$7x =$ the number multiplied by 7
$$7x = 42$$
$$\frac{7x}{7} = \frac{42}{7}$$
$$x = 6$$

19. Let $x =$ the number
$12 + 5x = 12$ increased by 5 times the number
$$12 + 5x = 47$$
$$12 - 12 + 5x = 47 - 12$$
$$5x = 35$$
$$\frac{5x}{5} = \frac{35}{5}$$
$$x = 7$$

20. Let $x =$ the number
$4x - 10 = 4$ times the number decreased by 10
$$4x - 10 = 42$$
$$4x - 10 + 10 = 42 + 10$$
$$4x = 52$$
$$\frac{4x}{4} = \frac{52}{4}$$
$$x = 13$$

21. Let $x =$ the number
$8x + 16 = 16$ more than 8 times the number
$$8x + 16 = 88$$
$$8x + 16 - 16 = 88 - 16$$
$$8x = 72$$
$$\frac{8x}{8} = \frac{72}{8}$$
$$x = 9$$

22. Let $x =$ the number
$5x + 6 = 6$ more than 5 times the number
$7x - 18 = 7$ times the number decreased by 18
$$5x + 6 = 7x - 18$$
$$5x - 7x + 6 = 7x - 7x - 18$$
$$-2x + 6 = -18$$
$$-2x + 6 - 6 = -18 - 6$$
$$-2x = -24$$
$$\frac{-2x}{-2} = \frac{-24}{-2}$$
$$x = 12$$

23. Let $x =$ the number
$x + 11 =$ the number increased by 11
$3x + 1 = 1$ more than 3 times the number
$$x + 11 = 3x + 1$$
$$x - x + 11 = 3x - x + 1$$
$$11 = 2x + 1$$
$$11 - 1 = 2x + 1 - 1$$
$$10 = 2x$$
$$\frac{10}{2} = \frac{2x}{2}$$
$$5 = x$$

24. Let $x =$ the number
$\dfrac{x}{3} =$ the number divided by 3
$x - 4 = 4$ less than the number
$$\frac{x}{3} = x - 4$$
$$3\left(\frac{x}{3}\right) = 3(x - 4)$$
$$x = 3x - 12$$
$$x - 3x = 3x - 3x - 12$$
$$-2x = -12$$
$$\frac{-2x}{-2} = \frac{-12}{-2}$$
$$x = 6$$

25. Let $x =$ the number
$x+3 = 3$ more than the number
$5(x+7) = 5$ times the sum of the number and 7

$$x+3 = 5(x+7)$$
$$x+3 = 5x+35$$
$$x-x+3 = 5x-x+35$$
$$3 = 4x+35$$
$$3-35 = 4x+35-35$$
$$-32 = 4x$$
$$\frac{-32}{4} = \frac{4x}{4}$$
$$-8 = x$$

26. Let $x =$ the number
$3x =$ the product of 3 and the number
$3x-4 =$ the product of 3 and the number, decreased by 4
$4x = 4$ times the number

$$3x-4 = 4x$$
$$3x-3x-4 = 4x-3x$$
$$-4 = x$$

27. Let $x =$ amount invested in mutual funds
$2x =$ amount invested in bonds

$$x+2x = 9000$$
$$3x = 9000$$
$$\frac{3x}{3} = \frac{9000}{3}$$
$$x = \$3000 \text{ in mutual funds}$$
$$2x = 2(3000) = \$6000 \text{ in bonds}$$

28. Let $x =$ cost of cheaper pair
$x+10 =$ cost of more expensive pair

$$x+(x+10) = 60$$
$$2x+10 = 60$$
$$2x+10-10 = 60-10$$
$$2x = 50$$
$$\frac{2x}{2} = \frac{50}{2}$$
$$x = \$25 \text{ for the cheaper pair}$$
$$x+10 = 25+10 = \$35 \text{ for the more expensive pair}$$

29. Let $x =$ number of years until the population reaches $12{,}200$
$500x =$ the amount the population increases by each year

$$6200+500x = 12{,}200$$
$$6200-6200+500x = 12{,}200-6200$$
$$500x = 6000$$
$$\frac{500x}{500} = \frac{6000}{500}$$
$$x = 12 \text{ years}$$

30. Let $x =$ the total Vito will need to spend
$0.08x =$ the amount saved on spending x dollars

$$0.08x = 80$$
$$\frac{0.08x}{0.08} = \frac{80}{0.08}$$
$$x = \$1000$$

31. Let $x =$ the original price before tax
$0.10x =$ amount saved on spending x dollars

$$x-0.10x = 15.72$$
$$0.9x = 15.72$$
$$\frac{0.9x}{0.9} = \frac{15.72}{0.9}$$
$$x \approx \$17.47$$

32. Let $x =$ the number of copies Ronnie must make
$0.08x =$ the amount spent on x copies

$$0.08x = 250$$
$$\frac{0.08x}{0.08} = \frac{250}{0.08}$$
$$x = 3125 \text{ copies}$$

33. Let $x =$ number of discs for Samantha
$3x =$ number of discs for Josie
$$x + 3x = 12$$
$$4x = 12$$
$$\frac{4x}{4} = \frac{12}{4}$$
$$x = 3 \text{ discs for Samantha}$$
$$3x = 3(3) = 9 \text{ discs for Josie}$$

34. Let $x =$ the amount of cardboard
$3x =$ the amount of newspaper
$$x + 3x = 28$$
$$4x = 28$$
$$\frac{4x}{4} = \frac{28}{4}$$
$$x = 7 \text{ tons of cardboard}$$
$$3x = 3(7) = 21 \text{ tons of newspaper}$$

35. Let $x =$ the number of miles traveled
$0.20x =$ the amount spent for x miles at $\$.20$ per mile
$$60 + 0.20x = 100$$
$$60 - 60 + 0.20x = 100 - 60$$
$$0.20x = 40$$
$$\frac{0.20x}{0.20} = \frac{40}{0.20}$$
$$x = 200 \text{ miles}$$

36. Let $w =$ the width
$w + 3 =$ the length
$$2w + 2(w + 3) = P$$
$$2w + 2(w + 3) = 54$$
$$2w + 2w + 6 = 54$$
$$4w + 6 = 54$$
$$4w + 6 - 6 = 54 - 6$$
$$4w = 48$$
$$\frac{4w}{4} = \frac{48}{4}$$
width $= 12$ ft.
length $= w + 3 = 12 + 3 = 15$ ft.

37. a) Let $x =$ area of smaller ones
$3x =$ area of largest one
$$x + x + 3x = 45,000$$
$$5x = 45,000$$
$$\frac{5x}{5} = \frac{45,000}{5}$$
$$x = 9000 \ ft.^2 \text{ for the two smaller barns}$$
$$3x = 3(9000) = 27,000 \ ft.^2 \text{ for the largest barn}$$
   b) Yes

38. Let $x =$ the hourly rate
$40x =$ the amount paid for 40 hours
$1.5x =$ the hourly amount paid for overtime
$$40x + 1.5x(15) = 500$$
$$40x + 22.5x = 500$$
$$62.5x = 500$$
$$\frac{62.5x}{62.5} = \frac{500}{62.5}$$
$$x = \$8$$

39. Let $x =$ the weight on Earth
$\dfrac{1}{6}x =$ the weight on the moon
$$x + \frac{1}{6}x = 203$$
$$\frac{7}{6}x = 203$$
$$\frac{6}{7}\left(\frac{7}{6}x\right) = \frac{6}{7}(203)$$
$$x = 174 \text{ lbs. on Earth}$$

40. Let $x =$ the cost of the car before tax
$0.05x = 5\%$ of the cost of the car (tax)
$$x + 0.05x = 14{,}512$$
$$1.05x = 14{,}512$$
$$\frac{1.05x}{1.05} = \frac{14{,}512}{1.05}$$
$$x = \$13{,}820.95238 \approx \$13{,}820.95$$

41. Let $w =$ width
     $2w =$ length of entire enclosed region
     $3w + 2(2w) =$ total amount of fencing
     $3w + 2(2w) = 140$
     $\quad 3w + 4w = 140$
     $\qquad 7w = 140$
     $\qquad \dfrac{7w}{7} = \dfrac{140}{7}$
     width $= 20$ ft., length $= 2w = 2(20) = 40$ ft.

42. Let $l =$ length of a shelf
     $l + 2 =$ height of the bookcase
     $4l + 2(l + 2) =$ total amount of wood
     $4l + 2(l + 2) = 32$
     $\quad 4l + 2l + 4 = 32$
     $\qquad 6l + 4 = 32$
     $\quad 6l + 4 - 4 = 32 - 4$
     $\qquad 6l = 28$
     $\qquad \dfrac{6l}{6} = \dfrac{28}{6}$
     length $= 4\dfrac{4}{6} = 4\dfrac{2}{3}$ ft. $= 4$ ft. 8 in.
     height $= l + 2 = 4$ ft. 8 in. $+ 2$ ft. $= 6$ ft. 8 in.

43. Let $x =$ the number of months
     $70x =$ cost of laundry for x months
     $70x = 760$
     $\dfrac{70x}{70} = \dfrac{760}{70}$
     $\quad x = 10.85714286$ months ≈ 11 months

44. Let $x =$ number of visits per month
     $56 =$ cost of Plan A for 1 month
     $20 + 3x =$ cost of Plan B for 1 month
     $56 = 20 + 3x$
     $56 - 20 = 20 - 20 + 3x$
     $\quad 36 = 3x$
     $\quad \dfrac{36}{3} = \dfrac{3x}{3}$
     $\qquad x = 12$ visits per month

45. Let $x =$ regular fare
     $0.50x =$ half off regular fare
     $0.07x =$ tax on regular fare
     $0.50x + 0.07x = 227$
     $\qquad 0.57x = 227$
     $\qquad \dfrac{0.57x}{0.57} = \dfrac{227}{0.57}$
     $x = \$398.245614 \approx \$398.25$ regular fare
     regular fare including tax:
     $\$398.25 + 0.07(\$398.25)$
     $= \$398.25 + \$27.88 = \$426.13$

46. Let $x =$ number of miles in one day
     $35 + 0.20x =$ U-Haul charge per day
     $25 + 0.32x =$ Ryder charge per day
     $\quad 35 + 0.20x = 25 + 0.32x$
     $35 + 0.20x - 25 = 25 - 25 + 0.32x$
     $\quad 10 + 0.20x = 0.32x$
     $10 + 0.20x - 0.20x = 0.32x - 0.20x$
     $\qquad 10 = 0.12x$
     $\qquad \dfrac{10}{0.12} = \dfrac{0.12x}{0.12}$
     $\qquad x = 83.\overline{3}$ miles $= 83\dfrac{1}{3}$ miles

47. Let $x =$ amount of tax reduction to be deducted from Mr. McAdam's income
$3640 - x =$ amount of tax reduction to be deducted from Mrs. McAdam's income
$$24{,}200 - x = 26{,}400 - (3640 - x)$$
$$24{,}200 - x = 26{,}400 - 3640 + x$$
$$24{,}200 - x = 22{,}760 + x$$
$$24{,}200 - x + x = 22{,}760 + x + x$$
$$24{,}200 = 22{,}760 + 2x$$
$$24{,}200 - 22{,}760 = 22{,}760 - 22{,}760 + 2x$$
$$1440 = 2x$$
$$\frac{1440}{2} = \frac{2x}{2}$$
$x = \$720$ deducted from Mr. McAdam's income
$3640 - x = 3640 - 720 = \$2920$ deducted from Mrs. McAdam's income

48. a) A number increased by 3 is 13.
    b) 3 times a number increased by 5 is 8.
    c) 3 times a number decreased by 8 is 7.

49. Let $x =$ the first integer
$x + 1 =$ the second integer
$x + 2 =$ the third integer (the largest)
$$x + (x + 1) + (x + 2) = 3(x + 2) - 3$$
$$3x + 3 = 3x + 6 - 3$$
$$3x + 3 = 3x + 3$$

50. a) Let $x =$ number of years for the amount saved to equal the price of the course
$0.10(600) = \$60$ saved per year
$$60x = 45$$
$$\frac{60x}{60} = \frac{45}{60}$$
$$x = \frac{3}{4} \text{ year} = \frac{3}{4}(12) = 9 \text{ months}$$
b) $25 - 18 = 7$ years
$7(60) = \$420$ saved before paying for course
$\$420 - \$45 = \$375$ total savings

Exercise Set 6.5

1. **Direct variation -** As one variable increases, so does the other, and as one variable decreases, so does the other.
2. **Inverse variation -** As one variable increases, the other decreases and vice-versa.
3. **Joint variation -** One quantity varies directly as the product of two or more other quantities.
4. **Combined variation -** uses at least two forms of variation

5. Inverse
6. Direct
7. Direct
8. Direct
9. Direct
10. Direct
11. Inverse
12. Direct
13. Inverse
14. Direct
15. Inverse
16. Inverse
17. Direct
18. Inverse
19. Direct
20. Inverse

21. Answers will vary.
22. Answers will vary.
23. $r = ks$
$r = 3(11) = 33$
24. $C = kZ^2$
$C = 2(5)^2 = 2(25) = 50$

25. $y = \dfrac{k}{x^2}$

$y = \dfrac{320}{(8)^2} = \dfrac{320}{64} = 5$

26. $x = \dfrac{k}{y}$

$x = \dfrac{5}{25} = 0.2$

27. $R = \dfrac{k}{W}$

$R = \dfrac{8}{160} = 0.05$

28. $D = \dfrac{kJ}{C}$

$D = \dfrac{5(10)}{25} = \dfrac{50}{25} = 2$

29. $F = kDE$
$F = 7(3)(10) = 210$

30. $A = \dfrac{kR_1R_2}{L^2}$

$A = \dfrac{\frac{3}{2}(120)(8)}{(5)^2} = \dfrac{(1.5)(120)(8)}{25} = \dfrac{1440}{25} = 57.6$

31. $T = \dfrac{kD^2}{F}$

$T = \dfrac{12(8)^2}{15} = \dfrac{12(64)}{15} = \dfrac{768}{15} = 51.2$

32. $x = kyz$
$72 = k(18)(2)$
$72 = 36k$
$\dfrac{72}{36} = \dfrac{36k}{36}$
$k = 2$
$x = 2yz$
$x = 2(36)(1) = 72$

33. $Z = kWY$
$12 = k(9)(4)$
$12 = 36k$
$\dfrac{12}{36} = \dfrac{36k}{36}$
$k = \dfrac{1}{3}$
$Z = \dfrac{1}{3}WY$
$Z = \dfrac{1}{3}(50)(6) = \dfrac{300}{3} = 100$

34. $y = kR^2$
$4 = k(4)^2$
$4 = 16k$
$\dfrac{4}{16} = \dfrac{16k}{16}$
$k = 0.25$
$y = 0.25R^2$
$y = 0.25(8)^2 = 0.25(64) = 16$

35. $H = kL$
$15 = k(50)$
$\dfrac{15}{50} = \dfrac{50k}{50}$
$k = 0.3$
$H = 0.3L$
$H = 0.3(10) = 3$

36. $C = \dfrac{k}{J}$

$7 = \dfrac{k}{0.7}$
$k = 7(0.7) = 4.9$
$C = \dfrac{4.9}{J}$
$C = \dfrac{4.9}{12} = 0.408\overline{3} \approx 0.41$

37. $A = kB^2$

$245 = k(7)^2$

$245 = 49k$

$\dfrac{245}{49} = \dfrac{49k}{49}$

$k = 5$

$A = 5B^2$

$A = 5(9)^2 = 5(81) = 405$

38. $F = \dfrac{kM_1 M_2}{d^2}$

$20 = \dfrac{k(5)(10)}{(0.2)^2}$

$20 = \dfrac{50k}{0.04}$

$50k = 0.8$

$k = \dfrac{0.8}{50} = 0.016$

$F = \dfrac{0.016 M_1 M_2}{d^2}$

$F = \dfrac{0.016(10)(20)}{(0.4)^2} = \dfrac{3.2}{0.16} = 20$

39. $F = \dfrac{kq_1 q_2}{d^2}$

$8 = \dfrac{k(2)(8)}{(4)^2}$

$8 = \dfrac{16k}{16}$

$k = 8$

$F = \dfrac{8q_1 q_2}{d^2}$

$F = \dfrac{8(28)(12)}{(2)^2} = \dfrac{2688}{4} = 672$

40. $S = k\,I\,T^2$

$8 = k(20)(4)^2$

$8 = 320k$

$k = \dfrac{8}{320} = 0.025$

$S = 0.025\,I\,T^2$

$S = 0.025(2)(2)^2 = 0.025(2)(4) = 0.2$

41. $F = km$

$256 = k(8)$

$k = \dfrac{256}{8} = 32$

$F = 32m$

$F = 32(50) = 1600$ **newtons**

42. $I = k\,r$

$40 = k(0.04)$

$k = \dfrac{40}{0.04} = 1000$

$I = 1000\,r$

$I = 1000(0.06) = \$60$

43. $l = \dfrac{k}{d^2}$

$20 = \dfrac{k}{(6)^2}$

$k = 20(36) = 720$

$l = \dfrac{720}{d^2}$

$l = \dfrac{720}{(3)^2} = \dfrac{720}{9} = 80$ **dB.**

44. $w = km$

$256 = k(8)$

$k = \dfrac{256}{8} = 32$

$w = 32m$

$120 = 32m$

$m = \dfrac{120}{32} = 3.75$ **slugs**

45. $R = \dfrac{kA}{P}$

$4800 = \dfrac{k(600)}{3}$

$600k = 14{,}400$

$k = \dfrac{14{,}400}{600} = 24$

$R = \dfrac{24A}{P}$

$R = \dfrac{24(700)}{3.50} = \dfrac{16{,}800}{3.50} = 4800\,\text{tapes}$

46. $W = \dfrac{k}{d^2}$

$140 = \dfrac{k}{(4000)^2}$

$k = 140(16{,}000{,}000) = 2{,}240{,}000{,}000$

$W = \dfrac{2{,}240{,}000{,}000}{d^2}$

$W = \dfrac{2{,}240{,}000{,}000}{(4100)^2}$

$W = \dfrac{2{,}240{,}000{,}000}{16{,}810{,}000} = 133.2540155 \approx 133.25\,\text{lbs.}$

47. $W = kI^2 R$

$1 = k(0.1)^2(100)$

$1 = 1k$

$k = \dfrac{1}{1} = 1$

$W = 1I^2 R$

$W = 1(0.4)^2(250) = 0.16(250) = 40\,\text{watts}$

48. $R = \dfrac{kL}{A}$

$0.2 = \dfrac{k(200)}{0.05}$

$200k = 0.01$

$k = \dfrac{0.01}{200} = 0.00005$

$R = \dfrac{0.00005L}{A}$

$R = \dfrac{0.00005(5000)}{0.01} = \dfrac{0.25}{0.01} = 25\,\text{ohms}$

49. $N = \dfrac{kp_1 p_2}{d}$

$100{,}000 = \dfrac{k(60{,}000)(200{,}000)}{300}$

$12{,}000{,}000{,}000k = 30{,}000{,}000$

$k = \dfrac{30{,}000{,}000}{12{,}000{,}000{,}000} = 0.0025$

$N = \dfrac{0.0025 p_1 p_2}{d}$

$N = \dfrac{0.0025(125{,}000)(175{,}000)}{450}$

$N = \dfrac{54{,}687{,}500}{450} = 121{,}527.7778 \approx 121{,}528\,\text{calls}$

50. **a)** $y = kx$

$y = 2x$

$\dfrac{y}{2} = \dfrac{2x}{2}$

$x = \dfrac{y}{2} = 0.5y$

Directly

b) $k = 0.5$

51. a) $y = \dfrac{k}{x}$

$y = \dfrac{0.3}{x}$

$xy = 0.3$

$\dfrac{xy}{y} = \dfrac{0.3}{y}$

$x = \dfrac{0.3}{y}$

Inversely

b) $k = 0.3$

52. $I = \dfrac{k}{d^2}$

$\dfrac{1}{16} = \dfrac{k}{(4)^2}$

$\dfrac{1}{16} = \dfrac{k}{16}$

$k = 1$

$I = \dfrac{1}{d^2}$

$I = \dfrac{1}{(3)^2} = \dfrac{1}{9}$

53. $W = \dfrac{kTA\sqrt{F}}{R}$

$68 = \dfrac{k(78)(1000)\sqrt{4}}{5.6}$

$156{,}000k = 380.8$

$k = \dfrac{380.8}{156{,}000} = 0.0024410256$

$W = \dfrac{0.0024410256TA\sqrt{F}}{R}$

$W = \dfrac{0.0024410256(78)(1500)\sqrt{6}}{5.6}$

$W = \dfrac{699.5742588}{5.6} = 124.9239748 \approx \$124.92$

Exercise Set 6.6

1. $a < b$ means that a is less than b, $a \le b$ means that a is less than or equal to b, $a > b$ means that a is greater than b, $a \ge b$ means that a is greater than or equal to b

2. **a)** An **inequality** consists of two (or more) expressions joined by an inequality sign.
   b) $2 < 7$, $3 > -1$, $5x + 2 \ge 9$

3. When both sides of an inequality are multiplied or divided by a negative number, the direction of the inequality symbol must be reversed.

4. Yes, the inequality symbol points to the -3 in both cases.

5. Yes, the inequality symbol points to the x in both cases.

6. You should use an open circle if the solution does not include the number. You should use a closed circle if the solution includes the number.

7. $x \le 10$

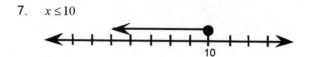

8. $x > 5$

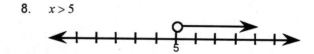

9.
$$x + 5 < 11$$
$$x + 5 - 5 < 11 - 5$$
$$x < 6$$

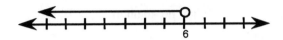

10.
$$5x \geq 15$$
$$\frac{5x}{5} \geq \frac{15}{5}$$
$$x \geq 3$$

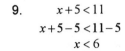

11.
$$-3x \leq 18$$
$$\frac{-3x}{-3} \geq \frac{18}{-3}$$
$$x \geq -6$$

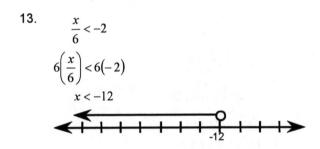

12.
$$-4x < 12$$
$$\frac{-4x}{-4} > \frac{12}{-4}$$
$$x > -3$$

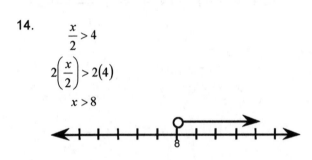

13.
$$\frac{x}{6} < -2$$
$$6\left(\frac{x}{6}\right) < 6(-2)$$
$$x < -12$$

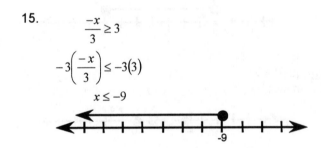

14.
$$\frac{x}{2} > 4$$
$$2\left(\frac{x}{2}\right) > 2(4)$$
$$x > 8$$

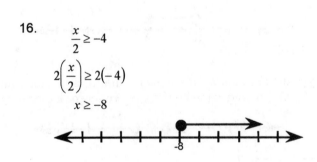

15.
$$\frac{-x}{3} \geq 3$$
$$-3\left(\frac{-x}{3}\right) \leq -3(3)$$
$$x \leq -9$$

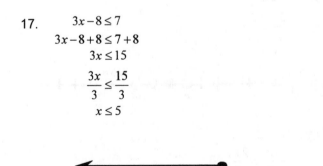

16.
$$\frac{x}{2} \geq -4$$
$$2\left(\frac{x}{2}\right) \geq 2(-4)$$
$$x \geq -8$$

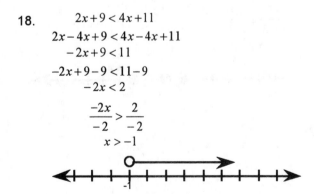

17.
$$3x - 8 \leq 7$$
$$3x - 8 + 8 \leq 7 + 8$$
$$3x \leq 15$$
$$\frac{3x}{3} \leq \frac{15}{3}$$
$$x \leq 5$$

18.
$$2x + 9 < 4x + 11$$
$$2x - 4x + 9 < 4x - 4x + 11$$
$$-2x + 9 < 11$$
$$-2x + 9 - 9 < 11 - 9$$
$$-2x < 2$$
$$\frac{-2x}{-2} > \frac{2}{-2}$$
$$x > -1$$

19. $2(x+6) \leq 15$

$2x + 12 \leq 15$

$2x + 12 - 12 \leq 15 - 12$

$2x \leq 3$

$\dfrac{2x}{2} \leq \dfrac{3}{2}$

$x \leq \dfrac{3}{2}$

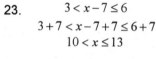

20. $-4(x+2) - 2x > -6x + 2$

$-4x - 8 - 2x > -6x + 2$

$-6x - 8 > -6x + 2$

$-6x + 6x - 8 > -6x + 6x + 2$

$-8 > 2$

False, no solution

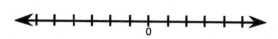

21. $3(x+4) - 2 < 3x + 10$

$3x + 12 - 2 < 3x + 10$

$3x + 10 < 3x + 10$

False, no solution

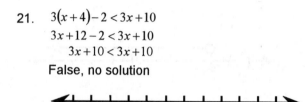

22. $-2 \leq x \leq 1$

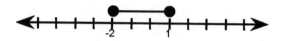

23. $3 < x - 7 \leq 6$

$3 + 7 < x - 7 + 7 \leq 6 + 7$

$10 < x \leq 13$

24. $\dfrac{1}{2} < \dfrac{x+4}{2} \leq 4$

$2\left(\dfrac{1}{2}\right) < 2\left(\dfrac{x+4}{2}\right) \leq 2(4)$

$1 < x + 4 \leq 8$

$1 - 4 < x + 4 - 4 \leq 8 - 4$

$-3 < x \leq 4$

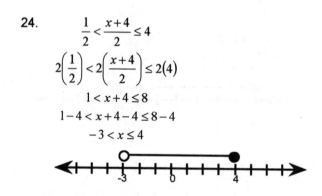

25. $x \geq 3$

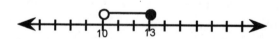

26. $-4 < x$

$x > -4$

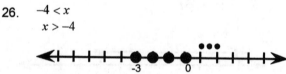

27. $-3x \leq 27$

$\dfrac{-3x}{-3} \geq \dfrac{27}{-3}$

$x \geq -9$

28. $3x \geq 27$

$\dfrac{3x}{3} \geq \dfrac{27}{3}$

$x \geq 9$

29. $x + 3 < 6$

$x + 3 - 3 < 6 - 3$

$x < 3$

30. $-7x \leq 21$

$\dfrac{-7x}{-7} \geq \dfrac{21}{-7}$

$x \geq -3$

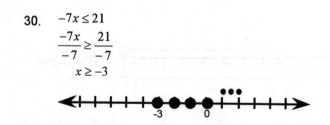

31.
$$\frac{x}{6} < -2$$

$$6\left(\frac{x}{6}\right) < 6(-2)$$

$$x < -12$$

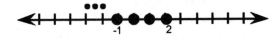

32.
$$\frac{x}{3} > -3$$

$$3\left(\frac{x}{3}\right) > 3(-3)$$

$$x > -9$$

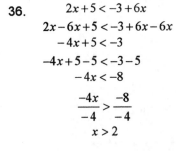

33.
$$\frac{-x}{6} \ge 3$$

$$-6\left(\frac{-x}{6}\right) \le -6(3)$$

$$x \le -18$$

34.
$$\frac{2x}{3} \le 4$$

$$\frac{3}{2}\left(\frac{2x}{3}\right) \le \frac{3}{2}(4)$$

$$x \le 6$$

35.
$$-11 < -5x + 4$$
$$-11 - 4 < -5x + 4 - 4$$
$$-15 < -5x$$
$$\frac{-15}{-5} > \frac{-5x}{-5}$$
$$3 > x$$
$$x < 3$$

36.
$$2x + 5 < -3 + 6x$$
$$2x - 6x + 5 < -3 + 6x - 6x$$
$$-4x + 5 < -3$$
$$-4x + 5 - 5 < -3 - 5$$
$$-4x < -8$$
$$\frac{-4x}{-4} > \frac{-8}{-4}$$
$$x > 2$$

37.
$$3(x+4) \ge 4x + 13$$
$$3x + 12 \ge 4x + 13$$
$$3x - 4x + 12 \ge 4x - 4x + 13$$
$$-x + 12 \ge 13$$
$$-x + 12 - 12 \ge 13 - 12$$
$$-x \ge 1$$
$$\frac{-x}{-1} \le \frac{1}{-1}$$
$$x \le -1$$

38.
$$-2(x-1) < 3(x-4) + 5$$
$$-2x + 2 < 3x - 12 + 5$$
$$-2x + 2 < 3x - 7$$
$$-2x - 3x + 2 < 3x - 3x - 7$$
$$-5x + 2 < -7$$
$$-5x + 2 - 2 < -7 - 2$$
$$-5x < -9$$
$$\frac{-5x}{-5} > \frac{-9}{-5}$$
$$x > \frac{9}{5}$$

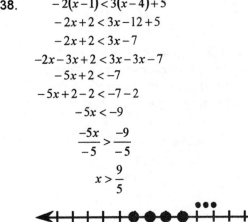

39.
$$5(x+4)-6 \le 2x+8$$
$$5x+20-6 \le 2x+8$$
$$5x+14 \le 2x+8$$
$$5x-2x+14 \le 2x-2x+8$$
$$3x+14 \le 8$$
$$3x+14-14 \le 8-14$$
$$3x \le -6$$
$$\frac{3x}{3} \le \frac{-6}{3}$$
$$x \le -2$$

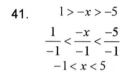

40. $-3 \le x < 5$

41.
$$1 > -x > -5$$
$$\frac{1}{-1} < \frac{-x}{-1} < \frac{-5}{-1}$$
$$-1 < x < 5$$

42.
$$-2 < 2x+3 < 6$$
$$-2-3 < 2x+3-3 < 6-3$$
$$-5 < 2x < 3$$
$$\frac{-5}{2} < \frac{2x}{2} < \frac{3}{2}$$
$$-\frac{5}{2} < x < \frac{3}{2}$$

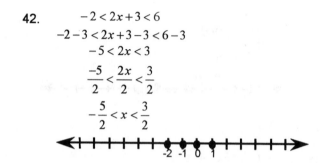

43.
$$0.2 < \frac{x-3}{10} \le 0.4$$
$$10(0.2) < 10\left(\frac{x-3}{10}\right) \le 10(0.4)$$
$$2 < x-3 \le 4$$
$$2+3 < x-3+3 \le 4+3$$
$$5 < x \le 7$$

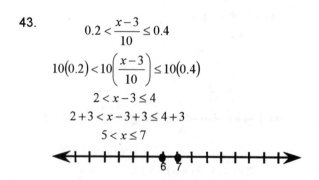

44.
$$-\frac{1}{3} \le \frac{x-3}{6} < \frac{1}{2}$$
$$6\left(-\frac{1}{3}\right) \le 6\left(\frac{x-3}{6}\right) < 6\left(\frac{1}{2}\right)$$
$$-2 \le x-3 < 3$$
$$-2+3 \le x-3+3 < 3+3$$
$$1 \le x < 6$$

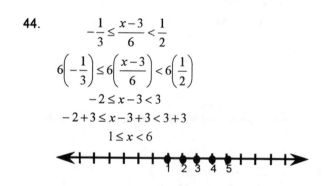

45. Let $x =$ the number of miles
$110+0.25x =$ cost of renting from Fred's
$$110+0.25x < 200$$
$$110-110+0.25x < 200-110$$
$$0.25x < 90$$
$$\frac{0.25x}{0.25} < \frac{90}{0.25}$$
$$x < 360 \text{ miles}$$

46. Let $x =$ the number of units
Option A: $9.90+1.10x$
Option B: $12.70+0.75x$
$$9.90+1.10x > 12.70+0.75x$$
$$9.90+1.10x-0.75x > 12.70+0.75x-0.75x$$
$$9.90+0.35x > 12.70$$
$$9.90-9.90+0.35x > 12.70-9.90$$
$$0.35x > 2.8$$
$$\frac{0.35x}{0.35} > \frac{2.8}{0.35}$$
$$x > 8$$

Greg must produce more than 8 units.

47. a) Let $x =$ the number of boxes of books
$60x =$ the weight of x boxes of books
$60x + 180 \leq 1200$

b) $60x + 180 - 180 \leq 1200 - 180$
$60x \leq 1020$

$$\frac{60x}{60} \leq \frac{1020}{60}$$

$x \leq 17$

The maximum number of boxes is 17.

48. Let $x =$ the cost of the meal
$0.07x =$ the tax on the meal
$0.15x =$ the tip on the meal
$x + 0.07x + 0.15x \leq 19$
$1.22x \leq 19$

$$\frac{1.22x}{1.22} \leq \frac{19}{1.22}$$

$x \leq 15.57377049$

Mrs. Franklin can select a meal for $x \leq \$15.57$.

49. $12x > 2x + 200$
$12x - 2x > 2x - 2x + 200$
$10x > 200$

$$\frac{10x}{10} > \frac{200}{10}$$

$x > 20$

More than 20 books must be sold weekly to make a profit.

50. $36 < 84 - 32t < 68$
$36 - 84 < 84 - 84 - 32t < 68 - 84$
$-48 < -32t < -16$

$$\frac{-48}{-32} > \frac{-32t}{-32} > \frac{-16}{-32}$$

$1.5 > t > 0.5$
$0.5 < t < 1.5$

The velocity will be between $36 \frac{ft.}{sec.}$ and

$68 \frac{ft.}{sec.}$ when t is between $0.5 \sec.$ and $1.5 \sec.$

51. Let $x =$ Devon's grade on the fifth test
$$80 \leq \frac{78 + 64 + 88 + 76 + x}{5} < 90$$

$$80 \leq \frac{306 + x}{5} < 90$$

$$5(80) \leq 5\left(\frac{306 + x}{5}\right) < 5(90)$$

$400 \leq 306 + x < 450$
$400 - 306 \leq 306 - 306 + x < 450 - 306$
$94 \leq x < 144$

Devon must have a score of $94 \leq x \leq 100$, assuming 100 is the highest grade possible.

52. Let $x =$ the number of miles
distance $=$ rate $\times$ time
$40(4) \leq x \leq 55(4)$
$160 \leq x \leq 220$

53. Let $x =$ the number of people enrolled
$18,000 \leq 8000 + 175x \leq 24,000$
$18,000 - 8,000 \leq 8000 - 8000 + 175x \leq 24,000 - 8000$
$10,000 \leq 175x \leq 16,000$

$$\frac{10,000}{175} \leq \frac{175x}{175} \leq \frac{16,000}{175}$$

$57.14285714 \leq x \leq 91.42857143$

Minimum: 58   Maximum: 91

54. Let $x =$ the number of gallons
$250x = 2750$ and $400x = 2750$

$$x = \frac{2750}{250} , \quad x = \frac{2750}{400}$$

$x = 11$, $x = 6.875$
$6.875 \leq x \leq 11$

55. Let $x =$ the final exam grade

The semester average $= \dfrac{86 + 74 + 68 + 96 + 72}{5} = \dfrac{396}{5} = 79.2$

The final grade is found by taking $\dfrac{2}{3}$ of the semester average and adding this to $\dfrac{1}{3}$ of the final exam. The

final grade is $\dfrac{2}{3}(79.2) + \dfrac{1}{3}x = 52.8 + \dfrac{1}{3}x$. In order for Teresa to receive a final grade of B in the course, she must have an average greater than or equal to 80 and less than 90.

$$80 \le 52.8 + \frac{1}{3}x < 90$$

$$80 - 52.8 \le 52.8 - 52.8 + \frac{1}{3}x < 90 - 52.8$$

$$27.2 \le \frac{1}{3}x < 37.2$$

$$3(27.2) \le 3\left(\frac{1}{3}x\right) < 3(37.2)$$

$$81.6 \le x < 111.6$$

Thus, Teresa must receive $81.6 \le x \le 100$, assuming 100 is the highest grade possible.

56. Student's answer: $\qquad -\dfrac{1}{3}x \le 4$

$$-3\left(-\frac{1}{3}x\right) \le -3(4)$$

$$x \le -12$$

Correct answer: $\qquad -\dfrac{1}{3}x \le 4$

$$-3\left(-\frac{1}{3}x\right) \ge -3(4)$$

$$x \ge -12$$

Yes, -12 is in both solution sets.

Exercise Set 6.7

1. A **graph** is an illustration of all the points whose coordinates satisfy an equation.

2. To find the **y-intercept**, set $x = 0$ and solve the equation for y.

3. To find the **x-intercept**, set $y = 0$ and solve the equation for x.

4. The **slope of a line** is a ratio of the vertical change to the horizontal change for any two points on the line.

5. a) Divide the difference between the $y-$coordinates by the difference between the $x-$coordinates.

b) $m = \dfrac{5 - 2}{-3 - 6} = \dfrac{3}{-9} = -\dfrac{1}{3}$

6. Plotting points, using intercepts, and using the slope and $y-$intercept

7. - 14.

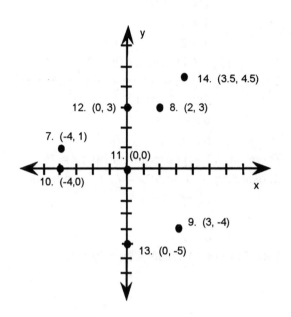

15. - 22.

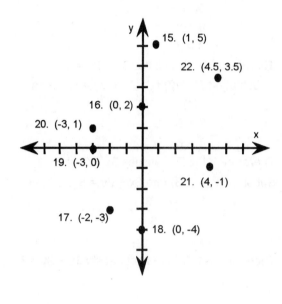

23. (2, 2)   24. (4, 3)   25. (0, 2)   26. (-2, 4)   27. (-2, 0)

28. (-3, 1)   29. (-5, -3)   30. (0, -3)   31. (2, -3)   32. (4, 0)

33. Substituting (2, -1) into x – 3y = 8, we have
$$2 – 3(-1) = 8$$
$$2 + 3 = 8$$
$$5 \neq 8$$
Therefore, (2, -1) does not satisfy x – 3y = 8.
Substituting (2, -2) into x – 3y = 8 , we have
$$2 – 3(-2) = 8$$
$$2 + 6 = 8$$
$$8 = 8$$
Therefore, (2, -2) satisfies x – 3y= 8.
Substituting (2, -3) into x – 3y = 8, we have
$$2 – 3(-3) = 8$$
$$2 + 9 = 8$$
$$11 \neq 8$$
Therefore, (2, -3) does not satisfy x – 3y = 8.

34. Substituting (0, 5) into 2x + 2y = 10, we have
$$2(0) + 2(5) = 10$$
$$0 + 10 = 10$$
$$10 = 10$$
Therefore, (0, 5) satisfies 2x + 2y = 10.
Substituting (1, 3) into 2x + 2y = 10, we have
$$2(1) + 2(3) = 10$$
$$2 + 6 = 10$$
$$8 \neq 10$$
Therefore, (1, 3) does not satisfy 2x + 2y = 10.
Substituting (-1, 5) into 2x + 2y = 10, we have
$$2(-1) + 2(5) = 10$$
$$-2 + 10 = 10$$
$$8 \neq 10$$
Therefore, (-1, 5) does not satisfy 2x + 2y = 10.

35. Substituting (0, 4) into $3x + 2y = 8$, we have

$$3(0) + 2(4) = 8$$
$$0 + 8 = 8$$
$$8 = 8$$

Therefore, (0, 4) satisfies $3x + 2y = 8$.

Substituting (1, 5/2) into $3x + 2y = 8$, we have

$$3(1) + 2(5/2) = 8$$
$$3 + 5 = 8$$
$$8 = 8$$

Therefore, (1, 5/2) satisfies $3x + 2y = 8$.

Substituting (-1, 3) into $3x + 2y = 8$, we have

$$3(-1) + 2(3) = 8$$
$$-3 + 6 = 8$$
$$3 \neq 8$$

Therefore, (-1, 3) does not satisfy $3x + 2y = 8$.

36. Substituting (1, 1/7) into $2x = 7y + 1$, we have

$$2(1) = 7(1/7) + 1$$
$$2 = 1 + 1$$
$$2 = 2$$

Therefore, (1, 1/7) satisfies $2x = 7y + 1$.

Substituting (3, -1) into $2x = 7y + 1$, we have

$$2(3) = 7(-1) + 1$$
$$6 = -7 + 1$$
$$6 \neq -6$$

Therefore, (3, -1) does not satisfy $2x = 7y + 1$.

Substituting (4, 1) into $2x = 7y + 1$, we have

$$2(4) = 7(1) + 1$$
$$8 = 7 + 1$$
$$8 = 8$$

Therefore, (4, 1) satisfies $2x = 7y + 1$.

37. Substituting (1, -1) into $7y = 3x - 5$, we have

$$7(-1) = 3(1) - 5$$
$$-7 = 3 - 5$$
$$-7 \neq -2$$

Therefore, (1, -1) does not satisfy $7y = 3x - 5$.

Substituting (-3, -2) into $7y = 3x - 5$, we have

$$7(-2) = 3(-3) - 5$$
$$-14 = -9 - 5$$
$$-14 = -14$$

Therefore, (-3, -2) satisfies $7y = 3x - 5$.

Substituting (2, 5) into $7y = 3x - 5$, we have

$$7(5) = 3(2) - 5$$
$$35 = 6 - 5$$
$$35 \neq 1$$

Therefore, (2, 5) does not satisfy $7y = 3x - 5$.

38. Substituting (0, 4/3) into $x/2 + 3y = 4$, we have

$$0/2 + 3(4/3) = 4$$
$$0 + 4 = 4$$
$$4 = 4$$

Therefore, (0, 4/3) satisfies $x/2 + 3y = 4$.

Substituting (8, 0) into $x/2 + 3y = 4$, we have

$$8/2 + 3(0) = 4$$
$$4 + 0 = 4$$
$$4 = 4$$

Therefore, (8, 0) satisfies $x/2 + 3y = 4$.

Substituting (10, -2) into $x/2 + 3y = 4$, we have

$$10/2 + 3(-2) = 4$$
$$5 - 6 = 4$$
$$-1 \neq 4$$

Therefore, (10, -2) does not satisfy $x/2 + 3y = 4$.

39. Substituting (0, 8/3) into x/2 + 3y/4 = 2, we have

$$0/2 + 8/4 = 2$$

$$0 + 2 = 2$$

$$2 = 2$$

Therefore, (0, 8/3) satisfies x/2 + 3y/4 = 2.

Substituting (1, 11/4) into x/2 + 3y/4 = 2, we have   1/2 + 33/16 = 2

$$8/16 + 33/16 = 2$$

$$41/16 \neq 2$$

Therefore, (1, 11/4) does not satisfy

x/2 + 3y/4 = 2.

Substituting (4, 0) into x/2 + 3y/4 = 2, we have

$$4/2 + 0/4 = 2$$

$$2 + 0 = 2$$

$$2 = 2$$

Therefore, (4, 0) satisfies x/2 + 3y/4 = 2.

40. Substituting (2, 1) into 2x – 5y = -7, we have

$$2(2) - 5(1) = -7$$

$$4 - 5 = -7$$

$$-1 \neq -7$$

Therefore, (2, 1) does not satisfy 2x – 5y = -7.

Substituting (-1, 1) into 2x – 5y = -7, we have

$$2(-1) - 5(1) = -7$$

$$-2 - 5 = -7$$

$$-7 = -7$$

Therefore, (-1, 1) satisfies 2x – 5y = -7.

Substituting (4, 3) into 2x – 5y = -7, we have

$$2(4) - 5(3) = -7$$

$$8 - 15 = -7$$

$$-7 = -7$$

Therefore, (4, 3) satisfies 2x – 5y = -7.

41. Since the line is vertical, its slope is undefined.

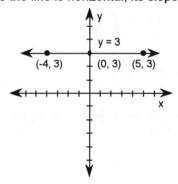

42. Since the line is vertical, its slope is undefined.

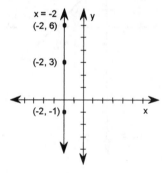

43. Since the line is horizontal, its slope is 0.

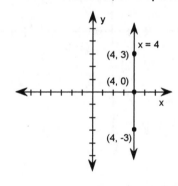

44. Since the line is horizontal, its slope is 0.

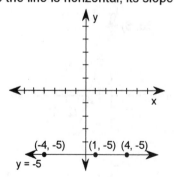

45. y = x - 2

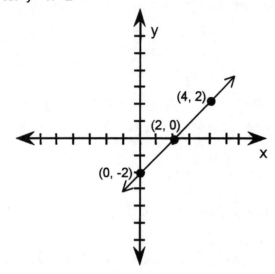

46. y = x + 4

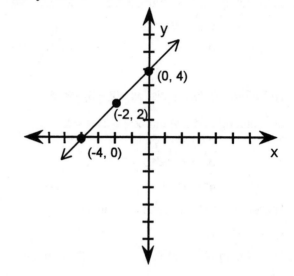

47. y = -x + 3

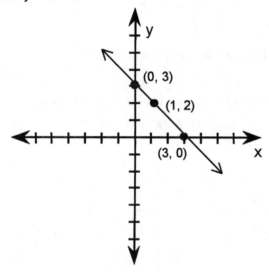

48. y = 2x - 2

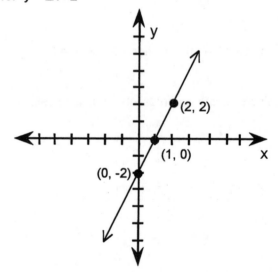

49. y + 3x = 6 or y = -3x + 6

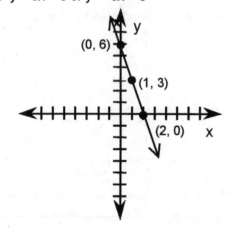

50. y − 4x = 8 or y = 4x + 8

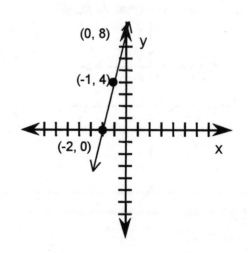

51. $y = \frac{1}{2}x + 4$

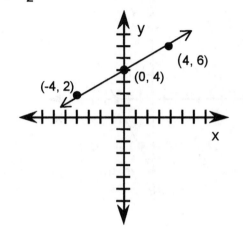

52. $3y = 2x - 3$ or $y = \frac{2}{3}x - 1$

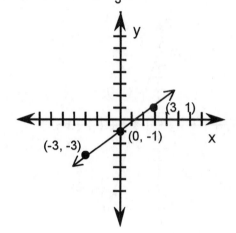

53. $2y = -x + 6$ or $y = -\frac{1}{2}x + 3$

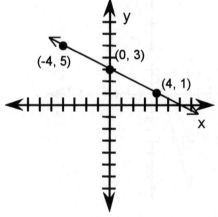

54. $y = -\frac{3}{4}x$

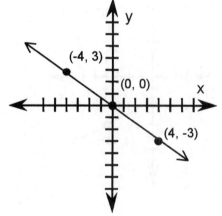

55. $x - y = 5$

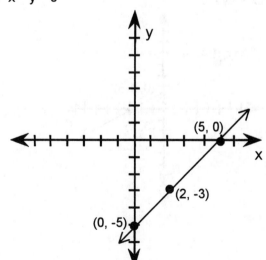

56. $x + y = 3$

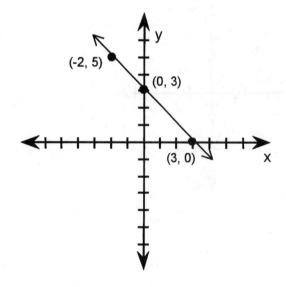

57. $3x + y = 6$

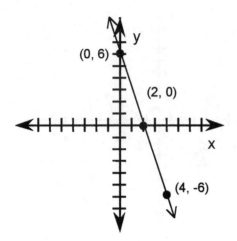

58. $4x - 2y = 12$

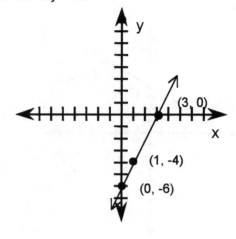

59. $2x = -4y - 8$

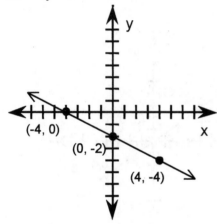

60. $y = 4x + 4$

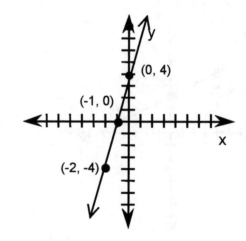

61. $y = -2x - 5$

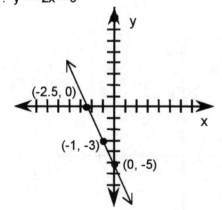

62. $2x + 4y = 6$

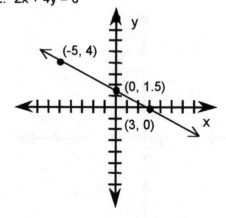

63. −3x + y = 4

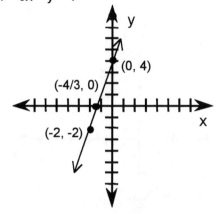

64. 5y = 3x + 10

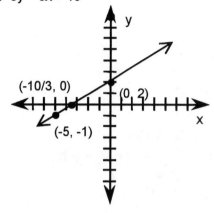

65. (2, 8), (4, 16) $m = \dfrac{16-8}{4-2} = \dfrac{8}{2} = 4$

66. (3, 7), (7, 3) $m = \dfrac{3-7}{7-3} = \dfrac{-4}{4} = -1$

67. (-1, -6), (3, 5) $m = \dfrac{5-(-6)}{3-(-1)} = \dfrac{11}{4}$

68. (3, -3), (-4, 9) $m = \dfrac{9-(-3)}{-4-3} = \dfrac{12}{-7} = -\dfrac{12}{7}$

69. (5, 2), (-3, 2) $m = \dfrac{2-2}{-3-5} = \dfrac{0}{-8} = 0$

70. (-3, -5), (-1, -2) $m = \dfrac{-2-(-5)}{-1-(-3)} = \dfrac{3}{2}$

71. (8, -3), (8, 3) $m = \dfrac{3-(-3)}{8-8} = \dfrac{6}{0}$ Undefined

72. (2, 6), (2, -3) $m = \dfrac{-3-6}{2-2} = \dfrac{-9}{0}$ Undefined

73. (-2, 3), (1, -1) $m = \dfrac{-1-3}{1-(-2)} = \dfrac{-4}{3} = -\dfrac{4}{3}$

74. (-7, -5), (5, -6) $m = \dfrac{-6-(-5)}{5-(-7)} = \dfrac{-1}{12} = -\dfrac{1}{12}$

75. y = x − 2

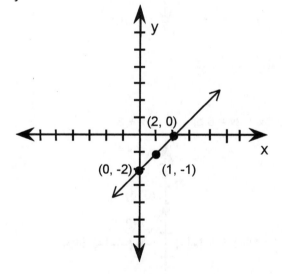

76. y = 3x + 2

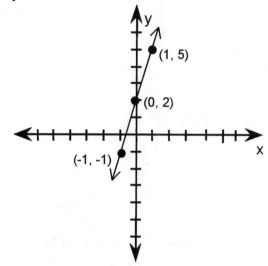

77. $y = -2x + 1$

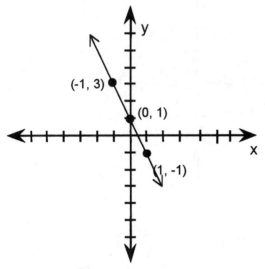

78. $y = -x - 4$

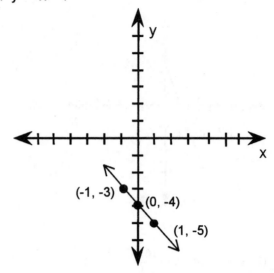

79. $y = -\dfrac{3}{5}x + 3$

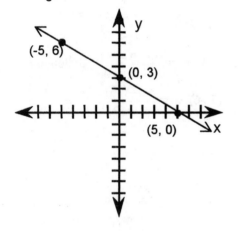

80. $y = -x - 2$

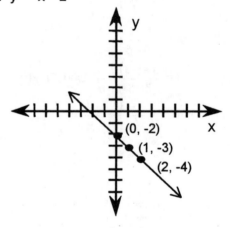

81. $7y = 4x - 7$ or $y = \dfrac{4}{7}x - 1$

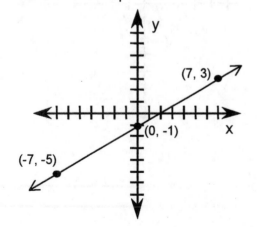

82. $3x + 2y = 6$ or $y = -\dfrac{3}{2}x + 3$

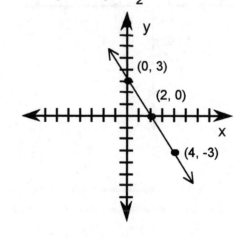

83. $3x - 2y + 6 = 0$ or $y = \frac{3}{2}x + 3$

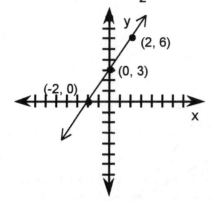

84. $3x + 4y - 8 = 0$ or $y = -\frac{3}{4}x + 2$

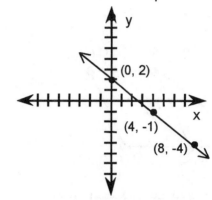

85. The y-intercept is 3; thus b = 3. The slope is negative since the graph falls from left to right. The change in y is 3, while the change in x is 4. Thus m, the slope, is $-\frac{3}{4}$. The equation is $y = -\frac{3}{4}x + 3$.

86. The y-intercept is 3; thus b = 3. The slope is positive since the graph rises from left to right. The change in y is 3, while the change in x is 2. Thus m, the slope, is $\frac{3}{2}$. The equation is $y = \frac{3}{2}x + 3$.

87. The y-intercept is -1; thus b = -1. The slope is positive since the graph rises from left to right. The change in y is 1, while the change in x is 2. Thus m, the slope, is $\frac{1}{2}$. The equation is $y = \frac{1}{2}x - 1$.

88. The y-intercept is 1 ; thus b = 1. The slope is negative since the graph falls from left to right. The change in y is 2, while the change in x is 1. Thus m, the slope, is -2. The equation is $y = -2x + 1$.

89. a)

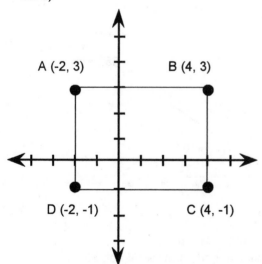

b) $A = l \times w = 6 \times 4 = 24$ square units

90. a)

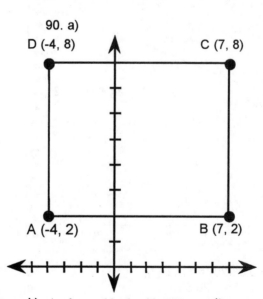

b) $A = l \times w = 11 \times 6 = 66$ square units

91.

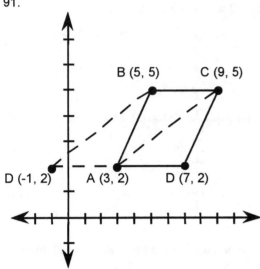

92.

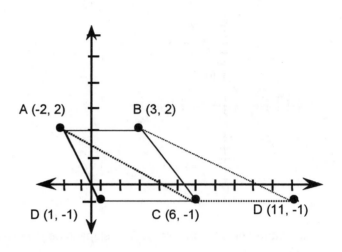

93. For the line joining points P and Q to be parallel to the x-axis, both ordered pairs must have the same y-value. Thus, b = 8.

94. For the line joining points P and Q to be parallel to the y-axis, both ordered pairs must have the same x-value. Thus, b = 5.

95. For the line joining points P and Q to be parallel to the y-axis, both ordered pairs must have the same x-value.
$$3b - 1 = 8$$
$$3b - 1 + 1 = 8 + 1$$
$$3b = 9$$
$$b = 3$$

96. For the line joining points P and Q to be parallel to the x-axis, both ordered pairs must have the same y-value.
$$2b + 1 = 7$$
$$2b + 1 - 1 = 7 - 1$$
$$2b = 6$$
$$b = 3$$

97. a)

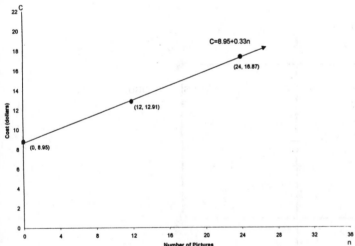

98. a)

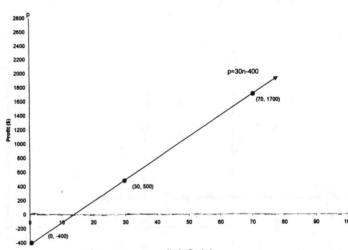

b) $8.95 + 0.33(20) = \$15.55$

c) $8.95 + 0.33n = 20.83$
$0.33n = 11.88$
$n = 36$ pictures

b) $30(50) - 400 = \$1100$

c) To break even, the profit would be $0.
$$30n - 400 = 0$$
$$30n = 400$$
$$n = 13\frac{1}{3} \text{ or } 14 \text{ vcrs (rounded upwards)}$$

99. a)

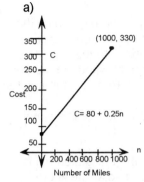

b) C = 80 + 0.25(600) = $230
c) 180 = 80 + 0.25n
   100 = 0.25n
   n = 400 miles

100. a)

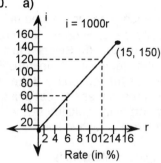

b) i = 1000(0.06) = $60
c) i = 1000(0.12) = $120

101. a) $m = \dfrac{96-53}{4-0} = \dfrac{43}{4} = 10.75$
   b) $y = 10.75x + 53$
   c) $y = 10.75(3) + 53 = 85.25$
   d) $80 = 10.75x + 53$
      $27 = 10.75x$
      $x = 2.511627907 \approx 2.5$ hours

102. a) $m = \dfrac{45-27.5}{5-0} = \dfrac{17.5}{5} = 3.5;\ 3.5(1000) = 3500$
   b) $y = 3500x + 27,500$
   c) $y = 3.5(4) + 27.5 = 41.5 \rightarrow 41.5(1000) = \$41,500$
   d) $45 = 3.5x + 27.5$
      $17.5 = 3.5x$
      $x = 5$ years

103. a) $m = \dfrac{790-370}{17-0} = \dfrac{420}{17} = 24.70588235 \approx 24.71$
   b) $y = 24.71x + 370$
   c) $y = 24.71(6) + 370 = \$518.26$
   d) $600 = 24.71x + 370$
      $230 = 24.71x$
      $x = 9.307972481 \approx 9.3$ years after 1980,
      or in 1989

104. a) $m = \dfrac{25,000-17,000}{9-0} = \dfrac{8000}{9} = 888.\overline{8} \approx 888.89$ million
   b) $y = 888.89x + 17,000$ (numbers in millions)
   c) $y = 888.89(4) + 17,000 = 20,555.56 \approx 20,556$ million
   d) $20,000 = 888.89x + 17,000$
      $3000 = 888.89x$
      $x = 3.374995781 \approx 3.37$ years after 1994, or in 1997

105. a) Solve the equations for y to put them in slope-intercept form. Then compare the slopes and y-intercepts. If the slopes are equal but the y-intercepts are different, then the lines are parallel.
   b) $2x - 3y = 6$ $4x = 6y + 6$
      $2x - 2x - 3y = -2x + 6$ $4x - 6 = 6y + 6 - 6$
          $-3y = -2x + 6$ $4x - 6 = 6y$
      $\dfrac{-3y}{-3} = \dfrac{-2x}{-3} + \dfrac{6}{-3}$ $\dfrac{4x}{6} - \dfrac{6}{6} = \dfrac{6y}{6}$
          $y = \dfrac{2}{3}x - 2$ $\dfrac{2}{3}x - 1 = y$

   Since the two equations have the same slope, m = $\dfrac{2}{3}$, the graphs of the equations are parallel lines.

106. Quadrants 1, 2, and 4. The graph of the line $x + y = 1$ is in quadrants 1, 2, and 4; therefore, the set of points that satisfy the equation is in these quadrants.

Exercise Set 6.8

1. (1) Mentally substitute the equal sign for the inequality sign and plot points as if you were graphing the equation. (2) If the inequality is < or >, draw a dashed line through the points. If the inequality is ≤ or ≥, draw a solid line through the points. (3) Select a test point not on the line and substitute the x- and y- coordinates into the inequality. If the substitution results in a true statement, shade in the area on the same side of the line as the test point. If the substitution results in a false statement, shade in the area on the opposite side of the line as the test point.

2. To indicate that the line is part of the solution set, we draw a solid line. To indicate that the line is not part of the solution set, we draw a dashed line.

3. Graph x = 2. Since the original statement is less than or equal to, a solid line is drawn. Since the point (0, 0) satisfies the inequality $x \leq 2$, all points on the line and in the half-plane to the left of the line x = 2 are in the solution set.

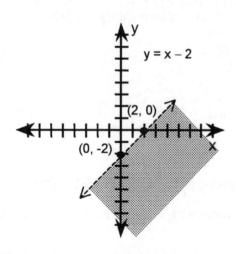

4. Graph y = 1. Since the original statement is greater than or equal to, a solid line is drawn. Since the point (0, 0) does not satisfy the inequality $y \geq 1$, all points on the line and in the half-plane above the line y = 1 are in the solution set.

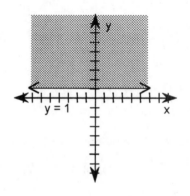

5. Graph y = x – 2. Since the original statement is strictly less than, a dashed line is drawn. Since the point (0, 0) does not satisfy the inequality $y < x - 2$, all points in the half-plane below the line y = x – 2 are in the solution set.

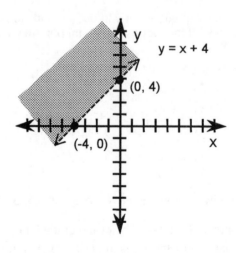

6. Graph y = x + 4. Since the original statement is strictly greater than, a dashed line is drawn. Since the point (0, 0) does not satisfy the inequality $y > x + 4$, all points in the half-plane above the line y = x + 4 are in the solution set.

7. Graph $y = 2x - 6$. Since the original statement is greater than or equal to, a solid line is drawn. Since the point $(0, 0)$ satisfies the inequality $y \geq 2x - 6$, all points on the line and in the half-plane above the line $y = 2x - 6$ are in the solution set.

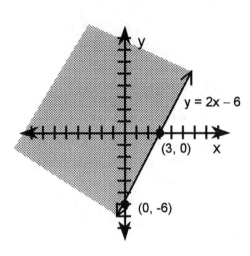

8. Graph $y = -2x + 2$. Since the original statement is strictly less than, a dashed line is drawn. Since the point $(0, 0)$ satisfies the inequality $y < -2x + 2$, all points in the half-plane below the line $y = -2x + 2$ are in the solution set.

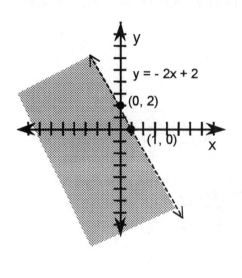

9. Graph $3x - 4y = 12$. Since the original statement is strictly greater than, a dashed line is drawn. Since the point $(0, 0)$ does not satisfy the inequality $3x - 4y > 12$, all points in the half-plane below the line $3x - 4y = 12$ are in the solution set.

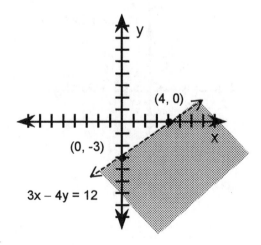

10. Graph $x + 2y = 4$. Since the original statement is strictly greater than, a dashed line is drawn. Since the point $(0, 0)$ does not satisfy the inequality $x + 2y > 4$, all points in the half-plane above the line $x + 2y = 4$ are in the solution set.

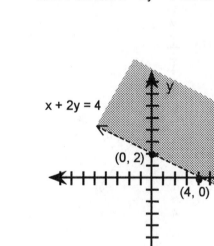

11. Graph $3x - 4y = 9$. Since the original statement is less than or equal to, a solid line is drawn. Since the point $(0, 0)$ satisfies the inequality $3x - 4y \leq 9$, all points on the line and in the half-plane above the line $3x - 4y = 9$ are in the solution set.

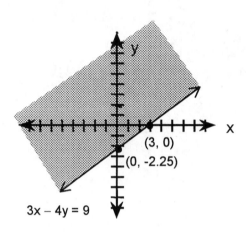

12. Graph $4y - 3x = 9$. Since the original statement is greater than or equal to, a solid line is drawn. Since the point $(0, 0)$ does not satisfy the inequality $4y - 3x \geq 9$, all points on the line and in the half-plane above the line $4y - 3x = 9$ are in the solution set.

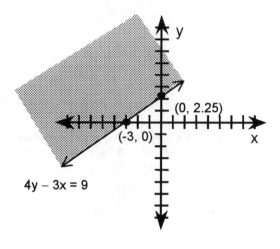

13. Graph $3x + 2y = 6$. Since the original statement is strictly less than, a dashed line is drawn. Since the point $(0, 0)$ satisfies the inequality $3x + 2y < 6$, all points in the half-plane to the left of the line $3x + 2y = 6$ are in the solution set.

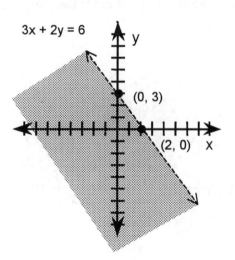

14. Graph $-x + 2y = 2$. Since the original statement is strictly less than, a dashed line is drawn. Since the point $(0, 0)$ satisfies the inequality $-x + 2y < 2$, all points in the half-plane below the line $-x + 2y = 2$ are in the solution set.

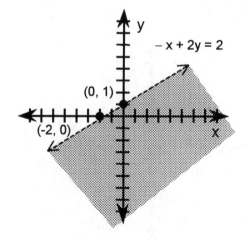

15. Graph x + y = 0. Since the original statement is strictly greater than, a dashed line is drawn. Since the point (1,1) satisfies the inequality x + y > 0, all points in the half-plane above the line x + y = 0 are in the solution set.

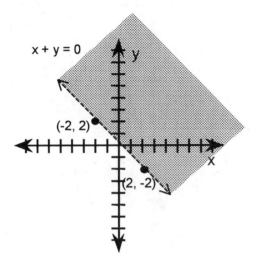

16. Graph x + 2y = 0. Since the original statement is less than or equal to, a solid line is drawn. Since the point (1, 1) does not satisfy the inequality x + 2y ≤ 0, all points on the line and in the half-plane below the line x + 2y = 0 are in the solution set.

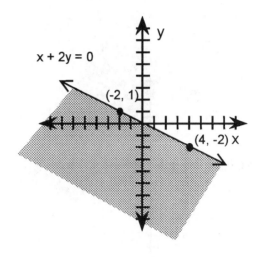

17. Graph 3y – 2x = 0. Since the original statement is less than or equal to, a solid line is drawn. Since the point (0, 1) does not satisfy the inequality 3y – 2x ≤ 0, all points on the line and in the half-plane below the line 3y – 2x = 0 are in the solution set.

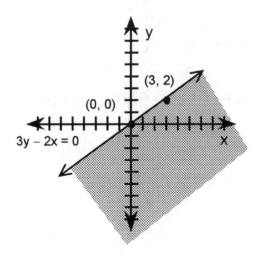

18. Graph y = 2x + 7. Since the original statement is greater than or equal to, a solid line is drawn. Since the point (0, 0) does not satisfy the inequality y ≥ 2x + 7, all points on the line and in the half-plane above the line y = 2x + 7 are in the solution set.

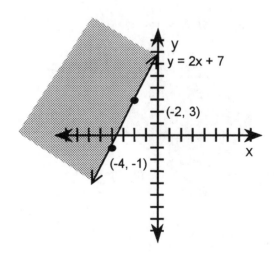

19. Graph $3x + 2y = 12$. Since the original statement is strictly greater than, a dashed line is drawn. Since the point $(0, 0)$ does not satisfy the inequality $3x + 2y > 12$, all points in the half-plane above the line $3x + 2y = 12$ are in the solution set.

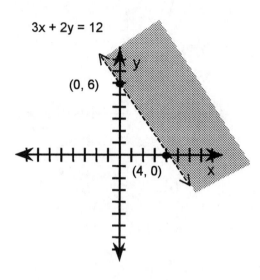

$3x + 2y = 12$

$(0, 6)$

$(4, 0)$

20. Graph $y = 3x - 4$. Since the original statement is less than or equal to, a solid line is drawn. Since the point $(0, 0)$ does not satisfy the inequality $y \leq 3x - 4$, all points on the line and in the half-plane below the line $y = 3x - 4$ are in the solution set.

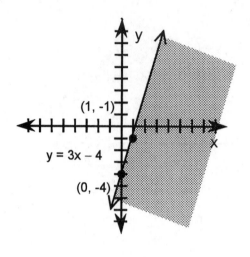

$(1, -1)$

$y = 3x - 4$

$(0, -4)$

21. Graph $(2/5)x - (1/2)y = 1$. Since the original statement is less than or equal to, a solid line is drawn. Since the point $(0, 0)$ satisfies the inequality $(2/5)x - (1/2)y \leq 1$, all points on the line and in the half-plane above the line $(2/5)x - (1/2)y = 1$ are in the solution set.

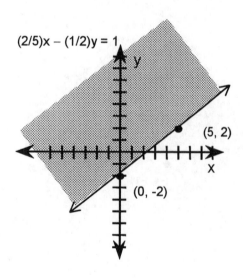

$(2/5)x - (1/2)y = 1$

$(5, 2)$

$(0, -2)$

22. Graph $0.1x + 0.3y = 0.4$. Since the original statement is less than or equal to, a solid line is drawn. Since the point $(0, 0)$ satisfies the inequality $0.1x + 0.3y \leq 0.4$, all points on the line and in the half-plane below the line $0.1x + 0.3y = 0.4$ are in the solution set.

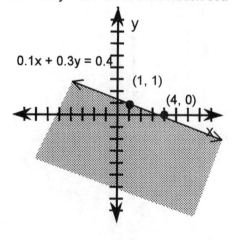

$0.1x + 0.3y = 0.4$

$(1, 1)$

$(4, 0)$

23. Graph 0.2x + 0.5y = 0.3. Since the original statement is less than or equal to, a solid line is drawn. Since the point (0, 0) satisfies the inequality 0.2x + 0.5y ≤ 0.3, all points on the line and in the half-plane below the line 0.2x + 0.5y = 0.3 are in the solution set.

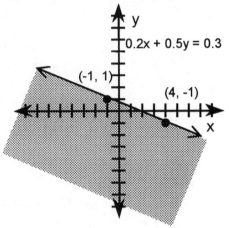

24. a) x + y ≤ 15

   b)

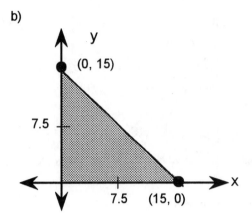

25. a) 2l + 2w ≤ 40 or l + w ≤ 20, where 0 ≤ l ≤ 20 and 0 ≤ w ≤ 20

   b) Let the x-coordinate represent w and the y-coordinate represent l.

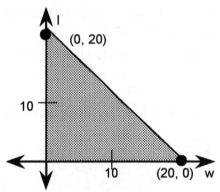

26. a) x = the number of acres of land, y = the number of square feet in the house

   b)

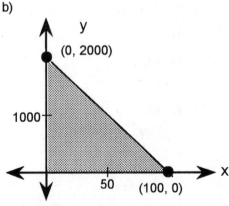

   c) 1500x + 75(1950) = 150,000
      1500x + 146,250 = 150,000
      1500x = 3750
      x = 2.5 acres or less
   d) 1500(5) + 75y = 150,000
      7500 + 75y = 150,000
      75y = 142,500
      y = 1900 ft.² or less

27. a) No, you can not have a negative number of shirts.

b)

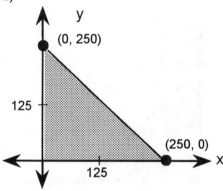

c) Answers will vary.

Exercise Set 6.9

1. A **binomial** is an expression that contains two terms in which each exponent that appears on the variable is a whole number. Examples: $2x+3$, $x-7$

2. A **trinomial** is an expression containing three terms in which each exponent that appears on the variable is a whole number. Examples: $2x^2-3x+1$, $-x^2+4x-6$, x^3-3x+2

3. The **foil method** is a method that obtains the products of the First, Outer, Inner, and Last terms of the binomials.

4. $ax^2+bx+c=0$, $a \neq 0$

5. If the product of two factors is 0, then one or both of the factors must have a value of 0.

6. $x = \dfrac{-b \pm \sqrt{b^2-4ac}}{2a}$

7. $x^2+10x+21=(x+3)(x+7)$

8. $x^2+4x+3=(x+3)(x+1)$

9. $x^2-4x-5=(x-5)(x+1)$

10. $x^2+4x-5=(x+5)(x-1)$

11. $x^2+2x-24=(x+6)(x-4)$

12. $x^2-6x+8=(x-2)(x-4)$

13. $x^2-2x-3=(x-3)(x+1)$

14. $x^2-5x-6=(x-6)(x+1)$

15. $x^2-10x+21=(x-3)(x-7)$

16. $x^2-25=(x+5)(x-5)$

17. $x^2-16=(x+4)(x-4)$

18. $x^2-x-56=(x-8)(x+7)$

19. $x^2+3x-28=(x+7)(x-4)$

20. $x^2+4x-32=(x+8)(x-4)$

21. $x^2+2x-63=(x+9)(x-7)$

22. $x^2-2x-48=(x-8)(x+6)$

23. $2x^2+5x+3=(2x+3)(x+1)$

24. $2x^2+13x-7=(2x-1)(x+7)$

25. $3x^2-14x-5=(3x+1)(x-5)$

26. $2x^2-13x-7=(2x+1)(x-7)$

27. $5x^2+12x+4=(5x+2)(x+2)$

28. $2x^2-9x+10=(2x-5)(x-2)$

29. $5x^2-13x-6=(5x+2)(x-3)$

30. $4x^2+20x+21=(2x+7)(2x+3)$

31. $5x^2-13x+6=(5x-3)(x-2)$

32. $6x^2-11x+4=(3x-4)(2x-1)$

33. $3x^2-14x-24=(3x+4)(x-6)$

34. $6x^2+5x+1=(2x+1)(3x+1)$

35. $(x+2)(x-5)=0$

$x+2=0$ or $x-5=0$

$x=-2 \qquad x=5$

36. $(2x-1)(3x+2)=0$

$2x-1=0$ or $3x+2=0$

$2x=1 \qquad 3x=-2$

$x=\dfrac{1}{2} \qquad x=-\dfrac{2}{3}$

37. $(2x-3)(3x+7)=0$

$2x-3=0$ or $3x+7=0$

$2x=3 \qquad 3x=-7$

$x=\dfrac{3}{2} \qquad x=-\dfrac{7}{3}$

38. $(x-6)(5x-4)=0$

$x-6=0$ or $5x-4=0$

$x=6 \qquad 5x=4$

$x=\dfrac{4}{5}$

39. $x^2+5x+6=0$

$(x+3)(x+2)=0$

$x+3=0$ or $x+2=0$

$x=-3 \qquad x=-2$

40. $x^2-6x-7=0$

$(x-7)(x+1)=0$

$x-7=0$ or $x+1=0$

$x=7 \qquad x=-1$

41. $x^2-6x+8=0$

$(x-4)(x-2)=0$

$x-4=0$ or $x-2=0$

$x=4 \qquad x=2$

42. $x^2+2x-15=0$

$(x+5)(x-3)=0$

$x+5=0$ or $x-3=0$

$x=-5 \qquad x=3$

43. $x^2-15=2x$

$x^2-2x-15=0$

$(x-5)(x+3)=0$

$x-5=0$ or $x+3=0$

$x=5 \qquad x=-3$

44. $x^2-7x=-6$

$x^2-7x+6=0$

$(x-1)(x-6)=0$

$x-1=0$ or $x-6=0$

$x=1 \qquad x=6$

45. $x^2=4x-3$

$x^2-4x+3=0$

$(x-1)(x-3)=0$

$x-1=0$ or $x-3=0$

$x=1 \qquad x=3$

46. $x^2-13x+40=0$

$(x-8)(x-5)=0$

$x-8=0$ or $x-5=0$

$x=8 \qquad x=5$

47. $x^2-81=0$

$(x+9)(x-9)=0$

$x+9=0$ or $x-9=0$

$x=-9 \qquad x=9$

48. $x^2-64=0$

$(x+8)(x-8)=0$

$x+8=0$ or $x-8=0$

$x=-8 \qquad x=8$

49. $x^2+5x-36=0$

$(x+9)(x-4)=0$

$x+9=0$ or $x-4=0$

$x=-9 \qquad x=4$

50. $x^2+12x+20=0$

$(x+2)(x+10)=0$

$x+2=0$ or $x+10=0$

$x=-2 \qquad x=-10$

51. $3x^2+7x=-2$

$3x^2+7x+2=0$

$(3x+1)(x+2)=0$

$3x+1=0$ or $x+2=0$

$3x=-1 \qquad x=-2$

$x=-\dfrac{1}{3}$

52. $4x^2+x=3$

$4x^2+x-3=0$

$(4x-3)(x+1)=0$

$4x-3=0$ or $x+1=0$

$4x=3 \qquad x=-1$

$x=\dfrac{3}{4}$

53. $5x^2 + 11x = -2$

$5x^2 + 11x + 2 = 0$

$(5x+1)(x+2) = 0$

$5x+1 = 0$ or $x+2 = 0$

$5x = -1 \qquad x = -2$

$x = -\dfrac{1}{5}$

54. $2x^2 = -5x + 3$

$2x^2 + 5x - 3 = 0$

$(2x-1)(x+3) = 0$

$2x-1 = 0$ or $x+3 = 0$

$2x = 1 \qquad x = -3$

$x = \dfrac{1}{2}$

55. $3x^2 - 4x = -1$

$3x^2 - 4x + 1 = 0$

$(3x-1)(x-1) = 0$

$3x-1 = 0$ or $x-1 = 0$

$3x = 1 \qquad x = 1$

$x = \dfrac{1}{3}$

56. $5x^2 + 16x + 12 = 0$

$(5x+6)(x+2) = 0$

$5x+6 = 0$ or $x+2 = 0$

$5x = -6 \qquad x = -2$

$x = -\dfrac{6}{5}$

57. $4x^2 - 9x + 2 = 0$

$(4x-1)(x-2) = 0$

$4x-1 = 0$ or $x-2 = 0$

$4x = 1 \qquad x = 2$

$x = \dfrac{1}{4}$

58. $6x^2 + x - 2 = 0$

$(3x+2)(2x-1) = 0$

$3x+2 = 0$ or $2x-1 = 0$

$3x = -2 \qquad 2x = 1$

$x = -\dfrac{2}{3} \qquad x = \dfrac{1}{2}$

59. $x^2 - x - 30 = 0$

$a = 1,\ b = -1,\ c = -30$

$x = \dfrac{-(-1) \pm \sqrt{(-1)^2 - 4(1)(-30)}}{2(1)}$

$x = \dfrac{1 \pm \sqrt{1+120}}{2} = \dfrac{1 \pm \sqrt{121}}{2} = \dfrac{1 \pm 11}{2}$

$x = \dfrac{12}{2} = 6$ or $x = \dfrac{-10}{2} = -5$

60. $x^2 + 9x + 14 = 0$

$a = 1,\ b = 9,\ c = 14$

$x = \dfrac{-9 \pm \sqrt{(9)^2 - 4(1)(14)}}{2(1)}$

$x = \dfrac{-9 \pm \sqrt{81-56}}{2} = \dfrac{-9 \pm \sqrt{25}}{2} = \dfrac{-9 \pm 5}{2}$

$x = \dfrac{-4}{2} = -2$ or $x = \dfrac{-14}{2} = -7$

61. $x^2 - 3x - 10 = 0$

$a = 1,\ b = -3,\ c = -10$

$x = \dfrac{-(-3) \pm \sqrt{(-3)^2 - 4(1)(-10)}}{2(1)}$

$x = \dfrac{3 \pm \sqrt{9+40}}{2} = \dfrac{3 \pm \sqrt{49}}{2} = \dfrac{3 \pm 7}{2}$

$x = \dfrac{10}{2} = 5$ or $x = \dfrac{-4}{2} = -2$

62. $x^2 - 5x - 14 = 0$

$a = 1,\ b = -5,\ c = -14$

$x = \dfrac{-(-5) \pm \sqrt{(-5)^2 - 4(1)(-14)}}{2(1)}$

$x = \dfrac{5 \pm \sqrt{25+56}}{2} = \dfrac{5 \pm \sqrt{81}}{2} = \dfrac{5 \pm 9}{2}$

$x = \dfrac{14}{2} = 7$ or $x = \dfrac{-4}{2} = -2$

63. $x^2 - 8x = 9$

$x^2 - 8x - 9 = 0$

$a = 1,\ b = -8,\ c = -9$

$$x = \frac{-(-8) \pm \sqrt{(-8)^2 - 4(1)(-9)}}{2(1)}$$

$$x = \frac{8 \pm \sqrt{64 + 36}}{2} = \frac{8 \pm \sqrt{100}}{2} = \frac{8 \pm 10}{2}$$

$$x = \frac{18}{2} = 9 \text{ or } x = \frac{-2}{2} = -1$$

64. $x^2 = -8x + 15$

$x^2 + 8x - 15 = 0$

$a = 1,\ b = 8,\ c = -15$

$$x = \frac{-8 \pm \sqrt{(8)^2 - 4(1)(-15)}}{2(1)}$$

$$x = \frac{-8 \pm \sqrt{64 + 60}}{2} = \frac{-8 \pm \sqrt{124}}{2} = \frac{-8 \pm 2\sqrt{31}}{2}$$

$$x = -4 \pm \sqrt{31}$$

65. $x^2 - 2x + 3 = 0$

$a = 1,\ b = -2,\ c = 3$

$$x = \frac{-(-2) \pm \sqrt{(-2)^2 - 4(1)(3)}}{2(1)}$$

$$x = \frac{2 \pm \sqrt{4 - 12}}{2} = \frac{2 \pm \sqrt{-8}}{2}$$

No real solution

66. $2x^2 - x - 3 = 0$

$a = 2,\ b = -1,\ c = -3$

$$x = \frac{-(-1) \pm \sqrt{(-1)^2 - 4(2)(-3)}}{2(2)}$$

$$x = \frac{1 \pm \sqrt{1 + 24}}{4} = \frac{1 \pm \sqrt{25}}{4} = \frac{1 \pm 5}{4}$$

$$x = \frac{6}{4} = \frac{3}{2} \text{ or } x = \frac{-4}{4} = -1$$

67. $x^2 - 4x + 2 = 0$

$a = 1,\ b = -4,\ c = 2$

$$x = \frac{-(-4) \pm \sqrt{(-4)^2 - 4(1)(2)}}{2(1)}$$

$$x = \frac{4 \pm \sqrt{16 - 8}}{2} = \frac{4 \pm \sqrt{8}}{2} = \frac{4 \pm 2\sqrt{2}}{2}$$

$$x = 2 \pm \sqrt{2}$$

68. $2x^2 - 5x - 2 = 0$

$a = 2,\ b = -5,\ c = -2$

$$x = \frac{-(-5) \pm \sqrt{(-5)^2 - 4(2)(-2)}}{2(2)}$$

$$x = \frac{5 \pm \sqrt{25 + 16}}{4} = \frac{5 \pm \sqrt{41}}{4}$$

69. $2x^2 - x = 4$

$2x^2 - x - 4 = 0$

$a = 2,\ b = -1,\ c = -4$

$$x = \frac{-(-1) \pm \sqrt{(-1)^2 - 4(2)(-4)}}{2(2)}$$

$$x = \frac{1 \pm \sqrt{1 + 32}}{4} = \frac{1 \pm \sqrt{33}}{4}$$

70. $5x^2 + 3x - 3 = 0$

$a = 5,\ b = 3,\ c = -3$

$$x = \frac{-3 \pm \sqrt{(3)^2 - 4(5)(-3)}}{2(5)}$$

$$x = \frac{-3 \pm \sqrt{9 + 60}}{10} = \frac{-3 \pm \sqrt{69}}{10}$$

71. $4x^2 - x - 1 = 0$

$a = 4,\ b = -1,\ c = -1$

$$x = \frac{-(-1) \pm \sqrt{(-1)^2 - 4(4)(-1)}}{2(4)}$$

$$x = \frac{1 \pm \sqrt{1 + 16}}{8} = \frac{1 \pm \sqrt{17}}{8}$$

72. $4x^2 - 5x - 3 = 0$

$a = 4,\ b = -5,\ c = -3$

$$x = \frac{-(-5) \pm \sqrt{(-5)^2 - 4(4)(-3)}}{2(4)}$$

$$x = \frac{5 \pm \sqrt{25 + 48}}{8} = \frac{5 \pm \sqrt{73}}{8}$$

73. $2x^2 + 7x + 5 = 0$

$a = 2$, $b = 7$, $c = 5$

$$x = \frac{-7 \pm \sqrt{(7)^2 - 4(2)(5)}}{2(2)}$$

$$x = \frac{-7 \pm \sqrt{49 - 40}}{4} = \frac{-7 \pm \sqrt{9}}{4} = \frac{-7 \pm 3}{4}$$

$$x = \frac{-4}{4} = -1 \text{ or } x = \frac{-10}{4} = -\frac{5}{2}$$

74. $3x^2 = 9x - 5$

$3x^2 - 9x + 5 = 0$

$a = 3$, $b = -9$, $c = 5$

$$x = \frac{-(-9) \pm \sqrt{(-9)^2 - 4(3)(5)}}{2(3)}$$

$$x = \frac{9 \pm \sqrt{81 - 60}}{6} = \frac{9 \pm \sqrt{21}}{6}$$

75. $3x^2 - 10x + 7 = 0$

$a = 3$, $b = -10$, $c = 7$

$$x = \frac{-(-10) \pm \sqrt{(-10)^2 - 4(3)(7)}}{2(3)}$$

$$x = \frac{10 \pm \sqrt{100 - 84}}{6} = \frac{10 \pm \sqrt{16}}{6} = \frac{10 \pm 4}{6}$$

$$x = \frac{14}{6} = \frac{7}{3} \text{ or } x = \frac{6}{6} = 1$$

76. $4x^2 + 7x - 1 = 0$

$a = 4$, $b = 7$, $c = -1$

$$x = \frac{-7 \pm \sqrt{(7)^2 - 4(4)(-1)}}{2(4)}$$

$$x = \frac{-7 \pm \sqrt{49 + 16}}{8} = \frac{-7 \pm \sqrt{65}}{8}$$

77. $4x^2 - 11x + 13 = 0$

$a = 4$, $b = -11$, $c = 13$

$$x = \frac{-(-11) \pm \sqrt{(-11)^2 - 4(4)(13)}}{2(4)}$$

$$x = \frac{11 \pm \sqrt{121 - 208}}{8} = \frac{11 \pm \sqrt{-87}}{8}$$

No real solution

78. $5x^2 + 9x - 2 = 0$

$a = 5$, $b = 9$, $c = -2$

$$x = \frac{-9 \pm \sqrt{(9)^2 - 4(5)(-2)}}{2(5)}$$

$$x = \frac{-9 \pm \sqrt{81 + 40}}{10} = \frac{-9 \pm \sqrt{121}}{10} = \frac{-9 \pm 11}{10}$$

$$x = \frac{2}{10} = \frac{1}{5} \text{ or } x = \frac{-20}{10} = -2$$

79. $45,000 = x^2 + 15x - 100$

$x^2 + 15x - 45,100 = 0$

$(x + 220)(x - 205) = 0$

$x + 220 = 0$ or $x - 205 = 0$

$x = -220 \qquad x = 205$

Cannot produce a negative number of air conditioners. Thus, $x = 205$.

80. a) Since the equation is equal to 6 and not 0, the zero-factor property cannot be used.

b) $(x - 4)(x - 7) = 6$

$x^2 - 11x + 28 = 6$

$x^2 - 11x + 22 = 0$

$a = 1$, $b = -11$, $c = 22$

$$x = \frac{-(-11) \pm \sqrt{(-11)^2 - 4(1)(22)}}{2(1)}$$

$$x = \frac{11 \pm \sqrt{121 - 88}}{2} = \frac{11 \pm \sqrt{33}}{2}$$

$x \approx 8.37$ or $x \approx 2.63$

81. $x = \dfrac{-b \pm \sqrt{b^2 - 4ac}}{2a}$

The $b^2 - 4ac$ is the radicand in the quadratic formula, the part under the square root sign.

a) If $b^2 - 4ac > 0$, then you are taking the square root of a positive number and there are two solutions.

These solutions are $x = \dfrac{-b + \sqrt{b^2 - 4ac}}{2a}$ and $x = \dfrac{-b - \sqrt{b^2 - 4ac}}{2a}$.

b) If $b^2 - 4ac = 0$, then you are taking the square root of zero and there is one solution. This solution

is $x = \dfrac{-b \pm \sqrt{0}}{2a} = \dfrac{-b}{2a}$.

c) If $b^2 - 4ac < 0$, then you are taking the square root of a negative number and there is no real solution.

Exercise Set 6.10

1. A **function** is a special type of relation where each value of the independent variable corresponds to a unique value of the dependent variable.
2. A **relation** is any set of ordered pairs.
3. The **domain** of a function is the set of values that can be used for the independent variable.
4. The **range** of a function is the set of values obtained for the dependent variable.
5. The vertical line test can be used to determine if a graph represents a function. If a vertical line can be drawn so that it intersects the graph at more than one point, then each value of x does not have a unique value of y and the graph does not represent a function. If a vertical line cannot be made to intersect the graph in at least two different places, then the graph represents a function.
6. The area of a square is a function of the length of a side, the average stopping distance of a car is a function of its speed, the cost of apples is a function of the number of apples

7. Function since each value of x is paired with a unique value of y.
   D: -2, -1, 1, 2, 3   R: -1, 1, 2, 3

8. Not a function since x = 2 is not paired with a unique value of y.

9. Function since each vertical line intersects the graph at only one point.
   D: all real numbers   R: all real numbers

10. Function since each vertical line intersects the graph at only one point.
    D: all real numbers   R: all real numbers

11. Function since each vertical line intersects the graph at only one point.
    D: all real numbers   R: y = 2

12. Not a function since x = -1 is not paired with a unique value of y.

13. Function since each vertical line intersects the graph at only one point.
    D: all real numbers   R: y ≥ -4

14. Function since each vertical line intersects the graph at only one point.
    D: all real numbers   R: y ≤ 10

15. Not a function since it is possible to draw a vertical line that intersects the graph at more than one point.

16. Function since each vertical line intersects the graph at only one point.
    D: 0 ≤ x ≤ 8   R: -1 ≤ y ≤ 1

17. Function since each vertical line intersects the graph at only one point.
    D: 0 ≤ x < 12   R: y = 1, 2, 3

18. Function since each vertical line intersects the graph at only one point.
    D: all real numbers   R: all real numbers

19. Not a function since it is possible to draw a vertical line that intersects the graph at more than one point.

20. Function since each vertical line intersects the graph at only one point.
    D: all real numbers   R: all real numbers

21. Function since each vertical line intersects the graph at only one point.
    D: all real numbers   R: y > 0

22. Function since each vertical line intersects the graph at only one point.
    D: $0 \leq x \leq 10$ R: $-1 \leq y \leq 3$

23. Function since each value of x is paired with a unique value of y.

24. Function since each value of x is paired with a unique value of y.

25. Not a function since x = 2 is paired with two different values of y.

26. Not a function since x = 1 is paired with three different values of y.

27. Function since each value of x is paired with a unique value of y.

28. Not a function since x = 1 is paired with three different values of y.

29. $f(x) = x + 6, \; x = 9$
    $f(9) = 9 + 6 = 15$

30. $f(x) = 3x + 10, \; x = 2$
    $f(2) = 3(2) + 10 = 6 + 10 = 16$

31. $f(x) = -2x - 7, \; x = -4$
    $f(-4) = -2(-4) - 7 = 8 - 7 = 1$

32. $f(x) = -5x + 3, \; x = -1$
    $f(-1) = -5(-1) + 3 = 5 + 3 = 8$

33. $f(x) = 10x - 6, \; x = 0$
    $f(0) = 10(0) - 6 = 0 - 6 = -6$

34. $f(x) = 7x - 6, \; x = 4$
    $f(4) = 7(4) - 6 = 28 - 6 = 22$

35. $f(x) = x^2 + 2x + 4, \; x = 6$
    $f(6) = (6)^2 + 2(6) + 4 = 36 + 12 + 4 = 52$

36. $f(x) = x^2 - 12, \; x = 6$
    $f(6) = (6)^2 - 12 = 36 - 12 = 24$

37. $f(x) = 2x^2 - 2x - 8, \; x = -2$
    $f(-2) = 2(-2)^2 - 2(-2) - 8 = 8 + 4 - 8 = 4$

38. $f(x) = -x^2 + 3x + 7, \; x = 2$
    $f(2) = -(2)^2 + 3(2) + 7 = -4 + 6 + 7 = 9$

39. $f(x) = -3x^2 + 5x + 4, \; x = -3$
    $f(-3) = -3(-3)^2 + 5(-3) + 4 = -27 - 15 + 4 = -38$

40. $f(x) = 5x^2 + 2x + 5, \; x = 4$
    $f(4) = 5(4)^2 + 2(4) + 5 = 80 + 8 + 5 = 93$

41. $f(x) = -6x^2 - 6x - 12, \; x = -3$
    $f(-3) = -6(-3)^2 - 6(-3) - 12 = -54 + 18 - 12 = -48$

42. $f(x) = -3x^2 + 5x - 9, \; x = -2$
    $f(-2) = -3(-2)^2 + 5(-2) - 9 = -12 - 10 - 9 = -31$

43.

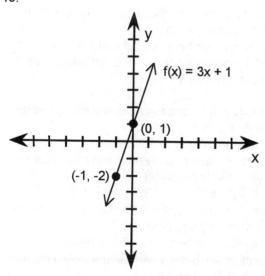

44.

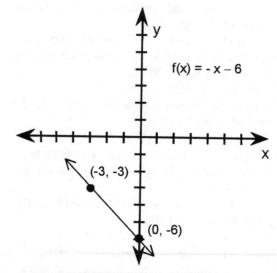

45.

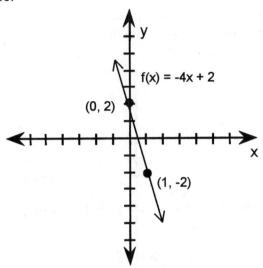

46.

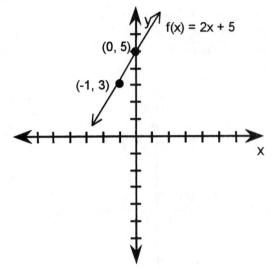

47.

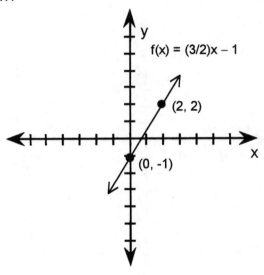

48.

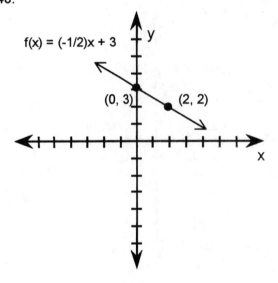

49. $y = x^2 - 1$

   a) $a = 1 > 0$, opens upward

   b) $x = 0$ c) (0, -1)   d) (0, -1)

   e)   (-1, 0), (1, 0)

   f)

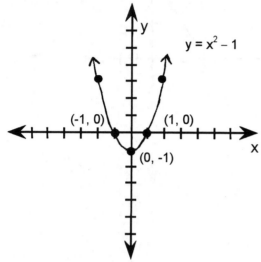

   g)   D: all real numbers   R: $y \geq -1$

50. $y = x^2 - 4$

   a) $a = 1 > 0$, opens upward

   b) $x = 0$ c) (0, -4)   d) (0, -4)

   e)   (-2, 0), (2, 0)

   f)

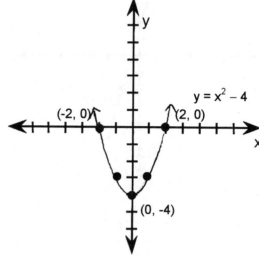

   g)   D: all real numbers   R: $y \geq -4$

51. $y = -x^2 + 4$

   a) $a = -1 < 0$, opens downward

   b) $x = 0$ c) (0, 4)   d) (0, 4)

   e)   (-2, 0), (2, 0)

   f)

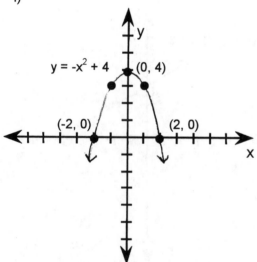

   g)   D: all real numbers   R: $y \leq 4$

52. $y = -x^2 + 16$

   a) $a = -1 < 0$, opens downward

   b) $x = 0$ c) (0, 16)   d) (0, 16)

   e)   (-4, 0), (4, 0)

   f)

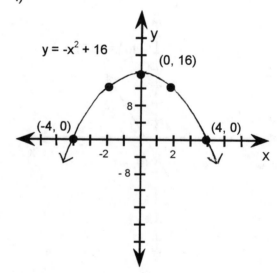

   g)   D: all real numbers   R: $y \leq 16$

53. f(x) = $-x^2 - 4$
   a) a = $-1 < 0$, opens downward
   b) x = 0   c) (0,-4)   d) (0,-4)
   e) no x-intercepts
   f)

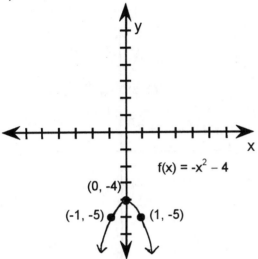

   g) D : all real numbers   R: y ≤ -4

54. y = $-2x^2 - 8$
   a) a = $-2 < 0$, opens downward
   b) x = 0   c) (0,-8)   d) (0,-8)
   e) no x-intercepts
   f)

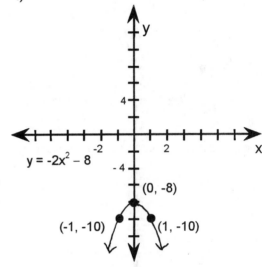

   g) D: all real numbers   R: y ≤ -8

55. y = $2x^2 - 3$
   a) a = 2 > 0, opens upward
   b) x = 0   c) (0,− 3)   d) (0,− 3)
   e) $(-1.22, 0)$, $(1.22, 0)$
   f)

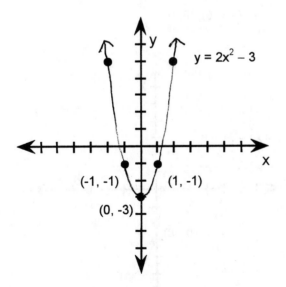

   g) D: all real numbers   R: y ≥ − 3

56. f(x) = $-3x^2 - 6$
   a) a = − 3 < 0, opens downward
   b) x = 0   c) (0,− 6)   d) (0,− 6)
   e) no x-intercepts
   f)

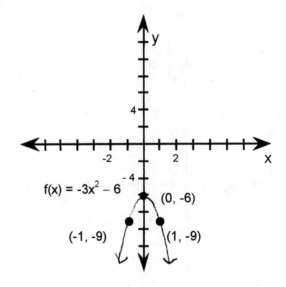

   g) D: all real numbers   R: y ≤ − 6

57. $f(x) = x^2 + 4x + 10$
   a) $a = 1 > 0$, opens upward
   b) $x = -2$ c) $(-2, 6)$ d) $(0, 10)$
   e) no x-intercepts
   f)

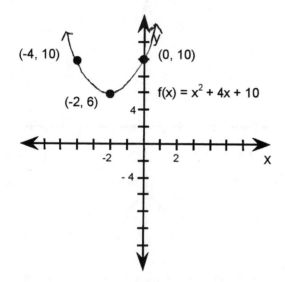

   g) D: all real numbers   R: $y \geq 6$

58. $y = x^2 - 2x + 8$
   a) $a = 1 > 0$, opens upward
   b) $x = 1$ c) $(1, 7)$ d) $(0, 8)$
   e) no x-intercepts
   f)

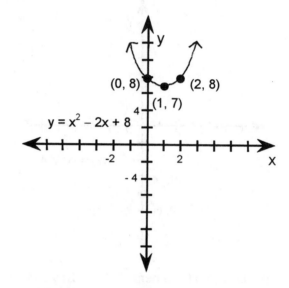

   g) D: all real numbers   R: $y \geq 7$

59. $y = x^2 + 5x + 6$
   a) $a = 1 > 0$, opens upward
   b) $x = -\dfrac{5}{2}$ c) $(-2.5, -0.25)$ d) $(0, 6)$
   e) $(-3, 0), (-2, 0)$
   f)

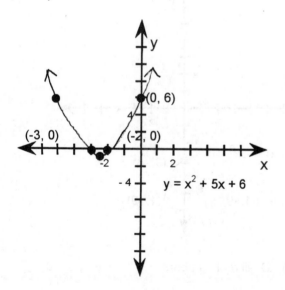

   g) D: all real numbers   R: $y \geq -0.25$

60. $y = x^2 - 7x - 8$
   a) $a = 1 > 0$, opens upward
   b) $x = \dfrac{7}{2}$ c) $\left(\dfrac{7}{2}, -\dfrac{81}{4}\right)$ d) $(0, -8)$
   e) $(-1, 0), (8, 0)$
   f)

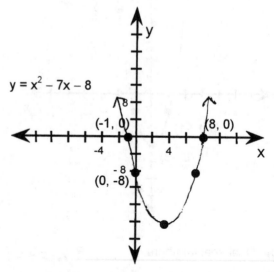

   g) D: all real numbers   R: $y \geq -\dfrac{81}{4}$

61. $y = -x^2 + 4x - 6$
   a) $a = -1 < 0$, opens downward
   b) $x = 2$ c) $(2, -2)$ d) $(0, -6)$
   e) no x-intercepts
   f)

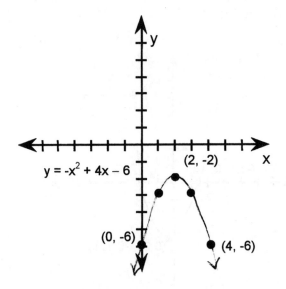

   g) D: all real numbers   R: $y \le -2$

62. $y = -x^2 + 8x - 8$
   a) $a = -1 < 0$, opens downward
   b) $x = 4$ c) $(4, 8)$ d) $(0, -8)$
   e) $(1.17, 0)$, $(6.83, 0)$
   f)

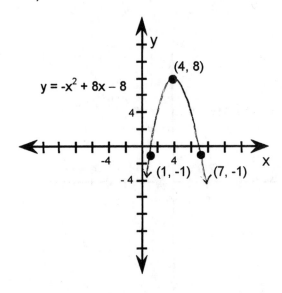

   g) D: all real numbers   R: $y \le 8$

63. $y = -3x^2 + 14x - 8$
    a) $a = -3 < 0$, opens downward
    b) $x = \dfrac{7}{3}$ c) $\left(\dfrac{7}{3}, \dfrac{25}{3}\right)$ d) $(0, -8)$
    e) $\left(\dfrac{2}{3}, 0\right), (4, 0)$
    f)

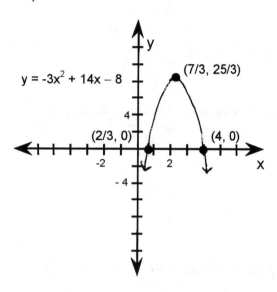

    g)   D: all real numbers   R: $y \leq \dfrac{25}{3}$

64. $y = 2x^2 - x - 6$
    a) $a = 2 > 0$, opens upward
    b) $x = \dfrac{1}{4}$ c) $\left(\dfrac{1}{4}, -6.125\right)$ d) $(0, -6)$
    e) $(2, 0), \left(-\dfrac{3}{2}, 0\right)$
    f)

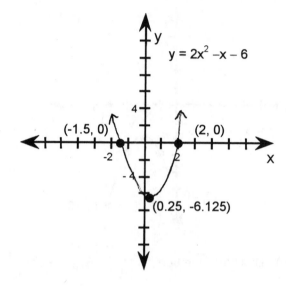

    g)   D: all real numbers   R: $y \geq -6.125$

65. $y = 3^x$

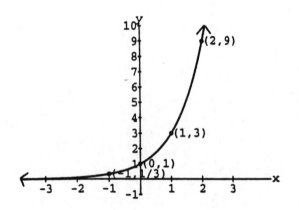

D: all real numbers   R: $y > 0$

66. $y = 4^x$

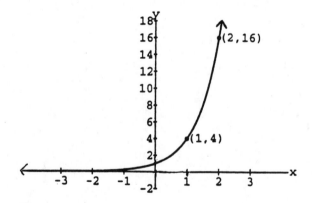

D: all real numbers   R: $y > 0$

67. $y = \left(\dfrac{1}{3}\right)^x$

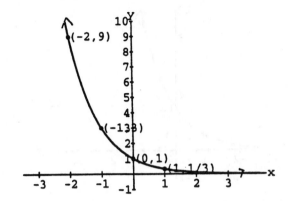

D: all real numbers   R: $y > 0$

68. $y = \left(\dfrac{1}{4}\right)^x$

D: all real numbers   R: $y > 0$

69. $y = 2^x + 1$

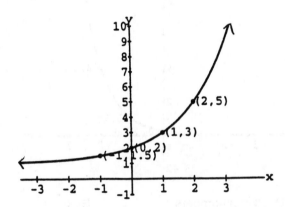

D: all real numbers   R: $y > 1$

70. $y = 3^x - 1$

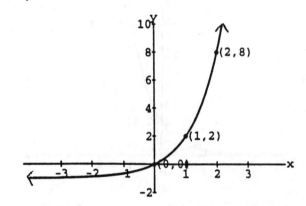

D: all real numbers   R: $y > -1$

71. $y = 4^x + 1$

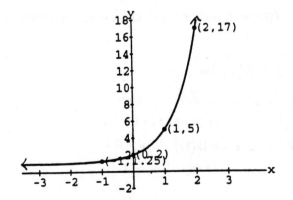

D: all real numbers   R: $y > 1$

72. $y = 2^x - 1$

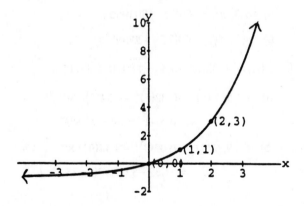

D: all real numbers   R: $y > -1$

73. $y = 3^{x-1}$

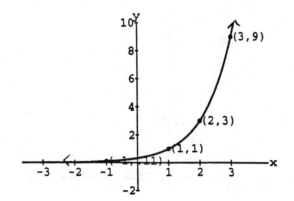

D: all real numbers   R: $y > 0$

74. $y = 3^{x+1}$

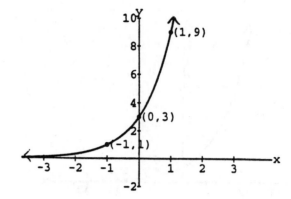

D: all real numbers   R: $y > 0$

75. $y = 4^{x+1}$

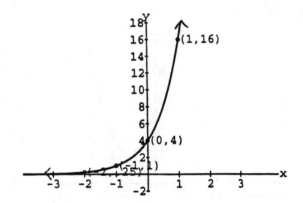

D: all real numbers   R: $y > 0$

76. $y = 4^{x-1}$

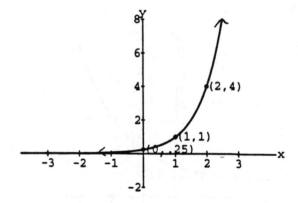

D: all real numbers   R: $y > 0$

77. $d(t) = 60t$

   a) $t = 3$, $d(3) = 60(3) = 180$ miles

   b) $t = 7$, $d(7) = 60(7) = 420$ miles

79. $T(A) = -0.02A^2 - 0.34A + 80$, $0 \le A \le 15$

   a) $A = 5$, $T(5) = -0.02(5)^2 - 0.34(5) + 80$

                $= -0.5 - 1.7 + 80 = 77.8°F$

   b) $A = 9$, $T(9) = -0.02(9)^2 - 0.34(9) + 80$

                $= -1.62 - 3.06 + 80 = 75.32°F$

78. $f(x) = 160 + 0.01x$

   $f(90{,}000) = 160 + 0.01(90{,}000) = 160 + 900 = \$1060$

80. $d = f(v) = 0.18v + 0.01v^2$

   a) $v = 88$, $d = 0.18(88) + 0.01(88)^2$

            $= 15.84 + 77.44 = 93.28$ m.

   b) $v = 72$, $d = 0.18(72) + 0.01(72)^2$

            $= 12.96 + 51.84 = 64.8$ m.

81. $P(x) = 4000(1.3)^{0.1x}$

    a) $x = 10$, $P(10) = 4000(1.3)^{0.1(10)}$

                $= 4000(1.3) = 5200$ people

    b) $x = 50$, $P(50) = 4000(1.3)^{0.1(50)}$

                $= 4000(3.71293)$

                $= 14{,}851.72 \approx 14{,}852$ people

82. $P = P_0 e^{-0.00003\,t}$

    $P = 2000 e^{-0.00003\,(50)}$

       $= 2000 e^{-0.0015}$

       $= 2000(0.9985011244)$

       $= 1997.002249 \approx 1997$ grams

83. a) Yes, the average salary increased rapidly from 1960 to 1995.

    b) $\approx \$700{,}000$

84. a) No, the average cost is increasing and then decreasing.

    b) $\approx \$1200$

85. $d = (21.9)(2)^{(20-x)/12}$

    a) $x = 19$, $d = (21.9)(2)^{(20-19)/12}$

              $= (21.9)(1.059463094) \approx 23.2$ cm.

    b) $x = 4$, $d = (21.9)(2)^{(20-4)/12}$

              $= (21.9)(2.519842099) \approx 55.2$ cm.

    c) $x = 0$, $d = (21.9)(2)^{(20-0)/12}$

              $= (21.9)(3.174802105) \approx 69.5$ cm.

86. $f(n) = 85{,}000(1.04)^n$

    a) $f(8) = 85{,}000(1.04)^8$

            $= 85{,}000(1.36856905) \approx 116{,}328$;

    The value of the house after 8 years is about $\$116{,}328$.

    b) 15 years since $f(14) \approx \$147{,}192.50$ and $f(15) \approx \$153{,}080.20$

87. $f(x) = -0.85x + 187$

    a) $f(20) = -0.85(20) + 187 = 170$ beats per minute

    b) $f(30) = -0.85(30) + 187 = 161.5 \approx 162$ beats per minute

    c) $f(50) = -0.85(50) + 187 = 144.5 \approx 145$ beats per minute

    d) $f(60) = -0.85(60) + 187 = 136$ beats per minute

    e) $-0.85x + 187 = 85$

       $-0.85x = -102$

       $x = 120$ years of age

88. $d(t) = 186{,}000t$

    a) $t = 1.3$, $d(1.3) = 186{,}000(1.3) = 241{,}800$ miles

    b) $186{,}000\,\dfrac{m}{\sec} \times 60\,\dfrac{\sec}{\min} = 11{,}160{,}000\,\dfrac{m}{\min}$

       $d(t) = 11{,}160{,}000t$

    c) $d(8.3) = 11{,}160{,}000(8.3) = 92{,}628{,}000$ miles

Review Exercises

1. $x = 4,\ x^2 + 7 = (4)^2 + 7 = 16 + 7 = 23$

2. $x = -3,\ -x^2 + 8 = -(-3)^2 + 8 = -9 + 8 = -1$

3. $x = 2,\ 4x^2 - 2x + 5 = 4(2)^2 - 2(2) + 5$
$$= 16 - 4 + 5 = 17$$

4. $x = \dfrac{1}{2},\ -x^2 + 7x - 3 = -\left(\dfrac{1}{2}\right)^2 + 7\left(\dfrac{1}{2}\right) - 3$
$$= -\dfrac{1}{4} + \dfrac{14}{4} - \dfrac{12}{4} = \dfrac{1}{4}$$

5. $x = -2,\ 4x^3 - 7x^2 + 3x + 1$
$$= 4(-2)^3 - 7(-2)^2 + 3(-2) + 1$$
$$= -32 - 28 - 6 + 1 = -65$$

6. $x = 2,\ y = -1,\ 4x^2 - 2xy + 3y^2$
$$= 4(2)^2 - 2(2)(-1) + 3(-1)^2$$
$$= 16 + 4 + 3 = 23$$

7. $2x + 5 - 8 - x = x - 3$

8. $3x + 4(x - 2) + 6x = 3x + 4x - 8 + 6x = 13x - 8$

9. $2(x - 4) + \dfrac{1}{2}(2x + 3) = 2x - 8 + x + \dfrac{3}{2}$
$$= 3x - \dfrac{16}{2} + \dfrac{3}{2} = 3x - \dfrac{13}{2}$$

10.
$$-2r - 8 = 20$$
$$-2r - 8 + 8 = 20 + 8$$
$$-2r = 28$$
$$\dfrac{-2r}{-2} = \dfrac{28}{-2}$$
$$r = -14$$

11.
$$3t + 8 = 6t - 13$$
$$3t - 3t + 8 = 6t - 3t - 13$$
$$8 = 3t - 13$$
$$8 + 13 = 3t - 13 + 13$$
$$21 = 3t$$
$$\dfrac{21}{3} = \dfrac{3t}{3}$$
$$7 = t$$

12.
$$\dfrac{x + 5}{6} = \dfrac{x - 3}{3}$$
$$3(x + 5) = 6(x - 3)$$
$$3x + 15 = 6x - 18$$
$$3x - 3x + 15 = 6x - 3x - 18$$
$$15 = 3x - 18$$
$$15 + 18 = 3x - 18 + 18$$
$$33 = 3x$$
$$\dfrac{33}{3} = \dfrac{3x}{3}$$
$$11 = x$$

13.
$$4(x - 2) = 3 + 5(x + 4)$$
$$4x - 8 = 3 + 5x + 20$$
$$4x - 8 = 5x + 23$$
$$4x - 4x - 8 = 5x - 4x + 23$$
$$-8 = x + 23$$
$$-8 - 23 = x + 23 - 23$$
$$-31 = x$$

14.
$$\dfrac{x}{3} + \dfrac{2}{5} = 4$$
$$15\left(\dfrac{x}{3} + \dfrac{2}{5}\right) = 15(4)$$
$$5x + 6 = 60$$
$$5x + 6 - 6 = 60 - 6$$
$$5x = 54$$
$$\dfrac{5x}{5} = \dfrac{54}{5}$$
$$x = \dfrac{54}{5}$$

15. $\dfrac{\dfrac{2}{1}}{\dfrac{1}{3}} = \dfrac{3}{x}$

$2x = 3\left(\dfrac{1}{3}\right)$

$2x = 1$

$\dfrac{2x}{2} = \dfrac{1}{2}$

$x = \dfrac{1}{2}$ cup

16. $1\,hr.\ 40\,min. = 100\,min.$

$\dfrac{120}{100} = \dfrac{450}{x}$

$120x = 100(450)$

$120x = 45,000$

$\dfrac{120x}{120} = \dfrac{45,000}{120}$

$x = 375\,mins.$ **or** $6\,hrs.\ 15\,mins.$

17. $A = lw$

$A = 13(8) = 104$

18. $V = 2\pi R^2 r^2$

$V = 2(3.14)(3)^2(1.75)^2$

$V = 2(3.14)(9)(3.0625)$

$V = 173.0925 \approx 173.1$

19. $Z = \dfrac{\bar{x} - \mu}{\dfrac{\sigma}{\sqrt{n}}}$

$2 = \dfrac{\bar{x} - 100}{\dfrac{3}{\sqrt{16}}}$

$\dfrac{2}{1} = \dfrac{\bar{x} - 100}{\dfrac{3}{4}}$

$2\left(\dfrac{3}{4}\right) = 1(\bar{x} - 100)$

$\dfrac{3}{2} = \bar{x} - 100$

$\dfrac{3}{2} + 100 = \bar{x} - 100 + 100$

$\dfrac{3}{2} + \dfrac{200}{2} = \bar{x}$

$\dfrac{203}{2} = \bar{x}$

$101.5 = \bar{x}$

20. $K = \dfrac{1}{2}mv^2$

$4500 = \dfrac{1}{2}m(30)^2$

$4500 = 450m$

$\dfrac{4500}{450} = \dfrac{450m}{450}$

$10 = m$

21. $\quad 4x - 6y = 12$

$4x - 4x - 6y = -4x + 12$

$-6y = -4x + 12$

$\dfrac{-6y}{-6} = \dfrac{-4x + 12}{-6}$

$y = \dfrac{-4x + 12}{-6} = \dfrac{-4}{-6}x + \dfrac{12}{-6} = \dfrac{2}{3}x - 2$

22. $\quad 5x + 6y = 18$

$5x - 5x + 6y = -5x + 18$

$6y = -5x + 18$

$\dfrac{6y}{6} = \dfrac{-5x + 18}{6}$

$y = \dfrac{-5x + 18}{6} = -\dfrac{5}{6}x + 3$

23.
$$2x - 3y + 52 = 30$$
$$2x - 2x - 3y + 52 = -2x + 30$$
$$-3y + 52 = -2x + 30$$
$$-3y + 52 - 52 = -2x + 30 - 52$$
$$-3y = -2x - 22$$
$$\frac{-3y}{-3} = \frac{-2x - 22}{-3}$$
$$y = \frac{-2x - 22}{-3} = \frac{2x + 22}{3} = \frac{2}{3}x + \frac{22}{3}$$

24.
$$-3x - 4y + 5z = 4$$
$$-3x + 3x - 4y + 5z = 3x + 4$$
$$-4y + 5z = 3x + 4$$
$$-4y + 5z - 5z = 3x - 5z + 4$$
$$-4y = 3x - 5z + 4$$
$$\frac{-4y}{-4} = \frac{3x - 5z + 4}{-4}$$
$$y = \frac{3x - 5z + 4}{-4} = \frac{-3x + 5z - 4}{4} = -\frac{3}{4}x + \frac{5}{4}z - 1$$

25. $A = lw$
$$\frac{A}{w} = \frac{lw}{w}$$
$$\frac{A}{w} = l$$

26.
$$P = 2l + 2w$$
$$P - 2l = 2l - 2l + 2w$$
$$P - 2l = 2w$$
$$\frac{P - 2l}{2} = \frac{2w}{2}$$
$$\frac{P - 2l}{2} = w$$

27.
$$L = 2(wh + lh)$$
$$L = 2wh + 2lh$$
$$L - 2wh = 2wh - 2wh + 2lh$$
$$L - 2wh = 2lh$$
$$\frac{L - 2wh}{2h} = \frac{2lh}{2h}$$
$$\frac{L - 2wh}{2h} = l \ \text{ or } \ l = \frac{L}{2h} - w$$

28.
$$a_n = a_1 + (n-1)d$$
$$a_n - a_1 = a_1 - a_1 + (n-1)d$$
$$a_n - a_1 = (n-1)d$$
$$\frac{a_n - a_1}{n-1} = \frac{(n-1)d}{n-1}$$
$$\frac{a_n - a_1}{n-1} = d$$

29. $7 - 4x$

30. $5x - 3$

31. $10 + 3r$

32. $\dfrac{8}{q} - 11$

33. Let $x =$ the number
$3x = 3$ times a number
$12 - 3x = 12$ decreased by 3 times a number
$$12 - 3x = 21$$
$$12 - 12 - 3x = 21 - 12$$
$$-3x = 9$$
$$\frac{-3x}{-3} = \frac{9}{-3}$$
$$x = -3$$

34. Let $x =$ the number
$3x =$ the product of 3 and a number
$3x + 8 =$ the product of 3 and a number increased by 8
$x - 6 = 6$ less than the number
$$3x + 8 = x - 6$$
$$3x - x + 8 = x - x - 6$$
$$2x + 8 = -6$$
$$2x + 8 - 8 = -6 - 8$$
$$2x = -14$$
$$\frac{2x}{2} = \frac{-14}{2}$$
$$x = -7$$

35. Let $x =$ the number

$x - 4 =$ the difference of a number and 4

$5(x - 4) = 5$ times the difference of a number and 4

$5(x - 4) = 45$

$5x - 20 = 45$

$5x - 20 + 20 = 45 + 20$

$5x = 65$

$\dfrac{5x}{5} = \dfrac{65}{5}$

$x = 13$

36. Let $x =$ the number

$10x = 10$ times a number

$10x + 14 = 14$ more than 10 times a number

$x + 12 =$ the sum of a number and 12

$8(x + 12) = 8$ times the sum of a number and 12

$10x + 14 = 8(x + 12)$

$10x + 14 = 8x + 96$

$10x - 8x + 14 = 8x - 8x + 96$

$2x + 14 = 96$

$2x + 14 - 14 = 96 - 14$

$2x = 82$

$\dfrac{2x}{2} = \dfrac{82}{2}$

$x = 41$

37. Let $x =$ Marie's income

$\dfrac{1}{3}x =$ Wesley's income

$x + \dfrac{1}{3}x = 48{,}000$

$\dfrac{4}{3}x = 48{,}000$

$\dfrac{3}{4}\left(\dfrac{4}{3}x\right) = \dfrac{3}{4}(48{,}000)$

$x = \$36{,}000$ Marie's income

$\dfrac{1}{3}x = \dfrac{1}{3}(36{,}000) = \$12{,}000$ Wesley's income

38. Let $x =$ number of lawn chairs

$9.50x =$ variable cost per lawn chair

$9.50x + 15{,}000 = 95{,}000$

$9.50x + 15{,}000 - 15{,}000 = 95{,}000 - 15{,}000$

$9.50x = 80{,}000$

$\dfrac{9.50x}{9.50} = \dfrac{80{,}000}{9.50}$

$x = 8421.052632 \approx 8421$ lawn chairs

39. Let $x =$ profit at restaurant B

$x + 12{,}000 =$ profit at restaurant A

$x + x + 12{,}000 = 68{,}000$

$2x + 12{,}000 = 68{,}000$

$2x + 12{,}000 - 12{,}000 = 68{,}000 - 12{,}000$

$2x = 56{,}000$

$\dfrac{2x}{2} = \dfrac{56{,}000}{2}$

$x = \$28{,}000$ for restaurant B

$x + 12{,}000 = 28{,}000 + 12{,}000 = \$40{,}000$ for restaurant A

40. Let $x =$ the number of rental hours

$15x =$ rental cost per hour

$15x = 300$

$\dfrac{15x}{15} = \dfrac{300}{15}$

$x = 20$ hours

41. $R = \dfrac{k}{S^2}$

    $8 = \dfrac{k}{(3)^2}$

    $k = 9(8) = 72$

    $R = \dfrac{72}{S^2}$

    $R = \dfrac{72}{(6)^2} = \dfrac{72}{36} = 2$

42. $m = kn$

    $80 = k(4)$

    $k = \dfrac{80}{4} = 20$

    $m = 20n$

    $m = 20(12) = 240$

43. $W = \dfrac{kL}{A}$

    $80 = \dfrac{k(100)}{20}$

    $100k = 1600$

    $k = \dfrac{1600}{100} = 16$

    $W = \dfrac{16L}{A}$

    $W = \dfrac{16(50)}{40} = \dfrac{800}{40} = 20$

44. $z = \dfrac{kxy}{r^2}$

    $12 = \dfrac{k(20)(8)}{(8)^2}$

    $160k = 768$

    $k = \dfrac{768}{160} = 4.8$

    $z = \dfrac{4.8xy}{r^2}$

    $z = \dfrac{4.8(10)(80)}{(3)^2} = \dfrac{3840}{9} = 426.\overline{6} \approx 426.7$

45. $\dfrac{1 \ in.}{30 \ mi.} = \dfrac{x \ in.}{120 \ mi.}$

    $30x = 120$

    $\dfrac{30x}{30} = \dfrac{120}{30}$

    $x = 4 \ in.$

46. $\dfrac{1 \ kWh}{\$0.162} = \dfrac{740 \ kWh}{x}$

    $x = \$119.88$

47. $d = kt^2$

    $16 = k(1)^2$

    $k = 16$

    $d = 16t^2$

    $d = 16(5)^2 = 16(25) = 400 \ ft.$

48. $A = kr^2$

    $78.5 = k(5)^2$

    $k = \dfrac{78.5}{25} = 3.14$

    $A = 3.14r^2$

    $A = 3.14(8)^2 = 3.14(64) = 200.96$

49.
$$6 + 7x \geq -3x - 4$$
$$6 - 6 + 7x \geq -3x - 4 - 6$$
$$7x \geq -3x - 10$$
$$7x + 3x \geq -3x + 3x - 10$$
$$10x \geq -10$$
$$\frac{10x}{10} \geq \frac{-10}{10}$$
$$x \geq -1$$

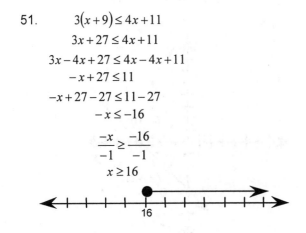

50.
$$3x + 7 \geq 5x + 9$$
$$3x - 5x + 7 \geq 5x - 5x + 9$$
$$-2x + 7 \geq 9$$
$$-2x + 7 - 7 \geq 9 - 7$$
$$-2x \geq 2$$
$$\frac{-2x}{-2} \leq \frac{2}{-2}$$
$$x \leq -1$$

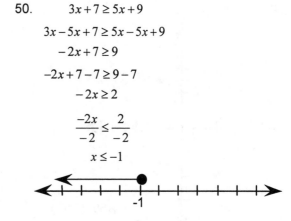

51.
$$3(x + 9) \leq 4x + 11$$
$$3x + 27 \leq 4x + 11$$
$$3x - 4x + 27 \leq 4x - 4x + 11$$
$$-x + 27 \leq 11$$
$$-x + 27 - 27 \leq 11 - 27$$
$$-x \leq -16$$
$$\frac{-x}{-1} \geq \frac{-16}{-1}$$
$$x \geq 16$$

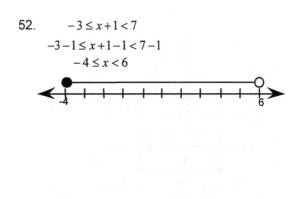

52.
$$-3 \leq x + 1 < 7$$
$$-3 - 1 \leq x + 1 - 1 < 7 - 1$$
$$-4 \leq x < 6$$

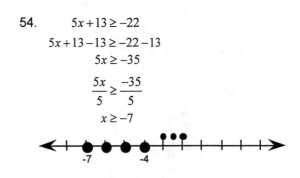

53.
$$2 + 7x > -12$$
$$2 - 2 + 7x > -12 - 2$$
$$7x > -14$$
$$\frac{7x}{7} > \frac{-14}{7}$$
$$x > -2$$

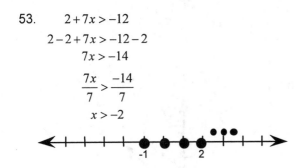

54.
$$5x + 13 \geq -22$$
$$5x + 13 - 13 \geq -22 - 13$$
$$5x \geq -35$$
$$\frac{5x}{5} \geq \frac{-35}{5}$$
$$x \geq -7$$

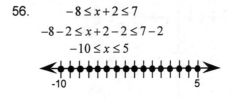

55. $-1 < x \leq 7$

56.
$$-8 \leq x + 2 \leq 7$$
$$-8 - 2 \leq x + 2 - 2 \leq 7 - 2$$
$$-10 \leq x \leq 5$$

57. - 60.

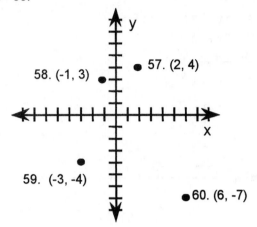

61.

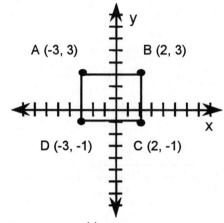

Area $= lw = 5(4) = 20$ square units

62.

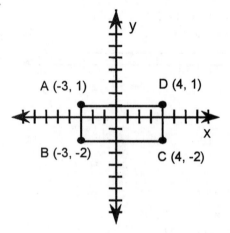

Area $= lw = 7(3) = 21$ square units

63. x - y = 4

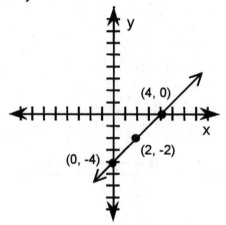

64. 2x + 3y = 12

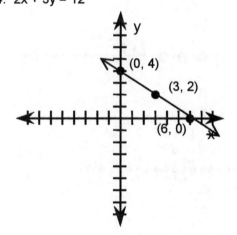

65. x = y

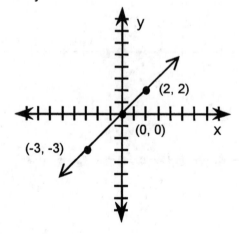

66. x = 3

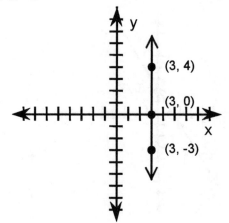

67. x + 4y = 8

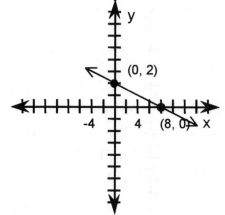

68. 3x - 2y = 6

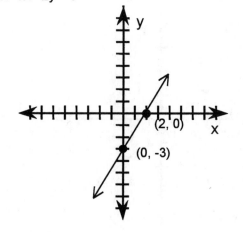

69. 4x - 3y = 12

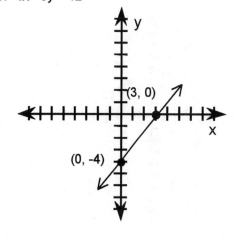

70. 2x + 3y = 9

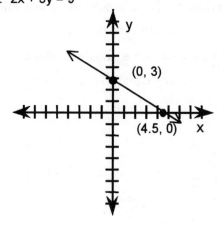

71. $m = \dfrac{2-3}{6-1} = -\dfrac{1}{5}$

72. $m = \dfrac{-4-(-1)}{5-3} = \dfrac{-4+1}{5-3} = -\dfrac{3}{2}$

73. $m = \dfrac{3-(-4)}{5-(-1)} = \dfrac{3+4}{5+1} = \dfrac{7}{6}$

74. $m = \dfrac{-2-2}{6-6} = \dfrac{-4}{0}$ Undefined

75. $y = 2x - 5$

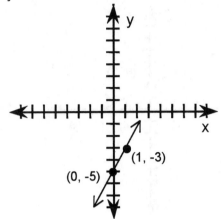

76. $2y - 4 = 3x$

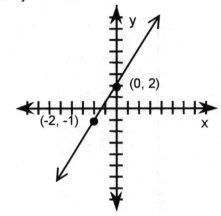

77. $2y + x = 8$

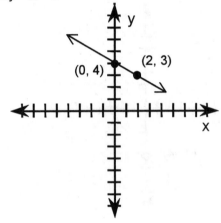

78. $y = -x - 1$

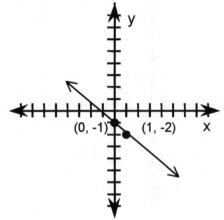

79. The y-intercept is 4, thus b = 4. Since the graph rises from left to right, the slope is positive. The change in y is 4 units while the change in x is 2. Thus, m, the slope is $\frac{4}{2}$ or 2. The equation is y = 2x + 4.

80. The y-intercept is 1, thus b = 1. Since the graph falls from left to right, the slope is negative. The change in y is 3 units while the change in x is 3. Thus, m, the slope is $\frac{-3}{3}$ or -1. The equation is y = -x + 1.

81. a)

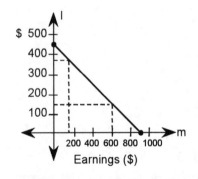

b) About $160
c) About $160

82. a)

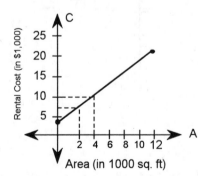

b) About $6400
c) About 4120 ft.^{2}

83. Graph 6x + 9y = 54. Since the original inequality is less than or equal to, a solid line is drawn. Since the point (0, 0) satisfies the inequality 6x + 9y ≤ 54, all points on the line and in the half-plane below the line 6x + 9y = 54 are in the solution set.

84. Graph 3x + 2y = 12. Since the original inequality is greater than or equal to, a solid line is drawn. Since the point (0, 0) does not satisfy the inequality 3x + 2y ≥ 12, all points in the half plane above the line 3x + 2y = 12 are in the solution set.

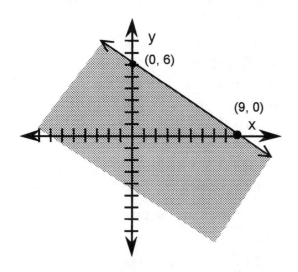

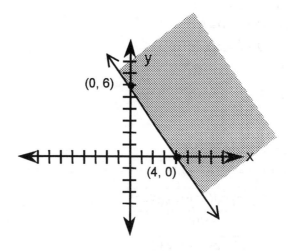

85. Graph 2x – 3y = 12. Since the original inequality is strictly greater than, a dashed line is drawn. Since the point (0, 0) does not satisfy the inequality 2x – 3y > 12, all points in the half-plane below the line 2x – 3y = 12 are in the solution set.

86. Graph -7x – 2y = 14. Since the original inequality is strictly less than, a dashed line is drawn. Since the point (0, 0) satisfies the inequality -7x – 2y < 14, all points in the half-plane to the right of the line -7x – 2y = 14 are in the solution set.

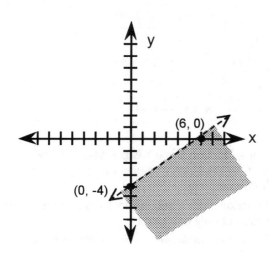

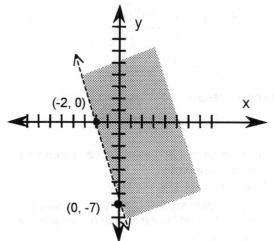

87. $x^2 + 9x + 18 = (x+3)(x+6)$

88. $x^2 + x - 20 = (x+5)(x-4)$

89. $x^2 - 10x + 24 = (x-6)(x-4)$

90. $x^2 - 9x + 20 = (x-4)(x-5)$

91. $2x^2 + x - 21 = (2x+7)(x-3)$

92. $3x^2 + 5x - 2 = (3x-1)(x+2)$

93. $x^2 + 5x + 6 = 0$

    $(x+2)(x+3) = 0$

    $x + 2 = 0$ or $x + 3 = 0$

    $x = -2 \qquad x = -3$

94. $x^2 - 6x = -5$

    $x^2 - 6x + 5 = 0$

    $(x-1)(x-5) = 0$

    $x - 1 = 0$ or $x - 5 = 0$

    $x = 1 \qquad x = 5$

95. $3x^2 - 17x + 10 = 0$

    $(3x-2)(x-5) = 0$

    $3x - 2 = 0$ or $x - 5 = 0$

    $3x = 2 \qquad x = 5$

    $x = \dfrac{2}{3}$

96. $3x^2 = -7x - 2$

    $3x^2 + 7x + 2 = 0$

    $(3x+1)(x+2) = 0$

    $3x + 1 = 0$ or $x + 2 = 0$

    $3x = -1 \qquad x = -2$

    $x = -\dfrac{1}{3}$

97. $x^2 - 3x - 7 = 0$

    $a = 1,\ b = -3,\ c = -7$

    $x = \dfrac{-(-3) \pm \sqrt{(-3)^2 - 4(1)(-7)}}{2(1)}$

    $x = \dfrac{3 \pm \sqrt{9+28}}{2} = \dfrac{3 \pm \sqrt{37}}{2}$

98. $x^2 - 3x + 2 = 0$

    $a = 1,\ b = -3,\ c = 2$

    $x = \dfrac{-(-3) \pm \sqrt{(-3)^2 - 4(1)(2)}}{2(1)}$

    $x = \dfrac{3 \pm \sqrt{9-8}}{2} = \dfrac{3 \pm \sqrt{1}}{2} = \dfrac{3 \pm 1}{2}$

    $x = \dfrac{4}{2} = 2$ or $x = \dfrac{2}{2} = 1$

99. $2x^2 - 3x + 4 = 0$

    $a = 2,\ b = -3,\ c = 4$

    $x = \dfrac{-(-3) \pm \sqrt{(-3)^2 - 4(2)(4)}}{2(2)}$

    $x = \dfrac{3 \pm \sqrt{9-32}}{4} = \dfrac{3 \pm \sqrt{-23}}{4}$

    No real solution

100. $2x^2 - x - 3 = 0$

    $a = 2,\ b = -1,\ c = -3$

    $x = \dfrac{-(-1) \pm \sqrt{(-1)^2 - 4(2)(-3)}}{2(2)}$

    $x = \dfrac{1 \pm \sqrt{1+24}}{4} = \dfrac{1 \pm \sqrt{25}}{4} = \dfrac{1 \pm 5}{4}$

    $x = \dfrac{6}{4} = \dfrac{3}{2}$ or $x = \dfrac{-4}{4} = -1$

101. Function since each value of x is paired with a unique value of y.

    D: x = -2, -1, 2, 3   R: y = -1, 0, 2

102. Not a function since it is possible to draw a vertical line that intersects the graph at more than one point.

103. Not a function since it is possible to draw a vertical line that intersects the graph at more than one point.

104. Function since each vertical line intersects the graph at only one point.

    D: all real numbers   R: all real numbers

105. $f(x) = 2x + 10,\ x = -3$

    $f(-3) = 2(-3) + 10 = -6 + 10 = 4$

106. $f(x) = -3x + 8,\ x = -2$

    $f(-2) = -3(-2) + 8 = 6 + 8 = 14$

107. $f(x) = 2x^2 - 3x + 4,\ x = 5$

    $f(5) = 2(5)^2 - 3(5) + 4 = 50 - 15 + 4 = 39$

108. $f(x) = -4x^2 + 7x + 9,\ x = 4$

    $f(4) = -4(4)^2 + 7(4) + 9 = -64 + 28 + 9 = -27$

109. $y = -x^2 - 4x + 21$
  a) $a = -1 < 0$, opens downward
  b) $x = -2$ c) $(-2, 25)$ d) $(0, 21)$
  e) $(-7, 0)$, $(3, 0)$
  f)

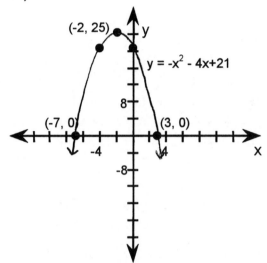

  g) D: all real numbers   R: $y \le 25$

110. $y = 3x^2 - 24x - 30$
  a) $a = 3 > 0$, opens upward
  b) $x = 4$ c) $(4, -78)$ d) $(0, -30)$
  e) $(4 - \sqrt{26}$, 0), $(4 + \sqrt{26}$, 0)
  f)

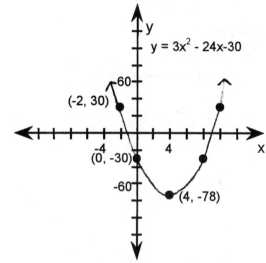

  g) D: all real numbers   R: $y \ge -78$

111. $y = 2^{2x}$

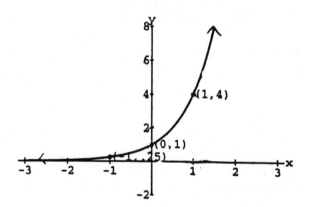

  D: all real numbers   R: $y > 0$

112. $y = \left(\dfrac{1}{2}\right)^x$

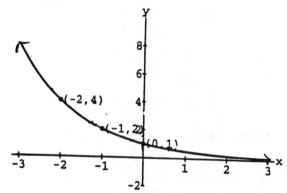

  D: all real numbers   R: $y > 0$

113. $m = 30 - 0.002n^2$, $n = 60$

  $m = 30 - 0.002(60)^2 = 30 - 0.002(3600)$
  $\qquad = 30 - 7.2 = 22.8$ miles per gallon

114. $n = 2a^2 - 80a + 5000$
  a) $a = 18$
  $\qquad n = 2(18)^2 - 80(18) + 5000$
  $\qquad\qquad = 648 - 1440 + 5000 = 4208$
  b) $a = 25$
  $\qquad n = 2(25)^2 - 80(25) + 5000$
  $\qquad\qquad = 1250 - 2000 + 5000 = 4250$

115. $P = 100(0.92)^x, \; x = 4.5$

 $P = 100(0.92)^{4.5}$

 $= 100(0.6871399881) = 68.71399881 \approx 68.7\%$

Chapter Test

1. $-3x^2 + 6x + 9, \; x = 2$

 $-3(2)^2 + 6(2) + 9 = -12 + 12 + 9 = 9$

2. $\quad 3x + 5 = 2(4x - 7)$

 $3x + 5 = 8x - 14$

 $3x - 8x + 5 = 8x - 8x - 14$

 $-5x + 5 = -14$

 $-5x + 5 - 5 = -14 - 5$

 $-5x = -19$

 $\dfrac{-5x}{-5} = \dfrac{-19}{-5}$

 $x = \dfrac{19}{5}$

3. $-2(x - 3) + 6x = 2x + 3(x - 4)$

 $-2x + 6 + 6x = 2x + 3x - 12$

 $4x + 6 = 5x - 12$

 $4x - 5x + 6 = 5x - 5x - 12$

 $-x + 6 = -12$

 $-x + 6 - 6 = -12 - 6$

 $-x = -18$

 $\dfrac{-x}{-1} = \dfrac{-18}{-1}$

 $x = 18$

4. Let $x =$ the number

 $3x =$ the product of a number and 3

 $3x - 10 =$ the product of a number and 3 decreased by 10

 $3x - 10 = 11$

 $3x - 10 + 10 = 11 + 10$

 $3x = 21$

 $\dfrac{3x}{3} = \dfrac{21}{3}$

 $x = 7$

5. Let $x =$ number of items

 $4.35x + 60 =$ his cost

 $7.75x =$ his revenue

 $7.75x = 4.35x + 60$

 $7.75x - 4.35x = 4.35x - 4.35x + 60$

 $3.4x = 60$

 $\dfrac{3.4x}{3.4} = \dfrac{60}{3.4}$

 $x = 17.64705882 \approx 18$ units

6. $L = ah + bh + ch; \; a = 3, \; b = 4, \; c = 5, \; h = 7$

 $L = 3(7) + 4(7) + 5(7)$

 $= 21 + 28 + 35 = 84$

7.
$$5x - 8y = 17$$
$$5x - 5x - 8y = -5x + 17$$
$$-8y = -5x + 17$$
$$\frac{-8y}{-8} = \frac{-5x + 17}{-8}$$
$$y = \frac{-5x + 17}{-8} = \frac{5x - 17}{8} = \frac{5}{8}x - \frac{17}{8}$$

8.
$$L = \frac{kMN}{P}$$
$$12 = \frac{k(8)(3)}{2}$$
$$24k = 24$$
$$k = \frac{24}{24} = 1$$
$$L = \frac{(1)MN}{P}$$
$$L = \frac{(1)(10)(5)}{15} = \frac{50}{15} = 3.\overline{3} = 3\frac{1}{3}$$

9.
$$l = \frac{k}{w}$$
$$15 = \frac{k}{9}$$
$$k = 15(9) = 135$$
$$l = \frac{135}{w}$$
$$l = \frac{135}{20} = 6.75 \text{ ft.}$$

10.
$$-3x + 11 \le 5x + 35$$
$$-3x - 5x + 11 \le 5x - 5x + 35$$
$$-8x + 11 \le 35$$
$$-8x + 11 - 11 \le 35 - 11$$
$$-8x \le 24$$
$$\frac{-8x}{-8} \ge \frac{24}{-8}$$
$$x \ge -3$$

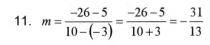

11. $m = \dfrac{-26 - 5}{10 - (-3)} = \dfrac{-26 - 5}{10 + 3} = -\dfrac{31}{13}$

12. y = 3x – 4

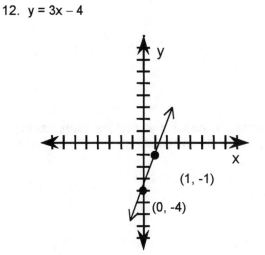

(1, -1)

(0, -4)

13. $2x - 3y = 15$

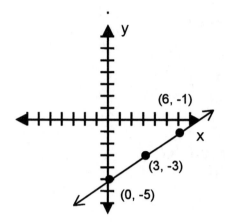

14. Graph $3y = 5x - 12$. Since the original statement is greater than or equal to, a solid line is drawn. Since the point $(0, 0)$ satisfies the inequality $3y \geq 5x - 12$, all points on the line and in the half-plane above the line

$3y = 5x - 12$ are in the solution set.

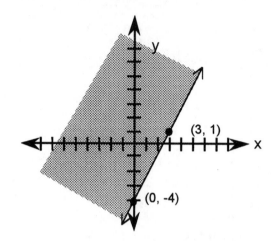

15. $x^2 - 3x = 28$

$x^2 - 3x - 28 = 0$

$(x - 7)(x + 4) = 0$

$x - 7 = 0$ or $x + 4 = 0$

$x = 7$ $\qquad$ $x = -4$

16. $3x^2 + 2x = 8$

$3x^2 + 2x - 8 = 0$

$a = 3, \ b = 2, \ c = -8$

$x = \dfrac{-2 \pm \sqrt{(2)^2 - 4(3)(-8)}}{2(3)}$

$x = \dfrac{-2 \pm \sqrt{4 + 96}}{6} = \dfrac{-2 \pm \sqrt{100}}{6} = \dfrac{-2 \pm 10}{6}$

$x = \dfrac{8}{6} = \dfrac{4}{3}$ or $x = \dfrac{-12}{6} = -2$

17. Function since each vertical line intersects the graph at only one point.

18. $f(x) = -4x^2 - 11x + 5, \ x = -2$

$f(-2) = -4(-2)^2 - 11(-2) + 5$

$\qquad = -16 + 22 + 5 = 11$

19. $y = x^2 - 2x + 4$

 a) $a = 1 > 0$, opens upward

 b) $x = 1$ c) $(1, 3)$ d) $(0, 4)$

 e) no x-intercepts

 f)

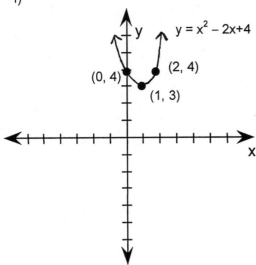

 g) D: all real numbers   R: $y \geq 3$

Group Projects

1. a) - b) Answers will vary.

 c) $h = 3.14H + 64.98 = 3.14(29.42) + 64.98 = 157.3588$ cm. ≈ 157.36 cm.

 Yes

 d) $h = 2.53T + 72.57$

 $167.64 = 2.53T + 72.57$

 $95.07 = 2.53T$

 $T = 37.5770751$ cm. ≈ 37.58 cm.

 e) i) $h = 3.14H + 64.98$

 $168 = 3.14H + 64.98$

 $103.02 = 3.14H$

 $H = 32.8089172 \approx 32.81$ cm.

 ii) $H = 32.81 - 0.06(30) = 32.81 - 1.8 = 31.01$ cm.

 f) Answers will vary.

2. a) - e) Answers will vary.

CHAPTER SEVEN

SYSTEMS OF LINEAR EQUATIONS AND INEQUALITIES

Exercise Set 7.1

1. Two or more linear equations form a system of linear equations.
2. A solution to a system of linear equations is the ordered pair or pairs that satisfy all equations in the system.
3. A consistent system of equations is a system that has a solution.
4. A dependent system of equations is a system that has an infinite number of solutions.
5. An inconsistent system of equations is a system that has no solution.
6. Graph each equation on the same axes. The point(s) of intersection of the graphs is the solution(s) to the system.
7. To check if $(2, -1)$ is a solution, replace x with 2 and y with (-1) in each equation.

$$x + 3y = -1 \qquad\qquad 2x + y = 2$$
$$2 + 3(-1) = -1 \qquad\quad 2(2) + (-1) = 2$$
$$2 - 3 = -1 \qquad\qquad\quad 4 - 1 = 2$$
$$-1 = -1 \;\; \text{True} \qquad\quad 3 = 2 \;\; \text{False}$$

Since $(2, -1)$ does not satisfy both equations, it is not a solution.

8. To check if $(-2, 4)$ is a solution, replace x with -2 and y with 4 in each equation.

$$x + 2y = 6 \qquad\qquad x - y = -6$$
$$-2 + 2(4) = 6 \qquad\quad -2 - 4 = -6$$
$$-2 + 8 = 6 \qquad\qquad -6 = -6 \;\; \text{True}$$
$$6 = 6 \;\; \text{True}$$

Since $(-2, 4)$ does satisfy both equations, it is a solution.

9.

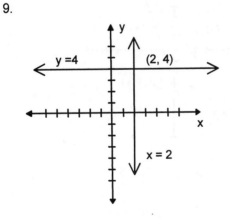

10.

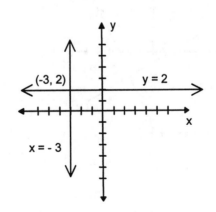

227

11.

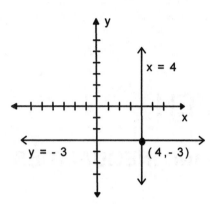

12.

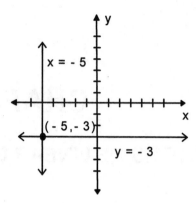

13.

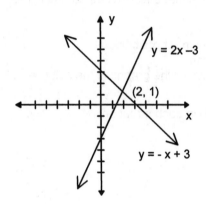

14.

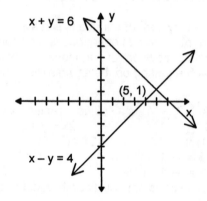

15.

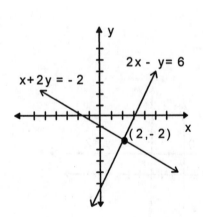

16.

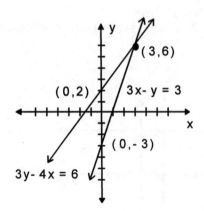

17.

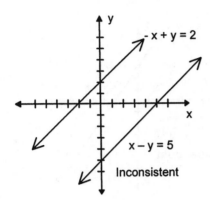

18.

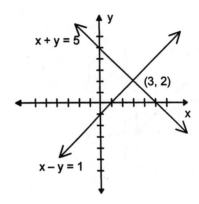

19.

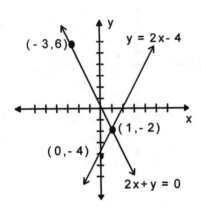

20.

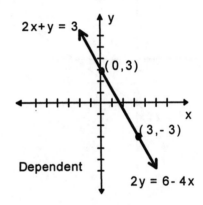

21.

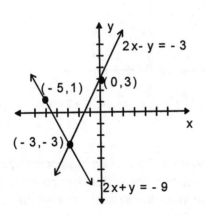

22.

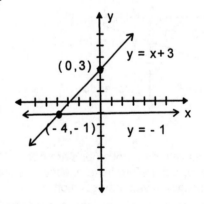

23.

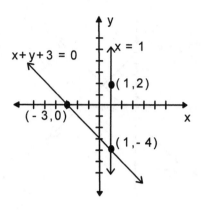

24.

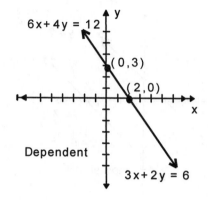

25.

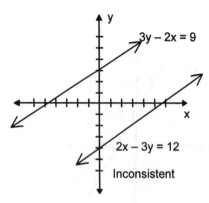

26.

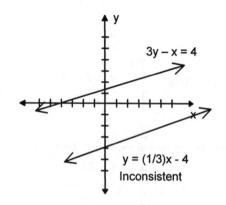

27.

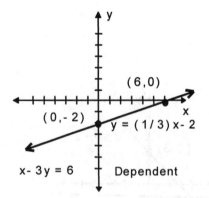

28.

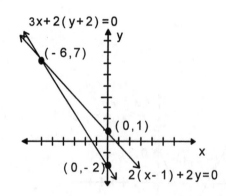

29. a)   Two lines with different slopes are not parallel, and therefore have exactly one point of intersection giving one solution.

    b)   Two lines with the same slope and different y- intercepts are distinct parallel lines and have no solution.

    c)   Two lines with the same slopes and y-intercepts have infinitely many solutions, each point on the line.

30. a)   Consistent; the system has one solution.
    b)   Inconsistent; the system has no solution.
    c)   Dependent; the system has infinitely many solutions.

In problems 31 - 42, solve each equation for y and then compare using the answer from problem #29.

31. $y = -3x + 8$
    $y = -3x + 8$
    same slope, same y-intercept;
    Infinite number of solutions

32. $y = -(2/3)x + 2$
    $y = -(2/3)x + 5/3$
    same slope, different y-intercepts;
    No solution

33. $y = -(1/2)x + 3/2$
    $y = x - 3$
    different slopes; One solution

34. $y = 2x - 8$
    $y = (1/2)x + 4$
    different slopes; One solution

35. $y = -3x + 7$
    $y = -3x + 9$
    same slope, different y-intercepts;
    No solution

36. $y = (2/3)x - 2$
    $y = (2/3)x - 2$
    same slope and y-intercept;
    Infinite number of solutions

37. $y = -(1/4)x + 3$
    $y = (1/4)x - (3/4)$
    different slopes; One solution

38. $y = (1/2)x - (5/6)$
    $y = (1/2)x - 3$
    same slope, different y-intercepts; No solution

39. $y = 2x + (4/3)$
    $y = 2x + (4/3)$
    same slope and y-intercept;
    Infinite number of solutions

40. $y = (1/2)x - 3$
    $y = -(1/2)x + 2$
    different slopes; One solution

41. $y = (12/5)x - (4/5)$
    $y = -(3/4)x + (3/2)$
    different slopes; One solution

42. $y = -(4/7)x + (2/7)$
    $y = (4/7)x - (6/7)$
    different slopes; One solution

43. $y = (2/5)x + 3$
    $y = (5/2)x + 1$
    $(2/5) \cdot (5/2) = 1 \neq -1$
    The lines are not perpendicular.

44. $y = (1/4)x + (3/2)$
    $y = x + 8$
    $(1/4) \cdot 1 = 1/4 \neq -1$
    The lines are not perpendicular.

45. $y = -2x + 3$
    $y = (1/2)x + 5/2$
    $-2 \cdot (1/2) = -(2/2) = -1$
    The lines are perpendicular.

46. $y = -(6/5)x + 3/5$
    $y = -(5/6)x - 1/6$
    $-(6/5) \cdot [-(5/6)] = 1 \neq -1$
    The lines are not perpendicular.

47. a) Let c = cost
    let h = number of hours
    (Tom's): c = 60h + 200
    (Lawn Per.): c = 25h + 305

b)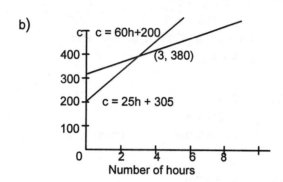

c) From the graph, the point of intersection of the two lines is (3, 380) indicating 3 hours.

48. Let c = cost
    let x = number of months
a) ABC: c = 18x + 3380
    SafeHomes: c = 29x + 2302

b)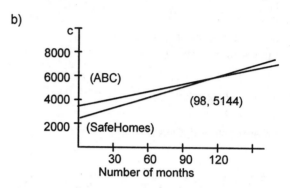

c) 98 months
d) Anytime after 98 months (8.2 yr) ABC would be less expensive.

49. a) Let c = cost of printing
    let b = number of books
    (Sivle): c = 6b + 1600
    (Yelserp): c = 8b + 1200

b)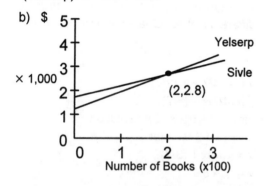

c) From the graph, the point of intersection of the two lines is (200, 2800) indicating 200 books.

d) Sivle: 6(100) + 1600 = $2200
    Yelserp: 8(100) + 1200 = $2000
    Yelserp is less expensive.

50. Let f = number of frames
a) Cost = 15f + 400
    Rev. = 25f

b)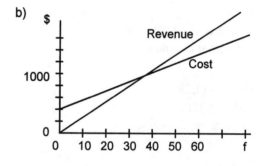

c) 40 frames
d) Profit = Rev. − Cost
    $$= 25f − (15f + 400)$$
    $$= 10f − 400$$
e) When f = 10, Profit = 10(10) − 400 = − 300
    A $300 loss.
f) Profit = 10f − 400
    $$1000 = 10f − 400$$
    $$1400 = 10f$$
    140 = f, He must sell 140 frames.

51. a) Let R = revenue, C = cost, and
     x = number of units.
     R = 165x
     C = 8400 + 95x

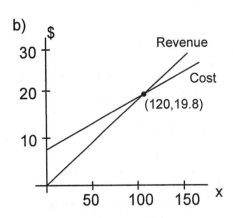

b)

c) Based on the graph, 120 units.
d) P = R − C = 165x − (8400 + 95x)
       = 70x − 8400
e) When x = 100, P = 70(100) − 8400 = − 1400
     A loss of $1400.
f) P = 70x − 8400 = 1250
           70x = 9650
             x ≈ 138 units

52. Solve each equation for y to determine the slope and y- intercept for each. If the slopes are not equal the equations are consistent. If the slopes and y- intercepts are equal the equations are dependent. If the slopes are equal and the y- intercepts are not equal the equations are inconsistent.

53. a) (1) s = 300 + 0.15v
          (2) s = 450
     b)

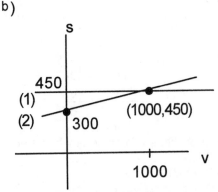

     c) $1000 sales volume.

54. a) (1) y = 0.20 + 0.10x
          (2) y = 0.26 + 0.08x
     b)

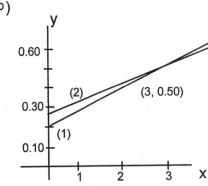

     c) At 3 minutes

55. a) one   b) three   c) six   d) ten
     e) number of equations: **2**   **3**   **4**   **5**   **6**
          points of intersection: 1   1+**2**=3   3+3=6   6+4=10   10+**5**=15

Exercise Set 7.2
1. Write the equations with the variables on one side and the constants on the other side. If necessary multiply one or both equations by a constant(s) so that when the equations are added one of the variables will be eliminated. Solve for the remaining variable and then substitute that value into one of the original equations to solve for the other variable.
2. Solve one of the equations for one of the variables in terms of the other variable. Then substitute that expression into the other equation and solve for the variable. Substitute the value found into one of the original equations and solve for the other variable.
3. The system is inconsistent if the result is a false statement.
4. The system is dependent if the result is of the form a = a.

5. $y = x - 6$
$y = -x + 4$
Substitute $(x - 6)$ in place of y in the second equation.

$$
\begin{aligned}
x - 6 &= -x + 4 \quad \text{(solve for x)} \\
\underline{+x \qquad\quad +x} & \\
2x - 6 &= 4 \\
\underline{+6 \qquad +6} & \\
2x &= 10 \\
\frac{2x}{2} &= \frac{10}{2} \\
x &= 5
\end{aligned}
$$

Now substitute 5 for x in the equation
$y = x - 6$
$y = 5 - 6 = -1$
The solution is $(5, -1)$.

6. $y = 5x + 7$
$y = 2x + 1$
Substitute $(5x + 7)$ in place of y in the second equation.

$$
\begin{aligned}
5x + 7 &= 2x + 1 \quad \text{(solve for x)} \\
\underline{-2x \qquad -2x} & \\
3x + 7 &= 1 \\
\underline{-7 \quad -7} & \\
3x &= -6 \\
x &= -2
\end{aligned}
$$

Now substitute -2 in place of x in the second equation.
$y = 5(-2) + 7 = -10 + 7 = -3$
The solution is $(-2, -3)$.

7. $2x - 4y = 12$
$2x + y = -3$
Solve the second equation for y.
$y = -3 - 2x$
Substitute $(-3 - 2x)$ in place of y in the first equation.

$$
\begin{aligned}
2x - 4(-3 - 2x) &= 12 \quad \text{(solve for x)} \\
2x + 12 + 8x &= 12 \\
10x + 12 &= 12 \\
10x + 12 - 12 &= 12 - 12 \\
10x &= 0 \\
x &= 0
\end{aligned}
$$

Now substitute 0 in place of x in the equation
$y = -3 - 2x$.
$$
\begin{aligned}
y &= -3 - 2(0) \\
y &= -3
\end{aligned}
$$
The solution is $(0, -3)$.

8. $x + 3y = 3$
$4y + 3x = -1$
Solve the first equation for x.
$x = 3 - 3y$
Substitute $(3 - 3y)$ in place of x in the second equation.

$$
\begin{aligned}
4y + 3(3 - 3y) &= -1 \quad \text{(solve for y)} \\
4y + 9 - 9y &= -1 \\
-5y + 9 &= -1 \\
-5y + 9 - 9 &= -1 - 9 \\
-5y &= -10 \\
\frac{-5y}{-5} &= \frac{-10}{-5} \\
y &= 2
\end{aligned}
$$

Now substitute 2 in place of y in the equation
$x = 3 - 3y$.
$x = 3 - 3(2) = 3 - 6 = -3$
The solution is $(-3, 2)$.

9. $y - x = 4$
$x - y = 3$
Solve the first equation for y.
$$
\begin{aligned}
y - x + x &= x + 4 \\
y &= x + 4
\end{aligned}
$$
Substitute $(x + 4)$ in place of y in the second equation.
$$
\begin{aligned}
x - (x + 4) &= 3 \quad \text{(combine like terms)} \\
-4 &= 3 \quad \text{False}
\end{aligned}
$$
Since -4 does not equal 3, there is no solution to this system. The equations are inconsistent.

10. $x + y = 3$
$y + x = 5$
Solve the second equation for y.
$$
\begin{aligned}
y + x - x &= -x + 5 \\
y &= -x + 5
\end{aligned}
$$
Substitute $(-x + 5)$ for y in the first equation.
$$
\begin{aligned}
x + (-x + 5) &= 3 \\
5 &= 3 \quad \text{False}
\end{aligned}
$$
Since 5 does not equal 3, there is no solution to this system. The equations are inconsistent.

11. $x = 5y - 12$
    $x - y = 0$
    Substitute $(5y - 12)$ in place of x in the second equation.
    $$5y - 12 - y = 0 \quad \text{(solve for y)}$$
    $$4y - 12 = 0$$
    $$4y = 12 \quad \text{(div. by 4)}$$
    $$y = 3$$
    Now substitute 3 for y in the second equation.
    $$x - 3 = 0$$
    $$x = 3$$
    The solution is $(3,3)$.

12. $3y + 2x = 4$
    $3y = 6 - x$
    Solve the second equation for x.
    $$3y = 6 - x$$
    $$3y - 6 = 6 - 6 - x$$
    $$3y - 6 = -x$$
    $$-3y + 6 = x$$
    Now substitute $(-3y + 6)$ in place of x in the first equation.
    $$3y + 2(6 - 3y) = 4 \quad \text{(solve for y)}$$
    $$3y + 12 - 6y = 4$$
    $$-3y = -8 \quad \text{(div. by } -3)$$
    $$y = 8/3$$
    Substitute 8/3 for y in the second eq.
    $$3(8/3) = 6 - x$$
    $$8 = 6 - x$$
    $$x = -2$$
    The solution is $(-2, 8/3)$

13. $y - 2x = 3$
    $2y = 4x + 6$
    Solve the first equation for y.
    $$y - 2x + 2x = 2x + 3$$
    $$y = 2x + 3$$
    Now substitute $(2x + 3)$ in place of y in the second equation.
    $$2(2x + 3) = 4x + 6$$
    $$4x + 6 = 4x + 6$$
    $$4x - 4x + 6 = 4x - 4x + 6$$
    $$6 = 6$$
    This statement is true for all values of x. The system is dependent.

14. $x = y + 3$
    $x = -3$
    Substitute -3 in place of x in the first equation.
    $$-3 = y + 3$$
    $$-3 - 3 = y + 3 - 3$$
    $$-6 = y$$
    The solution is $(-3, -6)$.

15. $y = 2$
    $y + x + 3 = 0$
    Substitute 2 in place of y in the second equation.
    $$2 + x + 3 = 0$$
    $$x + 5 = 0$$
    $$x + 5 - 5 = 0 - 5$$
    $$x = -5$$
    The solution is $(-5, 2)$.

16. $x + 2y = 6$
    $y = 2x + 3$
    Substitute $(2x + 3)$ in place of y in the first equation.
    $$x + 2(2x + 3) = 6$$
    $$x + 4x + 6 = 6$$
    $$5x + 6 - 6 = 6 - 6$$
    $$5x = 0$$
    $$\frac{5x}{5} = \frac{0}{5}$$
    $$x = 0$$
    Now substitute 0 in place of x in the second equation.
    $$y = 2(0) + 3 = 0 + 3 = 3$$
    The solution is $(0,3)$.

17. $y + 3x - 4 = 0$
$2x - y = 7$
Solve the first equation for y.
$$y + 3x - 4 = 0$$
$$y = 4 - 3x$$
Substitute $4 - 3x$ for y in the second eq.
$$2x - (4 - 3x) = 7 \text{ (solve for x)}$$
$$2x - 4 + 3x = 7$$
$$5x = 11$$
$$x = 11/5$$
Substitute 11/5 for x in the second eq.
$$2(11/5) - y = 7 \text{ (solve for y)}$$
$$22/5 - y = 7$$
$$-y = 13/5$$
$$y = -13/5$$
The solution is $(11/5, -13/5)$

18. $x + 4y = 7$
$2x + 3y = 5$
Solve the first equation for x.
$$x = 7 - 4y$$
Substitute $(7 - 4y)$ in place of x in the second equation.
$$2(7 - 4y) + 3y = 5 \text{ (solve for y)}$$
$$14 - 8y + 3y = 5$$
$$-5y = -9$$
$$y = 9/5$$
Now substitute $(9/5)$ in place of y in the equation $x + 4y = 7$.
$$x + 4(9/5) = 7$$
$$x + 36/5 = 35/5$$
$$x = -1/5$$
The solution is $(-1/5, 9/5)$.

19. $x = 2y + 3$
$y = 3x - 1$
Substitute $(3x - 1)$ in place of y in the first equation.
$$x = 2(3x - 1) + 3$$
$$x = 6x - 2 + 3$$
$$x = 6x + 1$$
$$x - 6x = 6x - 6x + 1$$
$$-5x = 1$$
$$\frac{-5x}{-5} = \frac{1}{-5}$$
$$x = -1/5$$
Substitute $-1/5$ in place of x in the second equation.
$$y = 3(-1/5) - 1 = -3/5 - 5/5 = -8/5$$
The solution is $(-1/5, -8/5)$.

20. $x + 4y = 9$
$2x - y - 6 = 0$
Solve the first equation for x.
$$x + 4y - 4y = 9 - 4y$$
$$x = 9 - 4y$$
Substitute $(9 - 4y)$ in place of x in the second equation.
$$2(9 - 4y) - y - 6 = 0$$
$$18 - 8y - y - 6 = 0$$
$$12 - 9y = 0$$
$$12 - 9y + 9y = 0 + 9y$$
$$12 = 9y$$
$$12/9 = y$$
Substitute $(12/9) = (4/3)$ for y in the equation
$x = 9 - 4y$
$$x = 9 - 4(4/3) = 27/3 - 16/3 = 11/3$$
The solution is $(11/3, 4/3)$.

21. $6x - y = 5$
$y = 6x - 3$
Substitute $(6x - 3)$ for y in the first equation.
$$6x - (6x - 3) = 5$$
$$6x - 6x + 3 = 5$$
$$3 = 5 \text{ False}$$
Since 3 does not equal 5, there is no solution to this system. The equations are inconsistent.

22. $x + 3y = 6$
$y = -(1/3)x + 2$
Substitute $[-(1/3)x + 2]$ for y in the first equation.
$$x + 3[-(1/3)x + 2] = 6$$
$$x - x + 6 = 6$$
$$6 = 6 \text{ True}$$
This statement is true for all values of x.
The system is dependent.

23. $4x + y = 9$
     $3x - y = 5$ (add the equations)
     $7x = 14$
     $x = 2$
Substitute 2 in place of x in the first equation.
     $4(2) + y = 9$ (solve for y)
     $8 + y = 9$
     $y = 1$
The solution is $(2, 1)$.

24. $3x + y = 10$
     $4x - y = 4$ (add the equations)
     $7x = 14$
     $x = 2$
Substitute 2 in place of x in the second equation.
     $4(2) - y = 4$
     $8 - y = 4$
     $-y = -4$, or $y = 4$
The solution is $(2, 4)$.

25. $-x + y = 5$
     $x + 3y = 3$ (add the equations)
     $4y = 8$
     $y = 2$
Substitute 2 in place of y in the 2nd equation.
     $x + 3(2) = 3$
     $x + 6 = 3$
     $x = -3$
The solution is $(-3, 2)$.

26. $2x - 6y = 8$
     $-2x + 4y = -10$ (add the equations)
     $-2y = -2$
     $y = 1$
Substitute 1 in place of y in the first equation.
     $2x - 6(1) = 8$
     $2x - 6 = 8$
     $2x = 14$
     $x = 7$
The solution is $(7, 1)$.

27. $2x - y = -4$
     $-3x - y = 6$
Multiplying the second equation by -1,
     $2x - y = -4$
     $3x + y = -6$ (add the equations)
     $5x = -10$
     $x = -2$
Substitute -2 in place of x in the first equation.
     $2(-2) - y = -4$
     $-4 - y = -4$
     $-y = 0$
     $y = 0$
The solution is $(-2, 0)$.

28. $x + y = 6$
     $-2x + y = -3$
Multiplying the second equation by -1,
     $x + y = 6$
     $2x - y = 3$ (add the equations)
     $3x = 9$
     $x = 3$
Substitute 3 in place of x in the first equation.
     $3 + y = 6$
     $y = 3$
The solution is $(3, 3)$.

29. $2x + y = 6$
     $3x + y = 5$
Multiplying the first equation by -1,
     $-2x - y = -6$
     $3x + y = 5$ (add the equations)
     $x = -1$
Substitute -1 in place of x in the first equation.
     $2(-1) + y = 6$
     $-2 + y = 6$
     $y = 8$
The solution is $(-1, 8)$.

30. $4x + 3y = -1$
     $2x - y = -13$
Multiplying the second equation by 3,
     $4x + 3y = -1$
     $6x - 3y = -39$ (add the equations)
     $10x = -40$
     $x = -4$
Substitute -4 in place of x in the 2nd equation.
     $2(-4) - y = -13$
     $-8 - y = -13$
     $y = 5$
The solution is $(-4, 5)$.

31. $2x + y = 11$
    $x + 3y = 18$
    Multiplying the second equation by -2,

    $\begin{array}{rl} 2x + y &= 11 \\ -2x - 6y &= -36 \quad \text{(add the equations)} \\ \hline -5y &= -25 \\ y &= 5 \end{array}$

    Substitute 5 in place of y in the 2nd equation.

    $\begin{array}{rl} x + 3(5) &= 18 \\ x + 15 &= 18 \\ x &= 3 \end{array}$

    The solution is (3, 5).

32. $5x - 2y = 11$
    $\underline{-3x + 2y = 1} \quad \text{(add the equations)}$

    $\begin{array}{rl} 2x &= 12 \\ x &= 6 \end{array}$

    Substitute 6 in place of x in the second equation.

    $\begin{array}{rl} -3(6) + 2y &= 1 \\ -18 + 2y &= 1 \\ 2y &= 19 \\ y &= 19/2 \end{array}$

    The solution is (6,19/2).

33. $3x - 4y = 11$
    $3x + 5y = -7$
    Multiplying the first equation by (-1),

    $\begin{array}{rl} -3x + 4y &= -11 \\ 3x + 5y &= -7 \quad \text{(add the equations)} \\ \hline 9y &= -18 \quad \text{(div. by 9)} \\ y &= -2 \end{array}$

    Substitute -2 in place of y in the first equation.

    $\begin{array}{rl} 3x - 4(-2) &= 11 \\ 3x &= 3 \\ x &= 1 \end{array}$

    The solution is (1,-2).

34. $4x - 2y = 6$
    $4y = 8x - 12$ or $8x - 4y = 12$
    Multiplying the first equation by (-2),

    $\begin{array}{rl} -8x + 4y &= -12 \\ 8x - 4y &= -12 \quad \text{(add the equations)} \\ \hline 0 &= 0 \quad \text{True} \end{array}$

    This system is dependent.

35. $4x + y = 6$
    $-8x - 2y = 13$
    Multiplying the first equation by 2,

    $\begin{array}{rl} 8x + 2y &= 12 \\ -8x - 2y &= 13 \quad \text{(add the equations)} \\ \hline 0 &= 25 \quad \text{False} \end{array}$

    Since this statement is not true for any values of x and y, the equations are inconsistent.

36. $2x + 3y = 6$
    $5x - 4y = -8$
    Multiplying the first equation by 5, and the second equation by (-2),

    $\begin{array}{rl} 10x + 15y &= 30 \\ -10x + 8y &= 16 \quad \text{(add the equations)} \\ \hline 23y &= 46 \\ y &= 2 \end{array}$

    Substitute 2 in place of y in the first equation.

    $\begin{array}{rl} 2x + 3(2) &= 6 \\ 2x + 6 &= 6 \\ 2x &= 0 \\ x &= 0 \end{array}$

    The solution is (0,2).

37.
$$7x + 8y = 11$$
$$5x + 6y = 7$$

Multiplying the first equation by (-5), and the second equation by (7).

$$-35x - 40y = -55$$
$$\underline{35x + 42y = 49} \text{ (add the equations)}$$
$$2y = -6 \text{ (div. by 2)}$$
$$y = -3$$

Substitute -3 in place of y in the first equation.

$$7x + 8(-3) = 11$$
$$7x - 24 = 11$$
$$7x = 35$$
$$x = 5$$

The solution is $(5, -3)$.

38.
$$8x + 3y = 7$$
$$3x + 2y = 9$$

Multiplying the first equation by (-3), and the second equation by (8).

$$-24x - 9y = -21$$
$$\underline{24x + 16y = 72} \text{ (add the equations)}$$
$$7y = 51$$
$$y = 51/7$$

Substitute $(51/7)$ in place of y in the first equation.

$$8x + 3\left(\frac{51}{7}\right) = 7$$
$$8x + \frac{153}{7} = 7$$
$$8x = \frac{49}{7} - \frac{153}{7}$$
$$8x = -\frac{104}{7}$$
$$x = -\frac{104}{7} \cdot \frac{1}{8}$$
$$x = -\frac{13}{7}$$

The solution is $\left(-\frac{13}{7}, \frac{51}{7}\right)$.

39. Let w = weekly salary

let s = amount of weekly sales

$$w = 300 + 0.04s$$
$$w = 0.16s$$
$$300 + 0.04s = 0.16s$$
$$300 = 0.12s$$
$$2500 = s$$

Thus, $2,500 in weekly sales will result in equal salaries.

40. Let x = no. of 2-pointers

y = no. of 3-pointers

(1) $x + y = 45$

(2) $2x + 3y = 101$

Solve equation (1) for y.

$$y = 45 - x \text{ (sub. for y in eq. (2))}$$
$$2x + 3(45 - x) = 101 \text{ (solve for x)}$$
$$2x + 135 - 3x = 101$$
$$-x = -34$$
$$x = 34$$

Substitute 34 for x in eq. (1).

$$34 + y = 45$$
$$y = 11$$

Answer: 34 two-pointers,

11 three-pointers

41. Let x = no. of games won
    y = no. of games tied.
    (1) $2x + 1y = 58$
    (2) $x = y + 23$
    Substitute y+23 for x in eq. (1)
    $2(y + 23) + y = 58$ (solve for y)
    $2y + 46 + y = 58$
    $3y = 12$
    $y = 4$
    Substitute 4 for y in equation (2).
    $x = 4 + 23$
    $x = 27$
    They won 27 games and tied 4 games.

42. Let x = fixed charge
    y = charge for each mph over limit
    (1) $x + 15y = 175$
    (2) $x + 20y = 200$
    Multiply eq. (1) by (– 1), then add the equations.
    (1) $-x - 15y = -175$
    (2) $\underline{x + 20y = 200}$
    $5y = 25$
    $y = 5$
    Sub. 5 for y in eq. (1) and solve for x.
    $x + 15(5) = 175$
    $x + 75 = 175$
    $x = 100$
    The fine is $100 plus $5 for each mph over 55 mph.

43. Let x = no. of pounds of soybean meal
    y = no. of pounds of corn meal
    (1) $x + y = 300$
    (2) $0.16x + .07y = .10(300)$
    Solve equation (1) for y.
    $y = 300 - x$, sub.(300–x) for y in eq. (2)
    $0.16x + .07(300 - x) = 30$ (solve for x)
    $0.16x + 21 - 0.07x = 30$
    $0.09x = 9$
    $x = 100$
    Substitute 100 for x in eq. (1).
    $100 + y = 300$
    $y = 200$
    Mix 100 pounds of soybean meal with 200 pounds of corn meal.

44. Let b = gallons of milk with butter fat
    let s = gallons of skim milk
    $b + s = 100$
    $0.05b + 0.0s = 100(0.035)$
    $0.05b = 3.5$
    $b = 3.5/0.05 = 70$
    $s = 100 - b = 100 - 70 = 30$
    Thus, Gina should mix 70 gallons of milk with 5% butter fat with 30 gallons of skim milk.

45. Let c = monthly cost
    let x = number of copies
    Eco. Sales: $c = 18 + 0.02x$
    Office Sup.: $c = 24 + 0.015x$ (set eqs. equal)
    $18 + 0.02x = 24 + 0.015x$
    $0.005x = 6$
    $x = 1200$
    1200 copies per month

46. a) Let c = monthly cost
    let x = number of minutes
    Cellular Two: $c = 25 + 0.05x$
    TGE: $c = 15 + 0.10x$
    $25 + 0.05x = 15 + 0.10x$
    $10 = 0.05x$
    $200 = x$, ans. 200 minutes per month
    b) Cellular Two: $c = 25 + 0.05(90)$
    $= 25 + 4.5 = \$29.50$
    TGE: $c = 15 + 0.10(90)$
    $= 15 + 9 = \$24$
    TGE would be less expensive.

47. Let x = no. of pounds of nuts
let y = no. of pounds of pretzels
$x + y = 20$
$3x + 1y = 30$
$y = 30 - x$ (equation 1 solved for y)
Substitute $(20 - x)$ for y in the second equation.
$$3x + (20 - x) = 30$$
$$3x + 20 - x = 30$$
$$2x = 10$$
$$x = 5$$
$y = 20 - 5 = 15$
Mix 5 lbs. of the nuts with 15 lbs. of the pretzels.

48. Let x = no. of students
let y = no. of adults
$x + y = 250$
$2x + 5y = 950$
$x = 250 - y$ (equation 1 solved for x)
Substitute $(250 - y)$ for x in the second equation.
$$2(250 - y) + 5y = 950$$
$$500 - 2y + 5y = 950$$
$$3y = 450$$
$$y = 150$$
$x = 250 - 150 = 100$
100 students and 150 adults.

49. Let a = number of grams of Mix A
let b = number of grams of Mix B
Protein: $0.10a + 0.20b = 20$
Carbohydrates: $0.06a + 0.02b = 6$
Multiplying the 2nd equation by $(- 10)$,
$$-0.60a - 0.20b = -60$$
$$\underline{0.10a + 0.20b = 20} \text{ (add)}$$
$$-0.50a = -40$$
$$a = 80 \text{ grams of Mix A}$$
Substitute 80 in place of a in the first equation.
$$0.10(80) + 0.20b = 20$$
$$8 + 0.20b = 20$$
$$0.20b = 12$$
$$b = 60 \text{ grams of Mix B}$$

50. Let c = total cost
r = no. of rounds of golf.
Chippers: $c = 3000 + 18r$
Birdies: $c = 2500 + 20r$
a) $3000 + 18r = 2500 + 20r$
$$500 = 2r$$
$$250 = r$$
A golfer must play 250 rounds for the cost to be the same at both clubs.
b) Chippers: $c = 3000 + 18(30) = \$3540$
Birdies: $c = 2500 + 20(30) = \$3100$
Ms. Passaro can play 30 rounds cheaper at Birdies.

51. Cassettes: $y = -29x + 450$
Comp.discs $y = 57x + 150$
$$-29x + 450 = 57x + 150$$
$$300 = 28x$$
$$x = \frac{300}{86} \approx 3.5$$
Approx. 3.5 years after 1988 (in 1991).
$y = 57(3.5) + 150 = 350$ million units.

52. Let c = cost
let n = number of checks written per month
Union: $c = 6 + 0.10n$
Citrus: $c = 2 + 0.20n$

a) $6 + 0.10n = 2 + 0.20n$
$$4 + 0.10n = 0.20n$$
$$4 = 0.10n$$
$$40 = n$$
The monthly cost is the same at both banks if 40 checks are written.

b) Union: $c = 6 + 0.10(14) = \$7.40$
Citrus: $c = 4 + 0.20(14) = \$6.80$
Citrus would be least expensive for Mr. Pickett.

53. (1) $\frac{1}{u} + \frac{2}{v} = 8$

   (2) $\frac{3}{u} - \frac{1}{v} = 3$

   Substitute x for $\frac{1}{u}$ and y for $\frac{1}{v}$.

   (1) $x + 2y = 8$
   (2) $3x - y = 3$

   Multiply eq. (2) by 2, then add.

   $x + 2y = 8$
   $\underline{6x - 2y = 6}$
   $7x = 14$

   $x = 2$, thus $u = \frac{1}{2}$

   Substitute 2 for x in eq. (1).

   $2 + 2y = 8$
   $2y = 6$

   $y = 3$, thus $v = \frac{1}{3}$

   Answer: $\left(\frac{1}{2}, \frac{1}{3}\right)$

54. Determine the equations of two lines that pass through (6,5) and another point.

   Example: $y = 5$
   $y = (5/6)x$

Exercise Set 7.3

1. A matrix is a rectangular array of elements.
2. The dimensions of a matrix are determined by the number of rows and columns.
3. A square matrix contains the same number of rows as columns.
4. They must have the same dimensions (the number of rows must be the same and the number of columns must be the same).
5. a) Add numbers in the same positions to produce an entry in that position.

   b) $\begin{bmatrix} 5 & 3 & -1 \\ 0 & 2 & 4 \end{bmatrix} + \begin{bmatrix} 4 & 5 & 6 \\ -1 & 3 & 2 \end{bmatrix} = \begin{bmatrix} 5+4 & 3+5 & -1+6 \\ 0-1 & 2+3 & 4+2 \end{bmatrix} = \begin{bmatrix} 9 & 8 & 5 \\ -1 & 5 & 6 \end{bmatrix}$

6. a) Subtract the entry in each position in the second matrix from the number in the same position in the first matrix.

   b) $\begin{bmatrix} 4 & 5 & 6 \\ -1 & 3 & 2 \end{bmatrix} - \begin{bmatrix} 5 & 3 & -1 \\ 0 & 2 & 4 \end{bmatrix} = \begin{bmatrix} 4-5 & 5-3 & 6+1 \\ -1-0 & 3-2 & 2-4 \end{bmatrix} = \begin{bmatrix} -1 & 2 & 7 \\ -1 & 1 & -2 \end{bmatrix}$

7. a) The number of rows of the first matrix must be the same as the number of columns of the second matrix.

   b) The dimensions of the resulting matrix will have the same number of rows as the first matrix and the same number of columns as the second matrix. The product of a 2 × 2 with a 2 × 3 matrix will yield a 2 × 3 matrix.

8. a) The numbers in the first row of the first matrix are multiplied by the numbers in the first column of the second matrix and the results are added together to produce the first entry of the result. Continue this procedure with each row of the first matrix and each column of the second matrix to obtain all the entries in the result matrix.

   b) $\begin{bmatrix} 6 & -1 \\ 5 & 0 \end{bmatrix}\begin{bmatrix} 2 & -3 \\ 1 & -4 \end{bmatrix} = \begin{bmatrix} 6(2)+(-1)(1) & 6(-3)+(-1)(-4) \\ 5(2)+0(1) & 5(-3)+0(-4) \end{bmatrix} = \begin{bmatrix} 11 & -14 \\ 10 & -15 \end{bmatrix}$

9. a) $\begin{bmatrix} 1 & 0 \\ 0 & 1 \end{bmatrix}$ b) $\begin{bmatrix} 1 & 0 & 0 \\ 0 & 1 & 0 \\ 0 & 0 & 1 \end{bmatrix}$

10. $\begin{array}{c} \\ A \\ B \\ C \end{array}\begin{bmatrix} \text{M} & \text{T} & \text{W} & \text{R} & \text{F} & \text{S} & \text{S} \\ 654 & 785 & 458 & 345 & 1478 & 2109 & 543 \\ 764 & 778 & 568 & 451 & 1024 & 1689 & 853 \\ 567 & 764 & 873 & 407 & 2034 & 2432 & 567 \end{bmatrix}$

11. $A + B = \begin{bmatrix} 2 & 7 \\ 1 & 6 \end{bmatrix} + \begin{bmatrix} -3 & -5 \\ 8 & 1 \end{bmatrix} = \begin{bmatrix} 2+(-3) & 7+(-5) \\ 1+8 & 6+1 \end{bmatrix} = \begin{bmatrix} -1 & 2 \\ 9 & 7 \end{bmatrix}$

12. $A + B = \begin{bmatrix} 2 & 5 & 1 \\ 6 & 0 & -1 \end{bmatrix} + \begin{bmatrix} -4 & -3 & 8 \\ 6 & 5 & 0 \end{bmatrix} = \begin{bmatrix} 2+(-4) & 5+(-3) & 1+8 \\ 6+6 & 0+5 & -1+0 \end{bmatrix} = \begin{bmatrix} -2 & 2 & 9 \\ 12 & 5 & -1 \end{bmatrix}$

13. $A + B = \begin{bmatrix} -1 & 0 \\ 0 & 4 \\ 6 & 2 \end{bmatrix} + \begin{bmatrix} 2 & 3 \\ 5 & 0 \\ 1 & -1 \end{bmatrix} = \begin{bmatrix} -1+2 & 0+3 \\ 0+5 & 4+0 \\ 6+1 & 2+(-1) \end{bmatrix} = \begin{bmatrix} 1 & 3 \\ 5 & 4 \\ 7 & 1 \end{bmatrix}$

14. $A + B = \begin{bmatrix} 1 & 5 & -3 \\ -1 & -6 & 4 \\ 2 & 0 & 5 \end{bmatrix} + \begin{bmatrix} -1 & 2 & 1 \\ 8 & -2 & 1 \\ 1 & 3 & 7 \end{bmatrix} = \begin{bmatrix} 1+(-1) & 5+2 & -3+1 \\ -1+8 & -6+(-2) & 4+1 \\ 2+1 & 0+3 & 5+7 \end{bmatrix} = \begin{bmatrix} 0 & 7 & -2 \\ 7 & -8 & 5 \\ 3 & 3 & 12 \end{bmatrix}$

15. $A - B = \begin{bmatrix} -2 & 5 \\ 9 & 1 \end{bmatrix} - \begin{bmatrix} 4 & -2 \\ -3 & 5 \end{bmatrix} = \begin{bmatrix} -2-4 & 5-(-2) \\ 9-(-3) & 1-5 \end{bmatrix} = \begin{bmatrix} -6 & 7 \\ 12 & -4 \end{bmatrix}$

16. $A - B = \begin{bmatrix} 1 & 2 \\ 0 & 6 \\ -3 & 9 \end{bmatrix} - \begin{bmatrix} 1 & 1 \\ 4 & 5 \\ -2 & 8 \end{bmatrix} = \begin{bmatrix} 1-0 & 2-1 \\ 0-4 & 6-5 \\ -3-(-2) & 9-8 \end{bmatrix} = \begin{bmatrix} 1 & 1 \\ -4 & 1 \\ -1 & 1 \end{bmatrix}$

17. $A - B = \begin{bmatrix} 5 & 3 & -1 \\ 7 & 4 & 2 \\ 6 & -1 & -5 \end{bmatrix} - \begin{bmatrix} 4 & 3 & 6 \\ -2 & -4 & 9 \\ 0 & -2 & 4 \end{bmatrix} = \begin{bmatrix} 5-4 & 3-3 & -1-6 \\ 7+2 & 4+4 & 2-9 \\ 6-0 & -1+2 & -5-4 \end{bmatrix} = \begin{bmatrix} 1 & 0 & -7 \\ 9 & 8 & -7 \\ 6 & 1 & -9 \end{bmatrix}$

18. $A - B = \begin{bmatrix} -4 & 3 \\ 6 & 2 \\ 1 & -5 \end{bmatrix} - \begin{bmatrix} -6 & -8 \\ -10 & -11 \\ 3 & -7 \end{bmatrix} = \begin{bmatrix} -4+6 & 3+8 \\ 6+10 & 2+11 \\ 1-3 & -5+7 \end{bmatrix} = \begin{bmatrix} 2 & 11 \\ 16 & 13 \\ -2 & 2 \end{bmatrix}$

19. $2B = 2\begin{bmatrix} 3 & 2 \\ 5 & 0 \end{bmatrix} = \begin{bmatrix} 2(3) & 2(2) \\ 2(5) & 2(0) \end{bmatrix} = \begin{bmatrix} 6 & 4 \\ 10 & 0 \end{bmatrix}$

20. $-3B = -3\begin{bmatrix} 3 & 2 \\ 5 & 0 \end{bmatrix} = \begin{bmatrix} -3(3) & -3(2) \\ -3(5) & -3(0) \end{bmatrix} = \begin{bmatrix} -9 & -6 \\ -15 & 0 \end{bmatrix}$

21. $2B + 3C = 2\begin{bmatrix} 3 & 2 \\ 5 & 0 \end{bmatrix} + 3\begin{bmatrix} -2 & 3 \\ 4 & 0 \end{bmatrix} = \begin{bmatrix} 6 & 4 \\ 10 & 0 \end{bmatrix} + \begin{bmatrix} -6 & 9 \\ 12 & 0 \end{bmatrix} = \begin{bmatrix} 6-6 & 4+9 \\ 10+12 & 0+0 \end{bmatrix} = \begin{bmatrix} 0 & 13 \\ 22 & 0 \end{bmatrix}$

22. $2B + 3A = 2\begin{bmatrix} 3 & 2 \\ 5 & 0 \end{bmatrix} + 3\begin{bmatrix} 1 & 2 \\ 0 & 5 \end{bmatrix} = \begin{bmatrix} 6 & 4 \\ 10 & 0 \end{bmatrix} + \begin{bmatrix} 3 & 6 \\ 0 & 15 \end{bmatrix} = \begin{bmatrix} 6+3 & 4+6 \\ 10+0 & 0+15 \end{bmatrix} = \begin{bmatrix} 9 & 10 \\ 10 & 15 \end{bmatrix}$

23. $3B - 2C = 3\begin{bmatrix} 3 & 2 \\ 5 & 0 \end{bmatrix} - 2\begin{bmatrix} -2 & 3 \\ 4 & 0 \end{bmatrix} = \begin{bmatrix} 9 & 6 \\ 15 & 0 \end{bmatrix} - \begin{bmatrix} -4 & 6 \\ 8 & 0 \end{bmatrix} = \begin{bmatrix} 9+4 & 6-6 \\ 15-8 & 0-0 \end{bmatrix} = \begin{bmatrix} 13 & 0 \\ 7 & 0 \end{bmatrix}$

24. $4C - 2A = 4\begin{bmatrix} -2 & 3 \\ 4 & 0 \end{bmatrix} - 2\begin{bmatrix} 1 & 2 \\ 0 & 5 \end{bmatrix} = \begin{bmatrix} -8 & 12 \\ 16 & 0 \end{bmatrix} - \begin{bmatrix} 2 & 4 \\ 0 & 10 \end{bmatrix} = \begin{bmatrix} -8-2 & 12-4 \\ 16-0 & 0-10 \end{bmatrix} = \begin{bmatrix} -10 & 8 \\ 16 & -10 \end{bmatrix}$

25. $A \times B = \begin{bmatrix} 2 & 1 \\ 3 & 0 \end{bmatrix} \times \begin{bmatrix} 1 & 4 \\ 2 & 6 \end{bmatrix} = \begin{bmatrix} 2(1)+1(2) & 2(4)+1(6) \\ 3(1)+0(2) & 3(4)+0(6) \end{bmatrix} = \begin{bmatrix} 4 & 14 \\ 3 & 12 \end{bmatrix}$

26. $A \times B = \begin{bmatrix} 1 & -1 \\ 2 & 6 \end{bmatrix} \times \begin{bmatrix} 3 & 2 \\ 5 & -2 \end{bmatrix} = \begin{bmatrix} 1(3)+(-1)(5) & 1(2)+(-1)(-2) \\ 2(3)+6(5) & 2(2)+6(-2) \end{bmatrix} = \begin{bmatrix} -2 & 4 \\ 36 & -8 \end{bmatrix}$

27. $A \times B = \begin{bmatrix} 2 & 3 & -1 \\ 0 & 4 & 6 \end{bmatrix} \times \begin{bmatrix} 2 \\ 4 \\ 1 \end{bmatrix} = \begin{bmatrix} 2(2)+3(4)-1(1) \\ 0(2)+4(4)+6(1) \end{bmatrix} = \begin{bmatrix} 15 \\ 22 \end{bmatrix}$

28. $A \times B = \begin{bmatrix} 1 & 1 \\ 1 & 1 \end{bmatrix} \times \begin{bmatrix} 1 & -1 \\ -1 & 2 \end{bmatrix} = \begin{bmatrix} 1(1)+1(-1) & 1(-1)+1(2) \\ 1(1)+1(-1) & 1(-1)+1(2) \end{bmatrix} = \begin{bmatrix} 0 & 1 \\ 0 & 1 \end{bmatrix}$

29. $A \times B = \begin{bmatrix} 5 & 1 & 6 \\ -2 & 3 & 1 \\ 4 & 7 & 2 \end{bmatrix} \times \begin{bmatrix} 1 & 0 & 0 \\ 0 & 1 & 0 \\ 0 & 0 & 1 \end{bmatrix} = \begin{bmatrix} 5(1)+1(0)+6(0) & 5(0)+1(1)+6(0) & 5(0)+1(0)+6(1) \\ -2(1)+3(0)+1(0) & -2(0)+3(1)+1(0) & -2(0)+3(0)+1(1) \\ 4(1)+7(0)+2(0) & 4(0)+7(1)+2(0) & 4(0)+7(0)+2(1) \end{bmatrix} = \begin{bmatrix} 5 & 1 & 6 \\ -2 & 3 & 1 \\ 4 & 7 & 2 \end{bmatrix}$

30. $A \times B = \begin{bmatrix} -3 & 1 \\ 2 & 7 \end{bmatrix} \times \begin{bmatrix} 4 & -1 \\ 0 & 6 \end{bmatrix} = \begin{bmatrix} -3(4)+1(0) & -3(-1)+1(6) \\ 2(4)+7(0) & 2(-1)+7(6) \end{bmatrix} = \begin{bmatrix} -12 & 9 \\ 8 & 40 \end{bmatrix}$

31. $A + B = \begin{bmatrix} 1 & 2 & -2 \\ 3 & 0 & 4 \end{bmatrix} + \begin{bmatrix} 5 & 1 & 3 \\ 2 & -2 & 1 \end{bmatrix} = \begin{bmatrix} 1+5 & 2+1 & -2+3 \\ 3+2 & 0+(-2) & 4+1 \end{bmatrix} = \begin{bmatrix} 6 & 3 & 1 \\ 5 & -2 & 5 \end{bmatrix}$

A and B cannot be multiplied because the number of columns in A is not equal to the number of rows in B.

32. A and B cannot be added because they do not have the same dimensions. A and B cannot be multiplied because the number of columns in A is not equal to the number of rows in B.

33. Matrices A and B cannot be added because they do not have the same dimensions.

$$A \times B = \begin{bmatrix} 4 & 5 & 3 \\ 6 & 2 & 1 \end{bmatrix} \times \begin{bmatrix} 3 & 2 \\ 4 & 6 \\ -2 & 0 \end{bmatrix} = \begin{bmatrix} 4(3)+5(4)+3(-2) & 4(2)+5(6)+3(0) \\ 6(3)+2(4)+1(-2) & 6(2)+2(6)+1(0) \end{bmatrix} = \begin{bmatrix} 26 & 38 \\ 24 & 24 \end{bmatrix}$$

34. $A + B = \begin{bmatrix} 1 & 2 \\ 3 & 4 \\ 5 & 6 \end{bmatrix} + \begin{bmatrix} 1 & 2 \\ 3 & 4 \\ 5 & 6 \end{bmatrix} = \begin{bmatrix} 1+1 & 2+2 \\ 3+3 & 4+4 \\ 5+5 & 6+6 \end{bmatrix} = \begin{bmatrix} 2 & 4 \\ 6 & 8 \\ 10 & 12 \end{bmatrix}$

A and B cannot be multiplied because the number of columns in A is not equal to the number of rows in B.

35. A and B cannot be added because they do not have the same dimensions.

$$A \times B = \begin{bmatrix} 1 & 2 \\ 3 & 4 \end{bmatrix} \times \begin{bmatrix} -3 \\ 2 \end{bmatrix} = \begin{bmatrix} 1(-3)+2(2) \\ 3(-3)+4(2) \end{bmatrix} = \begin{bmatrix} 1 \\ -1 \end{bmatrix}$$

36. $A + B = \begin{bmatrix} 5 & -1 \\ 6 & -2 \end{bmatrix} + \begin{bmatrix} 1 & 2 \\ 3 & 4 \end{bmatrix} = \begin{bmatrix} 5+1 & -1+2 \\ 6+3 & -2+4 \end{bmatrix} = \begin{bmatrix} 6 & 1 \\ 9 & 2 \end{bmatrix}$

$A \times B = \begin{bmatrix} 5 & -1 \\ 6 & -2 \end{bmatrix} \times \begin{bmatrix} 1 & 2 \\ 3 & 4 \end{bmatrix} = \begin{bmatrix} 5(1)+(-1)(3) & 5(2)+(-1)(4) \\ 6(1)+(-2)(3) & 6(2)+(-2)(4) \end{bmatrix} = \begin{bmatrix} 2 & 6 \\ 0 & 4 \end{bmatrix}$

37. $A + B = \begin{bmatrix} 1 & 3 \\ 2 & -3 \end{bmatrix} + \begin{bmatrix} 4 & 5 \\ 6 & 2 \end{bmatrix} = \begin{bmatrix} 1+4 & 3+5 \\ 2+6 & -3+2 \end{bmatrix} = \begin{bmatrix} 5 & 8 \\ 8 & -1 \end{bmatrix}$

$B + A = \begin{bmatrix} 4 & 5 \\ 6 & 2 \end{bmatrix} + \begin{bmatrix} 1 & 3 \\ 2 & -3 \end{bmatrix} = \begin{bmatrix} 4+1 & 5+3 \\ 6+2 & 2+(-3) \end{bmatrix} = \begin{bmatrix} 5 & 8 \\ 8 & -1 \end{bmatrix}$ Thus A + B = B + A

38. $A + B = \begin{bmatrix} -3 & 4 \\ 5 & 7 \end{bmatrix} + \begin{bmatrix} 0 & 6 \\ -1 & 5 \end{bmatrix} = \begin{bmatrix} -3+0 & 4+6 \\ 5+(-1) & 7+5 \end{bmatrix} = \begin{bmatrix} -3 & 10 \\ 4 & 12 \end{bmatrix}$

$B + A = \begin{bmatrix} 0 & 6 \\ -1 & 5 \end{bmatrix} + \begin{bmatrix} -3 & 4 \\ 5 & 7 \end{bmatrix} = \begin{bmatrix} 0+(-3) & 6+4 \\ -1+5 & 5+7 \end{bmatrix} = \begin{bmatrix} -3 & 10 \\ 4 & 12 \end{bmatrix}$ Thus A + B = B + A.

39. $A + B = \begin{bmatrix} 0 & -1 \\ 3 & -4 \end{bmatrix} + \begin{bmatrix} 8 & 1 \\ 3 & -4 \end{bmatrix} = \begin{bmatrix} 0+8 & -1+1 \\ 3+3 & -4-4 \end{bmatrix} = \begin{bmatrix} 8 & 0 \\ 6 & -8 \end{bmatrix}$

$B + A = \begin{bmatrix} 8 & 1 \\ 3 & -4 \end{bmatrix} + \begin{bmatrix} 0 & -1 \\ 3 & -4 \end{bmatrix} = \begin{bmatrix} 8+0 & 1-1 \\ 3+3 & -4-4 \end{bmatrix} = \begin{bmatrix} 8 & 0 \\ 6 & -8 \end{bmatrix}$ Thus A + B = B + A.

40. $A = \begin{bmatrix} 2 \\ 1 \end{bmatrix}$ $B = \begin{bmatrix} 0 \\ 3 \end{bmatrix}$ (Your choices for A and B may be different)

$A + B = \begin{bmatrix} 2 \\ 1 \end{bmatrix} + \begin{bmatrix} 0 \\ 3 \end{bmatrix} = \begin{bmatrix} 2+0 \\ 1+3 \end{bmatrix} = \begin{bmatrix} 2 \\ 4 \end{bmatrix}$

$B + A = \begin{bmatrix} 0 \\ 3 \end{bmatrix} + \begin{bmatrix} 2 \\ 1 \end{bmatrix} = \begin{bmatrix} 0+2 \\ 3+1 \end{bmatrix} = \begin{bmatrix} 2 \\ 4 \end{bmatrix}$ Thus, A + B = B + A.

41. $(A + B) + C = \left(\begin{bmatrix} 2 & 3 \\ 1 & 6 \end{bmatrix} + \begin{bmatrix} -1 & 4 \\ 5 & 0 \end{bmatrix} \right) + \begin{bmatrix} 3 & 4 \\ -2 & 7 \end{bmatrix} = \begin{bmatrix} 1 & 7 \\ 6 & 6 \end{bmatrix} + \begin{bmatrix} 3 & 4 \\ -2 & 7 \end{bmatrix} = \begin{bmatrix} 4 & 11 \\ 4 & 13 \end{bmatrix}$

$A + (B + C) = \begin{bmatrix} 2 & 3 \\ 1 & 6 \end{bmatrix} + \left(\begin{bmatrix} -1 & 4 \\ 5 & 0 \end{bmatrix} + \begin{bmatrix} 3 & 4 \\ -2 & 7 \end{bmatrix} \right) = \begin{bmatrix} 2 & 3 \\ 1 & 6 \end{bmatrix} + \begin{bmatrix} 2 & 8 \\ 3 & 7 \end{bmatrix} = \begin{bmatrix} 4 & 11 \\ 4 & 13 \end{bmatrix}$

Thus, (A + B) + C = A + (B + C).

42. $(A + B) + C = \left(\begin{bmatrix} -2 & -3 \\ -4 & -5 \end{bmatrix} + \begin{bmatrix} -9 & 1 \\ -7 & 2 \end{bmatrix} \right) + \begin{bmatrix} 6 & 3 \\ -3 & 6 \end{bmatrix} = \begin{bmatrix} -11 & -2 \\ -11 & -3 \end{bmatrix} + \begin{bmatrix} 6 & 3 \\ -3 & 6 \end{bmatrix} = \begin{bmatrix} -5 & 1 \\ -14 & 3 \end{bmatrix}$

$A + (B + C) = \begin{bmatrix} -2 & -3 \\ -4 & -5 \end{bmatrix} + \left(\begin{bmatrix} -9 & 1 \\ -7 & 2 \end{bmatrix} + \begin{bmatrix} 6 & 3 \\ -3 & 6 \end{bmatrix} \right) = \begin{bmatrix} -2 & -3 \\ -4 & -5 \end{bmatrix} + \begin{bmatrix} -3 & 4 \\ -10 & 8 \end{bmatrix} = \begin{bmatrix} -5 & 1 \\ -14 & 3 \end{bmatrix}$

Thus, (A + B) + C = A + (B + C).

43. $(A + B) + C = \left(\begin{bmatrix} 7 & 4 \\ 9 & -36 \end{bmatrix} + \begin{bmatrix} 5 & 6 \\ -1 & -4 \end{bmatrix} \right) + \begin{bmatrix} -7 & -5 \\ -1 & 3 \end{bmatrix} = \begin{bmatrix} 12 & 10 \\ 8 & -40 \end{bmatrix} + \begin{bmatrix} -7 & -5 \\ -1 & 3 \end{bmatrix} = \begin{bmatrix} 5 & 5 \\ 7 & -37 \end{bmatrix}$

$A + (B + C) = \begin{bmatrix} 7 & 4 \\ 9 & -36 \end{bmatrix} + \left(\begin{bmatrix} 5 & 6 \\ -1 & -4 \end{bmatrix} + \begin{bmatrix} -7 & -5 \\ -1 & 3 \end{bmatrix} \right) = \begin{bmatrix} 7 & 4 \\ 9 & -36 \end{bmatrix} + \begin{bmatrix} -2 & 1 \\ -2 & -1 \end{bmatrix} = \begin{bmatrix} 5 & 5 \\ 7 & -37 \end{bmatrix}$

Thus, (A + B) + C = A + (B + C).

44. $A = \begin{bmatrix} 1 \\ 1 \end{bmatrix}$, $B = \begin{bmatrix} 2 \\ 0 \end{bmatrix}$, $C = \begin{bmatrix} 3 \\ 3 \end{bmatrix}$ (Your choices may be different)

$(A + B) + C = \left(\begin{bmatrix} 1 \\ 1 \end{bmatrix} + \begin{bmatrix} 2 \\ 0 \end{bmatrix} \right) + \begin{bmatrix} 3 \\ 3 \end{bmatrix} = \begin{bmatrix} 3 \\ 1 \end{bmatrix} + \begin{bmatrix} 3 \\ 3 \end{bmatrix} = \begin{bmatrix} 6 \\ 4 \end{bmatrix}$

$A + (B + C) = \begin{bmatrix} 1 \\ 1 \end{bmatrix} + \left(\begin{bmatrix} 2 \\ 0 \end{bmatrix} + \begin{bmatrix} 3 \\ 3 \end{bmatrix} \right) = \begin{bmatrix} 1 \\ 1 \end{bmatrix} + \begin{bmatrix} 5 \\ 3 \end{bmatrix} = \begin{bmatrix} 6 \\ 4 \end{bmatrix}$ Thus, (A+B) + C = A + (B+C).

45. $A \times B = \begin{bmatrix} 2 & -1 \\ 4 & -3 \end{bmatrix} \times \begin{bmatrix} 2 & 4 \\ -1 & -3 \end{bmatrix} = \begin{bmatrix} 2(2)+(-1)(-1) & 2(4)+(-1)(-3) \\ 4(2)+(-3)(-1) & 4(4)+(-3)(-3) \end{bmatrix} = \begin{bmatrix} 5 & 11 \\ 11 & 25 \end{bmatrix}$

$B \times A = \begin{bmatrix} 2 & 4 \\ -1 & -3 \end{bmatrix} \times \begin{bmatrix} 2 & -1 \\ 4 & -3 \end{bmatrix} = \begin{bmatrix} 2(2)+4(4) & 2(-1)+4(-3) \\ -1(2)+(-3)(4) & (-1)(-1)+(-3)(-3) \end{bmatrix} = \begin{bmatrix} 20 & -14 \\ -14 & 10 \end{bmatrix}$

Thus, $A \times B \neq B \times A$.

46. Since B = I (identity matrix), and we know that $A \times I = I \times A = A$, we can conclude that $A \times B = B \times A$.

47. $A \times B = \begin{bmatrix} 4 & 2 \\ 1 & -3 \end{bmatrix} \times \begin{bmatrix} 2 & 4 \\ -3 & 1 \end{bmatrix} = \begin{bmatrix} 4(2)+2(-3) & 4(4)+2(1) \\ 1(2)+(-3)(-3) & 1(4)+(-3)(1) \end{bmatrix} = \begin{bmatrix} 2 & 18 \\ 11 & 1 \end{bmatrix}$

$B \times A = \begin{bmatrix} 2 & 4 \\ -3 & 1 \end{bmatrix} \times \begin{bmatrix} 4 & 2 \\ 1 & -3 \end{bmatrix} = \begin{bmatrix} 2(4)+4(1) & 2(2)+4(-3) \\ -3(4)+1(1) & -3(2)+1(-3) \end{bmatrix} = \begin{bmatrix} 12 & -8 \\ -11 & -9 \end{bmatrix}$

Thus, $A \times B \neq B \times A$.

48. $A \times B = \begin{bmatrix} -3 & 2 \\ 6 & -5 \end{bmatrix} \times \begin{bmatrix} -5/3 & -2/3 \\ -2 & -1 \end{bmatrix} = \begin{bmatrix} -3(-5/3)+2(-2) & -3(-2/3)+2(-1) \\ 6(-5/3)-5(-2) & 6(-2/3)-5(-1) \end{bmatrix} = \begin{bmatrix} 1 & 0 \\ 0 & 1 \end{bmatrix}$

$B \times A = \begin{bmatrix} -5/3 & -2/3 \\ -2 & -1 \end{bmatrix} \times \begin{bmatrix} -3 & 2 \\ 6 & -5 \end{bmatrix} = \begin{bmatrix} (-5/3)(-3)-(2/3)(6) & -(5/3)(2)-(2/3)(5) \\ -2(-3)-1(6) & -2(2)-1(-5) \end{bmatrix} = \begin{bmatrix} 1 & 0 \\ 0 & 1 \end{bmatrix}$

Thus, $A \times B = B \times A$.

49. Since $B = I$, (the identity matrix), and $A \times I = I \times A = A$ we can conclude that $A \times B = B \times A$.

50. $A = \begin{bmatrix} 1 & 1 \\ 0 & 2 \end{bmatrix}$, $B = \begin{bmatrix} 2 & 3 \\ 2 & 3 \end{bmatrix}$ (Your choices may be different)

$A \times B = \begin{bmatrix} 1 & 1 \\ 0 & 2 \end{bmatrix} \times \begin{bmatrix} 2 & 3 \\ 2 & 3 \end{bmatrix} = \begin{bmatrix} 1(2)+1(2) & 1(3)+1(3) \\ 0(2)+2(2) & 0(3)+2(3) \end{bmatrix} = \begin{bmatrix} 4 & 6 \\ 4 & 6 \end{bmatrix}$

$B \times A = \begin{bmatrix} 2 & 3 \\ 2 & 3 \end{bmatrix} \times \begin{bmatrix} 1 & 1 \\ 0 & 2 \end{bmatrix} = \begin{bmatrix} 2(1)+3(0) & 2(1)+3(2) \\ 2(1)+3(0) & 2(1)+3(2) \end{bmatrix} = \begin{bmatrix} 2 & 5 \\ 2 & 5 \end{bmatrix}$

Thus, $A \times B \neq B \times A$.

51. $(A \times B) \times C = \left(\begin{bmatrix} 1 & 2 \\ 4 & 0 \end{bmatrix} \begin{bmatrix} 2 & 1 \\ 3 & 0 \end{bmatrix} \right) \begin{bmatrix} 4 & 2 \\ 3 & 1 \end{bmatrix} = \begin{bmatrix} 1(2)+2(3) & 1(1)+2(0) \\ 4(2)+0(3) & 4(1)+0(0) \end{bmatrix} \begin{bmatrix} 4 & 2 \\ 3 & 1 \end{bmatrix}$

$= \begin{bmatrix} 8 & 1 \\ 8 & 4 \end{bmatrix} \begin{bmatrix} 4 & 2 \\ 3 & 1 \end{bmatrix} = \begin{bmatrix} 8(4)+1(3) & 8(2)+1(1) \\ 8(4)+4(3) & 8(2)+4(1) \end{bmatrix} = \begin{bmatrix} 35 & 17 \\ 44 & 20 \end{bmatrix}$

$A \times (B \times C) = \begin{bmatrix} 1 & 2 \\ 4 & 0 \end{bmatrix} \left(\begin{bmatrix} 2 & 1 \\ 3 & 0 \end{bmatrix} \begin{bmatrix} 4 & 2 \\ 3 & 1 \end{bmatrix} \right) = \begin{bmatrix} 1 & 2 \\ 4 & 0 \end{bmatrix} \begin{bmatrix} 2(4)+1(3) & 2(2)+1(1) \\ 3(4)+0(3) & 3(2)+0(1) \end{bmatrix}$

$= \begin{bmatrix} 1 & 2 \\ 4 & 0 \end{bmatrix} \begin{bmatrix} 11 & 5 \\ 12 & 6 \end{bmatrix} = \begin{bmatrix} 1(11)+2(12) & 1(5)+2(6) \\ 4(11)+0(12) & 4(5)+0(6) \end{bmatrix} = \begin{bmatrix} 35 & 17 \\ 44 & 20 \end{bmatrix}$

52. $(A \times B) \times C = \left(\begin{bmatrix} -2 & 3 \\ 0 & 4 \end{bmatrix} \begin{bmatrix} 4 & 0 \\ 3 & 5 \end{bmatrix} \right) \begin{bmatrix} 3 & 4 \\ -2 & 5 \end{bmatrix} = \begin{bmatrix} -2(4)+3(3) & -2(0)+3(5) \\ 0(4)+4(3) & 0(0)+4(5) \end{bmatrix} \begin{bmatrix} 3 & 4 \\ -2 & 5 \end{bmatrix}$

$= \begin{bmatrix} 1 & 15 \\ 12 & 20 \end{bmatrix} \begin{bmatrix} 3 & 4 \\ -2 & 5 \end{bmatrix} = \begin{bmatrix} 1(3)+15(-2) & 1(4)+15(5) \\ 12(3)+20(-2) & 12(4)+20(5) \end{bmatrix} = \begin{bmatrix} -27 & 79 \\ -4 & 148 \end{bmatrix}$

$A \times (B \times C) = \begin{bmatrix} -2 & 3 \\ 0 & 4 \end{bmatrix} \left(\begin{bmatrix} 4 & 0 \\ 3 & 5 \end{bmatrix} \begin{bmatrix} 3 & 4 \\ -2 & 5 \end{bmatrix} \right) = \begin{bmatrix} -2 & 3 \\ 0 & 4 \end{bmatrix} \begin{bmatrix} 4(3)+0(-2) & 4(4)+0(5) \\ 3(3)+5(-2) & 3(4)+5(5) \end{bmatrix}$

$= \begin{bmatrix} -2 & 3 \\ 0 & 4 \end{bmatrix} \begin{bmatrix} 12 & 16 \\ -1 & 37 \end{bmatrix} = \begin{bmatrix} -2(12)+3(-1) & -2(16)+3(37) \\ 0(12)+4(-1) & 0(16)+4(37) \end{bmatrix} = \begin{bmatrix} -27 & 79 \\ -4 & 148 \end{bmatrix}$

53. $(A \times B) \times C = \left(\begin{bmatrix} 4 & 3 \\ -6 & 2 \end{bmatrix} \begin{bmatrix} 1 & 2 \\ 0 & 1 \end{bmatrix} \right) \begin{bmatrix} 4 & 3 \\ 0 & -2 \end{bmatrix} = \begin{bmatrix} 4(1)+3(0) & 4(2)+3(1) \\ -6(1)+2(0) & -6(2)+2(1) \end{bmatrix} \begin{bmatrix} 4 & 3 \\ 0 & -2 \end{bmatrix}$

$= \begin{bmatrix} 4 & 11 \\ -6 & -10 \end{bmatrix} \begin{bmatrix} 4 & 3 \\ 0 & -2 \end{bmatrix} = \begin{bmatrix} 4(4)+11(0) & 4(3)+11(-2) \\ -6(4)-10(2) & -6(3)-10(-2) \end{bmatrix} = \begin{bmatrix} 16 & -10 \\ -24 & 2 \end{bmatrix}$

$A \times (B \times C) = \begin{bmatrix} 4 & 3 \\ -6 & 2 \end{bmatrix} \left(\begin{bmatrix} 1 & 2 \\ 0 & 1 \end{bmatrix} \begin{bmatrix} 4 & 3 \\ 0 & -2 \end{bmatrix} \right) = \begin{bmatrix} 4 & 3 \\ -6 & 2 \end{bmatrix} \begin{bmatrix} 1(4)+2(0) & 1(3)+2(-2) \\ 0(4)+1(0) & 0(3)+1(-2) \end{bmatrix}$

$= \begin{bmatrix} 4 & 3 \\ -6 & 2 \end{bmatrix} \begin{bmatrix} 4 & -1 \\ 0 & -2 \end{bmatrix} = \begin{bmatrix} 4(4)+3(0) & 4(-1)+3(-2) \\ -6(4)+2(0) & -6(-1)+2(-2) \end{bmatrix} = \begin{bmatrix} 16 & -10 \\ -24 & 2 \end{bmatrix}$

54. $(A \times B) \times C = (A \times I) \times C = A \times C$ and $A \times (B \times C) = A \times (I \times C) = A \times C$, thus
$(A \times B) \times C = A \times (B \times C)$.

55. $(A \times B) \times C = \left(\begin{bmatrix} 3 & 4 \\ -1 & -2 \end{bmatrix} \begin{bmatrix} 0 & 1 \\ 1 & 0 \end{bmatrix} \right) \begin{bmatrix} 2 & 0 \\ 3 & 0 \end{bmatrix} = \begin{bmatrix} 3(0)+4(1) & 3(1)+4(0) \\ -1(0)-2(1) & -1(1)-2(0) \end{bmatrix} \begin{bmatrix} 2 & 0 \\ 3 & 0 \end{bmatrix}$

$= \begin{bmatrix} 4 & 3 \\ -2 & -1 \end{bmatrix} \begin{bmatrix} 2 & 0 \\ 3 & 0 \end{bmatrix} = \begin{bmatrix} 4(2)+3(3) & 4(0)+3(0) \\ -2(2)-1(3) & -2(0)-1(0) \end{bmatrix} = \begin{bmatrix} 17 & 0 \\ -7 & 0 \end{bmatrix}$

$A \times (B \times C) = \begin{bmatrix} 3 & 4 \\ -1 & -2 \end{bmatrix} \left(\begin{bmatrix} 0 & 1 \\ 1 & 0 \end{bmatrix} \begin{bmatrix} 2 & 0 \\ 3 & 0 \end{bmatrix} \right) = \begin{bmatrix} 3 & 4 \\ -1 & -2 \end{bmatrix} \begin{bmatrix} 0(2)+1(3) & 0(0)+1(0) \\ 1(2)+0(3) & 1(0)+0(0) \end{bmatrix}$

$= \begin{bmatrix} 3 & 4 \\ -1 & -2 \end{bmatrix} \begin{bmatrix} 3 & 0 \\ 2 & 0 \end{bmatrix} = \begin{bmatrix} 3(3)+4(2) & 3(0)+4(0) \\ -1(3)-2(2) & -1(0)-2(0) \end{bmatrix} = \begin{bmatrix} 17 & 0 \\ -7 & 0 \end{bmatrix}$

56. $(A \times B) \times C = A \times (B \times C)$ for any choices of A, B, and C that can be multiplied.

57. $A \times B = \begin{bmatrix} 2 & 2 & .5 & 1 \\ 3 & 2 & 1 & 2 \\ 0 & 1 & 0 & 3 \\ .5 & 1 & 0 & 0 \end{bmatrix} \begin{bmatrix} 10 & 12 \\ 5 & 8 \\ 8 & 8 \\ 4 & 6 \end{bmatrix} = \begin{bmatrix} 2 \cdot 10+2 \cdot 5+.5 \cdot 8+1 \cdot 4 & 2 \cdot 12+2 \cdot 8+.5 \cdot 8+1 \cdot 6 \\ 3 \cdot 10+2 \cdot 5+1 \cdot 8+2 \cdot 4 & 3 \cdot 12+2 \cdot 8+1 \cdot 8+2 \cdot 6 \\ 0 \cdot 10+1 \cdot 5+0 \cdot 8+3 \cdot 4 & 0 \cdot 12+1 \cdot 8+0 \cdot 8+3 \cdot 6 \\ .5 \cdot 10+1 \cdot 5+0 \cdot 8+0 \cdot 4 & .5 \cdot 12+1 \cdot 8+0 \cdot 8+0 \cdot 6 \end{bmatrix} = \begin{bmatrix} 38 & 50 \\ 56 & 72 \\ 17 & 26 \\ 10 & 14 \end{bmatrix}$

58. a) Let C = [40 30 12 20].

    b) $C \times A = \begin{bmatrix} 40 & 30 & 12 & 20 \end{bmatrix} \begin{bmatrix} 2 & 2 & .5 & 1 \\ 3 & 3 & 1 & 2 \\ 0 & 1 & 0 & 3 \\ .5 & 1 & 0 & 0 \end{bmatrix} = [\underbrace{180}_{sug.}\ \underbrace{172}_{flr.}\ \underbrace{50}_{mlk.}\ \underbrace{136}_{eggs}]$

59. $C(A \times B) = \begin{bmatrix} 40 & 30 & 12 & 20 \end{bmatrix} \begin{bmatrix} 38 & 50 \\ 56 & 72 \\ 17 & 26 \\ 10 & 14 \end{bmatrix} = [3604\ \ 4752]$ cents or small \$36.04, lg. \$47.52

60. a) $A \times B = \begin{bmatrix} 28 & 32 & 25 \\ 33 & 26 & 31 \end{bmatrix} \begin{bmatrix} 2.45 & 2.95 & 3.15 \\ 1.35 & 0.99 & 1.00 \\ 1.40 & 0.92 & 1.20 \end{bmatrix} = \begin{bmatrix} 146.80 & 137.28 & 150.20 \\ 159.35 & 151.61 & 167.15 \end{bmatrix}$

    b) Burger Prince is the best deal for both clubs.

61. $A + B = \begin{bmatrix} 6 & 3 \\ 4 & -2 \end{bmatrix} + \begin{bmatrix} -6 & -3 \\ -2 & -4 \end{bmatrix} = \begin{bmatrix} 6 + (-6) & 3 + (-3) \\ 4 + (-2) & -2 + (-4) \end{bmatrix} = \begin{bmatrix} 0 & 0 \\ 2 & -6 \end{bmatrix}$

Since $A + B \ne I$ where I is the additive identity matrix, A and B are not additive inverses.

62. $A + B = \begin{bmatrix} 4 & 6 & 3 \\ 2 & 3 & -1 \\ -1 & 0 & 6 \end{bmatrix} + \begin{bmatrix} -4 & -6 & -3 \\ -2 & -3 & 1 \\ 1 & 0 & -6 \end{bmatrix} = \begin{bmatrix} 4 + (-4) & 6 + (-6) & 3 + (-3) \\ 2 + (-2) & 3 + (-3) & -1 + (1) \\ -1 + (1) & 0 + 0 & 6 + (-6) \end{bmatrix} = \begin{bmatrix} 0 & 0 & 0 \\ 0 & 0 & 0 \\ 0 & 0 & 0 \end{bmatrix}$

$B + A = \begin{bmatrix} -4 & -6 & -3 \\ -2 & -3 & 1 \\ 1 & 0 & -6 \end{bmatrix} + \begin{bmatrix} 4 & 6 & 3 \\ 2 & 3 & -1 \\ -1 & 0 & 6 \end{bmatrix} = \begin{bmatrix} -4 + (4) & -6 + (6) & -3 + (3) \\ -2 + (2) & -3 + (3) & 1 + (-1) \\ 1 + (-1) & 0 + (0) & -6 + (6) \end{bmatrix} = \begin{bmatrix} 0 & 0 & 0 \\ 0 & 0 & 0 \\ 0 & 0 & 0 \end{bmatrix}$

Thus, A and B are additive inverses.

63. $A \times B = \begin{bmatrix} 5 & -2 \\ -2 & 1 \end{bmatrix} \begin{bmatrix} 1 & 2 \\ 2 & 5 \end{bmatrix} = \begin{bmatrix} 5(1) - 2(2) & 5(2) - 2(5) \\ -2(1) + 1(2) & -2(2) + 1(5) \end{bmatrix} = \begin{bmatrix} 1 & 0 \\ 0 & 1 \end{bmatrix}$

$B \times A = \begin{bmatrix} 1 & 2 \\ 2 & 5 \end{bmatrix} \begin{bmatrix} 5 & -2 \\ -2 & 1 \end{bmatrix} = \begin{bmatrix} 1(5) + 2(-2) & 1(-2) + 2(1) \\ 2(5) + 5(-2) & 2(-2) + 5(1) \end{bmatrix} = \begin{bmatrix} 1 & 0 \\ 0 & 1 \end{bmatrix}$

Thus, A and B are multiplicative inverses.

64. $A \times B = \begin{bmatrix} 7 & 3 \\ 2 & 1 \end{bmatrix} \begin{bmatrix} 1 & -3 \\ -2 & 7 \end{bmatrix} = \begin{bmatrix} 7(1) + 3(-2) & 7(-3) + 3(7) \\ 2(1) + 1(-2) & 2(-3) + 1(7) \end{bmatrix} = \begin{bmatrix} 1 & 0 \\ 0 & 1 \end{bmatrix}$

$B \times A = \begin{bmatrix} 1 & -3 \\ -2 & 7 \end{bmatrix} \begin{bmatrix} 7 & 3 \\ 2 & 1 \end{bmatrix} = \begin{bmatrix} 1(7) - 3(2) & 1(3) - 3(1) \\ -2(7) + 7(2) & -2(3) + 7(1) \end{bmatrix} = \begin{bmatrix} 1 & 0 \\ 0 & 1 \end{bmatrix}$

Thus, A and B are multiplicative inverses.

65. False. Let $A = [1 \ 3]$ and $B = [2 \ 1]$. Then $A - B = [-1 \ 2]$ and $B - A = [1 \ -2] \ne A - B$.

66. True. For all scalars a and all matrices B and C, $a(B + C) = aB + aC$. As an example,
Let $a = 2$, $B = [1 \ 3]$, and $C = [2 \ 1]$. Then
$a(B + C) = 2([1 \ 3] + [2 \ 1]) = 2[3 \ 4] = [6 \ 8]$, and
$aB + aC = 2[1 \ 3] + 2[2 \ 1] = [2 \ 6] + [4 \ 2] = [6 \ 8] = a(B + C)$.

67. a) $1.4(14) + 0.7(10) + 0.3(7) = \$28.70$
    b) $2.7(12) + 2.8(9) + 0.5(5) = \$60.10$

    c) $L \times C = \begin{bmatrix} 28.7 & 24.6 \\ 41.3 & 35.7 \\ 69.3 & 60.1 \end{bmatrix} \begin{matrix} \text{small} \\ \text{medium} \\ \text{large} \end{matrix}$

    Ames Bay

This array shows the total cost of each boat at each plant.

Exercise Set 7.4

1. a) An augmented matrix is a matrix formed with the coefficients of the variables and the constants. The coefficients are separated from the constants by a vertical bar.

   b) $\begin{bmatrix} 1 & 3 & | & 7 \\ 2 & -1 & | & 4 \end{bmatrix}$

2. 1) Rows of a matrix can be interchanged.
   2) All values in a row can be multiplied by a nonzero real number.
   3) All the values in a row may be added to the corresponding values in another row.

3. If you obtain an augmented matrix in which a 0 appears across an entire row, the system of equations is dependent.

4. If you obtain an augmented matrix in which one row of numbers on the left side of the vertical line are all zeroes but a zero does not appear in the same row on the other side of the vertical line, the system is inconsistent.

NOTE: r_1 = row one, r_2 = row two

5. $$\begin{bmatrix} 1 & 1 & | & 3 \\ 2 & -1 & | & 9 \end{bmatrix}(r_2-2r_1) \begin{bmatrix} 1 & 1 & | & 3 \\ 0 & -3 & | & 3 \end{bmatrix}(r_2\div(-3)) \begin{bmatrix} 1 & 1 & | & 3 \\ 0 & 1 & | & -1 \end{bmatrix}(r_1-r_2) \begin{bmatrix} 1 & 0 & | & 4 \\ 0 & 1 & | & -1 \end{bmatrix}$$
   The solution is $(4,-1)$.

6. $$\begin{bmatrix} 1 & -1 & | & 3 \\ 2 & -1 & | & 7 \end{bmatrix}(r_2-2r_1) \begin{bmatrix} 1 & -1 & | & 3 \\ 0 & 1 & | & 1 \end{bmatrix}(r_1+r_2) \begin{bmatrix} 1 & 0 & | & 4 \\ 0 & 1 & | & 1 \end{bmatrix}$$ The solution is $(4,1)$

7. $$\begin{bmatrix} 1 & 2 & | & 4 \\ 2 & -1 & | & 3 \end{bmatrix}(r_2-2r_1) \begin{bmatrix} 1 & 2 & | & 4 \\ 0 & -5 & | & -5 \end{bmatrix}(r_2\div(-5)) \begin{bmatrix} 1 & 2 & | & 4 \\ 0 & 1 & | & 1 \end{bmatrix}(r_1-2r_2) \begin{bmatrix} 1 & 0 & | & 2 \\ 0 & 1 & | & 1 \end{bmatrix}$$
   The solution is $(2,1)$.

8. $$\begin{bmatrix} 1 & 1 & | & 1 \\ 2 & -5 & | & 9 \end{bmatrix}(r_2-2r_1) \begin{bmatrix} 1 & 1 & | & 1 \\ 0 & -7 & | & 7 \end{bmatrix}(r_2\div(-7)) \begin{bmatrix} 1 & 1 & | & 1 \\ 0 & 1 & | & -1 \end{bmatrix}(r_1-r_2) \begin{bmatrix} 1 & 0 & | & 2 \\ 0 & 1 & | & -1 \end{bmatrix}$$
   The solution is $(2,-1)$.

9. $$\begin{bmatrix} 2 & -5 & | & -6 \\ -4 & 10 & | & 12 \end{bmatrix}(r_2+2r_1) \begin{bmatrix} 2 & -5 & | & -6 \\ 0 & 0 & | & 0 \end{bmatrix} \Rightarrow \text{Dependent system.}$$
   The solution is all points on the line $2x - 5y = -6$.

10. $$\begin{bmatrix} 1 & 1 & | & 5 \\ 3 & -1 & | & 3 \end{bmatrix}(r_2-3r_1) \begin{bmatrix} 1 & 1 & | & 5 \\ 0 & -4 & | & -12 \end{bmatrix}(r_2\div(-4)) \begin{bmatrix} 1 & 1 & | & 5 \\ 0 & 1 & | & 3 \end{bmatrix}(r_1-r_2) \begin{bmatrix} 1 & 0 & | & 2 \\ 0 & 1 & | & 3 \end{bmatrix}$$
    The solution is $(2, 3)$.

11. $$\begin{bmatrix} 1 & 3 & | & 1 \\ -2 & 1 & | & 5 \end{bmatrix}(r_2+2r_1) \begin{bmatrix} 1 & 3 & | & 1 \\ 0 & 7 & | & 7 \end{bmatrix}(r_2\div7) \begin{bmatrix} 1 & 3 & | & 1 \\ 0 & 1 & | & 1 \end{bmatrix}(r_1-3r_2) \begin{bmatrix} 1 & 0 & | & -2 \\ 0 & 1 & | & 1 \end{bmatrix}$$
    The solution is $(-2,1)$.

12. $$\begin{bmatrix} 2 & -3 & | & 10 \\ 2 & 2 & | & 5 \end{bmatrix}\begin{matrix}(r_1\div2) \\ (r_2-2r_1)\end{matrix} \begin{bmatrix} 1 & \frac{3}{2} & | & 5 \\ 0 & 5 & | & -5 \end{bmatrix}(r_2\div(5)) \begin{bmatrix} 1 & -\frac{3}{2} & | & 5 \\ 0 & 1 & | & -1 \end{bmatrix}(r_1+\frac{3}{2}r_2) \begin{bmatrix} 1 & 0 & | & \frac{7}{2} \\ 0 & 1 & | & -1 \end{bmatrix}$$
    The solution is $(7/2, -1)$.

13. $$\begin{bmatrix} 2 & -4 & | & 0 \\ 1 & -3 & | & -1 \end{bmatrix}\begin{matrix}(r_1\div2) \\ = \end{matrix} \begin{bmatrix} 1 & -2 & | & 0 \\ 1 & -3 & | & -1 \end{bmatrix}(r_2-r_1) \begin{bmatrix} 1 & -2 & | & 0 \\ 0 & -1 & | & -1 \end{bmatrix}(r_2\div(-1)) \begin{bmatrix} 1 & -2 & | & 0 \\ 0 & 1 & | & 1 \end{bmatrix}(r_1+2r_2) \begin{bmatrix} 1 & 0 & | & 2 \\ 0 & 1 & | & 1 \end{bmatrix}$$
    The solution is $(2, 1)$.

14. $\begin{bmatrix} 4 & 2 & | & 6 \\ 5 & 4 & | & 9 \end{bmatrix} \begin{matrix} (r_1 \div 4) \\ = \end{matrix} \begin{bmatrix} 1 & \frac{1}{2} & | & \frac{3}{2} \\ 5 & 4 & | & 9 \end{bmatrix} \begin{matrix} \\ (r_2 - 5r_1) \end{matrix} \begin{matrix} = \\ \end{matrix} \begin{bmatrix} 1 & \frac{1}{2} & | & \frac{3}{2} \\ 0 & \frac{3}{2} & | & \frac{3}{2} \end{bmatrix} \begin{matrix} \\ (\frac{2}{3}r_2) \end{matrix} \begin{bmatrix} 1 & \frac{1}{2} & | & \frac{3}{2} \\ 0 & 1 & | & 1 \end{bmatrix} \begin{matrix} (r_1 - \frac{1}{2}r_2) \\ = \end{matrix} \begin{bmatrix} 1 & 0 & | & 1 \\ 0 & 1 & | & 1 \end{bmatrix}$

The solution is (1, 1).

15. $\begin{bmatrix} -3 & 6 & | & 5 \\ 2 & -4 & | & 8 \end{bmatrix} \begin{matrix} (r_1 \div (-3)) \\ = \end{matrix} \begin{bmatrix} 1 & -2 & | & \frac{-5}{3} \\ 2 & -4 & | & 8 \end{bmatrix} \begin{matrix} \\ (r_2 - 2r_1) \end{matrix} \begin{bmatrix} 1 & -2 & | & \frac{-5}{3} \\ 0 & 0 & | & \frac{34}{3} \end{bmatrix} \Rightarrow$ Inconsistent system.

No solution.

16. $\begin{bmatrix} 2 & -5 & | & 10 \\ 3 & 1 & | & 15 \end{bmatrix} = \begin{bmatrix} 1 & \frac{-5}{2} & | & 5 \\ 0 & \frac{15}{2} & | & 0 \end{bmatrix} = \begin{bmatrix} 1 & \frac{-5}{2} & | & 5 \\ 0 & 1 & | & 0 \end{bmatrix} = \begin{bmatrix} 1 & 0 & | & 5 \\ 0 & 1 & | & 0 \end{bmatrix}$ The solution is (5,0).

17. $\begin{bmatrix} 2 & 1 & | & 11 \\ 1 & 3 & | & 18 \end{bmatrix} \begin{matrix} (r_1 \div 2) \\ = \end{matrix} \begin{bmatrix} 1 & \frac{1}{2} & | & \frac{11}{2} \\ 1 & 3 & | & 18 \end{bmatrix} \begin{matrix} \\ (r_2 - r_1) \end{matrix} \begin{bmatrix} 1 & \frac{1}{2} & | & \frac{11}{2} \\ 0 & \frac{5}{2} & | & \frac{25}{2} \end{bmatrix} \begin{matrix} \\ (\frac{2}{5}r_2) \end{matrix} \begin{bmatrix} 1 & \frac{1}{2} & | & \frac{11}{2} \\ 0 & 1 & | & 5 \end{bmatrix} \begin{matrix} (r_1 - \frac{1}{2}r_2) \\ = \end{matrix} \begin{bmatrix} 1 & 0 & | & 3 \\ 0 & 1 & | & 5 \end{bmatrix}$

The solution is (3, 5)

18. $\begin{bmatrix} 4 & -3 & | & 7 \\ -2 & 5 & | & 14 \end{bmatrix} \begin{matrix} (r_1 \div 4) \\ = \end{matrix} \begin{bmatrix} 1 & -\frac{3}{4} & | & \frac{7}{4} \\ -2 & 5 & | & 14 \end{bmatrix} \begin{matrix} \\ (r_2 + 2r_1) \end{matrix} \begin{bmatrix} 1 & -\frac{3}{4} & | & \frac{7}{4} \\ 0 & \frac{7}{2} & | & \frac{35}{2} \end{bmatrix} \begin{matrix} \\ (\frac{2}{7}r_2) \end{matrix} \begin{bmatrix} 1 & -\frac{3}{4} & | & \frac{7}{4} \\ 0 & 1 & | & 5 \end{bmatrix} \begin{matrix} (r_1 + \frac{3}{4}r_2) \\ = \end{matrix} \begin{bmatrix} 1 & 0 & | & \frac{11}{2} \\ 0 & 1 & | & 5 \end{bmatrix}$

The solution is (11/2, 5)

19. Let x = cost of poster board $4x + 2y = 8$
    y = cost of a marker pen $8x + 5y = 18$

$\begin{bmatrix} 4 & 2 & | & 8 \\ 8 & 5 & | & 18 \end{bmatrix} \begin{matrix} (r_1 \div 4) \\ = \end{matrix} \begin{bmatrix} 1 & \frac{1}{2} & | & 2 \\ 8 & 5 & | & 18 \end{bmatrix} \begin{matrix} \\ (r_2 - 8r_1) \end{matrix} \begin{bmatrix} 1 & \frac{1}{2} & | & 2 \\ 0 & 1 & | & 2 \end{bmatrix} \begin{matrix} (r_1 - \frac{1}{2}r_2) \\ = \end{matrix} \begin{bmatrix} 1 & 0 & | & 1 \\ 0 & 1 & | & 2 \end{bmatrix}$ The solution is (1,2).

Poster board: \$1; markers: \$2.

20. Let x = length $x - y = 4$
    y = width $2x + 2y = 16$

$\begin{bmatrix} 1 & -1 & | & 4 \\ 2 & 2 & | & 16 \end{bmatrix} = \begin{bmatrix} 1 & -1 & | & 4 \\ 0 & 4 & | & 8 \end{bmatrix} = \begin{bmatrix} 1 & -1 & | & 4 \\ 0 & 1 & | & 2 \end{bmatrix} = \begin{bmatrix} 1 & 0 & | & 6 \\ 0 & 1 & | & 2 \end{bmatrix}$

length = 6 feet, width = 2 feet

21. Let x = cost per pound of cherries $2x + 3y = 23$
    y = cost per pound of mints $1x + 2y = 14$

$\begin{bmatrix} 2 & 3 & | & 23 \\ 1 & 2 & | & 14 \end{bmatrix} = \begin{bmatrix} 1 & \frac{3}{2} & | & \frac{23}{2} \\ 1 & 2 & | & 14 \end{bmatrix} = \begin{bmatrix} 1 & \frac{3}{2} & | & \frac{23}{2} \\ 0 & \frac{1}{2} & | & \frac{5}{2} \end{bmatrix} = \begin{bmatrix} 1 & \frac{3}{2} & | & \frac{23}{2} \\ 0 & 1 & | & 5 \end{bmatrix} = \begin{bmatrix} 1 & 0 & | & 4 \\ 0 & 1 & | & 5 \end{bmatrix}$

The cherries are \$4 per pound and the mints are \$5 per pound.

22. Let x = hours the truck driver worked $x + 2 = y$ or $x - y = -2$
    y = hours the laborer worked $10x + 8y = 144$ $10x + 8y = 144$

$\begin{bmatrix} 1 & -1 & | & -2 \\ 10 & 8 & | & 144 \end{bmatrix} = \begin{bmatrix} 1 & -1 & | & -2 \\ 0 & 18 & | & 164 \end{bmatrix} = \begin{bmatrix} 1 & -1 & | & -2 \\ 0 & 1 & | & \frac{82}{9} \end{bmatrix} = \begin{bmatrix} 1 & 0 & | & 7\frac{7}{9} \\ 0 & 1 & | & 9\frac{1}{9} \end{bmatrix}$

The truck driver worked $7^1/_9$ hours and the laborer worked $9^1/_9$ hours.

23. $\left.\begin{array}{c} 1.5x + 2y = 337.5 \\ x + y = 200 \end{array}\right\} \Rightarrow \begin{bmatrix} 1.5 & 2 & | & 337.5 \\ 1 & 1 & | & 200 \end{bmatrix} = \begin{bmatrix} 1 & 1.\overline{33} & | & 225 \\ 1 & 1 & | & 200 \end{bmatrix} = \begin{bmatrix} 1 & 1.\overline{33} & | & 225 \\ 1 & 1 & | & 200 \end{bmatrix} = \begin{bmatrix} 1 & 1.\overline{33} & | & 225 \\ 0 & -.\overline{33} & | & -25 \end{bmatrix}$

$$= \begin{bmatrix} 1 & 1.\overline{33} & | & 225 \\ 0 & 1 & | & 75 \end{bmatrix} = \begin{bmatrix} 1 & 0 & | & 125 \\ 0 & 1 & | & 75 \end{bmatrix}$$

The solution is 125 @ $1.50 and 75 @ $2.00.

Exercise Set 7.5

1. The solution set of a system of linear inequalities is the set of points that satisfy all inequalities in the system.

2. Graph and shade the solution set to each of the inequalities. The intersection of the shaded areas and any solid lines common to both inequalities is the solution set.

3.

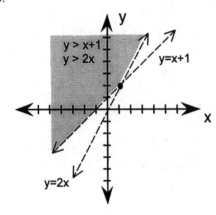

4.

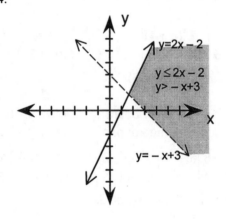

5.

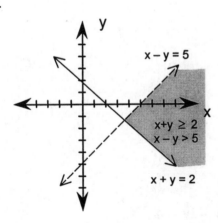

6.

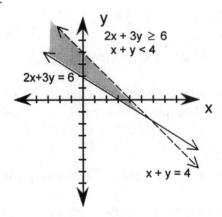

7.

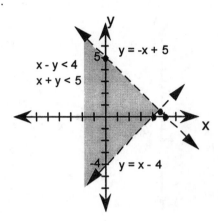

$x - y < 4$

$x + y < 5$

$y = -x + 5$

$y = x - 4$

8.

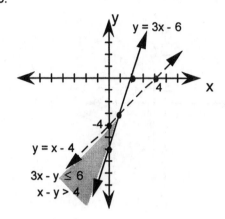

$y = 3x - 6$

$y = x - 4$

$3x - y \leq 6$

$x - y > 4$

9.

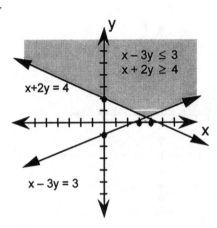

$x - 3y \leq 3$

$x + 2y \geq 4$

$x + 2y = 4$

$x - 3y = 3$

10.

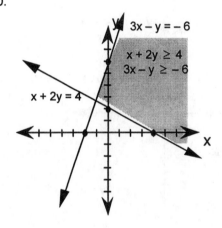

$3x - y = -6$

$x + 2y \geq 4$

$3x - y \geq -6$

$x + 2y = 4$

11.

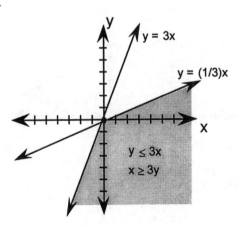

$y = 3x$

$y = (1/3)x$

$y \leq 3x$

$x \geq 3y$

12.

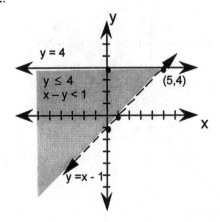

$y = 4$

$y \leq 4$

$x - y < 1$

$(5,4)$

$y = x - 1$

13.

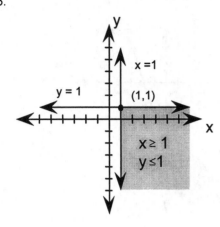

14.

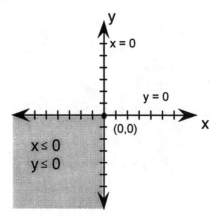

15.

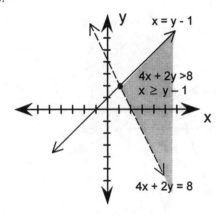

16.

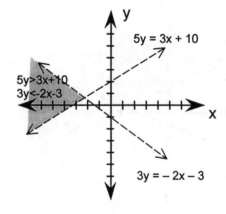

17.

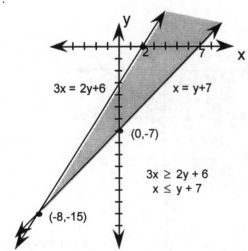

18.

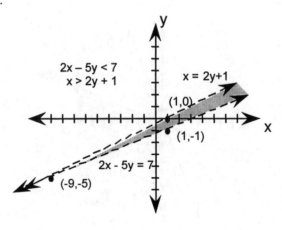

19. a) x + y < 500
        x ≥ 150
        y ≥ 150

    b)

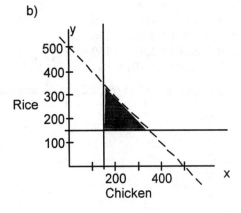

    c) (220, 220) means 220 calories of chicken
    and 220 calories of rice, or approx. 3.7 oz. of
    chicken and 8.8 oz. of rice.

20. x ≤ 0, y ≥ 0

21. a) No, if the lines are parallel there may not be
    a solution to the system.
    b) Example: y ≥ x
                  y ≤ x − 2
    This system has no solution.

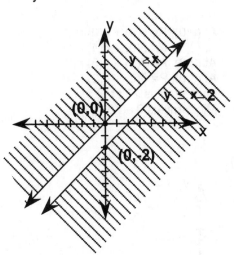

22. Yes. One example is x ≥ 0, y ≥ 0, x ≤ 0, y ≤ 0.

23. No. Every line divides the plane into two halves
    only one of which can be part of the solution.
    Therefore, the points in the other half cannot
    satisfy both inequalities and so do not solve the
    system.
    Example: y ≥ x
              x ≥ 2

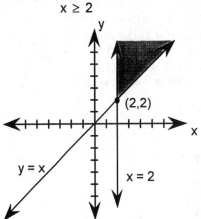

Exercise Set 7.6
1. Constraints are restrictions that are represented as linear inequalities.
2. The feasible region is formed by graphing the system of inequalities.
3. Vertices.
4. Objective function: K = Ax + By
5. If a linear equation of the form K = Ax + By is evaluated at each point in a closed polygonal region, the
   maximum and minimum values of the equation occur at a corner.

6. At (1, 1), P = 4(1) + 6(1) = 10
   At (1, 4), P = 4(1) + 6(4) = 28
   At (5, 1), P = 4(5) + 6(1) = 26
   At (7, 1), P = 4(7) + 6(1) = 34

   The maximum profit is 34.
   Determine the value of the profit function at
   each vertice; the largest profit value is the
   maximum.

7. At (0, 0), K= 3(0) + 4(0) = 0
   At (0, 4), K= 3(0) + 4(4) = 16
   At (2, 3), K= 3(2) + 4(3) = 18
   At (5, 0), K= 3(5) + 4(0) = 15

   The maximum value is 18 at (2, 3);
   minimum value is 0 at (0, 0).

8. At (10, 20), K = 2(10) + 3(20) = 80
    At (10, 40), K = 2(10) + 3(40) = 140
    At (50, 30), K = 2(50) + 3(30) = 190
    At (50, 10), K = 2(50) + 3(10) = 130
    At (20, 10), K = 2(20) + 3(10) = 70

    The maximum value is 190 at (50, 30); minimum value is 70 at (20, 10).

9. a)

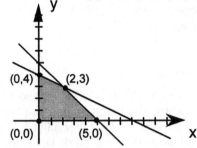

    b) P = 3x + 5y
        At (0,0), P = 3(0) + 5(0) = 0
        At (0,4), P = 3(0) + 5(4) = 20
        At (2,3), P = 3(2) + 5(3) = 21
        At (5,0), P = 3(5) + 5(0) = 15
        Max. profit is 21 at (2,3)
        Min. profit is 0 at (0,0)

10. a)

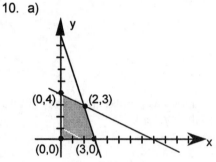

    b) P = 5x + 4y
        At (0,0), P= 5(0) + 4(0) = 0
        At (0,4), P= 5(0) + 4(4) = 16
        At (2,3), P= 5(2) + 4(3) = 22
        At (3,0), P= 5(3) + 4(0) = 15
        Max. profit is 22 at (2,3)
        Min. profit is 0 at (0,0)

11. a)

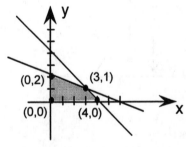

    b) P = 7x + 6y
        At (0,0), P = 7(0) + 6(0) = 0
        At (0,2), P = 7(0) + 6(2) = 12
        At (3,1), P = 7(3) + 6(1) = 27
        At (4,0), P = 7(4) + 6(0) = 28
        Max. profit is 28 at (4,0)
        Min. profit is 0 at (0,0)

12. a)

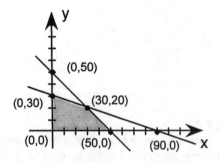

    b) P = 20x + 40y
        At (0,0), P = 20(0)+40(0) = 0
        At (0,30), P = 20(0)+40(30) = 120
        At (30,20), P = 20(30)+40(20) = 1400
        At (50,0), P = 20(50)+40(0) = 1000
        Max. profit is 1400 at (30,20)
        Min. profit is 0 at (0,0)

13. a)

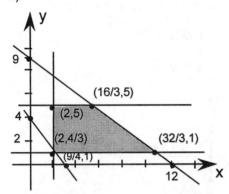

b) P = 2.20x + 1.65y

At (2,4/3), P= 2.20(2)+1.65(4/3) = 6.60

At (2,5), P= 2.20(2)+1.65(5) = 12.65

At (16/3,5), P=2.20(16/3)+1.65(5) = 19.98

At (32/3,1), P=2.20(32/3)+1.65(1) = 25.12

At (9/4,1), P=2.20(9/4)+1.65(1) = 6.60

Max. profit is 25.12 at (32/3,1)

Min. profit is 6.60 at (2,4/3), (9/4,1)

14. a)

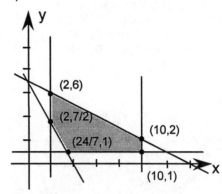

b) P = 15.13x + 9.35y

Max. profit is 170 at (10,2)

Min. profit is 61.22 at (24/7,1)

15. a) Let x = number of skateboards

y = number of in-line skates

x + y ≤ 20

x ≥ 3

x ≤ 6

y ≥ 2

b) P = 25x + 20y

c)

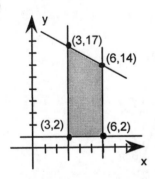

d) (3,2) (3,17) (6,14) (6,2)

e) At (3,2), P = 25(3) + 20(2) = 115

At (3,17), P = 25(3) + 20(17) = 415

At (6,14), P = 25(6) + 20(14) = 430

At (6,2), P = 25(6) + 20(2) = 190

Six skateboards and 14 pairs of in-line skates.

f) Max. profit = $430.

16. a) Let x = number of cars

y = number of trucks

x ≥ 2

y ≥ 2

y ≤ 5

x + y ≤ 15

b) P = 8x + 10y

c)

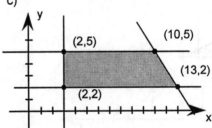

d) (2,2), (2,5), (10,5), (13,2)

e) Maximum profit occurs at (10,5).

f) Thus he should make 10 cars and 5 trucks for a profit of $130.

17. a) Let x = no. of cups of Trimfit.
       y = no. of cups of Usave.
       constraints: 60x + 50y ≥ 300 cal.
                    8x + 20y ≥ 80 A
                    6x + 30y ≥ 90 C
    b) C = 0.25x + 0.32y
    c)

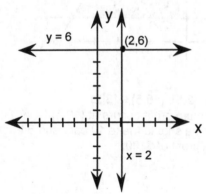

    d) (0,6), (5/2,3), (5,2) (15,0)
    e) C = .25x + .32y
        At (0,6) C = .25(0) + .32(6) = 1.92
        At (5/2,3) C = .25(5/2) + .32(3) = 1.59
        At (5,2) C = .25(5) + .32(2) = 1.89
        At (15,0) C = .25(15) + .32(0) = 3.75
        2.5 cups of Trimfit and 3 cups of Usave.
    f) Min. cost is $1.59

18. Let x = pounds of all-beef hot dogs
       y = pounds of regular hot dogs
           x + (1/2)y ≤ 200
           (1/2)y ≤ 150
           x ≥ 0
           y ≥ 0

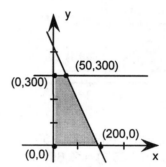

    P = 0.30y + 0.40x
    Maximum profit occurs at (50,300).
    Thus the manufacturer should make 50 lb. of
    the all-beef hot dogs and 300 lb. of the regular
    hot dogs for a profit of $110.

19. Let x = no. of 4-cylinder engines
       y = no. of 6 cylinder engines
    The vertices are: (0,0), (0,8), (2,7), (6,3), (8,0).
    P = 150x + 250y
    Max. profit is $2050 at (2,7)

    constraints: x ≥ 0, y ≥ 0
                   x + y ≤ 9 for cleaning
                   3x + 2y ≤ 24 for testing
                   5x + 10y ≤ 80 for overhauling

Review Exercises

1.

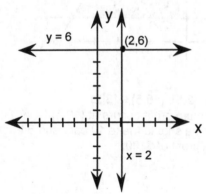

The solution is (2,6).

2.

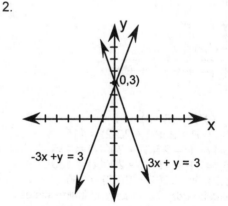

The solution is (0,3).

3.

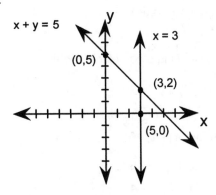

The solution is (3,2).

4.

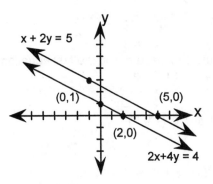

Inconsistent

5. y = (2/3)x + 5
    y = (2/3)x + 5
    Same slope and y-intercept.
    Infinitely many solutions.

6. y = (2/3)x + 5
    y = (2/3)x – 8/3
    Same slope but different
    y-intercepts. No solution.

7. 6y – 2x = 20 becomes y = (1/3)x + 10/3
    4y + 2x = 10 becomes y = – (1/2)x + 5/2
    Different slopes. One solution.

8. y = (1/2)x – 2
    y = 2x + 6
    Different slopes. One solution.

9. x – 2y = 1
    2x + y = 7
    Solve the first equation for x.
    x = 2y + 1
    Substitute (2y + 1) in place of x in the second
    equation.
         2(2y + 1) + y = 7 (solve for y)
            4y + 2 + y = 7
               5y + 2 = 7
                   5y = 5
                    y = 1
    Substitute 1 in place of y in the equation
    x = 2y + 1.
    x = 2(1) + 1 = 2 + 1 = 3
    The solution is (3,1).

10. x + 2y = – 11
    y = 2x – 3
    Substitute (2x – 3) in place of y in the first
    equation.
        x + 2(2x – 3) = – 11 (solve for x)
           x + 4x – 6 = – 11
               5x – 6 = – 11
                   5x = – 5
                    x = – 1
    Substitute (– 1) in place of x in the second
    equation.
    y = 2(– 1) – 3 = – 2– 3 = – 5
    The solution is (– 1,– 5).

11. 2x – y = 4
    3x – y = 2
    Solve for y in the first equation.
        2x – 2x – y = – 2x + 4
              – y = – 2x + 4
                y = 2x – 4
    Substitute 2x – 4 in place of y in the second
    equation.
        3x – (2x – 4) = 2 (solve for x)
          3x – 2x + 4 = 2
               x + 4 = 2
                   x = – 2
    Substitute – 2 in place of x in the equation
    y = 2x – 4.
    y = 2(– 2) – 4 = – 4 –4 = –8
    The solution is (– 2, – 8).

12. 3x + y = 1
    3y = – 9x – 4
    Solve the first equation for y.
    y = – 3x + 1
    Substitute (– 3x + 1) in place of y in the second
    equation.
        3(– 3x + 1) = – 9x – 4 (solve for x)
          – 9x + 3 = – 9x – 4
                 3 = – 4   False
    Since 3 does not equal – 4 we can conclude
    that there is no solution to this system. The
    equations are inconsistent.

13.

$$
\begin{aligned}
(1) \quad -x + y &= 12 \\
(2) \quad \underline{x + 2y} &= \underline{-3} \text{ (add)} \\
3y &= 9 \\
y &= 3
\end{aligned}
$$

Substitute 3 in place of y in the first equation.

$$
\begin{aligned}
-x + 3 &= 12 \\
-x &= 9 \\
x &= -9
\end{aligned}
$$

The solution is (−9,3).

14.

$$
\begin{aligned}
(1) \quad 2x + y &= 2 \\
(2) \quad \underline{-3x - y} &= \underline{5} \text{ (add)} \\
-x &= 7 \\
x &= -7
\end{aligned}
$$

Substitute (− 7) in place of x in the first equation.

$$
\begin{aligned}
2(-7) + y &= 2 \\
-14 + y &= 2 \\
y &= 16
\end{aligned}
$$

The solution is (− 7, 16).

15.

$$
\begin{aligned}
(1) \quad x + y &= 2 \\
(2) \quad x + 3y &= -2
\end{aligned}
$$

Multiply the first equation by –1.

$$
\begin{aligned}
-x - y &= -2 \\
\underline{x + 3y} &= \underline{-2} \text{ (add)} \\
2y &= -4 \\
y &= -2
\end{aligned}
$$

Substitute (–2) for y in equation (2).

$$
\begin{aligned}
x + 3(-2) &= -2 \\
x - 6 &= -2 \\
x &= 4
\end{aligned}
$$

The solution is (4,–2).

16.

$$
\begin{aligned}
(1) \quad 3x + 4y &= 6 \\
(2) \quad 2x - 3y &= 4
\end{aligned}
$$

Multiply the first equation by 2, and the second equation by − 3.

$$
\begin{aligned}
6x + 8y &= 12 \\
\underline{-6x + 9y} &= \underline{-12} \text{ (add)} \\
17y &= 0 \\
y &= 0
\end{aligned}
$$

Substitute 0 for y in the first equation.

$$
\begin{aligned}
3x + 4(0) &= 6 \\
3x &= 6 \text{ or } x = 2
\end{aligned}
$$

The solution is (2,0).

17.

$$
\begin{aligned}
(1) \quad 3x + 5y &= 15 \\
(2) \quad 2x + 4y &= 0
\end{aligned}
$$

Multiply the first equation by 2, and the second equation by (− 3).

$$
\begin{aligned}
6x + 10y &= 30 \\
\underline{-6x - 12y} &= \underline{0} \text{ (add)} \\
-2y &= 30 \\
y &= -15
\end{aligned}
$$

Substitute (− 15) for y in the second equation.

$$
\begin{aligned}
2x + 4(-15) &= 0 \\
2x - 60 &= 0 \\
2x &= 60 \text{ or } x = 30
\end{aligned}
$$

The solution is (30,− 15).

18.

$$
\begin{aligned}
3x + y &= 6 \\
-6x - 2y &= -12
\end{aligned}
$$

Multiply the first equation by 2.

$$
\begin{aligned}
6x + 2y &= 12 \\
\underline{6x - 2y} &= \underline{-12} \text{ (add)} \\
0 &= 0
\end{aligned}
$$

The system of equations is dependent.

19. $A + B = \begin{bmatrix} 1 & -3 \\ 2 & 4 \end{bmatrix} + \begin{bmatrix} -2 & -5 \\ 6 & 3 \end{bmatrix} = \begin{bmatrix} 1+(-2) & -3+(-5) \\ 2+6 & 4+3 \end{bmatrix} = \begin{bmatrix} -1 & -8 \\ 8 & 7 \end{bmatrix}$

20. $A - B = \begin{bmatrix} 1 & -3 \\ 2 & 4 \end{bmatrix} - \begin{bmatrix} -2 & -5 \\ 6 & 3 \end{bmatrix} = \begin{bmatrix} 1-(-2) & -3-(-5) \\ 2-6 & 4-3 \end{bmatrix} = \begin{bmatrix} 3 & 2 \\ -4 & 1 \end{bmatrix}$

21. $2A = 2\begin{bmatrix} 1 & -3 \\ 2 & 4 \end{bmatrix} = \begin{bmatrix} 2(1) & 2(-3) \\ 2(2) & 2(4) \end{bmatrix} = \begin{bmatrix} 2 & -6 \\ 4 & 8 \end{bmatrix}$

22. $3A - 2B = 3\begin{bmatrix} 1 & -3 \\ 2 & 4 \end{bmatrix} - 2\begin{bmatrix} -2 & -5 \\ 6 & 3 \end{bmatrix} = \begin{bmatrix} 3 & -9 \\ 6 & 12 \end{bmatrix} - \begin{bmatrix} -4 & -10 \\ 12 & 6 \end{bmatrix} = \begin{bmatrix} 3-(-4) & -9-(-10) \\ 6-12 & 12-6 \end{bmatrix} = \begin{bmatrix} 7 & 1 \\ -6 & 6 \end{bmatrix}$

23. $A \times B = \begin{bmatrix} 1 & -3 \\ 2 & 4 \end{bmatrix} \times \begin{bmatrix} -2 & -5 \\ 6 & 3 \end{bmatrix} = \begin{bmatrix} 1(-2)+(-3)6 & 1(-5)+(-3)3 \\ 2(-2)+4(6) & 2(-5)+4(3) \end{bmatrix} = \begin{bmatrix} -20 & -14 \\ 20 & 2 \end{bmatrix}$

24. $B \times A = \begin{bmatrix} -2 & -5 \\ 6 & 3 \end{bmatrix} \times \begin{bmatrix} 1 & -3 \\ 2 & 4 \end{bmatrix} = \begin{bmatrix} (-2)1+(-5)2 & (-2)(-3)+(-5)4 \\ 6(1)+3(2) & 6(-3)+3(4) \end{bmatrix} = \begin{bmatrix} -12 & -14 \\ 12 & -6 \end{bmatrix}$

25. $\begin{bmatrix} 1 & 2 & | & 4 \\ 1 & 1 & | & 2 \end{bmatrix}_{(r_2-r_1)} = \begin{bmatrix} 1 & 2 & | & 4 \\ 0 & -1 & | & -2 \end{bmatrix}_{(-1)r_2}^{(r_1-2r_2)} = \begin{bmatrix} 1 & 0 & | & 0 \\ 0 & 1 & | & 2 \end{bmatrix}$ The solution is (0, 2).

26. $\begin{bmatrix} -1 & 1 & | & 4 \\ 1 & 2 & | & 2 \end{bmatrix} = \begin{bmatrix} 1 & -1 & | & -4 \\ 0 & 3 & | & 6 \end{bmatrix} = \begin{bmatrix} 1 & 0 & | & -2 \\ 0 & 1 & | & 2 \end{bmatrix}$ The solution is (– 2, 2).

27. $\begin{bmatrix} 2 & 1 & | & 3 \\ 3 & -1 & | & 12 \end{bmatrix}_{=}^{(r_1 \div 2)}\begin{bmatrix} 1 & \frac{1}{2} & | & \frac{3}{2} \\ 3 & -1 & | & 12 \end{bmatrix}_{(r_2-3r_1)} = \begin{bmatrix} 1 & \frac{1}{2} & | & \frac{3}{2} \\ 0 & -\frac{5}{2} & | & \frac{15}{2} \end{bmatrix}_{(-\frac{2}{5}r_2)} = \begin{bmatrix} 1 & \frac{1}{2} & | & \frac{3}{2} \\ 0 & 1 & | & -3 \end{bmatrix}_{=}^{(-\frac{1}{2}r_2+r_1)}\begin{bmatrix} 1 & 0 & | & 3 \\ 0 & 1 & | & -3 \end{bmatrix}$

The solution is (3,– 3).

28. $\begin{bmatrix} 2 & 3 & | & 2 \\ 4 & -9 & | & 4 \end{bmatrix} = \begin{bmatrix} 1 & \frac{3}{2} & | & 1 \\ 0 & -15 & | & 0 \end{bmatrix} = \begin{bmatrix} 1 & \frac{3}{2} & | & 1 \\ 0 & 1 & | & 0 \end{bmatrix} = \begin{bmatrix} 1 & 0 & | & 1 \\ 0 & 1 & | & 0 \end{bmatrix}$ The solution is (1,0)

29. $\begin{bmatrix} 1 & 3 & | & 3 \\ 3 & -2 & | & 2 \end{bmatrix} = \begin{bmatrix} 1 & 3 & | & 3 \\ 0 & -11 & | & -7 \end{bmatrix} = \begin{bmatrix} 1 & 3 & | & 3 \\ 0 & 1 & | & \frac{7}{11} \end{bmatrix} = \begin{bmatrix} 1 & 0 & | & \frac{12}{11} \\ 0 & 1 & | & \frac{7}{11} \end{bmatrix}$ The solution is $\left(\frac{12}{11}, \frac{7}{11}\right)$

30. $\begin{bmatrix} 3 & -6 & | & 3 \\ 4 & 5 & | & 17 \end{bmatrix} = \begin{bmatrix} 1 & -2 & | & 1 \\ 0 & 13 & | & 13 \end{bmatrix} = \begin{bmatrix} 1 & -2 & | & 1 \\ 0 & 1 & | & 1 \end{bmatrix} = \begin{bmatrix} 1 & 0 & | & 3 \\ 0 & 1 & | & 1 \end{bmatrix}$ The solution is (3,1)

31. a) Let C = total cost for parking
        x = number of additional hours
        All-Day: C = 5 + 0.50x
        Sav-A-Lot: C = 4.25 + 0.75x
        5 + 0.50x = 4.25 + 0.75x
        0.75 = 0.25x
        3 = x
    The total cost will be the same after 3 additional hours or 4 hours total.
    b) After 5 hours or x = 4 additional hours:
        All-Day: C = 5 + 0.50(4) = $7.00
        Sav-A-Lot: C = 4.25 + 0.75(4) = $7.25
    All-Day would be less expensive.

32. Let s = liters of 80% acid solution
    let w = liters of 50% acid solution
    $\begin{aligned} s + w &= 100 \\ 0.80s + 0.50w &= 100(0.75) \\ 0.80s + 0.50w &= 75 \\ s &= 100 - w \\ 0.80(100 - w) + 0.50w &= 75 \\ 80 - 0.80w + 0.50w &= 75 \\ -0.30w &= -5 \\ w = -5/(-0.30) &= 16 \, 2/3 \text{ liters} \\ s = 100 - 16 \, 2/3 &= 83 \, 1/3 \text{ liters} \end{aligned}$

33. Let s = salary
    r = commission rate
    (1) s + 4000r = 660
    (2) s + 6000r = 740 (subtract 1 from 2)
        2000r = 80
        r = 80/2000
        r = 0.04
Substitute 0.04 for r in eq. 1.
s = 660 – 4000(.04)
s = 500
His salary is 500 per week and his commission rate is 4%.

34. Let x = number of quarters
    let y = number of dimes
        x + y = 40
        .25x + .10y = 5.50
Solve the first equation for y.
y = 40 – x
Substitute (40 – x) in place of y in the second equation.
.25x + .10(40 – x) = 5.50
.25x + 4.00 – .10x = 5.50
    .15x + 4.00 = 5.50
        .15x = 1.50 or x = 10
Substitute 10 in place of x in the equation
y = 40 – x.
y = 40 – 10 = 30
Cheryl has 10 quarters and 30 dimes.

35. Let c = total cost
    x = no. of months to operate
    a) model 1600A: c = 950 + 32x
       model 6070B: c = 1275 + 22x
           950 + 32x = 1275 + 22x
               10x = 325
                 x = 32.5 months
After 32.5 months of operation the total cost of the units will be equal.

b) After 32.5 months or 2.7 years, the most cost effective unit is the unit with the lower per month to operate cost. Thus model 6070B is the better deal in the long run.

36.

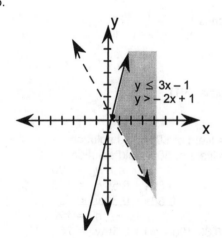

37.

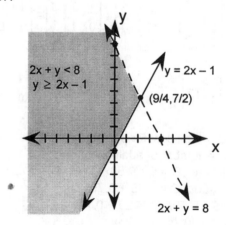

38.

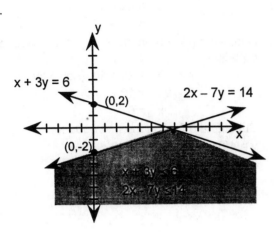

39.

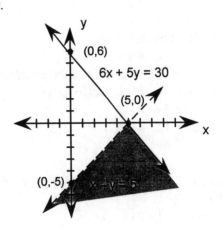

40. P = 6x + 5y
    At (0,0), P = 6(0) + 5(0) = 0
    At (0,10), P = 6(0) + 5(10) = 50
    At (9,0), P = 6(9) + 5(0) = 54

    The maximum profit is $54 at (9,0).

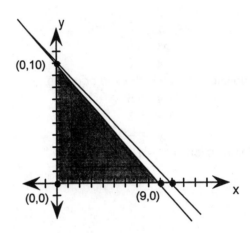

Chapter Test

1. If the lines do not intersect (parallel) the system of equations is inconsistent. The system of equations is consistent if the lines intersect only once. If both equations represent the same line then the system of equations is dependent.

2.

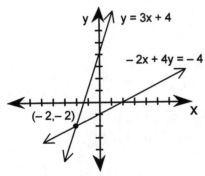

The solution is (− 2,− 2).

3. Write each equation in slope intercept form, then compare slopes and intercepts.

4x + 5y = 6	− 3x + 5y = 13
5y = − 4x + 6	5y = 3x + 13
y = − (4/5)x + 6/5	y = (3/5)x + 13/5

The slopes are different so there is only one solution.

4.
$$x - y = 5$$
$$2x + 3y = -5$$
Solve the first equation for x.
$$x = y + 5$$
Substitute (y + 5) for x in the second equation.
$$2(y + 5) + 3y = -5 \text{ (solve for y)}$$
$$2y + 10 + 3y = -5$$
$$5y + 10 = -5$$
$$5y = -15$$
$$y = -3$$
Substitute (− 3) for y in the equation x = y + 5.
$$x = -3 + 5 = 2$$
The solution is (2,− 3).

5.
$$y = 4x + 6$$
$$y = 2x + 18$$
Substitute (4x + 6) in place of y in the second equation.
$$4x + 6 = 2x + 18 \text{ (solve for x)}$$
$$2x = 12$$
$$x = 6$$
Substitute 6 for x in the first equation.
$$y = 4(6) + 6 = 24 + 6 = 30$$
The solution is (6,30).

6.
$$x - y = 4$$
$$\underline{2x + y = 5} \text{ (add)}$$
$$3x = 9$$
$$x = 3$$
Substitute 3 for x in the 2nd equation.
$$2(3) + y = 5$$
$$6 + y = 5$$
$$y = -1$$
The solution is (3,− 1).

7.
$$4x + 3y = 5$$
$$2x + 4y = 10$$
Multiply the second equation by (− 2).
$$4x + 3y = 5$$
$$\underline{-4x - 8y = -20} \text{ (add)}$$
$$-5y = -15$$
$$y = 3$$
Substitute 3 for y in the first equation.
$$4x + 3(3) = 5$$
$$4x + 9 = 5$$
$$4x = -4 \text{ or } x = -1$$
The solution is (−1,3).

8.
$$2x + 3y = 4$$
$$6x + 4y = 7$$
Multiply the first equation by − 3.
$$-6x - 9y = -12$$
$$\underline{6x + 4y = 7}$$
$$-5y = -5$$
$$y = 1$$
Substitute 1 for y in the first equation.
$$2x + 3(1) = 4 \text{ (solve for x)}$$
$$2x = 1$$
$$x = 1/2$$
The solution is (1/2,1).

9. $\left. \begin{array}{l} x + 3y = 4 \\ 5x + 7y = 4 \end{array} \right\} \left[\begin{array}{cc|c} 1 & 3 & 4 \\ 5 & 7 & 4 \end{array} \right] \underset{(-5r_1 + r_2)}{=} \left[\begin{array}{cc|c} 1 & 3 & 4 \\ 0 & -8 & -16 \end{array} \right] \underset{(r_2 \div (-8))}{=} \left[\begin{array}{cc|c} 1 & 3 & 4 \\ 0 & 1 & 2 \end{array} \right] \overset{(r_1 - 3r_2)}{=} \left[\begin{array}{cc|c} 1 & 0 & -2 \\ 0 & 1 & 2 \end{array} \right]$

The solution is (− 2,2).

10. $A + B = \begin{bmatrix} 2 & -5 \\ 4 & 6 \end{bmatrix} + \begin{bmatrix} -1 & 3 \\ 2 & 5 \end{bmatrix} = \begin{bmatrix} 2+(-1) & -5+3 \\ 4+2 & 6+5 \end{bmatrix} = \begin{bmatrix} 1 & -2 \\ 6 & 11 \end{bmatrix}$

11. $3A - B = 3\begin{bmatrix} 2 & -5 \\ 4 & 6 \end{bmatrix} - \begin{bmatrix} -1 & 3 \\ 2 & 5 \end{bmatrix} = \begin{bmatrix} 3(2)-(-1) & 3(-5)-3 \\ 3(4)-2 & 3(6)-5 \end{bmatrix} = \begin{bmatrix} 7 & -18 \\ 10 & 13 \end{bmatrix}$

12. $A \times B = \begin{bmatrix} 2 & -5 \\ 4 & 6 \end{bmatrix} \times \begin{bmatrix} -1 & 3 \\ 2 & 5 \end{bmatrix} = \begin{bmatrix} 2(-1)+(-5)(2) & 2(3)+(-5)(5) \\ 4(-1)+(6)(2) & 4(3)+(6)(5) \end{bmatrix} = \begin{bmatrix} -12 & -19 \\ 8 & 42 \end{bmatrix}$

13.

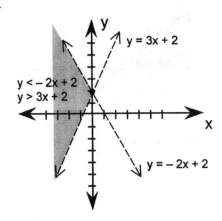

$y = 3x + 2$

$y < -2x + 2$
$y > 3x + 2$

$y = -2x + 2$

14. Let x = lb of $6.00 coffee
let y = lb of $7.50 coffee
x + y = 30
6x + 7.5y = 7.00(30)
Solve the first equation for y.
y = 30 − x
Substitute (30 − x) for y in the second equation.

$$6x + 7.5(30 - x) = 210$$
$$6x + 225 - 7.5x = 210$$
$$-1.5x = -15$$
$$x = 10$$

Substitute 10 for x in the equation y = 30 − x.
y = 30 − 10 = 20
Mix 10 lb of the $6.00 coffee with 20 lb of the $7.50 coffee.

15. Let x = no. of one bedroom units
let y = no. of two bedroom units
x + y = 20
425x + 500y = 9100
Solve the first equation for x.
x = 20 − y
Substitute (20 − y) for x in the second equation.

$$425(20 - y) + 500y = 9100$$
$$75y = 600$$
$$y = 8$$

Substitute 8 for y in the first equation.

$$x + 8 = 20$$
$$x = 12$$

The building has 12 one bedroom and 8 two bedroom apartments.

16. a)

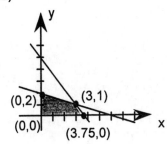

(0,2)
(3,1)
(0,0)
(3.75,0)

b) P = 2x + 3y
At (0,0) P = 2(0) + 3(0) = 0
At (0,2) P = 2(0) + 3(2) = 6
At (3,1) P = 2(3) + 3(1) = 9
At (3.75,0) P = 2(3.75) + 3(0) = 7.50
Max. is 9 at (3,1)
Min. is 0 at (0,0)

Group Projects

1. Answers will vary.

2. a) $5x + 4y \le 1000$

   $2x + 3y \le 600$

   $x \ge 40$

   $y \ge 50$

   b) $P = 75x + 125y$

   c)

   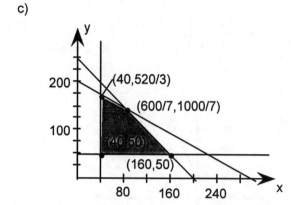

   d) Determine the maximum profit.

   At $(40,173)$ $P = 75(40) + 125(173) = \$24{,}625$

   At $(40,50)$ $P = 75(40) + 125(50) = \$9{,}250$

   At $(160,50)$ $P = 75(160) + 125(50) = \$18{,}250$

   At $(86,143)$ P $75(86) + 125(143) = \$24{,}325$

   Maximum profit occurs at 40 of model 01 and 173 of model 02

   e) Maximum profit = $\$24{,}625$

3. Answers will vary.

CHAPTER EIGHT

THE METRIC SYSTEM

Exercise Set 8.1

1. The metric system.
2. The U.S. customary system.
3. It is the worldwide accepted standard of measurement. There is only 1 basic unit of measurement for each quantity. It is based on the number 10 which makes many calculations easier.

4. a) meter   b) kilogram   c) liter   d) celsius

5. a) Move the decimal point one place for each change in unit of measure.

   b) 497.2 cm = $\dfrac{497.2}{100}$ m = 4.972 m = $\dfrac{4.972}{1000}$ km = 0.004972 km

   c) 30.8 hm = (30.8)(1000) dm = 30800 dm

6. a) mega   7. Student activity
   b) micro

8. a) 10,000 times greater   b) 1 hm = 10,000 cm   c) 1 cm = 0.0001 hm
9. a) 100 times greater   b) 1 dam = 100 dm   c) 1dm = 0.01 dam
10. a) 0° C   b) 100° C   c) 37° C

11. 2 pounds	12. 1 yard	13. 5 grams	14. 30° C
15. b	16. c	17. d	18. f
19. e	20. a	21. decigram	22. liter
23. gram	24. milliliter	25. dekaliter	26. meter
27. centimeter	28. kilometer	29. degree Celsius	30. hetogram

31. a) 10 liters   b) $\dfrac{1}{100}$ liter   c) $\dfrac{1}{1000}$ liter

     d) $\dfrac{1}{10}$ liter   e) 1000 liters   f) 100 liters

32. a) 100 grams   b) 0.001 gram   c) 1000 grams

     d) 0.01 gram   e) 10 grams   f) 0.1 gram

33. mg, 0.001 g   34. cg, 0.01 g   35. dg, 0.1 g
36. dag, 10 g   37. hg, 100 g   38. kg, 1 000 g

39. Max. load 320 kg = (320 × 1,000) g = 320 000 g
40. Max. load 320 kg = (320 × 1,000,000) mg = 320 000 000 mg
41. 9 m = (9 × 100) cm = 900 cm
42. 7 dam = (7 × 10) m = 70 m
43. 15.7 hg = (15.7 × 100) g = 1 570 g

44. 0.054 hl = (0.054)(100) = 5.4 l
45. 242.6 cm = (242.6)(0.0001) hm = 0.02426 hm
46. 1.34 ml = (1.34)(0.001) l = 0.00134 l
47. 974 g = (974)(0.01) hg = 9.74 hg
48. 14.27 kl = (14.27)(1000) l = 14 270 l
49. 1.34 hm = (1.34)(10000) cm = 13 400 cm
50. 0.00052 kg = 52 cg
51. 8.3 m = 830 cm
52. 94.5 kg = 94 500 g
53. 895 l = 895 000 ml
54. 24 dm = 0.0024 km
55. 130 cm = 0.013 hm
56. 6 049 mm = 6.049 m
57. 8 472 ml = 0.8472 dal
58. 17 200 ml = 17.2 l

59. 514 hm = 51400 m; 62 km = 62 000 m
    680 m, 514 hm, 62 km
60. 5.1 dam = 51 m; 0.47 km = 470 m;
    590 cm = 5.9 m
    590 cm, 5.1 dam, 0.47 km

61. 420 cl = 4.3 l; 0.045 kl = 45 l
    420 cl, 4.3 l, 0.045 kl
62. 2.2 kg, 2 400 g, 24 300 dg
    2.2 kg = 2 200 g; 24 300 dg = 2 430 g

63. 0.032 kl = 32 l; 460 dl = 46 l; 48 000 cl = 480 l
    0.032 kl, 460 dl, 48 000 cl
64. 203 000 mm = 203 m; 2.6 km = 2 600 m;
    52.6 hm = 5260 m
    203 000 mm, 2.6 km, 52.6 hm

65. The side with the 5 kg weight would go down. 5 kg = 5(2.2 lbs.) = 11 lbs.
66. Jim, since a meter is longer than a yard.
67. The pump that removes 1 dal of water per min. 1 dekaliter is more than 1 deciliter.
68. 1 hectometer in 10 min. A hectometer is longer than a dekameter.

69. a) Perimeter= 2l + 2w= 2(74) + 2(99)= 346 cm

    b) 346 cm = (346 × 1000) mm = 346 000 mm

70. a) (4)(27 m) = 108 m   b) 108 m = 0.108 km

    c) 108 m = 108 000 mm

71. a) 14 × 250 mg = 3 500 mg per week

    b) 3 500 mg = 3.5 g

72. $30 \text{ l} = (30 \text{ l})\left(\dfrac{1000 \text{ ml}}{1 \text{ l}}\right)\left(\dfrac{1 \text{ min}}{360 \text{ ml}}\right) = 83.333\ldots \text{ min. or 1 hr 23.333}\ldots \text{min.}$

73. a) $\dfrac{1200 \text{ km}}{187 \text{ l}} = 6.417 \text{ km/l}$

    b) 6.417 km/l = 6 417 m/l

74. 8 × 400 m = 3 200 m;   3 200 m = 3.2 km

75. 3 × 2 l = 6 l of soda; 6 l = 6000 ml; $\dfrac{6000}{12}$ = 500 ml per person

76. a) 6 × 360 ml = 2160 ml

    b) 2160 ÷ 1000 = 2.16 l

    c) 2.45 ÷ 2.16 = $1.13 per liter

77. $0.96 per l × 24.3 l = $23.33

78. a) cost = 5.8 kg × $6.30 per kg = $36.54   b) 5.8 kg = 5 800 g; $\frac{5800 \text{ g}}{14 \text{ people}}$ = 414.3 g/person

79. 1000 meters
80. 0.001 micrograms
81. 1×10^{24} picoliters
82. 1×10^{15} nanograms
83. 288 mg = 0.288 g, 0.8 ÷ 0.288 = 2.8 cups
84. 27 mg = 0.027 g, 0.8 ÷ 0.027 ≈ 29.6 eggs
85. 1.6 mg = 0.0016 g, 0.8 ÷ 0.016 = 500, 500 × 49 = 24500 g
86. 195 mg = 0.195 g, 0.8 ÷ 0.195 = 4.1 cups

87. 9 dam
88. 2 m
89. 4 dm
90. 3 hm
91. 2 dam
92. 5 m

Exercise Set 8.2

1. length
2. volume
3. area
4. length
5. volume
6. volume
7. volume
8. volume
9. area
10. volume
11. volume
12. area
13. answers will vary
14. answers will vary
15. answers will vary
16. answers will vary
17. answers will vary
18. answers will vary
19. A cubic decimeter
20. A kiloliter
21. cubic centimeter
22. area
23. 2.5 acres
24. square kilometers
25. meters or cm
26. centimeters
27. kilometers
28. millimeters
29. centimeters
30. centimeters
31. millimeters
32. millimeters
33. centimeters
34. centimeters
35. cm or mm
36. kilometers
37. student activity
38. student activity
39. (a)
40. (b)
41. (a)
42. (c)
43. (b)
44. (b)
45. (c)
46. (c)
47. student activity
48. student activity
49. student activity
50. student activity
51. student activity
52. student activity
53. cm or km
54. kilometer
55. meter
56. meter
57. centimeter
58. kilometer

59. square meters
60. square kilometers
61. square millimeters or square centimeters
62. square meters
63. square meters or hectares
64. square meters or hectares
65. square millimeters or square centimeters
66. square kilometers
67. square centimeters
68. square meters

69. (a)
70. (b)
71. (a)
72. (b)
73. (c)
74. (a)
75. (a)
76. (c)
77. student activity
78. student activity
79. student activity
80. student activity
81. student activity
82. student activity
83. kiloliters
84. liters
85. milliliters
86. cubic centimeters
87. liters or milliliters
88. liters
89. cubic meters
90. cubic meters
91. liters
92. cubic meters
93. (c)
94. (a)
95. (c)
96. (b)
97. (b)
98. (a)
99. (b)
100. (a)

101. b) v = 2 × 1.5 × 0.25 = 0.75 m^3
102. b) v ≈ 3.14 × (0.25)^2 × 1 = 0.20 m^3
103. b) v = $\pi r^2 h$ ≈ 3.14 × (0.5)^2 × 10 = 7.85 cm^3
104. b) v = $\pi r^2 h$ ≈ 3.14 × (0.20)^2 × 2 = 0.25 m^3

105. long side = 4 cm, short side = 1.8 cm,
   height = 1.5 cm;
   P = sum of all sides = 4+4+1.8+1.8 = 11.6 cm
   A = base × height = 4 × 1.5 = 6 cm^2

106. r ≈ 1.2 cm;
   C = 2π r ≈ 2 × 3.14 × 1.2 = 7.54 cm
   A = π r^2 ≈ 3.14 × (1.2)^2 = 4.52 cm^2

107. A = $l \cdot w$;
   matted area = total area − picture area
   $$= (82 \times 62) - (50 \times 42)$$
   $$= 5084 - 2100 = 2984 \text{ cm}^2$$

108. a) 43 × 67 = 2881 m2
   b) 2881 − (40 × 64) = 2881 − 2560 = 321 m^2

109. a) A = $l \cdot w$ = 1.4 × 3.75 = 5.25 km^2
   b) 5.25 × 100 = 525 ha

110. a) A = $l \cdot w$ = 22.5 × 18.3 = 411.75 m^2
   b) 411.75 × 0.0001 ≈ 0.041 ha

111. a) V = lwh, l = 18 m, w = 10 m , h = 2.5 m,
   V = (18)(10)(2.5) = 450 m^3
   b) 450 m^3 = 450 kl

112. a) V = lwh = 70 × 40 × 20 = 56 000 cm^3
   b) 56 000 cm^3 = 56 000 ml
   c) 56 000 ml = $\dfrac{56000}{1000}$ l = 56 l

113. Total Surface Area of 4 walls = 2lh + 2wh = 2(20)(6) + 2(12)(6) = 384 m^2

   Liters for first coat = (384 m^2)($\dfrac{1 \text{ l}}{10 \text{ m}^2}$) = 38.4 l

   Liters for second coat = (384 m^2)($\dfrac{1 \text{ l}}{15 \text{ m}^2}$) = 25.6 l

   Total liters = 38.4 + 25.6 = 64 l
   Total cost = (64)($4.75) = $304

114. V = π r^{2}h ≈ 3.14 × (4.0)^2 × (12.5) = 628 cm^3

115. 100^2 = 10,000 times larger

116. 10^2 = 100 times larger

117. 10^3 = 1000 times larger

118. 10^3 = 1000 times larger

119. 1 000 000 mm^2

120. 1000 000 000 cm^2

121. 100 hm^2

122. 0.000 1 m^2

123. 10 000 mm^2

124. 0.0000000001 hm^2

125. 1 000 000 cm^3

126. 0.001 km^3

127. 620 l

128. 0.620 l

129. 76 m^3

130. 4 200 cm^3

131. 6.7 kl = 6.7 m^3 = (6.7 × 10^3) dm^3 = 6 700 dm^3

132. 1.4 ha = 14000 m^2 = (14000 × 100^2) cm^2 = 140 000 000 cm^2

133. a) 1 sq mi = 1 mi^2 × (5280)^2 $\dfrac{ft^2}{mi^2}$ = 27,878,400 ft^2

   27,878,400 ft^2 × (12)^2 $\dfrac{in^2}{ft^2}$ = 4,014,489,600 in^2

   b) It is easier to convert in the metric system because it is a base 10 system.

134. a) 6 yd3 = 6 yd3 × (36)^3 $\dfrac{in^3}{yd^3}$ = 279,936 in^3

   b) It is easier to convert in the metric system because it is a base 10 system.

Exercise Set 8.3

1. kilogram
2. 2 lb
3. 5 g
4. metric tonne
5. approx. 35° C
6. approx. − 15° C
7. Answers will vary

8. a) Yes; mass is a measure of the amount of matter in an object.
   b) No; weight is a measure of gravitational force.

9. kilograms or grams
10. kilograms
11. grams
12. kilograms or grams
13. grams
14. metric tonnes
15. metric tonnes
16. milligrams
17. grams
18. grams
19. (b)
20. (b)
21. (c)
22. (c)
23. (b)
24. (c)
25. Answers will vary
26. Answers will vary
27. Answers will vary
28. Answers will vary
29. (c)
30. (b)
31. (b)
32. (c)
33. (b)
34. (b)
35. (c)
36. (c)

37. $F = \dfrac{9}{5}(20) + 32 = 36 + 32 = 68^\circ\,F$

38. $F = \dfrac{9}{5}(-5) + 32 = -9 + 32 = 23^\circ\,F$

39. $C = \dfrac{5}{9}(92 - 32) = \dfrac{5}{9}(60) = 33.3^\circ\,C$

40. $C = \dfrac{5}{9}(-25 - 32) = \dfrac{5}{9}(-57) = -31.7^\circ\,C$

41. $C = \dfrac{5}{9}(350 - 32) = \dfrac{5}{9}(318) = 176.7^\circ\,C$

42. $C = \dfrac{5}{9}(98 - 32) = \dfrac{5}{9}(66) = 36.7^\circ\,C$

43. $F = \dfrac{9}{5}(37) + 32 = 66.6 + 32 = 98.6^\circ\,F$

44. $F = \dfrac{9}{5}(-4) + 32 = -7.2 + 32 = 24.8^\circ\,F$

45. $C = \dfrac{5}{9}(13 - 32) = \dfrac{5}{9}(-19) = -10.6^\circ\,C$

46. $C = \dfrac{5}{9}(75 - 32) = \dfrac{5}{9}(43) = 23.9^\circ\,C$

47. $F = \dfrac{9}{5}(45) + 32 = 81 + 32 = 113^\circ\,F$

48. $F = \dfrac{9}{5}(10) + 32 = 18 + 32 = 50^\circ\,F$

49. $C = \dfrac{5}{9}(113 - 32) = \dfrac{5}{9}(81) = 45^\circ\,C$

50. $C = \dfrac{5}{9}(425 - 32) = \dfrac{5}{9}(393) = 218.3^\circ\,C$

51. $F = \dfrac{9}{5}(22) + 32 = 39.6 + 32 = 71.6^\circ\,F$

52. $F = \dfrac{9}{5}(35.1) + 32 = 63.2 + 32 = 95.2^\circ\,F$

53. $F = \dfrac{9}{5}(15.6) + 32 = 28.1 + 32 = 60.1^\circ\,F$

54. $F = \dfrac{9}{5}(32.3) + 32 = 58.1 + 32 = 90.1° \text{ F}$

55. low: $F = \dfrac{9}{5}(17.8) + 32 = 32 + 32 = 64° \text{ F}$

    high: $F = \dfrac{9}{5}(23.5) + 32 = 42.3 + 32 = 74.3° \text{ F}$

56. low: $F = \dfrac{9}{5}(22) + 32 = 39.6 + 32 = 71.6° \text{ F}$

    high: $F = \dfrac{9}{5}(34) + 32 = 61.2 + 32 = 93.2° \text{ F}$

57. cost = $4.5 \times 0.70 = \$3.15$ 58. cost = $0.75 \times 0.80 = \$0.60$

59. total mass = 45 g + 29 g + 370 ml = 45 g + 29 g + 370 g = 444 g

60. fuel used = $4320 \times 17 = 73440$ kg, $73440 \text{ kg} \cdot \dfrac{1 \text{ t}}{1000 \text{ kg}} = 73.44$ t

61. a) V = lwh, l = 16 m, w = 12 m, h = 12 m, $V = 16(12)(12) = 2304 \text{ m}^3$
    b) $2304 \text{ m}^3 = 2304$ kl
    c) 2304 kl = 2304 t

62. a) $V = \pi r^2 h$, r = 50 cm = 0.50 m, h = 150 cm = 1.5 m, $V = 3.14(0.50)^2(1.50) = 1.1775 \text{ m}^3$
    b) $1.1775 \text{ m}^3 = 1.1775$ kl = (1.1775×1000) l = 1177.5 l
    c) 1177.5 l = 1177.5 kg

63. $3.6 \text{ kg} = 3.6 \text{ kg} \times \dfrac{1 \text{ t}}{1000 \text{ kg}} = 0.0036$ t

64. $9.52 \text{ t} = 9.52 \text{ t} \times \dfrac{1000 \text{ kg}}{1 \text{ t}} = 9520$ kg

65. $42.6 \text{ t} = 42.6 \text{ t} \times \dfrac{1000 \text{ kg}}{1 \text{ t}} = 42\,600 \text{ kg} = 42\,600\,000$ g

66. $1\,460\,000 \text{ mg} = 1.46 \text{ kg} = 1.46 \text{ kg} \times \dfrac{1 \text{ t}}{1000 \text{ kg}} = 0.001\,46$ t

67. Yes, $78° \text{ F} = \dfrac{5}{9}(78 - 32) \approx 25.6° \text{ C}$, not 20° C

68. Normal body temperature is 98.6° F or 37° C. Maria's temperature is 38.2° C which is above normal. She should take an aspirin.

69. a) V = lwh, l = 1 yd = 3 ft, w = 15 in = 1.25 ft, h = 1.5 ft; $V = (3)(1.25)(1.5) = 5.625$ cubic feet
    b) $5.625 \text{ ft}^3 \times 62.5 \dfrac{\text{lbs}}{\text{ft}^3} = 351.6$ lb
    c) $351.6 \text{ lb} \times \dfrac{1 \text{ gal}}{8.3 \text{ lb}} = 42.4$ gal

70. $-40° \text{ C} = \dfrac{9}{5}(-40) + 32 = -72 + 32 = -40° \text{ F}$

Exercise Set 8.4

1. **Dimensional analysis** is a procedure used to convert from one unit of measurement to a different unit of measurement.

2. A **unit fraction** is a fraction in which the numerator and denominator contain different units and the value of the fraction is 1.

3. $\dfrac{60\,seconds}{1\,minute}$ or $\dfrac{1\,minute}{60\,seconds}$ because $60\,seconds = 1\,minute$

4. $\dfrac{3\,ft}{1\,yd}$ or $\dfrac{1\,yd}{3\,ft}$ because $3\,ft = 1\,yd$

5. $\dfrac{1\,lb}{0.45\,kg}$ Since we need to eliminate kilograms, kg must appear in the denominator. Since we need to convert to pounds, lb must appear in the numerator.

6. $\dfrac{1\,ft}{30\,cm}$ Since we need to eliminate centimeters, cm must appear in the denominator. Since we need to convert to feet, ft must appear in the numerator.

7. $\dfrac{0.8\,m^2}{1\,yd^2}$ Since we need to eliminate square yards, yd^2 must appear in the denominator. Since we need to convert to square meters, m^2 must appear in the numerator.

8. $\dfrac{3.8\,l}{1\,gal}$ Since we need to eliminate gallons, gal must appear in the denominator. Since we need to convert to liters, l must appear in the numerator.

9. $147\,km = \left(147\,km\right)\left(\dfrac{1\,mi}{1.6\,km}\right) = 91.875\,mi$

10. $9\,lb = \left(9\,lb\right)\left(\dfrac{0.45\,kg}{1\,lb}\right) = 4.05\,kg$

11. $4.2\,ft = \left(4.2\,ft\right)\left(\dfrac{30\,cm}{1\,ft}\right)\left(\dfrac{1\,m}{100\,cm}\right) = 1.26\,m$

12. $11\,in = \left(11\,in\right)\left(\dfrac{2.54\,cm}{1\,in}\right) = 27.94\,cm$

13. $15\,yd^2 = \left(15\,yd^2\right)\left(\dfrac{0.8\,m^2}{1\,yd^2}\right) = 12\,m^2$

14. $160\,kg = \left(160\,kg\right)\left(\dfrac{1\,lb}{0.45\,kg}\right) = 355.\overline{5} \approx 355.6\,lb$

15. $39\,mi = \left(39\,mi\right)\left(\dfrac{1.6\,km}{1\,mi}\right) = 62.4\,km$

16. $765\,mm = \left(765\,mm\right)\left(\dfrac{1\,cm}{10\,mm}\right)\left(\dfrac{1\,in}{2.54\,cm}\right) = 30.11811024 \approx 30.12\,in$

17. $675\,ha = \left(675\,ha\right)\left(\dfrac{1\,acre}{0.4\,ha}\right) = 1687.5\,acres$

18. $346\,g = \left(346\,g\right)\left(\dfrac{1\,oz}{28\,g}\right) = 12.35714286 \approx 12.36\,oz$

19. $10.4\,c = (10.4\,c)\left(\dfrac{0.24\,l}{1\,c}\right) = 2.496\,l$

20. $4\,T = (4\,T)\left(\dfrac{0.9\,t}{1\,T}\right) = 3.6\,t$

21. $45.6\,ml = (45.6\,ml)\left(\dfrac{1\,fl\,oz}{30\,ml}\right) = 1.52\,fl\,oz$

22. $1.6\,km^2 = (1.6\,km^2)\left(\dfrac{1\,mi^2}{2.6\,km^2}\right) = 0.6153846154 \approx 0.62\,mi^2$

23. $120\,lb = (120\,lb)\left(\dfrac{0.45\,kg}{1\,lb}\right) = 54\,kg$

24. $6.2\,acres = (6.2\,acres)\left(\dfrac{0.4\,ha}{1\,acre}\right) = 2.48\,ha$

25. $28\,grams, 0.45\,kilogram$

26. $28\,grams$

27. $2.54\,centimeters, 1.6\,kilometers$

28. $0.45\,kilogram$

29. $5\,ft = (5\,ft)\left(\dfrac{12\,in}{1\,ft}\right)\left(\dfrac{2.54\,cm}{1\,in}\right) = 152.4\,cm$

    $2\,in = (2\,in)\left(\dfrac{2.54\,cm}{1\,in}\right) = 5.08\,cm$

    $152.4\,cm + 5.08\,cm = 157.48\,centimeters$

    $157.48\,cm = (157.48\,cm)\left(\dfrac{1\,m}{100\,cm}\right) = 1.5748 \approx 1.57\,meters$

30. $1.6\,kilometers$

31. $10\,yd = (10\,yd)\left(\dfrac{0.9\,m}{1\,yd}\right) = 9\,meters$

32. $0.9\,meter$

33. $505\,m = (505\,m)\left(\dfrac{1\,yd}{0.9\,m}\right) = 561.\overline{1} \approx 561.11\,yd$

34. $175\,m = (175\,m)\left(\dfrac{1\,yd}{0.9\,m}\right) = 194.\overline{4} \approx 194.4\,yd$

35. $344\,m = (344\,m)\left(\dfrac{100\,cm}{1\,m}\right)\left(\dfrac{1\,ft}{30\,cm}\right) = 1146.\overline{6} \approx 1146.67\,ft$

36. $303\,m = (303\,m)\left(\dfrac{100\,cm}{1\,m}\right)\left(\dfrac{1\,ft}{30\,cm}\right) = 1010\,ft$

37. $18\,km = \left(18\,km\right)\left(\dfrac{1\,mi}{1.6\,km}\right) = 11.25\,mi$

38. $105\,mi = \left(105\,mi\right)\left(\dfrac{1.6\,km}{1\,mi}\right) = 168\,km$

39. $\left(6\,yd\right)\left(9\,yd\right) = 54\,yd^{2}$

 $54\,yd^{2} = \left(54\,yd^{2}\right)\left(\dfrac{0.8\,m^{2}}{1\,yd^{2}}\right) = 43.2\,m^{2}$

40. $210\,mi = \left(210\,mi\right)\left(\dfrac{1.6\,km}{1\,mi}\right) = 336\,km$

41. $70\,mi = \left(70\,mi\right)\left(\dfrac{1.6\,km}{1\,mi}\right) = 112\,kph$

42. $80\,km = \left(80\,km\right)\left(\dfrac{1\,mi}{1.6\,km}\right) = 50\,mph$

43. $8\,fl\,oz = \left(8\,fl\,oz\right)\left(\dfrac{30\,ml}{1\,fl\,oz}\right) = 240\,ml$

44. $1776\,km = \left(1776\,km\right)\left(\dfrac{1\,mi}{1.6\,km}\right) = 1110\,mi$

45. $\left(50\,ft\right)\left(30\,ft\right)\left(8\,ft\right) = 12{,}000\,ft^{3}$

 $12{,}000\,ft^{3} = \left(12{,}000\,ft^{3}\right)\left(\dfrac{0.03\,m^{3}}{1\,ft^{3}}\right) = 360\,m^{3}$

46. $1189\,mi^{2} = \left(1189\,mi^{2}\right)\left(\dfrac{2.6\,km^{2}}{1\,mi^{2}}\right) = 3091.4\,km^{2}$

47. $1\,kg = \left(1\,kg\right)\left(\dfrac{1\,lb}{0.45\,kg}\right) = 2.\overline{2}\,lb$

 $\dfrac{\$1.10}{2.\overline{2}} = \$0.495\,per\,pound$

48. a) $1.3\,t = \left(1.3\,t\right)\left(\dfrac{1\,T}{0.9\,t}\right) = 1.\overline{4} \approx 1.44\,T$

 b) $1.\overline{4}\,T = \left(1.\overline{4}\,T\right)\left(\dfrac{2000\,lb}{1\,T}\right) = 2888.\overline{8} \approx 2888.9\,lb$

49. $34.5\,kl = \left(34.5\,kl\right)\left(\dfrac{1000\,l}{1\,kl}\right)\left(\dfrac{1\,gal}{3.8\,l}\right) = 9078.947368 \approx 9078.95\,gal$

50. $0.25\,oz = \left(0.25\,oz\right)\left(\dfrac{28\,g}{1\,oz}\right) = 7\,g$

 $\dfrac{\$80}{7} = 11.42857143 \approx \$11.43\,per\,gram$

51. a) $8\,stones = (8\,stones)\left(\dfrac{70\,kg}{11\,stones}\right) = 50.\overline{90} \approx 50.91\,kg$

    b) $50.\overline{90}\,kg = (50.\overline{90}\,kg)\left(\dfrac{1\,lb}{0.45\,kg}\right) = 113.\overline{13} \approx 113.13\,lb$

52. $\dfrac{1}{8}\,carat = (0.125\,carat)\left(\dfrac{1\,g}{5\,carat}\right) = 0.025\,g$

53. a) $-282\,ft = (-282\,ft)\left(\dfrac{30\,cm}{1\,ft}\right) = -8460\,cm$

    b) $-8460\,cm = (-8460\,cm)\left(\dfrac{1\,m}{100\,cm}\right) = -84.6\,m$

54. a) $1.5\,mm = (1.5\,mm)\left(\dfrac{1\,cm}{10\,mm}\right)\left(\dfrac{1\,in}{2.54\,cm}\right) = 0.0590551181 \approx 0.059\,in$

    b) $4.5\,m = (4.5\,m)\left(\dfrac{100\,cm}{1\,m}\right)\left(\dfrac{1\,in}{2.54\,cm}\right) = 177.1653543 \approx 177.165\,in$

    c) $2.5\,cm = (2.5\,cm)\left(\dfrac{1\,in}{2.54\,cm}\right) = 0.9842519685 \approx 0.984\,in$

    d) $45\,cm = (45\,cm)\left(\dfrac{1\,in}{2.54\,cm}\right) = 17.71653543 \approx 17.717\,in$

55. a) $1\,m^2 = (1\,m^2)\left(\dfrac{(3.3)^2\,ft^2}{1\,m^2}\right) = 10.89\,ft^2$

    b) $1\,m^3 = (1\,m^3)\left(\dfrac{(3.3)^3\,ft^3}{1\,m^3}\right) = 35.937\,ft^3$

56. a) $1\,ft^2 = (1\,ft^2)\left(\dfrac{(30)^2\,cm^2}{1\,ft^2}\right) = 900\,cm^2$

    b) $1\,ft^3 = (1\,ft^3)\left(\dfrac{(30)^3\,cm^3}{1\,ft^3}\right) = 27\,000\,cm^3$

57. $56\,lb = (56\,lb)\left(\dfrac{0.45\,kg}{1\,lb}\right)\left(\dfrac{1\,mg}{1\,kg}\right) = 25.2\,mg$

58. $170\,lb = (170\,lb)\left(\dfrac{0.45\,kg}{1\,lb}\right)\left(\dfrac{1.5\,mg}{1\,kg}\right) = 114.75\,mg$

59. $76\,lb = (76\,lb)\left(\dfrac{0.45\,kg}{1\,lb}\right)\left(\dfrac{200\,mg}{1\,kg}\right) = 6840\,mg$

    $6840\,mg = (6840\,mg)\left(\dfrac{1\,g}{1000\,mg}\right) = 6.84\,g$

60. $82\,lb = (82\,lb)\left(\dfrac{0.45\,kg}{1\,lb}\right)\left(\dfrac{5\,mg}{1\,kg}\right) = 184.5\,mg$

61. a) $2 \text{ teaspoons} = (2 \text{ teaspoons})\left(\dfrac{12.5\,mg}{1 \text{ teaspoon}}\right) = 25\,mg$

b) $12\,fl\,oz = (12\,fl\,oz)\left(\dfrac{30\,ml}{1\,fl\,oz}\right)\left(\dfrac{12.5\,mg}{5\,ml}\right) = 900\,mg$

62. a) $2 \text{ tablespoons} = (2 \text{ tablespoons})\left(\dfrac{236\,mg}{1 \text{ tablespoon}}\right) = 472\,mg$

b) $8\,fl\,oz = (8\,fl\,oz)\left(\dfrac{30\,ml}{1\,fl\,oz}\right)\left(\dfrac{1\,tablespoon}{15\,ml}\right)\left(\dfrac{236\,mg}{1\,tablespoon}\right) = 3776\,mg$

63. $(0.5\,c)\left(\dfrac{0.24\,l}{1\,c}\right) = 0.12\,l$ graham cracker crumbs

$(12\,oz)\left(\dfrac{28\,g}{1\,oz}\right) = 336\,g$ nuts

$(8\,oz)\left(\dfrac{28\,g}{1\,oz}\right) = 224\,g$ chocolate pieces

$\left(\dfrac{4}{3}\,c\right)\left(\dfrac{0.24\,l}{1\,c}\right) = 0.32\,l$ flaked coconut

$\left(\dfrac{4}{3}\,c\right)\left(\dfrac{0.24\,l}{1\,c}\right) = 0.32\,l$ condensed milk

$(9\,in)\left(\dfrac{2.54\,cm}{1\,in}\right) \times (13\,in)\left(\dfrac{2.54\,cm}{1\,in}\right) = 22.86\,cm \times 33.02\,cm$ baking pan

$350°F = \dfrac{5}{9}(350-32) = 176.\overline{6} \approx 176.7°C$

$(1.5\,in)\left(\dfrac{2.54\,cm}{1\,in}\right) \times (3\,in)\left(\dfrac{2.54\,cm}{1\,in}\right) = 3.81\,cm \times 7.62\,cm$ bars

64. a) $(37\,m)\left(\dfrac{1\,yd}{0.9\,m}\right) = 41.\overline{1} \approx 41.1\,yd$

b) $(370\,140\,km)\left(\dfrac{1\,mi}{1.6\,km}\right) = 231{,}337.5\,mi$

c) $(44\,km)\left(\dfrac{1\,mi}{1.6\,km}\right) = 27.5\,mi$

d) $1260°C = \dfrac{9}{5}(1260)+32 = 2300°F$

e) $(335\,km)\left(\dfrac{1\,mi}{1.6\,km}\right) = 209.375\,mph$

f) $(29\,484\,kg)\left(\dfrac{1\,lb}{0.45\,kg}\right) = 65{,}520\,lb$

g) $(4.5\,m)\left(\dfrac{1\,yd}{0.9\,m}\right) \times (18\,m)\left(\dfrac{1\,yd}{0.9\,m}\right) = 5\,yd \times 20\,yd$

64. h) $(171396\,l)\left(\dfrac{1\,gal}{3.8\,l}\right) = 45{,}104.21053 \approx 45{,}104.21\,gal\,/\,min$

   i) $(63\,588\,l)\left(\dfrac{1\,gal}{3.8\,l}\right) = 16{,}733.68421 \approx 16{,}733.68\,gal\,/\,min$

   j) $(46.89\,m)\left(\dfrac{1\,yd}{0.9\,m}\right) = 52.1\,yd$

   k) $(8.4\,m)\left(\dfrac{1\,yd}{0.9\,m}\right) = 9.\overline{3}\,yd \approx 9.33\,yd$

   l) $(632\,772\,kg)\left(\dfrac{1\,lb}{0.45\,kg}\right) = 1{,}406{,}160\,lb$

   m) $(106\,142\,kg)\left(\dfrac{1\,lb}{0.45\,kg}\right) = 235{,}871.\overline{1} \approx 235{,}871.11\,lb$

   n) $-251°C = \dfrac{9}{5}(-251) + 32 = -419.8°F$

65. $(0.2\,mg)\left(\dfrac{1\,grain}{60\,mg}\right)\left(\dfrac{1\,ml}{\frac{1}{300}\,grain}\right) = 1.0\,cc$ **or b)**

66. $15(130\,lb) = 1950\,lb$

   $(1950\,lb)\left(\dfrac{0.18\,kg}{100\,lb}\right)\left(\dfrac{1\,lb}{0.45\,kg}\right) = 7.8\,lb$

67. a) $(3.6\,l)\left(\dfrac{1000\,ml}{1\,l}\right)\left(\dfrac{1\,cm^3}{1\,ml}\right) = 3600\,cm^3$

   b) $(3600\,cm^3)\left(\dfrac{1\,in^3}{(2.54)^3\,cm^3}\right) = 219.6854787 \approx 219.7\,in^3$

Review Exercises

1. $\dfrac{1}{100}$ of base unit
2. $1000\times$ base unit
3. $\dfrac{1}{1000}$ of base unit
4. $100\times$ base unit
5. $10\times$ base unit
6. $\dfrac{1}{10}$ of base unit

7. 80 mg = 0.080 g
8. 3.2 l = 320 cl
9. 0.197 cm = 1.97 mm
10. 1 000 000 mg = 1 kg
11. 4.62 kl = 4620 l
12. 192.6 dag = 19 260 dg
13. 2.67 kl = 2 670 000 ml
   14 630 cl = 146 300 ml
   3000 ml, 14 630 cl, 2.67 kl
14. 0.047 km = 47 m
   47 000 cm = 470 m
   0.047 km, 47 000 cm,
   4700 m
15. Centimeters

16. Kilograms or grams
17. Degrees Celsius
18. Millimeters
19. Square meters
20. Milliliters or cubic centimeters
21. Millimeters

22. Kilograms or tonnes
23. Kilometers
24. Liters
25. Answers will vary.
26. Answers will vary.
27. c

28. b   **29.** c   **30.** a
31. a   **32.** b

33. $1640\,kg = \left(1640\,kg\right)\left(\dfrac{1\,lb}{0.45\,kg}\right)\left(\dfrac{1\,T}{2000\,lb}\right)\left(\dfrac{0.9\,t}{1\,T}\right) = 1.64\,t$

34. $6.3\,t = \left(6.3\,t\right)\left(\dfrac{1\,T}{0.9\,t}\right)\left(\dfrac{2000\,lb}{1\,T}\right)\left(\dfrac{0.45\,kg}{1\,lb}\right)\left(\dfrac{1000\,g}{1\,kg}\right) = 6\,300\,000\,g$

35. $28^{\circ}C = \dfrac{9}{5}(28)+32 = 82.4^{\circ}F$ **36.** $68^{\circ}F = \dfrac{5}{9}(68-32) = 20^{\circ}C$

37. $-6^{\circ}F = \dfrac{5}{9}(-6-32) = -21.\overline{1} \approx -21.1^{\circ}C$ **38.** $39^{\circ}C = \dfrac{9}{5}(39)+32 = 102.2^{\circ}F$

39. $l = 4\,cm, w = 1.6\,cm,\ P = 4+4+1.6+1.6 = 11.2\,cm,\ A = lw = 4(1.6) = 6.4\,cm^2$

40. base $= 3.2\,cm$, height $= 2.5\,cm$, hypotenuse $= 4.1\,cm$, $P = 3.2+2.5+4.1 = 9.8\,cm$,

   $A = \dfrac{1}{2}bh = \dfrac{1}{2}(3.2)(2.5) = 4\,cm^2$

41. a) $V = lwh = (10)(4)(2) = 80\,m^3$

   b) $\left(80\,m^3\right)\left(\dfrac{1\,kl}{1\,m^3}\right)\left(\dfrac{1000\,l}{1\,kl}\right)\left(\dfrac{1\,kg}{1\,l}\right) = 80\,000\,kg$

42. a) $A = lw = 30(22) = 660\,m^2$

   b) $660\,m^2 = \left(660\,m^2\right)\left(\dfrac{1\,km^2}{(1000)^2\,m^2}\right) = 0.000\,66\,km^2$

43. a) $V = lwh = (80)(40)(30) = 96\,000\,cm^3$

   b) $96\,000\,cm^3 = \left(96\,000\,cm^3\right)\left(\dfrac{1\,m^3}{(100)^3\,cm^3}\right) = 0.096\,m^3$

   c) $96\,000\,cm^3 = \left(96\,000\,cm^3\right)\left(\dfrac{1\,ml}{1\,cm^3}\right) = 96\,000\,ml$

   d) $0.096\,m^3 = \left(0.096\,m^3\right)\left(\dfrac{1\,kl}{1\,m^3}\right) = 0.096\,kl$

44. Since $1\,km = 100 \times 1\,dam, 1\,km^2 = 100^2 \times 1\,dam^2 = 10\,000\,dam^2$. Thus 1 square kilometer is $10{,}000$ times larger than a square dekameter.

45. $\left(27\,in\right)\left(\dfrac{2.54\,cm}{1\,in}\right) = 68.58\,cm$ **46.** $\left(105\,kg\right)\left(\dfrac{1\,lb}{0.45\,kg}\right) = 233.\overline{3} \approx 233.3\,lb$

47. $\left(83\,yd\right)\left(\dfrac{0.9\,m}{1\,yd}\right) = 74.7\,m$ **48.** $\left(100\,m\right)\left(\dfrac{1\,yd}{0.9\,m}\right) = 111.\overline{1} \approx 111.1\,yd$

49. $\left(45\,mi\right)\left(\dfrac{1.6\,km}{1\,mi}\right) = 72\,kph$ **50.** $\left(200\,lb\right)\left(\dfrac{0.45\,kg}{1\,lb}\right) = 90\,kg$

51. $(15\,gal)\left(\dfrac{3.8\,l}{1\,gal}\right) = 57\,l$

52. $(40\,m^3)\left(\dfrac{1\,yd^3}{0.76\,m^3}\right) = 52.63157895 \approx 52.6\,yd^3$

53. $(72\,lb)\left(\dfrac{0.45\,kg}{1\,lb}\right) = 32.4\,kg$

54. $(4\,qt)\left(\dfrac{0.95\,l}{1\,qt}\right) = 3.8\,l$

55. $(15\,yd^3)\left(\dfrac{0.76\,m^3}{1\,yd^3}\right) = 11.4\,m^3$

56. $(62\,mi)\left(\dfrac{1.6\,km}{1\,mi}\right) = 99.2\,km$

57. $(27\,cm)\left(\dfrac{1\,ft}{30\,cm}\right) = 0.9\,ft$

58. $(3.25\,in)\left(\dfrac{2.54\,cm}{1\,in}\right)\left(\dfrac{10\,mm}{1\,cm}\right) = 82.55\,mm$

59. a) $700(1.5\,kg) = 1050\,kg$

    b) $1050\,kg = (1050\,kg)\left(\dfrac{1\,lb}{0.45\,kg}\right) = 2333.\overline{3} \approx 2333.3\,lb$

60. $A = lw = (24)(15) = 360\,ft^2$

    $360\,ft^2 = (360\,ft^2)\left(\dfrac{0.09\,m^2}{1\,ft^2}\right) = 32.4\,m^2$

61. a) $(2.5\,hr)\left(\dfrac{461.6\,km}{1\,hr}\right) = 1154\,km$

    b) $1154\,km = (1154\,km)\left(\dfrac{1\,mi}{1.6\,km}\right) = 721.25\,mi$

62. a) $35\,mi = (35\,mi)\left(\dfrac{1.6\,km}{1\,mi}\right) = 56\,kph$

    b) $56\,km = (56\,km)\left(\dfrac{1000\,m}{1\,km}\right) = 56\,000\ \text{meters per hour}$

63. a) $V = lwh = (90)(70)(40) = 252\,000\,cm^3$

    $252\,000\,cm^3 = (252\,000\,cm^3)\left(\dfrac{1\,ml}{1\,cm^3}\right)\left(\dfrac{1\,l}{1000\,ml}\right) = 252\,l$

    b) $252\,l = (252\,l)\left(\dfrac{1\,kg}{1\,l}\right) = 252\,kg$

64. $1\,kg = (1\,kg)\left(\dfrac{1\,lb}{0.45\,kg}\right) = 2.\overline{2}\,lb$

    $\dfrac{\$2.75}{2.\overline{2}} = \$1.2375 \approx \$1.24\ \text{per pound}$

Chapter Test

1. $67\,km = (67\,km)\left(\dfrac{1\,000\,000\,mm}{1\,km}\right) = 67\,000\,000\,mm$

2. $96\,cg = \left(96\,cg\right)\left(\dfrac{1\,hg}{10\,000\,cg}\right) = 0.0096\,hg$

3. $1\,km = \left(1\,km\right)\left(\dfrac{100\,dam}{1\,km}\right) = 100\,dam$ or 100 times greater

4. $300\left(6\right) = 1800\,m$

   $1800\,m\left(\dfrac{1\,km}{1000\,m}\right) = 1.8\,km$

5. b

6. a

7. c

8. b

9. b

10. $1\,m^2 = \left(1\,m^2\right)\left(\dfrac{100^2\,cm^2}{1\,m^2}\right) = 10\,000\,cm^2$ or $10{,}000$ times greater

11. $1\,m^3 = \left(1\,m^3\right)\left(\dfrac{1000^3\,mm^3}{1\,m^3}\right) = 1\,000\,000\,000\,mm^3$ or $1{,}000{,}000{,}000$ times greater

12. $452\,in = \left(452\,in\right)\left(\dfrac{2.54\,cm}{1\,in}\right) = 1148.08\,cm$

13. $8\,km = \left(8\,km\right)\left(\dfrac{1\,mi}{1.6\,km}\right) = 5\,mph$

14. $50°F = \dfrac{5}{9}\left(50 - 32\right) = 10°C$

15. $50°C = \dfrac{9}{5}\left(50\right) + 32 = 122°F$

16. $12\,ft = \left(12\,ft\right)\left(\dfrac{30\,cm}{1\,ft}\right) = 360\,cm$ or $12\,ft = \left(12\,ft\right)\left(\dfrac{12\,in}{1\,ft}\right)\left(\dfrac{2.54\,cm}{1\,in}\right) = 365.76\,cm$

17. a) $V = lwh = 20\left(20\right)\left(8\right) = 3200\,m^3$

    b) $3200\,m^3 = \left(3200\,m^3\right)\left(\dfrac{1000\,l}{1\,m^3}\right) = 3\,200\,000\,l$ or $3\,200\,000\,l = \left(3\,200\,000\,l\right)\left(\dfrac{1\,kl}{1000\,l}\right) = 3200\,kl$

    c) $3\,200\,000\,l = \left(3\,200\,000\,l\right)\left(\dfrac{1\,kg}{1\,l}\right) = 3\,200\,000\,kg$

18. Total surface area: $2lh + 2wh = 2\left(20\right)\left(6\right) + 2\left(15\right)\left(6\right) = 420\,m^2$

    Liters needed for first coat: $\left(420\,m^2\right)\left(\dfrac{1\,l}{10\,m^2}\right) = 42\,l$

    Liters needed for second coat: $\left(420\,m^2\right)\left(\dfrac{1\,l}{15\,m^2}\right) = 28\,l$

    Total liters needed: $42 + 28 = 70\,l$

    Total cost: $\left(70\,l\right)\left(\dfrac{\$3.50}{1\,l}\right) = \$245$

Group Projects

1. a) $\left(196\, lb\right)\left(\dfrac{0.45\, kg}{1\, lb}\right)\left(\dfrac{20\, mg}{1\, kg}\right) = 1764\, mg$

    b) $\left(\dfrac{250\, cc}{1\, hr}\right)\left(\dfrac{1\, hr}{60\, min}\right) = 4.1\overline{6} \approx 4.17\, cc\,/\,min$

2. a) $\left(60\, lb\right)\left(\dfrac{0.45\, kg}{1\, lb}\right) = 27\, kg$

    Child's dose: $\dfrac{27\, kg}{67.5\, kg}\left(70\, mg\right) = 28\, mg$

    b) $\dfrac{child's\ weight\ in\ kg}{67.5\, kg} \times 70\, mg = 70\, mg$

    $\dfrac{child's\ weight\ in\ kg}{67.5\, kg} = 1$

    Child's weight: $67.5\, kg = \left(67.5\, kg\right)\left(\dfrac{1\, lb}{0.45\, kg}\right) = 150\, lb$

3. a) $5\, ft\, 2\, in = 62\, in$

    $62\, in = \left(62\, in\right)\left(\dfrac{2.54\, cm}{1\, in}\right) = 157.48\, cm$

    b) $8695.5\, yen = \left(8695.5\, yen\right)\left(\dfrac{1\, dollar}{102.30\, yen}\right) = \$85$

    c) $6\, lb = \left(6\, lb\right)\left(\dfrac{0.45\, kg}{1\, lb}\right)\left(\dfrac{1000\, g}{1\, kg}\right) = 2700\, g$

    $2700\, g = \left(2700\, g\right)\left(\dfrac{6\, pesos}{100\, g}\right)\left(\dfrac{0.1320\, dollar}{1\, pesos}\right) = 21.384 \approx \$21.38$

    d) To fill the tank in Niagara Falls, New York:

    $\$1.39(18) = \$25.02\ U.S.$

    To fill the tank in Niagara Falls, Canada:

    $18\, gal = \left(18\, gal\right)\left(\dfrac{3.8\, l}{1\, gal}\right) = 68.4\, l$

    $\$0.57(68.4) = \$38.988\ Canadian$

    $\$38.988\ Canadian = \left(\$38.988\ Canadian\right)\left(\dfrac{\$0.689\ U.S.}{1\ Canadian}\right) = 26.862732 \approx \$26.86\ U.S.$

    It is more expensive in Canada by $\$1.84\ U.S.\ currency$

CHAPTER NINE

GEOMETRY

Exercise Set 9.1

1. An **axiom (postulate)** is a statement accepted as being true on the basis of its "obviousness" and its relation to the physical world. A **theorem** is a statement that has been proven using undefined terms, definitions, and axioms.

2. a) Undefined terms, definitions, postulates (axioms), and theorems

   b) First, Euclid introduced **undefined terms**. Second, he introduced certain **definitions**. Third, he stated primitive propositions called **postulates (axioms)** about the undefined terms and definitions. Fourth, he proved, using deductive reasoning, other propositions called **theorems**.

3. Two lines in the same plane that do not intersect are **parallel lines**.

4. Two lines that do not lie in the same plane and do not intersect are called **skewed lines**.

5. Two angles in the same plane are **adjacent angles** when they have a common vertex and a common side but no common interior points.

6. Two angles the sum of whose measures is 90° are called **complementary angles**.

7. Two angles the sum of whose measures is 180° are called **supplementary angles**.

8. An angle whose measure is 90° is a **right angle**.

9. An angle whose measure is less than 90° is an **acute angle**.

10. An angle whose measure is greater than 90° but less than 180° is an **obtuse angle**.

11. An angle whose measure is 180° is a **straight angle**.

12. In the pair of intersecting lines below, ∡ 1 and ∡ 3 are vertical angles as are ∡ 2 and ∡ 4.

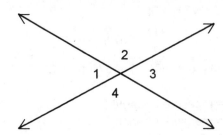

13. Ray $\overrightarrow{BA}$

14. Open line segment $\overset{\circ\!\!-\!\!\circ}{AB}$

15. Line $\overleftrightarrow{AB}$

16. Half line $\overset{\circ\!\!-\!\!\rightarrow}{BA}$

17. Ray $\overrightarrow{AB}$

18. Line segment $\overline{AB}$

19. Half open line segment $\underset{\circ}{AB}$

20. Half line $\overset{\circ\!\!-\!\!\rightarrow}{AB}$

21. $\overleftrightarrow{EG}$

22. $\measuredangle$ BFC

23. $\overleftrightarrow{AD}$

24. $\overrightarrow{BD}$

25. $\varnothing$

26. {C}

27. {C}

28. $\overline{BC}$

29. $\overleftrightarrow{BC}$

30. $\overleftrightarrow{BC}$

31. $\triangle$ BCF

32. $\varnothing$

33. $\overrightarrow{ED}$

34. $\varnothing$

35. $\overline{DE}$

36. $\overleftrightarrow{BC}$

37. $\measuredangle$ FBE

38. $\measuredangle$ ABE

39. {B}

40. $\measuredangle$ EBC

41. $\varnothing$

42. $\overleftrightarrow{AC}$

43. {B}

44. $\overline{BE}$

45. Straight

46. Obtuse

47. Acute

48. Straight

49. None of these

50. Right

51. Right

52. None of these

53. $90° - 51° = 39°$

54. $90° - 73° = 17°$

56. $90° - 17.4° = 72.6°$

55. $90° - 25\frac{1}{2}° = 64\frac{1}{2}°$

57. $90° - 89° = 1°$

58. $90° - 15\frac{1}{8}° = 74\frac{7}{8}°$

59. $180° - 76° = 104°$

60. $180° - 19° = 161°$

61. $180° - 135° = 45°$

62. $180° - 2\frac{5}{8}° = 177\frac{3}{8}°$

64. $180° - 156.8° = 23.2°$

63. $180° - 99\frac{1}{5}° = 80\frac{4}{5}°$

65. b

66. c

67. f

68. e

69. a

70. d

71. Let x = measure of angle 2
    7x = measure of angle 1
    $x + 7x = 90$
    $8x = 90$
    $x = \frac{90}{8} = 11.25°$, m $\measuredangle$ 2
    $7x = 7(11.25) = 78.75°$, m $\measuredangle$ 1

72. Let x = measure of angle 1
    90 - x = measure of angle 2
    $x - (90 - x) = 24$
    $x - 90 + x = 24$
    $2x - 90 = 24$
    $2x = 114$
    $x = \frac{114}{2} = 57°$, m $\measuredangle$ 1
    $90 - x = 90 - 57 = 33°$, m $\measuredangle$ 2

73. Let x = measure of angle 1
    180 - x = measure of angle 2
    $x - (180 - x) = 74$
    $x - 180 + x = 74$
    $2x - 180 = 74$
    $2x = 254$
    $x = \frac{254}{2} = 127°$, m $\measuredangle$ 1
    $180 - x = 180 - 127 = 53°$, m $\measuredangle$ 2

74. Let x = measure of angle 2
    8x = measure of angle 1
    $x + 8x = 180$
    $9x = 180$
    $x = \frac{180}{9} = 20°$, m $\measuredangle$ 2
    $8x = 8(20) = 160°$, m $\measuredangle$ 1

75. m ∠ 1 + 125° = 180°
    m ∠ 1 = 55°
    m ∠ 2 = m ∠ 1 (vertical angles)
    m ∠ 3 = 125° (vertical angles)
    m ∠ 5 = m ∠ 2 (alternate interior angles)
    m ∠ 4 = m ∠ 3 (alternate interior angles)
    m ∠ 7 = m ∠ 4 (vertical angles)
    m ∠ 6 = m ∠ 5 (vertical angles)
    Measures of angles 3, 4, and 7 are each 125°.
    Measures of angles 1, 2, 5, and 6 are each 55°.

76. m ∠ 3 + 30° = 180°
    m ∠ 3 = 150°
    m ∠ 1 = 30° (vertical angles)
    m ∠ 2 = m ∠ 3 (vertical angles)
    m ∠ 4 = m ∠ 1 (corresponding angles)
    m ∠ 7 = m ∠ 4 (vertical angles)
    m ∠ 6 = m ∠ 3 (alternate interior angles)
    m ∠ 5 = m ∠ 6 (vertical angles)
    Measures of angles 1, 4, and 7 are each 30°
    Measures of angles 2, 3, 5, and 6 are each 150°.

77. m ∠ 3 + 120° = 180°
    m ∠ 3 = 60°
    m ∠ 4 = 120° (vertical angles)
    m ∠ 7 = m ∠ 3 (vertical angles)
    m ∠ 6 = m ∠ 3 (alternate interior angles)
    m ∠ 1 = m ∠ 6 (vertical angles)
    m ∠ 5 = m ∠ 4 (alternate exterior angles)
    m ∠ 2 = m ∠ 5 (vertical angles)
    Measures of angles 2, 4, and 5 are each 120°.
    Measures of angles 1, 3, 6, and 7 are each 60°.

78. m ∠ 1 + 25° = 180°
    m ∠ 1 = 155°
    m ∠ 3 = m ∠ 1 (vertical angles)
    m ∠ 2 = 25° (vertical angles)
    m ∠ 4 = m ∠ 3 (alternate interior angles)
    m ∠ 7 = m ∠ 4 (vertical angles)
    m ∠ 5 = m ∠ 2 (corresponding angles)
    m ∠ 6 = m ∠ 5 (vertical angles)
    Measures of angles 2, 5, and 6 are each 25°.
    Measures of angles 1, 3, 4, and 7 are each 155°.

79.
$$x + 5x + 6 = 90$$
$$6x + 6 = 90$$
$$6x = 84$$
$$x = \frac{84}{6} = 14°, \text{ m } ∠ 2$$
$$5x + 6 = 5(14) + 6 = 76°, \text{ m } ∠ 1$$

80.
$$x + 4x - 10 = 90$$
$$5x - 10 = 90$$
$$5x = 100$$
$$x = \frac{100}{5} = 20°, \text{ m } ∠ 1$$
$$4x - 10 = 4(20) - 10 = 70°, \text{ m } ∠ 2$$

81.
$$x + 2x - 3 = 90$$
$$3x - 3 = 90$$
$$3x = 93$$
$$x = \frac{93}{3} = 31°, \text{ m } ∠ 1$$
$$2x - 3 = 2(31) - 3 = 59°, \text{ m } ∠ 2$$

82.
$$x + 4x + 5 = 90$$
$$5x + 5 = 90$$
$$5x = 85$$
$$x = \frac{85}{5} = 17°, \text{ m } ∠ 2$$
$$4x + 5 = 4(17) + 5 = 73°, \text{ m } ∠ 1$$

83.
$$x + 3x - 12 = 180$$
$$4x - 12 = 180$$
$$4x = 192$$
$$x = \frac{192}{4} = 48°, \text{ m } ∠ 2$$
$$3x - 12 = 3(48) - 12 = 132°, \text{ m } ∠ 1$$

84.
$$x + 12x - 2 = 180$$
$$13x - 2 = 180$$
$$13x = 182$$
$$x = \frac{182}{13} = 14°, \text{ m } ∠ 2$$
$$12x - 2 = 12(14) - 2 = 166°, \text{ m } ∠ 1$$

85. $x + 5x - 18 = 180$
$6x - 18 = 180$
$6x = 198$
$x = \dfrac{198}{6} = 33°, m \not\angle 1$
$5x - 18 = 5(33) - 18 = 147°, m \not\angle 2$

86. $x + 14x + 15 = 180$
$15x + 15 = 180$
$15x = 165$
$x = \dfrac{165}{15} = 11°, m \not\angle 1$
$14x + 15 = 14(11) + 15 = 169°, m \not\angle 2$

87. a) An infinite number of lines can be drawn through a given point.
    b) An infinite number of planes can be drawn through a given point.
88. If the two planes are not parallel, the intersection is a straight line.
89. An infinite number of planes can be drawn through a given line.
90. a) Yes, any three non collinear points always determine a plane.
    b) No, the plane determined is unique.
    c) An infinite number of planes can be drawn through three collinear points.

In exercises 91 - 96, there may be more than one answer.

91. Plane AGB ∩ plane GBC = $\overleftrightarrow{BG}$

92. Plane AGB ∩ plane ABC ∩ plane BCD = {B}

93. Plane HGD ∩ plane FGD ∩ plane BGD = $\overleftrightarrow{GD}$

94. $\overleftrightarrow{BC}$ ∩ plane ABG = {B}

95. $\overleftrightarrow{AB}$ ∩ plane ABG = $\overleftrightarrow{AB}$

96. $\overleftrightarrow{BG}$ ∩ $\overleftrightarrow{HG}$ ∩ $\overleftrightarrow{GD}$ = {G}

97. Always true. If any two lines are parallel to a third line, then they must be parallel to each other.
98. Sometimes true. A triangle must always contain at least two acute angles. Some triangles contain three acute angles.
99. Sometimes true. Vertical angles are only complementary when each is equal to 45°.
100. Sometimes true. Alternate exterior angles are only supplementary when each is equal to 90°.
101. Sometimes true. Alternate interior angles are only complementary when each is equal to 45°.
102. Never true. The sum of two obtuse angles is greater than 180°.

103.   104.

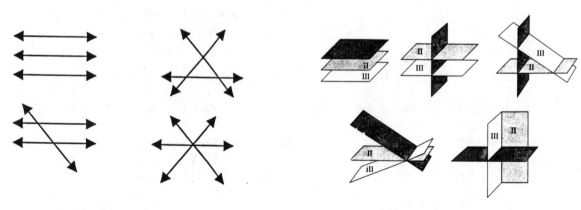

105.

i. Three parallel lines, two on the same plane ($\ell_1 \parallel \ell_3 \parallel \ell_9$)
ii. Three lines on the same plane intersecting in three distinct points (ℓ_9, ℓ_{10}, ℓ_{13})
iii. Three lines in the same plane, two are $\parallel$ and the third intersects the other two ($\ell_2 \parallel \ell_4$ and ℓ_1 intersects ℓ_2 and ℓ_4)
iv. Three lines intersect at a point, two lines on the same plane (ℓ_1, ℓ_2, ℓ_6)
v. Two lines intersect. A 3rd line is $\parallel$ the 1st line and skewed to the 2nd. (ℓ_9 and ℓ_{10} intersect, $\ell_2 \parallel \ell_{10}$, ℓ_2 and ℓ_9 are skewed.)
vi. Three lines that are skew to each other (ℓ_3, ℓ_6, ℓ_{13})
vii. Three $\parallel$ lines in the same plane. ($\ell_2 \parallel \ell_4 \parallel \ell_{14}$)
viii. Three lines in the same plane intersecting in a single point (ℓ_{10}, ℓ_{11}, ℓ_{13})
ix. Two $\parallel$ lines and a third line skewed to the other two. ($\ell_6 \parallel \ell_8$ and ℓ_{13} is skewed to ℓ_6 and ℓ_8)

Exercise Set 9.2

1. A **polygon** is a closed figure in a plane determined by three or more straight line segments.
2. The union of the sides of a polygon and its interior is a **polygonal region**.
3. A **regular polygon** is one whose sides are all the same length and whose interior angles all have the same measure; other polygons may have sides of different length and interior angles with different meaures.
4. Take the number of sides of the polygon and subtract 2; then multiply this difference by 180°.
5. Figures that have the same shape but may be of different sizes are **similar figures**.
6. If the corresponding sides of two similar figures are the same length, the figures are **congruent figures**.

7. Octagon	8. Quadrilateral	9. Pentagon	10. Hexagon
11. Equilateral	12. Scalene	13. Scalene	14. Scalene
15. Isosceles	16. Equilateral	17. Right	18. Acute
19. Obtuse	20. Obtuse	21. Right	22. Right
23. Rectangle	24. Parallelogram	25. Trapezoid	26. Rhombus
27. Square	28. Trapezoid		

29. The measure of one angle of the triangle is 75° (by vertical angles). The measure of another angle of the triangle is 180° - 133° = 47°. The measure of the third angle of the triangle is 180° - 75° - 47° = 58°. Since angle x is a vertical angle with the 58° angle, the measure of angle x is 58°.
30. The measures of the other two angles of the triangle are 138° and 25° (by vertical angles). Therefore, the measure of angle x is 180° - 138° - 25° = 17°.
31. The given measure of one angle of the triangle is 35°. The measure of another angle of the triangle is 30° (by vertical angles). The measure of the third angle of the triangle is 180° - 35° - 30° = 115°. The measure of angle x is 180° - 115° = 65° (The 115° angle and angle x form a straight angle.).
32. The measure of one angle of the triangle is 27° (by vertical angles). The measure of another angle of the triangle is 180° - 57° = 123°. The measure of the third angle of the triangle is 180° - 27° - 123° = 30°. The measure of angle x is 180° - 30° = 150° (The 30° angle and angle x form a straight angle.).

33.

Angle	Measure	Reason
1	90°	∡ 1 and ∡ 7 are vertical angles
2	50°	∡ 2 and ∡ 4 are corresponding angles
3	130°	∡ 3 and ∡ 4 form a straight angle
4	50°	Vertical angle with the given 50° angle
5	50°	∡ 2 and ∡ 5 are vertical angles
6	40°	Vertical angle with the given 40° angle
7	90°	∡ 2, ∡ 6, and ∡ 7 form a straight angle
8	130°	∡ 3 and ∡ 8 are vertical angles
9	140°	∡ 9 and ∡ 10 form a straight angle
10	40°	∡ 10 and ∡ 12 are vertical angles
11	140°	∡ 9 and ∡ 11 are vertical angles
12	40°	∡ 6 and ∡ 12 are corresponding angles

34.

Angle	Measure	Reason
1	50°	∡ 1 and ∡ 5 are vertical angles
2	63°	Vertical angle with the given 63° angle
3	67°	∡ 1, ∡ 2, and ∡ 3 form a straight angle
4	67°	∡ 3 and ∡ 4 are vertical angles
5	50°	∡ 5 and ∡ 12 are corresponding angles
6	113°	∡ 6 and the given 67° angle form a straight angle
7	50°	The sum of the measures of the interior angles of a triangle is 180°
8	130°	∡ 8 and ∡ 12 form a straight angle
9	67°	∡ 4 and ∡ 9 are corresponding angles
10	113°	∡ 6 and ∡ 10 are vertical angles
11	130°	∡ 8 and ∡ 11 are vertical angles
12	50°	∡ 7 and ∡ 12 are vertical angles

35. $n = 8$
$(8 - 2) \times 180° = 6 \times 180° = 1080°$

36. $n = 20$
$(20 - 2) \times 180° = 18 \times 180° = 3240°$

37. $n = 7$
$(7 - 2) \times 180° = 5 \times 180° = 900°$

38. $n = 12$
$(12 - 2) \times 180° = 10 \times 180° = 1800°$

39. The sum of the measures of the interior angles of a quadrilateral is $(4 - 2) \times 180° = 2 \times 180° = 360°$. Dividing by 4, the number of angles, each interior angle measures 90°. Each exterior angle measures $180° - 90° = 90°$.

40. The sum of the measures of the interior angles of a triangle is 180°. Dividing by 3, the number of angles, each interior angle measures 60°. Each exterior angle measures $180° - 60° = 120°$.

41. The sum of the measures of the interior angles of a pentagon is $(5 - 2) \times 180° = 3 \times 180° = 540°$. Dividing by 5, the number of angles, each interior angle measures 108°. Each exterior angle measures $180° - 108° = 72°$.

42. The sum of the measures of the interior angles of a hexagon is $(6 - 2) \times 180° = 4 \times 180° = 720°$. Dividing by 6, the number of angles, each interior angle measures 120°. Each exterior angle measures $180° - 120° = 60°$.

43. The sum of the measures of the interior angles of a heptagon is $(7 - 2) \times 180° = 5 \times 180° = 900°$. Dividing by 7, the number of angles, each interior angle measures $128\frac{4}{7}°$. Each

exterior angle measures $180° - 128\frac{4}{7}° = 51\frac{3}{7}°$.

44. The sum of the measures of the interior angles of an octagon is $(8 - 2) \times 180° = 6 \times 180° = 1080°$. Dividing by 8, the number of angles, each interior angle measures $135°$. Each exterior angle measures $180° - 135° = 45°$.

45. $180° - 125° = 55°$
47. $180° - 90° - 55° = 35°$

46. $55°$
48. $90° + 35° = 125°$

49. Let $x = A'C'$

$$\frac{A'C'}{AC} = \frac{A'B'}{AB}$$

$$\frac{x}{10} = \frac{2}{5}$$

$$5x = 20$$

$$x = 4$$

Let $y = B'C'$

$$\frac{B'C'}{BC} = \frac{A'B'}{AB}$$

$$\frac{y}{8} = \frac{2}{5}$$

$$5y = 16$$

$$y = \frac{16}{5}$$

50. Let $x = BC$

$$\frac{BC}{B'C'} = \frac{AB}{A'B'}$$

$$\frac{x}{2.4} = \frac{10}{4}$$

$$4x = 24$$

$$x = 6$$

Let $y = A'C'$

$$\frac{A'C'}{AC} = \frac{A'B'}{AB}$$

$$\frac{y}{8} = \frac{4}{10}$$

$$10y = 32$$

$$y = \frac{32}{10} = \frac{16}{5}$$

51. Let $x = AB$

$$\frac{AB}{A'B'} = \frac{AD}{A'D'}$$

$$\frac{x}{5} = \frac{5}{12}$$

$$12x = 25$$

$$x = \frac{25}{12}$$

Let $y = C'D'$

$$\frac{C'D'}{CD} = \frac{A'D'}{AD}$$

$$\frac{y}{1} = \frac{12}{5}$$

$$5y = 12$$

$$y = \frac{12}{5}$$

52. Let $x = CD$

$$\frac{CD}{C'D'} = \frac{AB}{A'B'}$$

$$\frac{x}{6} = \frac{4}{10}$$

$$10x = 24$$

$$x = \frac{24}{10} = \frac{12}{5}$$

Let $y = B'D'$

$$\frac{B'D'}{BD} = \frac{A'B'}{AB}$$

$$\frac{y}{3} = \frac{10}{4}$$

$$4y = 30$$

$$y = \frac{30}{4} = \frac{15}{2}$$

53. Let $x = DC$

$$\frac{DC}{AC} = \frac{DE}{AB}$$

$$\frac{x}{10} = \frac{2}{6}$$

$$6x = 20$$

$$x = \frac{20}{6} = \frac{10}{3}$$

54. Let $x = BC$

$$\frac{BC}{EC} = \frac{AB}{DE}$$

$$\frac{x}{2} = \frac{6}{2}$$

$$2x = 12$$

$$x = 6$$

55. $BE = BC - EC = 6 - 2 = 4$

56. $AD = AC - DC = 10 - \dfrac{10}{3} = \dfrac{30}{3} - \dfrac{10}{3} = \dfrac{20}{3}$

57. A' B' = AB = 14

58. B' C' = BC = 30

59. AC = A'C' = 28

60. m ∡ B'A'C' = m ∡ BAC = 84°

61. m ∡ ACB = m ∡ A'C'B' = 28°

62. m ∡ ABC = m ∡ A'B'C' = 180° - 84° - 28° = 68°

63. A'B' = AB = 8

64. AD = A'D' = 6

65. B'C' = BC = 16

66. m ∡ BCD = m ∡ B'C'D' = 50°

67. m ∡ A'D'C' = m ∡ ADC = 70°

68. m ∡ DAB = m ∡ D'A'B'
    = 360° - 130° - 70° - 50° = 110°

69. m ∡ x = 50°, m ∡ y = 130°

70. a)

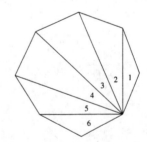

b) The sum of the measures of the angles in each triangle is 180°. The sum of the measures of the angles in the octagon is 180° × 6 = 1080°.

c) n = 8, (8 - 2) × 180° = 6 × 180° = 1080°

71. m ∡ w = 180° - 100° = 80°

72. m ∡ x = 100° (corresponding angles)

73. m ∡ y = 180° - 80° = 100°

74. m ∡ z = 80° (alternate interior angles)

75. a) m ∠ CED = m ∠ ABC;

   m ∠ ACB = m ∠ DCE (vertical angles);

   m ∠ BAC = m ∠ CDE (alternate interior angles)

   b) Let $x = DE$

$$\frac{x}{AB} = \frac{CE}{BC}$$

$$\frac{x}{543} = \frac{1404}{356}$$

$$356x = 762{,}372$$

$$x \approx 2141.49 \, \text{ft.}$$

76. a) m ∠ CED = m ∠ CBA (corresponding angles);

   m ∠ EDC = m ∠ BAC (corresponding angles);

   m ∠ ECD = m ∠ BCA (same angle)

   b) Let $x = AB$; 12 in. = 1 ft.

$$\frac{x}{1} = \frac{192}{2}$$

$$2x = 192$$

$$x = 96 \, \text{ft.}$$

77. Answers will vary.

78. a) m ∠ HMF = m ∠ TMB, m ∠ HFM = m ∠ TBM, m ∠ MHF = m ∠ MTB

   b) Let $x =$ height of the wall

$$\frac{x}{20} = \frac{5.5}{2.5}$$

$$2.5x = 110$$

$$x = \frac{110}{2.5} = 44 \, \text{ft.}$$

Exercise Set 9.3

1. a) The **perimeter** of a two-dimensional figure is the sum of the lengths of the sides of the figure.

   b) The **area** of a two-dimensional figure is the region within the boundaries of the figure.

   c)

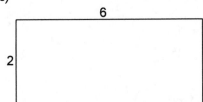

$$A = lw = 6(2) = 12 \text{ square units}$$
$$p = 2l + 2w = 2(6) + 2(2) = 12 + 4 = 16 \text{ units}$$

2. The radius of a circle is half the diameter or the diameter of a circle is twice the radius.

3. $A = \frac{1}{2}bh = \frac{1}{2}(10)(7) = 35 \, in.^2$

4. $A = \frac{1}{2}bh = \frac{1}{2}(7)(5) = 17.5 \, cm.^2$

5. $3 \, yd. = 3(3) = 9 \, ft.$

   $A = \frac{1}{2}bh = \frac{1}{2}(1)(9) = 4.5 \, ft.^2 = \frac{4.5}{9} = 0.5 \, yd.^2$

6. $A = \frac{1}{2}bh = \frac{1}{2}(2)(\sqrt{3}) = \sqrt{3} \, m.^2$

7. $A = lw = (15)(7) = 105 \, ft.^2$

   $p = 2l + 2w = 2(15) + 2(7) = 44 \, ft.$

8. $A = bh = (7)(5) = 35 \, in.^2$

   $p = 2b + 2w = 2(7) + 2(6) = 26 \, in.$

9. $2\,ft. = 2(12) = 24\,in.$

$A = \dfrac{1}{2}h(b_1 + b_2) = \dfrac{1}{2}(24)(5 + 19)$

$\qquad = \dfrac{1}{2}(24)(24) = 288\,in.^2$

$p = s_1 + s_2 + b_1 + b_2 = 25 + 25 + 5 + 19 = 74\,in.$

10. $2\,yd. = 2(3) = 6\,ft.$

$A = s^2 = (6)^2 = 36\,ft.^2$

$p = 4s = 4(6) = 24\,ft.$

11. $A = \dfrac{1}{2}h(b_1 + b_2) = \dfrac{1}{2}(12)(6 + 16)$

$\qquad = \dfrac{1}{2}(12)(22) = 132\,in.^2$

$p = s_1 + s_2 + b_1 + b_2 = 13 + 13 + 6 + 16 = 48\,in.$

12. $3\,m. = 3(100) = 300\,cm.$

$A = bh = 300(20) = 6000\,cm.^2$

$p = 2b + 2w = 2(300) + 2(27) = 654\,cm.$

In exercises 13-16 and the other exercises involving π, the π key on a scientific calculator was used to determine the answers. If you use 3.14 for π, your answers may vary slightly.

13. $A = \pi r^2 = \pi(5)^2 = 25\pi \approx 78.54\,in.^2$

$C = 2\pi r = 2\pi(5) = 10\pi \approx 31.42\,in.$

14. $r = \dfrac{22}{2} = 11\,cm.$

$A = \pi r^2 = \pi(11)^2 = 121\pi \approx 380.13\,cm.^2$

$C = 2\pi r = 2\pi(11) = 22\pi \approx 69.12\,cm.$

15. $r = \dfrac{7}{2} = 3.5\,ft.$

$A = \pi r^2 = \pi(3.5)^2 = 12.25\pi \approx 38.48\,ft.^2$

$C = 2\pi r = 2\pi(3.5) = 7\pi \approx 21.99\,ft.$

16. $A = \pi r^2 = \pi(15)^2 = 225\pi \approx 706.86\,mm.^2$

$C = 2\pi r = 2\pi(15) = 30\pi \approx 94.25\,mm.$

17. $c^2 = 5^2 + 12^2$

$c^2 = 25 + 144$

$c^2 = 169$

$c = \sqrt{169} = 13\,ft.$

18. $a^2 + 12^2 = 15^2$

$a^2 + 144 = 225$

$a^2 = 81$

$a = \sqrt{81} = 9\,in.$

19. $b^2 + 15^2 = 39^2$

$b^2 + 225 = 1521$

$b^2 = 1296$

$b = \sqrt{1296} = 36\,m.$

20. $c^2 = 10^2 + 24^2$

$c^2 = 100 + 576$

$c^2 = 676$

$c = \sqrt{676} = 26\,cm.$

21. Area of square: $(10)^2 = 100\,m.^2$

Area of circle: $\pi(5)^2 = 25\pi = 78.53981634\,m.^2$

Shaded area:

$100 - 78.53981634 = 21.46018366 \approx 21.46\,m^2$

22. Area of larger circle:

$\pi(4)^2 = 16\pi = 50.26548246\,cm.^2$

Area of smaller circle:

$\pi(3)^2 = 9\pi = 28.27433388\,cm.^2$

Shaded area:

$50.26548246 - 28.27433388 = 21.99114858$

$\approx 21.99\,cm.^2$

23. Area of rectangle: $7(4) = 28 \, ft.^2$

    Area of trapezoid: $\frac{1}{2}(4)(3+7) = \frac{1}{2}(4)(10) = 20 \, ft.^2$

    Shaded area: $28 - 20 = 8 \, ft.^2$

24. Use the Pythagorean Theorem to find the length of a side of the shaded square.

    $x^2 = 2^2 + 2^2$

    $x^2 = 4 + 4$

    $x^2 = 8$

    $x = \sqrt{8}$

    Shaded area: $\sqrt{8}\left(\sqrt{8}\right) = 8 \, in.^2$

25. Area of circle: $\pi(5)^2 = 25\pi = 78.53981634 \, m.^2$

    Area of rectangle: $8(6) = 48 \, m.^2$

    Shaded area:
    $78.53981634 - 48 = 30.53981634 \approx 30.54 \, m.^2$

26. Area of trapezoid: $\frac{1}{2}(8)(6+9) = \frac{1}{2}(8)(15) = 60 \, in.^2$

    Area of circle: $\pi(4)^2 = 16\pi = 50.26548246 \, in.^2$

    Shaded area:
    $60 - 50.26548246 = 9.73451754 \approx 9.73 \, in.^2$

27. Area of small rectangle on the right side:
    $12(6) = 72 \, ft.^2$

    Area of semi-circle on the right side:

    $\frac{1}{2}\pi(6)^2 = 18\pi = 56.54866776 \, ft.^2$

    Area of shaded region on the right side:
    $72 - 56.54866776 = 15.45133224 \, ft.^2$

    Area of shaded region on the left side:
    $15.45133224 \, ft.^2$

    Area of triangle: $\frac{1}{2}(14)(12) = 84 \, ft.^2$

    Shaded area:
    $15.45133224 + 15.45133224 + 84 \approx 114.90 \, ft.^2$

28. Radius of larger circle: $\frac{28}{2} = 14 \, cm.$

    Area of large circle:
    $\pi(14)^2 = 196\pi = 615.7521601 \, cm.^2$

    Radius of each smaller circle: $\frac{14}{2} = 7 \, cm.$

    Area of each smaller circle:
    $\pi(7)^2 = 49\pi = 153.93804 \, cm.^2$

    Shaded area:
    $615.7521601 - 153.93804 - 153.93804$
    $\approx 307.88 \, cm.^2$

29. $\frac{1}{x} = \frac{9}{15.2}$

    $9x = 15.2$

    $x = \frac{15.2}{9} \approx 1.69 \, yd.^2$

30. $\frac{1}{x} = \frac{9}{107}$

    $9x = 107$

    $x = \frac{107}{9} \approx 11.89 \, yd.^2$

31. $\frac{1}{18.3} = \frac{9}{x}$

    $x = 18.3(9) = 164.7 \, ft.^2$

32. $\frac{1}{14.7} = \frac{9}{x}$

    $x = 14.7(9) = 132.3 \, ft.^2$

33. $\frac{1}{14.7} = \frac{10,000}{x}$

    $x = 14.7(10,000) = 147\,000 \, cm.^2$

34. $\frac{1}{23.4} = \frac{10,000}{x}$

    $x = 23.4(10,000) = 234\,000 \, cm.^2$

35. $\frac{1}{x} = \frac{10,000}{608}$

    $10,000x = 608$

    $x = \frac{608}{10,000} = 0.0608 \, m.^2$

36. $\frac{1}{x} = \frac{10,000}{1075}$

    $10,000x = 1075$

    $x = \frac{1075}{10,000} = 0.1075 \, m.^2$

37. First floor: $A = 20(28) + 22(25) = 1110 \, ft.^2$

    Second floor: $A = 20(28) = 560 \, ft.^2$

    Total area: $1110 + 560 = 1670 \, ft.^2$

    Cost: $1670(\$65) = \$108,550$

38. $A = 22(25) = 550 \, ft.^2$

    Cost: $550(\$4.50) = \$2475$

39. Bedroom 1: $A = 10(20) = 200 \, ft.^2$

    Bedroom 2: $A = 10(14) = 140 \, ft.^2$

    Bedroom 3: $A = 10(14) = 140 \, ft.^2$

    Total area: $480 \, ft.^2 = \dfrac{480}{9} = 53\dfrac{1}{3} \approx 54 \, yd.^2$

    Cost: $\$14.95(54) = \$807.30$

40. Kitchen: $A = 12(14) = 168 \, ft.^2$

    Bathroom 1: $A = 8(14) = 112 \, ft.^2$

    Bathroom 2: $A = 6(10) = 60 \, ft.^2$

    Total area: $340 \, ft.^2 = \dfrac{340}{9} = 37\dfrac{7}{9} \approx 38 \, yd.^2$

    Cost: $\$25(38) = \$950$

41. Area of larger rectangle: $42(27) = 1134 \, ft.^2$

    Area of pool: $30(15) = 450 \, ft.^2$

    Area of deck: $1134 - 450 = 684 \, ft.^2$

42. Area of larger rectangle: $25(31) = 775 \, in.^2$

    Area of portrait: $19(25) = 475 \, in.^2$

    Area of picture frame: $775 - 475 = 300 \, in.^2$

43. Area of entire lawn if all grass:
    $200(100) = 20,000 \, ft.^2$

    Area of patio: $40(10) = 400 \, ft.^2$

    Area of shed: $10(8) = 80 \, ft.^2$

    Area of house: $50(25) = 1250 \, ft.^2$

    Area of drive: $30(10) = 300 \, ft.^2$

    Area of pool: $\pi(12)^2 = 144\pi = 452.3893421 \, ft.^2$

    Area of lawn:
    $20,000 - 400 - 80 - 1250 - 300 - 452.3893421$

    $= 17,517.61066 \, ft.^2 = \dfrac{17,517.61066}{9}$

    $= 1946.401184 \, yd.^2$

    Cost: $1946.401184(\$0.02) \approx \$38.93$

44. Area of entire lawn if all grass:
    $400(300) = 120,000 \, ft.^2$

    Area of house: $\dfrac{1}{2}(50)(100 + 150) = 6250 \, ft.^2$

    Area of goldfish pond:
    $\pi(20)^2 = 400\pi = 1256.637061 \, ft.^2$

    Area of privacy hedge: $200(20) = 4000 \, ft.^2$

    Area of garage: $70(30) = 2100 \, ft.^2$

    Area of driveway: $40(25) = 1000 \, ft.^2$

    Area of lawn:
    $120,000 - 6250 - 1256.637061 - 4000 - 2100 - 1000$

    $= 105,393.3629 \, ft.^2 = \dfrac{105,393.3629}{9}$

    $= 11,710.37366 \, yd.^2$

    Cost: $11,710.37366(\$0.02) \approx \$234.21$

45. $A = 36(60) + 36(24) + \dfrac{1}{2}(24)(24)$

    $= 2160 + 864 + 288 = 3312 \, in.^2$

    $= \dfrac{3312}{36 \times 36} = \dfrac{3312}{1296} \approx 2.56 \, yd.^2$

46. a) $A = 11.5(15.4) = 177.1 \, m.^2$

    b) $\dfrac{1}{x} = \dfrac{10,000}{177.1}$

    $10,000x = 177.1$

    $x = \dfrac{177.1}{10,000} = 0.01771 \, hectares$

47. $A = \dfrac{1}{2}s^2 = 72\,cm.^2$

$s^2 = 144\,cm.^2$

$s = \sqrt{144} = 12$

The legs are each $12\ cm.$

The hypotenuse:

$c^2 = 12^2 + 12^2$

$c^2 = 144 + 144$

$c^2 = 288$

$c = \sqrt{288} \approx 16.97\,cm.$

48. Wendy's hamburger: $A = 3(3) = 9\,in.^2$

Burger King hamburger:

$A = \pi\left(\dfrac{3.5}{2}\right)^2 = \pi(1.75)^2 = 3.0625\pi \approx 9.62\,in.^2$

Burger King's hamburger is larger by

$9.62 - 9 = 0.62\,in.^2$

49. a) $A = s^2$

b) $A = (2s)^2 = 4s^2$

c) The area of the square in part b) is four times larger than the area of the square in part a).

50. a) $A = \dfrac{1}{2}bh$

b) $A = \dfrac{1}{2}(2b)(2h) = 2bh$

c) The area of the triangle in part b) is four times larger than the area of the triangle in part a).

51. a) $A = bh$

b) $A = 2b(2h) = 4bh$

c) The area of the parallelogram in part b) is four times larger than the area of the parallelogram in part a).

52. a) Area to be painted if no windows or doors:

$2\left[16(30) + 16(40) + \dfrac{1}{2}(30)(10)\right]$

$= 2(1270) = 2540\,ft.^2$

Area of windows: $12\left(\dfrac{27}{12}\right)\left(\dfrac{40}{12}\right) = 90\,ft.^2$

Area of doors: $2\left(\dfrac{80}{12}\right)\left(\dfrac{36}{12}\right) = 40\,ft.^2$

Area to be painted: $2540 - 90 - 40 = 2410\,ft.^2$

b) $\dfrac{1}{x} = \dfrac{500}{2410}$

$500x = 2410$

$x = \dfrac{2410}{500} = 4.82\,\text{gallons per coat}$

2 coats: $4.82(2) = 9.64\,\text{gallons} \approx 10\,\text{gallons}$

c) $10(\$24.95) = \$249.50$

53. Area of top and bottom:

$$2\left(\pi(3)^2\right) = 18\pi = 56.54866776 \, in.^2$$

The side of the cylinder laid out flat would be a rectangle whose length is equal to the circumference of the circle and width is the height of the cylinder.

$$C = 2\pi(3) = 6\pi = 18.84955592 \, in.$$

Area of side: $7(18.84955592) \approx 131.9468915 \, in.^2$

Total area:

$$56.54866776 + 131.9468915 \approx 188.50 \, in.^2$$

54. Area of top and bottom: $2(5 \times 3) = 30 \, ft.^2$

Area of sides: $2(4 \times 3) + 2(4 \times 5) = 64 \, ft.^2$

Total area: $30 + 64 = 94 \, ft.^2$

55. $s = \dfrac{1}{2}(a + b + c) = \dfrac{1}{2}(8 + 6 + 10) = 12$

$$A = \sqrt{12(12 - 8)(12 - 6)(12 - 10)}$$
$$= \sqrt{12(4)(6)(2)} = \sqrt{576} = 24 \, cm.^2$$

56. First piece: $s = \dfrac{1}{2}(15 + 25 + 35) = 37.5$

Area of first piece:

$$\sqrt{37.5(37.5 - 15)(37.5 - 25)(37.5 - 35)}$$
$$\sqrt{37.5(22.5)(12.5)(2.5)} = \sqrt{26,367.1875}$$
$$\approx 162.3797632 \, ft.^2$$

Second piece: $s = \dfrac{1}{2}(60 + 100 + 140) = 150$

Area of second piece:

$$\sqrt{150(150 - 60)(150 - 100)(150 - 140)}$$
$$\sqrt{150(90)(50)(10)} = \sqrt{6,750,000}$$
$$\approx 2598.076211 \, ft.^2$$

The area of the larger piece is 16 times the area of the smaller piece, but only 8 times the price. Therefore, the larger piece of land is least expensive.

Exercise Set 9.4

In this section we use the π key on the calculator to determine answers in calculations involving pi.
If you use 3.14 for π your answers may vary slightly.

1. **Volume** is a measure of the capacity of a figure.
2. **Solid geometry** is the study of three-dimensional solid figures.
3. A **polyhedron** is a closed surface formed by the union of polygonal regions. A **regular polyhedron** is one whose faces are all regular polygons of the same size and shape.
4. A **prism** is a polyhedron whose bases are congruent polygons and whose sides are parallelograms.
   A **right prism** is one in which all of the lateral faces are rectangles.
5. For any polyhedron, the number of vertices minus the number of edges plus the number of faces equals two.
6. A **prism** and a **pyramid** are both polyhedrons, but a prism has a top and a bottom base while a pyramid only has one base.

7. $V = lwh = 2(2)(2) = 8 \, ft.^3$

8. $V = lwh = 7(2)(2) = 28 \, ft.^3$

9. $2\,ft. = 2(12) = 24\,in.$

   $V = \pi r^2 h = \pi(6)^2(24) = 864\pi$

   $= 2714.336053 \approx 2714.34\,in.^3$

10. $1\,ft. = 12\,in.$

    $V = \pi r^2 h = \pi(2)^2(12) = 48\pi$

    $= 150.7964474 \approx 150.80\,in.^3$

11. $V = \dfrac{1}{3}\pi r^2 h = \dfrac{1}{3}\pi(3)^2(14) = 42\pi$

    $= 131.9468915 \approx 131.95\,cm.^3$

12. $r = \dfrac{10}{2} = 5\,ft.$

    $V = \dfrac{1}{3}\pi r^2 h = \dfrac{1}{3}\pi(5)^2(24) = 200\pi$

    $= 628.3185307 \approx 628.32\,ft.^3$

13. Area of the base: $B = \dfrac{1}{2}bh = \dfrac{1}{2}(8)(8) = 32\,in.^2$

    $V = Bh = 32(12) = 384\,in.^3$

14. Area of the base:

    $B = \dfrac{1}{2}h(b_1 + b_2) = \dfrac{1}{2}(10)(8+12) = 100\,in.^2$

    $V = Bh = 100(24) = 2400\,in.^3$

15. $r = \dfrac{13}{2} = 6.5\,cm.$

    $V = \dfrac{4}{3}\pi r^3 = \dfrac{4}{3}\pi(6.5)^3 = 366.1\overline{6}\pi$

    $= 1150.34651 \approx 1150.35\,cm.^3$

16. $V = \dfrac{4}{3}\pi r^3 = \dfrac{4}{3}\pi(7)^3 = 457.\overline{3}\pi$

    $= 1436.75504 \approx 1436.76\,cm.^3$

17. Area of the base: $B = s^2 = (11)^2 = 121\,cm.^2$

    $V = \dfrac{1}{3}Bh = \dfrac{1}{3}(121)(13) = 524.\overline{3} \approx 524.33\,cm.^3$

18. Area of the base: $B = \dfrac{1}{2}bh = \dfrac{1}{2}(9)(15) = 67.5\,ft.^2$

    $V = \dfrac{1}{3}Bh = \dfrac{1}{3}(67.5)(13) = 292.5\,ft.^3$

19. Area of the base:

    $B = \dfrac{1}{2}h(b_1 + b_2) = \dfrac{1}{2}(5)(7+9) = 40\,in.^2$

    $V = \dfrac{1}{3}Bh = \dfrac{1}{3}(40)(8) = 106.\overline{6} \approx 106.67\,in.^3$

20. Area of the base: $B = lw = 18(15) = 270\,in.^2$

    $V = \dfrac{1}{3}Bh = \dfrac{1}{3}(270)(10) = 900\,in.^3$

21. $V = $ volume of rect. solid - volume of cylinder

    $= 4(4)(25) - \pi(2)^2(25) = 400 - 100\pi$

    $= 400 - 314.1592654 = 85.84073464 \approx 85.84\,yd.^3$

22. $V = $ volume of cylinder - volume of cone

    $= \pi(2)^2(9) - \dfrac{1}{3}\pi(2)^2(9) = 36\pi - 12\pi = 24\pi$

    $= 75.39822369 \approx 75.40\,cm.^3$

23. $V = $ volume of rect. solid - volume of cylinder

    $= 6(4)(3) - \pi(1)^2(4) = 72 - 4\pi$

    $= 72 - 12.56637061 = 59.43362939 \approx 59.43\,m.^3$

24. $V = $ volume of rect. solid - volume of sphere

    $= 4(4)(4) - \dfrac{4}{3}\pi(2)^3 = 64 - 33.51032164$

    $= 30.48967836 \approx 30.49\,ft.^3$

25. $V = $ vol. of large sphere - vol. of small sphere

    $= \dfrac{4}{3}\pi(6)^3 - \dfrac{4}{3}\pi(3)^3 = 288\pi - 36\pi = 252\pi$

    $= 791.6813487 \approx 791.68\,cm.^3$

26. $V = $ vol. of large cylinder - vol. of small cylinder

    $= \pi(1.5)^2(5) - \pi(0.5)^2(5) = 11.25\pi - 1.25\pi = 10\pi$

    $= 31.41592654 \approx 31.42\,m.^3$

27. V = volume of cylinder - volume of 3 spheres

$$= \pi(3.5)^2(20.8) - 3\left[\frac{4}{3}\pi(3.45)^3\right]$$

$$= 254.8\pi - 164.2545\pi = 90.5455\pi$$

$$= 284.4570776 \approx 284.46\, cm.^3$$

28. V = volume of rect. solid - volume of pyramid

$$= 3(3)(4) - \frac{1}{3}(3)^2(4) = 36 - 12 = 24\, ft.^3$$

29. $5\, yd.^3 = 5(27) = 135\, ft.^3$

30. $4.1\, yd.^3 = 4.1(27) = 110.7\, ft.^3$

31. $212\, ft.^3 = \dfrac{212}{27} = 7.\overline{851} \approx 7.85\, yd.^3$

32. $84\, ft.^3 = \dfrac{84}{27} = 3.\overline{1} \approx 3.11\, yd.^3$

33. $2.7\, m.^3 = 2.7(1,000,000) = 2\,700\,000\, cm.^3$

34. $5.9\, m.^3 = 5.9(1,000,000) = 5\,900\,000\, cm.^3$

35. $4\,000\,000\, cm.^3 = \dfrac{4,000,000}{1,000,000} = 4\, m.^3$

36. $6\,800\,000\, cm.^3 = \dfrac{6,800,000}{1,000,000} = 6.8\, m.^3$

37. Tubs: $V = \pi r^2 h = \pi(3)^2(5) = 45\pi$

$$= 141.3716694 \approx 141.37\, in.^3$$

Boxes: $V = s^3 = (5)^3 = 125\, in.^3$

38. a) $V = 46(25)(25) = 28,750\, in.^3$

b) $(1\, ft.)^3 = (12\, in.)(12\, in.)(12\, in.) = 1728\, in.^3$

$$28,750\, in.^3 = \dfrac{28,750}{1728} = 16.63773148 \approx 16.64\, ft.^3$$

39. Wendy's Volume: $4(4)\left(\dfrac{3}{16}\right) = 3\, in.^3$

Magic Burger's Volume:

$$\pi\left(\dfrac{4.5}{2}\right)^2(0.25) = \pi(2.25)^2(0.25)$$

$$= 3.976078202 \approx 3.98\, in.^3$$

The Magic Burger has the greater volume by $0.98\, in.^3$

40. $V = 12(4)(3) = 144\, in.^3$

$$144\, in.^3 = 144(0.01736) = 2.49984 \approx 2.50\, qt.$$

41. a) Cylinder 1:

$$V = \pi\left(\dfrac{10}{2}\right)^2(12) = 300\pi = 942.4777961 \approx 942.48\, in.^3$$

Cylinder 2:

$$V = \pi\left(\dfrac{12}{2}\right)^2(10) = 360\pi = 1130.973355 \approx 1130.97\, in.^3$$

The container with the larger diameter holds more.

b) $1130.97 - 942.48 = 188.49 \approx 188.50\, in.^3$

42. a) $V = 80(50)(30) = 120\,000\, cm.^3$

b) $120\,000\, ml.$

c) $120\,000\, ml. = \dfrac{120,000}{1000} = 120\, l.$

43. a) $V = 15(9)(2) = 270\, m.^3$

b) $270\, kl.$

44. $V = \dfrac{1}{3}Bh = \dfrac{1}{3}(720)^2(480) = 82,944,000\, ft.^3$

45. $V = \pi r^2 h = \pi\left(\dfrac{2.25}{2}\right)^2(3.5) = 13.91627371\, in.^3$

$$2(13.91627371) = 27.83254742 \approx 27.83\, in.^3$$

46. $V = \dfrac{4}{3}\pi r^3 = \dfrac{4}{3}\pi\left(\dfrac{1.2}{2}\right)^3 = 0.288\pi$

$$= 0.9047786842 \approx 0.90\, mm.^3$$

47. a) $4\,in. = \dfrac{4}{12} = \dfrac{1}{3}\,ft.$

$V = lwh = 80(12.5)\left(\dfrac{1}{3}\right) = 333.\overline{3} \approx 333.33\,ft.^3$

b) $333.\overline{3}\,ft.^3 = \dfrac{333.\overline{3}}{27} = 12.34567901 \approx 12.35\,yd.^3$

48. a) Round pan:

$A = \pi r^2 = \pi\left(\dfrac{9}{2}\right)^2 = 20.25\pi$

$= 63.61725124 \approx 63.62\,in.^2$

Rectangular pan: $A = lw = 7(9) = 63\,in.^2$

b) Round pan:

$V = \pi r^2 h \approx 63.62(2) = 127.24\,in.^3$

Rectangular pan: $V = lwh = 7(9)(2) = 126\,in.^3$

c) Round pan

49. $V = \dfrac{1}{3}\pi r^2 h = \dfrac{1}{3}\pi\left(\dfrac{3}{2}\right)^2(6) = 4.5\pi$

$= 14.13716694 \approx 14.14\,in.^3$

50. a) $9\,in. = \dfrac{9}{12} = 0.75\,ft.$

$V = lwh = 6(4)(0.75) = 18\,ft.^3$

b) Weight of water in mattress:
$18(62.5) = 1125\,lb.$

c) Number of gallons of water:

$\dfrac{1125}{8.3} = 135.5421687 \approx 135.54\,\text{gal.}$

51. a) $C = 2\pi r = 2\pi\left(\dfrac{19.6}{2}\right) = 19.6\pi$

$= 61.57521601 \approx 61.58\,m.$

b) $V = \pi r^2 h = \pi\left(\dfrac{19.6}{2}\right)^2(60) = 5762.4\pi$

$= 18{,}103.11351 \approx 18103.11\,m.^3$

52. a) $B = \text{area of trapezoid} = \dfrac{1}{2}(9)(8+12) = 90\,in.^2$

$4\,ft. = 4(12) = 48\,in.$

$V = Bh = 90(48) = 4320\,in.^3$

b) $1\,ft.^3 = (12)(12)(12) = 1728\,in.^3$

$4320\,in.^3 = \dfrac{4320}{1728} = 2.5\,ft.^3$

53. $12 - 16 + x = 2$
$-4 + x = 2$
$x = 6\ \text{faces}$

54. $8 - x + 3 = 2$
$11 - x = 2$
$-x = -9$
$x = 9\ \text{edges}$

55. $x - 8 + 4 = 2$
$x - 4 = 2$
$x = 6\ \text{vertices}$

56. $7 - 12 + x = 2$
$-5 + x = 2$
$x = 7\ \text{faces}$

57. $11 - x + 5 = 2$
$16 - x = 2$
$-x = -14$
$x = 14\ \text{edges}$

58. $x - 10 + 4 = 2$
$x - 6 = 2$
$x = 8\ \text{vertices}$

59. Compare $V = x^3$ to $V = (2x)^3 = 8x^3$

The new volume is eight times the original volume.

60. Compare $V = \pi r^2 h$ to $V = \pi(2r)^2 h = 4\pi r^2 h$

The new volume is four times the original volume.

61. Compare $V = \dfrac{4}{3}\pi r^3$ to $V = \dfrac{4}{3}\pi (2r)^3 = 8\left(\dfrac{4}{3}\right)\pi r^3$

    The new volume is eight times the original volume.

62. Volume of a half-inch cube: $\left(\dfrac{1}{2}\right)^3 = \dfrac{1}{8}\, in.^3$

    Volume of a half cubic inch: $\dfrac{1}{2}(1)^3 = \dfrac{1}{2}\, in.^3$

    No. The volumes are different.

63. Regular cone container: $V = \dfrac{1}{3}\pi r^2 h$

    Right circular cylinder container: $V = \pi r^2 h$

    Yes. The cylinder has three times the volume of the cone, but the customer is only charged twice as much.

64. $6\, cm.$ grapefruit: $V = \dfrac{4}{3}\pi r^3 = \dfrac{4}{3}\pi(6)^3 = 288\pi = 904.778\,684\,2\, cm.^3$

    Cost of $6\, cm.$ grapefruit: $\dfrac{0.33}{904.7786842} \approx \$0.000365\, per\, cm.^3$

    $7\, cm.$ grapefruit: $V = \dfrac{4}{3}\pi r^3 = \dfrac{4}{3}\pi(7)^3 = 457.\overline{3}\pi = 1436.755\,04\, cm.^3$

    Cost of $7\, cm.$ grapefruit: $\dfrac{0.49}{1436.75504} \approx \$0.000341\, per\, cm.^3$

    The grapefruit with the $7\, cm.$ radius is the better buy.

65. Let $r =$ the radius of one of the cans of orange juice
    The length of the box $= 6r$ and the width of the box $= 4r$
    Volume of box - volume of cans:

    $lwh - 6\left(\pi r^2 h\right) = (6r)(4r)h - 6\pi r^2 h = 24r^2 h - 6\pi r^2 h = 6r^2 h(4 - \pi)$

    Percent of the volume of the interior of the box that is not occupied by the cans:

    $\dfrac{6r^2 h(4-\pi)}{lwh} = \dfrac{6r^2(4-\pi)}{(6r)(4r)} = \dfrac{4-\pi}{4} = 0.2146018366 \approx 21.46\%$

66. $1\, day:\ 12\,\dfrac{drops}{min.} \times \dfrac{60\, mins.}{1\, hr.} \times \dfrac{24\, hrs.}{1\, day} = 17{,}280\, drops\, per\, day$

    $17{,}280(30) = 518{,}400\, drops$

    $\dfrac{518{,}400}{20} = 25{,}920\, ml.$

    $\dfrac{25{,}920}{1000} = 25.92\, l.$

67. a) Find the volume of each numbered region. Since the length of each side is $a+b$, the sum of the volumes of each region will equal $(a+b)^3$.

    b) $V_1 = a(a)(a) = a^3$ $V_2 = a(a)(b) = a^2 b$ $V_3 = a(a)(b) = a^2 b$ $V_4 = a(b)(b) = ab^2$

    $V_5 = a(a)(b) = a^2 b$ $V_6 = a(b)(b) = ab^2$ $V_7 = b(b)(b) = b^3$

    c) The volume of the piece not shown is ab^2.

68. i) $P = 2l + 2w = 2(12) + 2(10) = 24 + 20 = 44$ *ft.*

   ii) Wall space: $44(8) = 352$ *ft.*^{2}

   iii) $\dfrac{352}{30} = 11.7\overline{3}$ or 12 *rolls*

   iv) $12 - 1 - 1 = 10$ *rolls*

Exercise Set 9.5

1. A **Mobius strip** is a one-sided, one-edged surface.
2. You can construct a Mobius strip by taking a strip of paper, giving one end a half twist, and taping the ends together.
3. A **Klein bottle** is a topological object that resembles a bottle but has only one side.
4. Four
5. a) Six
   b) Seven
6. A **Jordan curve** is a topological object that can be thought of as a circle twisted out of shape.
7. Two figures are **topologically equivalent** if one figure can be elastically twisted, stretched, bent, or shrunk into the other figure without puncturing or ripping the original figure.
8. The number of holes in the object determines the **genus** of an object.

9. One   10. One   11. One   12. Two

13. a) No, it has an inside and an outside.
    b) Two
    c) Two
    d) Two strips, one inside the other
14. The smaller one is a Mobius strip, the larger one is not.
15. No, it does not.
16. Yes. "Both sides" of the belt experience wear.
17. - 22. 1 - Red; 2, 5 - Yellow; 3, 6 - Blue; 4, 7 - Green
23. - 24. Answers will vary.

25. Outside; a straight line from point A to a point clearly outside the curve crosses the curve an even number of times.
26. Inside; a straight line from point B to a point clearly outside the curve crosses the curve an odd number of times.
27. Outside; a straight line from point A to a point clearly outside the curve crosses the curve an even number of times.
28. Outside; a straight line from point B to a point clearly outside the curve crosses the curve an even number of times.
29. Outside; a straight line from point C to a point clearly outside the curve crosses the curve an even number of times.
30. Outside; a straight line from point D to a point clearly outside the curve crosses the curve an even number of times.
31. Inside; a straight line from point E to a point clearly outside the curve crosses the curve an odd number of times.

32. Since you must cross the curve to get from inside to outside, two crosses puts you back where you started. Thus, if you cross the curve twice (or any even number of times) to get outside, you must have started outside. Also, if you cross the curve once (or any odd number of times) to get outside, you must have started inside.

33. 1	34. 1	35. 5	36. 1
37. 0	38. 1	39. 4	40. 5
41. 3	42. 0		

43. - 46. Answers will vary.

Exercise Set 9.6

1. Janos Bolyai - discovered hyperbolic geometry
2. Carl Friedrich Gauss - discovered hyperbolic geometry
3. Nikolay Ivanovich Lobachevsky - discovered hyperbolic geometry
4. Girolamo Saccheri - proved many theorems of hyperbolic geometry
5. G.F. Bernhard Riemann - discovered elliptical geometry
6. a) Euclidean - Given a line and a point not on the line, one and only one line can be drawn parallel to the given line through the given point.

   b) Hyperbolic - Given a line and a point not on the line, two or more lines can be drawn through the given point parallel to the given line.

   c) Elliptical - Given a line and a point not on the line, no line can be drawn through the given point parallel to the given line.
7. a) Euclidean - The sum of the measures of the angles of a triangle is 180°.

   b) Hyperbolic - The sum of the measures of the angles of a triangle is less than 180°.

   c) Elliptical - The sum of the measures of the angles of a triangle is greater than 180°.
8. Plane
9. Sphere
10. Pseudosphere
11. Each type of geometry can be used in its own frame of reference.
12. Einstein conjectured that mass caused space to be curved.
13. Spherical - elliptical geometry; Flat - Euclidean geometry; Saddle shaped - hyperbolic geometry
14. The area is finite because it encloses a finite region.

    The perimeter is infinite because it consists of an infinite number of pieces.
15.

16.

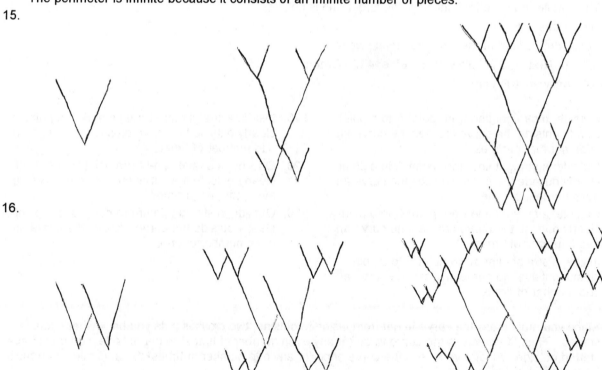

17.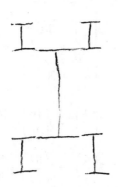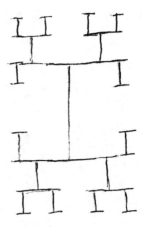

18.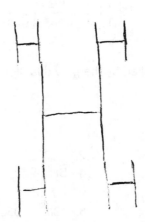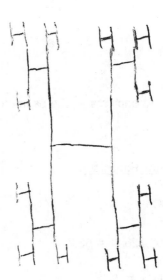

19. a)

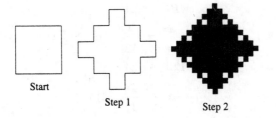

b) Infinite since it is infinitely subdivided.
c) Finite since it covers a finite or closed area.

20. a)

Step	Perimeter
1	$3\left(\dfrac{4}{3}\right)^0 = 3(1) = 3$
2	$3\left(\dfrac{4}{3}\right)^1 = 3\left(\dfrac{4}{3}\right) = 4$
3	$3\left(\dfrac{4}{3}\right)^2 = 3\left(\dfrac{16}{9}\right) = \dfrac{16}{3}$
4	$3\left(\dfrac{4}{3}\right)^3 = 3\left(\dfrac{64}{27}\right) = \dfrac{64}{9}$
5	$3\left(\dfrac{4}{3}\right)^4 = 3\left(\dfrac{256}{81}\right) = \dfrac{256}{27}$
6	$3\left(\dfrac{4}{3}\right)^5 = 3\left(\dfrac{1024}{243}\right) = \dfrac{1024}{81}$

b) At each stage, the perimeter is $\dfrac{4}{3}$ multiplied by the previous perimeter.

Review Exercises

1. {F}

2. $\triangle$ BFC

3. $\overline{BC}$

4. $\overleftrightarrow{BH}$

5. {F}

6. { }

7. $90° - 26.3° = 63.7°$

8. $180° - 105.2° = 74.8°$

9. Let $x = BC$

$$\frac{BC}{B'C} = \frac{AC}{A'C}$$

$$\frac{x}{3.4} = \frac{12}{4}$$

$$4x = 40.8$$

$$x = \frac{40.8}{4} = 10.2 \text{ in.}$$

10. Let $x = A'B'$

$$\frac{A'B'}{AB} = \frac{A'C}{AC}$$

$$\frac{x}{6} = \frac{4}{12}$$

$$12x = 24$$

$$x = \frac{24}{12} = 2 \text{ in.}$$

11. m $\angle$ ABC = m $\angle$ A'B'C

m $\angle$ A'B'C = 180° - 88° = 92°

Thus, m $\angle$ ABC = 92°

m $\angle$ BAC = 180° - 30° - 92° = 58°

12. m $\angle$ ABC = m $\angle$ A'B'C

m $\angle$ A'B'C = 180° - 88° = 92°

Thus, m $\angle$ ABC = 92°

13. The measure of the top angle of the triangle is $45°$, by vertical angles. The measure of the angle on the bottom right of the triangle is $180° - 120° = 60°$. Therefore, m $\angle$ 1 = $180° - 45° - 60° = 75°$.

   m $\angle$ 6 = $75°$ (angle 1 and angle 6 are vertical angles)

   m $\angle$ 2 = $60°$ (angle 2 and the angle on the bottom right of the triangle are vertical angles)

   The measure of the alternate interior angle of angle 2 is $60°$. Thus, m $\angle$ 3 = $180° - 60° = 120°$.

   The measure of the alternate interior angle of angle 6 is $75°$. Thus, m $\angle$ 5 = $180° - 75° = 105°$.

   m $\angle$ 4 = $180° - 105° = 75°$.

14. $n = 6$

   $(n - 2)180° = (6 - 2)180° = 4(180°) = 720°$

15. $A = lw = 7(4) = 28\,cm.^2$

16. $A = \dfrac{1}{2}bh = \dfrac{1}{2}(16)(7) = 56\,in.^2$

17. $A = \dfrac{1}{2}h(b_1 + b_2) = \dfrac{1}{2}(2)(4 + 9) = 13\,in.^2$

18. $A = bh = 12(7) = 84\,in.^2$

19. $A = \pi r^2 = \pi(11)^2 = 121\pi$

   $= 380.1327111 \approx 380.13\,cm.^2$

20. $A = lw = 14(16) = 224\,ft.^2$

   $224\,ft.^2 = \dfrac{224}{9} = 24.\overline{8}\,yd.^2 \approx 25\,yd.^2$

   $25(\$18.50) = \$462.50$

21. $V = \pi r^2 h = \pi(2)^2(6) = 24\pi$

   $= 75.39822369 \approx 75.40\,in.^3$

22. $V = lwh = 10(3)(4) = 120\,cm.^3$

23. If h represents the height of the triangle which is the base of the pyramid, then

$$\begin{aligned} h^2 + 3^2 &= 5^2 \\ h^2 + 9 &= 25 \\ h^2 &= 16 \\ h &= \sqrt{16} = 4\,ft. \end{aligned}$$

   $B = \dfrac{1}{2}bh = \dfrac{1}{2}(6)(4) = 12\,ft.^2$

   $V = \dfrac{1}{3}Bh = \dfrac{1}{3}(12)(7) = 28\,ft.^3$

24. If h represents the height of the triangle which is the base of the solid, then

$$\begin{aligned} h^2 + 5^2 &= 13^2 \\ h^2 + 25 &= 169 \\ h^2 &= 144 \\ h &= \sqrt{144} = 12\,m. \end{aligned}$$

   $B = \dfrac{1}{2}bh = \dfrac{1}{2}(10)(12) = 60\,m.^2$

   $V = Bh = 60(9) = 540\,m.^3$

25. $V = \dfrac{1}{3}\pi r^2 h = \dfrac{1}{3}\pi(5)^2(15) = 125\pi$

   $= 392.6990817 \approx 392.70\,mm.^3$

26. $V = \frac{4}{3}\pi r^3 = \frac{4}{3}\pi(5)^3 = 166.\overline{6}\pi$

$= 523.5987756 \approx 523.60\ ft.^3$

27.
$$h^2 + 1^2 = 3^2$$
$$h^2 + 1 = 9$$
$$h^2 = 8$$
$$h = \sqrt{8}$$

$A = \frac{1}{2}h(b_1 + b_2) = \frac{1}{2}(\sqrt{8})(2+4) = 8.485281374\ ft.^2$

a) $V = Bh = 8.485281374(8)$

$= 67.88225099 \approx 67.88\ ft.^3$

b) Weight:
$67.88(62.5) + 375 = 4617.5\ lbs.$

Yes, it will support the trough filled with water.

c) $(4617.5 - 375) = 4242.5\ lbs.\ of\ water$

$\frac{4242.5}{8.3} = 511.1445783 \approx 511.1\ gal.$

28. 4

29. 1, 7 - Green; 2, 5 - Red; 3, 8 - Blue;
4, 6 - Yellow

30. Outside; a straight line from point A to a point clearly outside the curve crosses the curve an even number of times.

31. Euclidean: Given a line and a point not on the line, one and only one line can be drawn parallel to the given line through the given point.

Elliptical: Given a line and a point not on the line, no line can be drawn through the given point parallel to the given line.

Hyperbolic: Given a line and a point not on the line, two or more lines can be drawn through the given point parallel to the given line.

32.

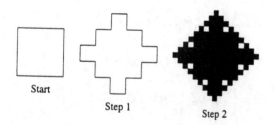

Start

Step 1

Step 2

Chapter Test

1. $\overset{\circ}{\overrightarrow{EF}}$

2. $\triangle$ BCD

3. {D}

4. $\overleftrightarrow{AC}$

5. 90° - 17.4° = 72.6°

6. 180° - 93.6° = 86.4°

7. The other two angles of the triangle are 52° (by vertical angles) and 180° - 115° = 65°. Thus, the measure of angle x = 180° - 52° - 65° = 63°.

8. n = 8

(n - 2)180° = (8 - 2)180° = 6(180°) = 1080°

9. Let $x = B'C'$

$$\frac{B'C'}{BC} = \frac{A'C'}{AC}$$

$$\frac{x}{14} = \frac{10}{26}$$

$$26x = 140$$

$$x = \frac{140}{26} = 5.384615385 \approx 5.38\,cm.$$

10. a) $\quad x^2 + 5^2 = 13^2$

$$x^2 + 25 = 169$$

$$x^2 = 144$$

$$x = \sqrt{144} = 12\,in.$$

b) $\quad p = 5 + 13 + 12 = 30\,in.$

c) $\quad A = \dfrac{1}{2}bh = \dfrac{1}{2}(5)(12) = 30\,in.^2$

11. $\quad r = \dfrac{16}{2} = 8\,cm.$

$$V = \frac{4}{3}\pi r^3 = \frac{4}{3}\pi(8)^3 = 682.\overline{6}\pi$$

$$= 2144.660585 \approx 2144.66\,cm.^3$$

12. $\quad B = 18(28) + \pi(9)^2 = 504 + 81\pi = 758.4690049$

$$V = Bh = 758.4690049(6) = 4550.81403\,ft.^3$$

$$4550.81403\,ft.^3 = \frac{4550.81403}{27}$$

$$= 168.5486678 \approx 168.55\,yd.^3$$

13. $\quad B = lw = 3(9) = 27\,ft.^2$

$$V = \frac{1}{3}Bh = \frac{1}{3}(27)(14) = 126\,ft.^3$$

14. Answers will vary.

15. A **Mobius strip** is a one-sided, one-edged surface.

16. Answers will vary.

Group Projects

1. a) $\quad B = \pi r^2 = \pi\left(\dfrac{12}{2}\right)^2 = 36\pi = 113.0973355$

$$V = Bh = 113.0973355(4) = 452.3893421 \approx 452\,ft.^3$$

b) $452.3893421(7.5) = 3392.920066 \approx 3393\,gal.$

c) $452.3893421(52.4) = 23{,}705.20153 \approx 23{,}705\,lbs.$

d) Weight of Jacuzzi and water: $475 + 23{,}705.20153 = 24{,}180.20153\,lbs.$
    Yes

e) Weight of Jacuzzi, water, and four people: $24{,}180.20153 + 4(115) = 24{,}640.20153\,lbs.$
    Yes

2. **a)** 12 *ft.*

   b) $4\,in. \times 3\,ft.\,6\,in. \times 12\,ft.\,6\,in.$

   c) $V = \dfrac{4}{12}\,ft. \times 3.5\,ft. \times 12.5\,ft. = 14.58\overline{3}\,ft.^3$

   $14.58\overline{3}\,ft.^3 = \dfrac{14.58\overline{3}}{27} = 0.5401234568\,yd.^3$

   d) $0.5401234568(45) = 24.30\overline{5} \approx \$24.31$

   e) 1 sheet

   f) \$18.95

   g) Five 8 *ft.* $2 \times 4's$

   h) $5(\$2.14) = \$10.70$

   i) $B = \dfrac{1}{2}bh = \dfrac{1}{2}(2)(12) = 12\,ft.^2$

   $V = Bh = 12(3) = 36\,ft.^3$

   $36\,ft.^3 = \dfrac{36}{27} = 1.\overline{3}\,yd.^3 \approx 1.33\,yd.^3$

   j) $1.\overline{3}(\$45) = \$60$

   k) $\$24.31 + \$18.95 + \$10.70 + \$60 = \$113.96$

   l) $2^2 + 12^2 = x^2$

   $4 + 144 = x^2$

   $x^2 = 148$

   $x = \sqrt{148} = 12.16552506 \approx 12.17\,ft.$

   m) 8 boards

   n) $8(\$6.47) = \$51.76$

   o) $10(\$2.44) = \$24.40$

   p) $\$24.31 + \$51.76 + \$24.40 = \$100.47$

   q) The materials are less expensive for the wooden ramp.

CHAPTER TEN

MATHEMATICAL SYSTEMS

Exercise Set 10.1

1. A binary operation is an operation that is performed on two elements, and the result is a single element.

2. A set of elements and at least one binary operation.

3. Each of these operations can be performed on only two elements at a time and the result is always a single element.

   a) $2 + 3 = 5$ b) $5 - 3 = 2$ c) $2 \times 3 = 6$ d) $6 \div 3 = 2$

4. Closure, identity, each element must have a unique inverse, associative property.

5. Closure, identity, each element must have a unique inverse, associative property, commutative property.

6. Abelian group

7. If a binary operation is performed on any two elements of a set and the result is an element of the set, then that set is closed under the given binary operation. For all integers a and b, $a + b$ is an integer. Therefore, the set of integers is closed under the operation of addition.

8. An identity element is an element in a set such that when a binary operation is performed on it and any given element in the set, the result is the given element. The additive identity element is 0, and the multiplicative identity element is 1.
   Examples: $5 + 0 = 5$, $5 \times 1 = 5$

9. When a binary operation is performed on two elements in a set and the result is the identity element for the binary operation, then each element is said to be the inverse of the other. The additive inverse of 2 is (-2) since $2 + (-2) = 0$, and the multiplicative inverse of 2 is $(1/2)$ since $2 \times 1/2 = 1$.

10. A specific example illustrating that a specific property is not true is called a counterexample.

11. The associative property of addition states that $(a + b) + c = a + (b + c)$, for any elements a, b, and c.
    Example: $(3 + 4) + 5 = 3 + (4 + 5)$

12. The associative property of multiplication states that $(a \times b) \times c = a \times (b \times c)$, for any real numbers a, b, and c. Example: $(3 \times 4) \times 5 = 3 \times (4 \times 5)$

13. The commutative property of addition stated that $a + b = b + a$, for any elements a, b, and c.
    Example: $3 + 4 = 4 + 3$

14. The commutative property of multiplication stated that $a \times b = b \times a$, for any real numbers a, b, and c.
    Example: $3 \times 4 = 4 \times 3$

15. $7 - 3 = 4$, but $3 - 7 = -4$

16. $8 \div 4 = 2$, but $4 \div 8 = 1/2$

17. $(6 - 3) - 2 = 3 - 2 = 1$, but $6 - (3 - 2) = 6 - 1 = 5$

18. $(16 \div 4) \div 2 = 4 \div 2, = 2$ but $16 \div (4 \div 2) = 16 \div 2 = 8$

19. No; no identity element. $3 + \underline{?} = 3$, where ? must be a positive number.

20. No; not all elements have an inverse. $4 \times \underline{?} = 1$, where ? must be an integer.

21. Yes. Closure: The sum of any two rational numbers is a rational number.
    Identity element is zero.
    Example: $5 + 0 = 0 + 5 = 5$
    Associative property holds:
    Example: $(2 + 3) + 4 = 2 + (3 + 4)$

    Each element has a unique inverse.
    Example: $6 + (-6) = 0$
    Commutative property holds:
    Example: $3 + 8 = 8 + 3$

22. No; the system is not closed, $2 - 5 = -3$ is not a positive integer.
23. No; subtraction is not associative, $(6 - 3) - 2 = 3 - 2 = 1$, but $6 - (3 - 2) = 6 - 1 = 5$.
24. Square root, absolute value. Each of these operations is performed on only one element. A binary operation (such as addition) requires two elements.
25. No; the system is not closed, $\pi + (-\pi) = 0$ which is not an irrational number.
26. No; $\pi \times (1/\pi) = 1$ which is not an irrational number.

27. Yes. Closure: The sum of any two real numbers is a real number.
    The identity element is zero.
    Example: $5 + 0 = 0 + 5 = 5$
    Each element has a unique inverse.
    Example: $6 + (-6) = 0$
    Associative property holds:
    Example: $(2 + 3) + 4 = 2 + (3 + 4)$

28. No. Closure: The product of any two real numbers is a real number.
    The identity element is one.
    Example: $5 \times 1 = 1 \times 5 = 5$
    Not every element has an inverse.
    Example: $0 \times \underline{?} = 1$
    Associative property holds:
    Example: $(2 \times 3) \times 4 = 2 \times (3 \times 4)$

29. Student activity problem.

Exercise Set 10.2

1. The clock addition table is formed by adding all pairs of integers between 1 and 12 using the 12 hour clock to determine the result. Example: If the clock is at 7 and we add 8, then the clock will read 3. Thus $7 + 8 = 3$ in clock arithmetic.
2. $12 + 12 = 12$. Start at 12 move clockwise 12 hours, the result is 12.
3. a) First add $(6 + 9)$ on the clock, then add that result to 5 on the clock to obtain the final answer.
   b) $(6 + 9) + 5 = (3) + 5 = 8$
4. a) Start at the first number on the face of the clock, then count counterclockwise the number being subtracted. The number you end at is the difference.
   b) $5 - 9 = 8$
5. a) First add 12 to 3 to get 15, then subtract $15 - 10$.
   b) $3 - 10 = (12 + 3) - 10 = 15 - 10 = 5$.
   c) Since 12 is the identity element, you can add 12 to any number without changing the answer.
6. The system is commutative if the elements in the table are symmetric about the main diagonal.
7. If a binary operation is performed on any two elements of a set and the result is an element of the set, then that set is closed under the given binary operation. For all integers a and b, $a + b$ is an integer. Therefore, the set of integers is closed under the operation of addition.
8. Yes. 12
9. Yes. One and 11 are inverses, 2 and 10 are inverses, 3 and 9 are inverses, 4 and 8 are inverses, 5 and 7 are inverses, 6 is its own inverse, and 12 is its own inverse.
10. $(2 + 3) + 8 = 2 + (3 + 8)$
    $5 + 8 = 2 + 11$
    $1 = 1$
11. Yes. $6 + 9 = 3$ and $9 + 6 = 3$

12. Yes, the five properties are met.
    1) The system is closed. All results are from the set {1, 2, 3, 4, 5, 6, 7, 8, 9, 10, 11, 12}
    2) The identity element is 12.
    3) Each element has an inverse.
    4) The associative property holds true.
    5) The system is commutative.

13. $3 + 9 = 12$

14. $9 + 5 = 2$

15. $9 + 8 = 5$

16. $10 + 4 = 2$

17. $5 + 12 = 5$

18. $12 + 12 = 12$

19. $2 + (9 + 9) = 2 + 6 = 8$

20. $(8 + 7) + 6 = 3 + 6 = 9$

21. $(6 + 4) + 8 = 10 + 8 = 6$

22. $(10 + 6) + 12 = 4 + 12 = 4$

23. $(7 + 8) + (9 + 6) = 3 + 3 = 6$

24. $(7 + 11) + (9 + 5) = 6 + 2 = 8$

25. $10 - 4 = 6$

26. $12 - 8 = 4$

27. $4 - 7 = 9$

28. $3 - 9 = 6$

29. $5 - 10 = 7$

30. $3 - 10 = 5$

31.

+	1	2	3	4	5	6
1	2	3	4	5	6	1
2	3	4	5	6	1	2
3	4	5	6	1	2	3
4	5	6	1	2	3	4
5	6	1	2	3	4	5
6	1	2	3	4	5	6

32. $5 + 4 = 3$

33. $3 + 4 = 1$

34. $6 + 4 = 4$

35. $5 - 2 = 3$

36. $3 - 5 = 4$

37. $2 - 6 = 2$

38. $3 - 4 = 5$

39. $(4 - 5) - 6 = 5 - 6 = 5$

40. $2 + (1 - 3) = 2 + 4 = 6$

41.

+	1	2	3	4	5	6	7
1	2	3	4	5	6	7	1
2	3	4	5	6	7	1	2
3	4	5	6	7	1	2	3
4	5	6	7	1	2	3	4
5	6	7	1	2	3	4	5
6	7	1	2	3	4	5	6
7	1	2	3	4	5	6	7

42. $3 + 6 = 2$

43. $4 + 5 = 2$

44. $4 + 4 = 1$

45. $7 + 6 = 6$

46. $2 - 6 = 3$

47. $3 - 6 = 4$

48. $2 - 4 = 5$

49. $(3 - 5) - 6 = 5 - 6 = 6$

50. $4 + (2 - 6) = 4 + 3 = 7$

51. Yes. The system is <u>closed</u> since all the elements in the table are from the set {1,2,3,4,5,6,7}.

    The <u>identity</u> element is 7.

    Each element has an <u>inverse</u>. 1 and 6 are inverses, 2 and 5 are inverses, 3 and 4 are inverses and 7 is its own inverse.

    The <u>associative</u> property holds.

    Example: $(1 + 3) + 2 = 1 + (3 + 2)$
    $4 + 2 = 1 + 5$
    $6 = 6$

    The system is <u>commutative</u> since the table is symmetric about the main diagonal.

    Since all 5 properties are satisfied, the system does form a commutative group.

52. No. One reason is that the system may not have an identity. For example, the system shown in the table below does not have an identity element.

*	1	2	3
1	3	2	1
2	2	1	3
3	1	3	2

53. a) {0, 1, 2, 3}   b) ✈
    c) Yes. Whenever the binary operation is performed on any two elements of the set, the result is an element of the set.
    d) Identity element is 0.
    e) Yes; $0 - 0, 1 - 3, 2 - 2, 3 - 1$
    f) $(1 ✈ 2) ✈ 3 = 3 ✈ 3 = 2$
       and $1 ✈ (2 ✈ 3) = 1 ✈ 1 = 2$
    g) Yes; $3 ✈ 2 = 1 = 2 ✈ 3$
    h) Yes, the system satisfies all five properties.

54. a) {15, 19, 23}   b) ⚠
    c) Yes. Whenever the binary operation is performed on any two elements of the set, the result is an element of the set.
    d) Identity element is 23.
    e) Yes; $15 - 19, 19 - 15, 23 - 23$
    f) $(15 ⚠ 19) ⚠ 23 = 23 ⚠ 23 = 23$
       and $15 ⚠ (19 ⚠ 23) = 15 ⚠ 19 = 23$
    g) Yes; $15 ⚠ 19 = 23 = 19 ⚠ 15$
    h) Yes, the system satisfies all five properties.

55. a) {5, 8, 9, 11}   b) ⚘
    c) Yes. Whenever the binary operation is performed on any two elements of the set, the result is an element of the set.
    d) Yes, the identity element is 9.
    e) Yes; $5 - 5, 8 - 11, 9 - 9, 11 - 8$
    f) $(5 ⚘ 8) ⚘ 11 = 11 ⚘ 11 = 5$
       and $5 ⚘ (8 ⚘ 11) = 5 ⚘ 9 = 5$
    g) Yes; $5 ⚘ 8 = 11 = 8 ⚘ 5$
    h) Yes, the system satisfies all five properties.

56. a) {3, 5, 8, 4}   b) ✷
    c) Yes. Whenever the binary operation is performed on any two elements of the set, the result is an element of the set.
    d) Identity element is 4.
    e) Yes. $3 - 8, 5 - 5, 8 - 3, 4 - 4$
    f) $(5 ✷ 8) ✷ 4 = 3 ✷ 4 = 3$
       and $5 ✷ (8 ✷ 4) = 5 ✷ 8 = 3$
    g) Yes. $8 ✷ 5 = 3 = 5 ✷ 8$
    h) Yes, the system satisfies all five properties.

57. a) No, there is no identity element.
    b) $(1 \; w \; 3) \; w \; 4 \neq 1 \; w \; (3 \; w \; 4)$
       $4 \; w \; 4 \neq 1 \; w \; 3$
       $2 \neq 3$

58. a) {f, r, o, m}   b) 🐕
    c) The system is closed. All elements in the table are elements of the set.
    d) $(r \; 🐕 \; o) \; 🐕 \; f = m \; 🐕 \; f = m$
    e) $(f \; 🐕 \; r) \; 🐕 \; m) = r \; 🐕 \; m = f$
    f) Identity element is f.
    g) Inverse of r is m since $m \; 🐕 \; r = f$.
    h) Inverse of m is r since $r \; 🐕 \; m = f$.

59. Not associative: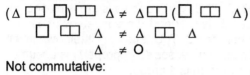

$$(\Delta \square \square) \square \Delta \neq \Delta \square (\square \square \Delta)$$
$$\square \square \Delta \neq \Delta \square \Delta$$
$$\Delta \neq O$$

Not commutative:

$$\square \square \Delta \neq \Delta \square \square$$
$$\Delta \neq \square$$

60. Not closed: $y \wedge x = a$ and $a \notin \{w, x, y\}$
No identity element and therefore no inverses.
Not associative:

$$(x \wedge w) \wedge x \neq x \wedge (w \wedge x)$$
$$y \wedge x \neq x \wedge y$$
$$a \neq w$$

Not commutative: $y \wedge x \neq x \wedge y$
$$a \neq w$$

61. No inverses for ~ and *.
Not associative:

$$(\sim \varnothing L) \varnothing L \neq \sim \varnothing (L \varnothing L)$$
$$* \varnothing L \neq \sim \varnothing P$$
$$\sim \neq *$$

62. Not associative:

$$(a \ \text{☺} \ a) \ \text{☺} \ \Delta \neq a \ \text{☺} \ (a \ \text{☺} \ \Delta)$$
$$\Delta \ \text{☺} \ \Delta \neq a \ \text{☺} \ 0$$
$$\Delta \neq \pi$$

Not commutative:

$$\Delta \ \text{☺} \ \pi \neq \pi \ \text{☺} \ \Delta$$
$$\pi \neq a$$

63. No identity element and therefore no inverses.
Not associative:

$$(d \Leftrightarrow e) \Leftrightarrow d \neq d \Leftrightarrow (e \Leftrightarrow d)$$
$$d \Leftrightarrow d \neq d \Leftrightarrow e$$
$$e \neq d$$

Not commutative:

$$e \Leftrightarrow d \neq d \Leftrightarrow e$$
$$e \neq d$$

64. No inverses for 0, 2, 3, and 4.

65. a)

+	E	O
E	E	O
O	O	E

b) The system is closed, the identity element is E, each element is its own inverse, and the system is commutative since the table is symmetric about the main diagonal. Since the system has fewer than 6 elements satisfying the above properties, it is a commutative group.

66. a)

×	E	O
E	E	E
O	E	O

b) The identity is 0, but since E has no inverse, the system is not a group.

67. Student activity problem.

68. Student activity problem.

Examples of associativity:
$(2 \infty 3) \infty 4 = 5 \infty 4 = 3$ and
$2 \infty (3 \infty 4) = 2 \infty 5 = 3$
$(1 \infty 3) \infty 5 = 4 \infty 5 = 2$ and
$1 \infty (3 \infty 5) = 1 \infty 4 = 2$

69. a) All elements in the table are in the set {1, 2, 3, 4, 5, 6} so the system is closed. The identity is 6. 5 and 1 are inverses of each other, and 2, 3, 4, and 6 are their own inverses. Thus, if the associative property is assumed, the system is a group.

b) $4 \infty 5 = 2$, but $5 \infty 4 = 3$

70. $4^3 = 64$ ways

71. $5^3 = 125$ ways

72. a)

*	R	S	T	U	V	I
R	V	T	U	S	I	R
S	U	I	V	R	T	S
T	S	R	I	V	U	T
U	T	V	R	I	S	U
V	I	U	S	T	R	V
I	R	S	T	U	V	I

Example of associativity:
$(R * S) * V = T * V = U$
$R * (S * V) = R * T = U$

b) All elements in the table are in the set
$\{R, S, T, U, V, I\}$ so the system is closed. The
identity is I. R and V are inverses of each
other, and S, T, U, and I are their own inverses.
Thus, if the associative property is assumed,
the system is a group.

c) The system is not commutative since
$R * S = T$, but $S * R = U$.

Exercise Set 10.3

1. A modulo m system consists of m elements, 0 through m – 1, and a binary operation.

2. a is congruent to b modulo m, written a ≡ b (mod m), means a and b have the same remainder when divided by m.

3. In a modulo 5 system there will be 5 modulo classes. When a number is divided by 5 the remainder will be a number from 0 – 4.

0	1	2	3	4
0	1	2	3	4
5	6	7	8	9
10	11	12	13	14
•	•	•	•	•

4. In any modulo system, modulo classes are developed by placing all numbers with the same remainder in the same modulo class.

5. In a modulo 12 system there will be 12 modulo classes. When a number is divided by 12 the remainder will be a number 0 – 11.

6. In a modulo n system there will be n modulo classes. When a number is divided by n the remainder will be a number from 0 – (n–1).

7. 4 + 20 = 24 and
24 ÷ 7 = 3, remainder 3
day 3 = Wednesday

8. 4 + 161 = 165 and
165 ÷ 7 = 23, remainder 4
day 4 = Thursday

9. 4 + 366 = 370 and
370 ÷ 7 = 52, remainder 6
day 6 = Saturday

10. 5 years = (5 × 365) days = 1825 days
4 + 1825 = 1829 and
1829 ÷ 7 = 261, remainder 2
day 2 = Tuesday

11. 3 years, 34 days = (3 × 365 + 34) days
= 1129 days
4 + 1129 = 1133 and
1133 ÷ 7 = 161, remainder 6
day 6 = Saturday

12. 4 + 463 = 467 and
467 ÷ 7 = 66, remainder 5
day 5 = Friday

Answers to 13-18 will vary depending on the month used as the reference point.

13. 7 ÷ 12 = 0, remainder 7
A remainder of 7 indicates 7 months from now.

14. 36 ÷ 12 = 3, remainder 0
A remainder of 0 indicates 0 months from now.

15. 3 years, 5 months = (3 × 12 + 5) months
= 41 months
41 ÷ 12 = 3, remainder 5
A remainder of 5 indicates 5 months from now.

16. 4 years, 8 months = 56 months
56 ÷ 12 = 4, remainder 8
A remainder of 8 indicates 8 months from now.

17. Eight years from this month it will be this same month again.

18. 83 ÷ 12 = 6, remainder 11
A remainder of 11 indicates 11 months from now.

19. 6 + 6 = 12 and 12 ÷ 5 = 2, remainder 2
Thus 6 + 6 ≡ 2 (mod 5).

20. 5 + 10 = 15 and 15 ÷ 5 = 3, remainder 0
Thus 5 + 10 ≡ 0 (mod 5).

21. $4 + 7 + 12 = 23$ and
    $23 \div 5 = 4$, remainder 3
    Thus $4 + 7 + 12 \equiv 3$ (mod 5).

22. $9 - 3 = 6$ and $6 \div 5 = 1$, remainder 1
    Thus $9 - 3 \equiv 1$ (mod 5).

23. $3 - 9 \equiv (3 + 10) - 9 = 13 - 9 = 4$ and
    $4 \div 5 = 0$, remainder 4
    Thus $3 - 9 \equiv 4$ (mod 5).

24. $7 \times 4 = 28$ and $28 \div 5 = 5$, remainder 3
    Thus $7 \times 4 \equiv 3$ (mod 5).

25. $7 \times 9 = 63$ and
    $63 \div 5 = 12$, remainder 3
    Thus $7 \times 9 \equiv 3$ (mod 5).

26. $10 - 15 = (10+5) - 15 = 0$ and
    $0 \div 5 = 0$, remainder 0
    Thus $10 - 15 \equiv 0$ (mod 5).

27. $4 - 8 \equiv (4 + 5) - 8 = 9 - 8 = 1$
    Thus $4 - 8 \equiv 1$ (mod 5).

28. $3 - 7 \equiv (3 + 5) - 7 = 8 - 7 = 1$
    Thus $3 - 7 \equiv 1$ (mod 5).

29. $(15 \cdot 4) - 8 = 60 - 8 = 52$ and
    $52 \div 5 = 10$, remainder 2
    Thus $(15 \cdot 4) - 8 \equiv 2$ (mod 5).

30. $(4 - 9) \cdot 7 = [(4 + 5) - 9] \cdot 7$
    $= (9 - 9) \cdot 7 = 0 \cdot 6 = 0$ and
    $0 \div 5 = 0$, remainder 0.
    Thus $(4 - 9) \cdot 7 \equiv 0$ (mod 5).

31. $13 \div 4 = 3$, remainder 1
    $13 \equiv 1$ (mod 4)

32. $23 \div 7 = 3$, remainder 2
    $23 \equiv 2$ (mod 7)

33. $84 \div 12 = 7$, remainder 0
    $84 \equiv 0$ (mod 12)

34. $43 \div 6 = 7$, remainder 1
    $43 \equiv 1$ (mod 6)

35. $38 \div 9 = 4$, remainder 2
    $38 \equiv 2$ (mod 9)

36. $75 \div 8 = 9$, remainder 3
    $75 \equiv 3$ (mod 8)

37. $34 \div 7 = 4$, remainder 6
    $34 \equiv 6$ (mod 7)

38. $53 \div 4 = 13$, remainder 1
    $53 \equiv 1$ (mod 4)

39. $-6 \equiv -6 + 7 = 1$
    $-6 \equiv 1$ (mod 7)

40. $-7 \equiv -7 + 2(4) = -7 + 8 = 1$
    $-7 \equiv 1$ (mod 4)

41. $-13 \equiv -13 + 2(11) = -13 + 22 = 9$
    $-13 \equiv 9$ (mod 11)

42. $-11 \equiv -11 + 13 = 2$
    $-11 \equiv 2$ (mod 13)

43. $4 + 4 = 8$
    $8 \div 6 = 1$, remainder 2
    Thus, $4 + 4 \equiv 2$ (mod 6)

44. $? + 9 \equiv 7$ (mod 8)
    $0 + 9 = 9 \equiv 1$ (mod 8)
    $1 + 9 = 10 \equiv 2$ (mod 8)
    $2 + 9 = 11 \equiv 3$ (mod 8)
    $3 + 9 = 12 \equiv 4$ (mod 8)
    $4 + 9 = 13 \equiv 5$ (mod 8)
    $5 + 9 = 14 \equiv 6$ (mod 8)
    $\boxed{6 + 9 = 15 \equiv 7 \text{ (mod 8)}}$
    Thus, to make the statement true, replace ?
    with 6.

45. $3 + ? \equiv 4$ (mod 5)
    $3 + 0 \equiv 3$ (mod 5)
    $\boxed{3 + 1 \equiv 4 \text{ (mod 5)}}$
    Thus, to make the statement true replace ?
    with 1.

46. $4 + ? \equiv 3$ (mod 6)
    $4 + 0 = 4 \equiv 4$ (mod 6)
    $4 + 1 = 5 \equiv 5$ (mod 6)
    $4 + 2 = 6 \equiv 0$ (mod 6)
    $4 + 3 = 7 \equiv 1$ (mod 6)
    $4 + 4 = 8 \equiv 2$ (mod 6)
    $\boxed{4 + 5 = 9 \equiv 3 \text{ (mod 6)}}$
    Thus, to make the statement true replace ?
    with 5.

47. $2 - ? \equiv 5 \pmod 6$
 $2 - 0 \equiv 2 \pmod 6$
 $2 - 1 \equiv 1 \pmod 6$
 $\underline{2 - 2 \equiv 0 \pmod 6}$
 $\boxed{(2+6) - 3 \equiv 5 \pmod 6}$
 Thus, to make the statement true replace ?
 with 3.

48. $4 \cdot 5 = 20$ and $20 \div 7 = 2$, remainder 6
 Thus, the ? is replaced with 6 since
 $4 \cdot 5 = 20 \equiv 6 \pmod 7$.

49. $5 \cdot ? \equiv 7 \pmod 9$
 $5 \cdot 0 = 0 \equiv 0 \pmod 9$
 $5 \cdot 1 = 5 \equiv 5 \pmod 9$
 $5 \cdot 2 = 10 \equiv 1 \pmod 9$
 $5 \cdot 3 = 15 \equiv 6 \pmod 9$
 $5 \cdot 4 = 20 \equiv 2 \pmod 9$
 $\boxed{5 \cdot 5 = 25 \equiv 7 \pmod 9}$
 Thus $5 \cdot 5 \equiv 7 \pmod 9$ and the ?
 is replaced with 5.

50. $3 \cdot ? \equiv 5 \pmod 6$
 $3 \cdot 0 = 0 \equiv 0 \pmod 6$
 $3 \cdot 1 = 3 \equiv 3 \pmod 6$
 $3 \cdot 2 = 6 \equiv 0 \pmod 6$
 $3 \cdot 3 = 9 \equiv 3 \pmod 6$
 $3 \cdot 4 = 12 \equiv 0 \pmod 6$
 $3 \cdot 5 = 15 \equiv 3 \pmod 6$
 None of the numbers 0, 1, 2, 3, 4, 5, make the
 statement true. There is no solution for ?.

51. $2 \cdot ? \equiv 3 \pmod 4$
 $2 \cdot 0 = 0 \equiv 0 \pmod 4$
 $2 \cdot 1 = 2 \equiv 2 \pmod 4$
 $2 \cdot 2 = 4 \equiv 0 \pmod 4$
 $2 \cdot 3 = 6 \equiv 2 \pmod 4$
 None of the numbers 0, 1, 2, or 3 make the
 statement true. Thus, there is no solution for ?.

52. $3 \cdot ? \equiv 3 \pmod{12}$
 $3 \cdot 0 = 0 \equiv 0 \pmod{12}$
 $\boxed{3 \cdot 1 = 3 \equiv 3 \pmod{12}}$
 $3 \cdot 2 = 6 \equiv 6 \pmod{12}$
 $3 \cdot 3 = 9 \equiv 9 \pmod{12}$
 $\underline{3 \cdot 4 = 12 \equiv 0 \pmod{12}}$
 $\boxed{3 \cdot 5 = 15 \equiv 3 \pmod{12}}$
 $3 \cdot 6 = 18 \equiv 6 \pmod{12}$
 $3 \cdot 7 = 21 \equiv 9 \pmod{12}$
 $\underline{3 \cdot 8 = 24 \equiv 0 \pmod{12}}$
 $\boxed{3 \cdot 9 = 27 \equiv 3 \pmod{12}}$
 $3 \cdot 10 = 30 \equiv 6 \pmod{12}$
 $3 \cdot 11 = 33 \equiv 9 \pmod{12}$
 Thus, there are 3 numbers, 1, 5, and 9 that can
 replace ?.

53. $3 \cdot ? \equiv 2 \pmod 8$
 $3 \cdot 0 = 0 \equiv 0 \pmod 8$
 $3 \cdot 1 = 3 \equiv 3 \pmod 8$
 $3 \cdot 2 = 6 \equiv 6 \pmod 8$
 $3 \cdot 3 = 9 \equiv 9 \pmod 8$
 $3 \cdot 4 = 12 \equiv 4 \pmod 8$
 $\underline{3 \cdot 5 = 15 \equiv 7 \pmod 8}$
 $\boxed{3 \cdot 6 = 18 \equiv 2 \pmod 8}$
 $3 \cdot 7 = 21 \equiv 5 \pmod 8$
 Thus, $3 \cdot 6 \equiv 2 \pmod 8$ and so ?
 is replaced with 6.

54. $\quad\quad 4 - 6 \equiv ? \pmod 8$
 $(8 + 4) - 6 \equiv ? \pmod 8$
 $\quad\quad 12 - 6 \equiv ? \pmod 8$
 $\quad\quad\quad\quad 6 \equiv 6 \pmod 8$
 Thus, the ? is replaced with 6.

55. $\quad\quad 5 - 7 \equiv ? \pmod{12}$
 $(12 + 5) - 7 \equiv ? \pmod{12}$
 $\quad\quad 17 - 7 \equiv ? \pmod{12}$
 $\quad\quad\quad 10 \equiv 10 \pmod{12}$
 Thus, the ? is replaced with 10.

56. $\quad\quad 6 - ? \equiv 8 \pmod 9$
 $(9 + 6) - ? \equiv 8 \pmod 9$
 $\quad\quad 15 - ? \equiv 8 \pmod 9$
 $\quad\quad 15 - 7 \equiv 8 \pmod 9$
 Thus, the ? is replaced with 7.

57. a) The next five presidential election years are 2012, 2016, 2020, 2024 and 2028.
    b) Election years are always evenly divisible by 4. Since 3000 is evenly divisible by 4, it is an election year, and the first one following it is 3004.
    c) 2550 ÷ 4 = 637, remainder 2, so the next election year is 2 years after 2550. The election years between 2550 and 2575 are 2552, 2556, 2560, 2564, 2568, 2572.

58. The pilot's schedule is repeated every 8 days. If today, the second day of her shift, is considered day 0, then in mod 8, her activity on any day is given by the following table:

Day (mod 8)	0	1	2	3	4	5	6	7
rest/fly	rest	rest	fly	fly	fly	fly	fly	rest

a) 60 ÷ 8 = 7, remainder 4
    A remainder of 4 indicates she will be flying 60 days from today.

b) 90 ÷ 8 = 11, remainder 2
    A remainder of 2 indicates she will be flying 90 days from today.

c) 240 ÷ 8 = 30, remainder 0
    A remainder of 0 indicates she will be on her rest shift 240 days from today.

d) $-6 \equiv 8 - 6 \equiv 2$ (mod 8) which indicates that she was flying 6 days ago.

e) $-20 \equiv 24 - 20 \equiv 4$ (mod 8) which indicates that she was flying 20 days ago.

59. The manager's schedule is repeated every seven weeks. If this is week two of her schedule then this is her second weekend that she works, or week 1 in a mod 7 system. In mod 7 her schedule on any given weekend is shown in the following table:

Weekend (mod 7):	0	1	2	3	4	5	6
work/off :	work	**work**	work	work	work	work	off

a) If this is weekend 1, then in 5 more weeks (1 + 5 = 6) she will have the weekend off.

b) 25 ÷ 7 = 3, remainder 4. Thus 25 ≡ 4 (mod 7) and 4 weeks from weekend 1 will be weekend 5. She will not have off.

c) 50 ÷ 7 = 7, remainder 1. One week from weekend 1 will be weekend 2. It will be 4 more weeks before she has off. Thus, in 54 weeks she will have the weekend off.

60. a) 6 ≡ 1 (mod 5)
    If this is week 3, then 3 + 1 ≡ 4 (mod 5) indicates the 3 P.M. - 11 P.M. shift.
    b) 7 ≡ 2 (mod 5)
    If this is week 4, then 4 + 2 ≡ 1 (mod 5) indicates the 7 A.M. - 3 P.M. shift.
    c) 11 ≡ 1 (mod 5)
    If this is week 1, then 1 + 1 ≡ 2 (mod 5) indicates the 7 A.M. - 3 P.M. shift.

61. The waiter's schedule in a mod 14 system is given in the following table:

Day:	0	1	2	3	4	5	6	7	8	9	10	11	12	13
shift:	d	d	d	d	d	e	e	d	d	d	d	e	e	

    Note: This is his second day shift which is day 1 in the mod 14 system.
a) 20 ÷ 14 = 1, remainder 6. Six days from day 1 is day 7 which is the evening shift.
b) 52 ÷ 14 = 3, remainder 10. Ten days from day 1 is day 11, which is the day shift.
c) 365 ÷ 14 = 26, remainder 1. One day from day 1 is day 2, which is the day shift.

62. The truck driver's schedule is repeated every 17 days as indicated by the following table:

Days	Activity
0 - 2	N.Y. - Chicago
3	Rest in Chicago
4 - 6	Chicago - L.A.
7 - 8	Rest in L.A.
9 - 13	L.A. - N.Y.
14 - 16	Rest in N.Y.

a) 30 ≡ 13 (mod 17) indicates that he will be driving from L.A. to N.Y.

b) 70 ≡ 2 (mod 17) indicates that he will be driving from N.Y. to Chicago.

c) 2 years = 730 days ≡ 16 (mod 17) indicates that he will be resting in N.Y.

63. a)

+	0	1	2	3
0	0	1	2	3
1	1	2	3	0
2	2	3	0	1
3	3	0	1	2

b) Yes. All the numbers in the table are from the set {0, 1, 2, 3}.

c) The identity element is 0.

d) Yes.

elem.	+	inverse	=	identity
0	+	0	=	0
1	+	3	=	0
2	+	2	=	0
3	+	1	=	0

e) $(1 + 3) + 2 = 1 + (3 + 2)$
    $0 + 2 = 1 + 1$
    $2 = 2$

f) Yes, the table is symmetric about the main diagonal.
   $1 + 3 = 0 = 3 + 1$

g) Yes; all five properties are satisfied.

h) Yes; mod n under addition is a commutative group for all n. The system is closed since all elements in the system are from the set {0, 1, 2, ..., n}. The identity element is 0. The inverse for any number a is $n - a$. Addition is associative and commutative for any mod n system.

64. a)

+	0	1	2	3	4	5	6	7
0	0	1	2	3	4	5	6	7
1	1	2	3	4	5	6	7	0
2	2	3	4	5	6	7	0	1
3	3	4	5	6	7	0	1	2
4	4	5	6	7	0	1	2	3
5	5	6	7	0	1	2	3	4
6	6	7	0	1	2	3	4	5
7	7	0	1	2	3	4	5	6

b) Yes. All the numbers in the table are from the set {0, 1, 2, 3, 4, 5, 6, 7}.

c) The identity element is 0.

d)

elem.	+	inverse	=	identity
0	+	0	=	0
1	+	7	=	0
2	+	6	=	0
3	+	5	=	0
4	+	4	=	0
5	+	3	=	0
6	+	2	=	0
7	+	1	=	0

e) $(1 + 2) + 5 = 1 + (2 + 5)$
    $3 + 5 = 1 + 7$
    $0 = 0$

f) Yes. $2 + 4 = 4 + 2$
    $6 = 6$

g) Yes. All five properties are satisfied.
h) Same answer as problem 63 part h.

65. a)

×	0	1	2	3
0	0	0	0	0
1	0	1	2	3
2	0	2	0	2
3	0	3	2	1

b) Yes. All the elements in the table are from the set {0, 1, 2, 3}.

c) Yes. The identity element is 1.

d)

elem.	×	inverse	=	identity
0	×	none	=	1
1	×	1	=	1
2	×	none	=	1
3	×	3	=	1

Elements 0 and 2 do not have inverses.

e) $(1 × 3) × 0 = 1 × (3 × 0)$
    $3 × 0 = 1 × 0$
    $0 = 0$

f) Yes. $2 × 3 = 3 × 2$
    $2 = 2$

g) No. Not all elements have inverses.

66. a)

×	0	1	2	3	4	5	6
0	0	0	0	0	0	0	0
1	0	1	2	3	4	5	6
2	0	2	4	6	1	3	5
3	0	3	6	2	5	1	4
4	0	4	1	5	2	6	3
5	0	5	3	1	6	4	2
6	0	6	5	4	3	2	1

b) Yes. All the elements in the table are from the set $\{0, 1, 2, 3, 4, 5, 6\}$.

c) Yes. The identity element is 1.

d) No.

elem.	inverse
0	none
1	1
2	4
3	5
4	2
5	3
6	6

The element 0 does not have an inverse.

e) $(1 \times 2) \times 4 = 1 \times (2 \times 4)$
$2 \times 4 = 1 \times 1$
$1 = 1$

f) Yes. $2 \times 3 = 3 \times 2$
$6 = 6$

g) No. 0 does not have an inverse.

For the operation of division in modular systems, we define $n \div d = n \cdot i$ where i is the multiplicative inverse of d.

67. $5 \div 7 \equiv ? \pmod 9$
Since $7 \cdot 4 = 28 \equiv 1 \pmod 9$,
4 is the inverse of 7. Thus
$5 \div 7 \equiv 5 \cdot 4 \equiv 20 \equiv 2 \pmod 9$
Replace ? with 2.

68. $? \div 5 \equiv 5 \pmod 9$
Since $5 \cdot 2 \equiv 10 \equiv 1 \pmod 9$,
2 is the inverse of 5.
$? \div 5 \equiv ? \cdot 2 \equiv 5 \pmod 9$
$0 \cdot 2 = 0 \equiv 0 \pmod 9$
$1 \cdot 2 = 2 \equiv 2 \pmod 9$
$2 \cdot 2 = 4 \equiv 4 \pmod 9$
$3 \cdot 2 = 6 \equiv 6 \pmod 9$
$4 \cdot 2 = 8 \equiv 8 \pmod 9$
$5 \cdot 2 = 10 \equiv 1 \pmod 9$
$6 \cdot 2 = 12 \equiv 3 \pmod 9$
$7 \cdot 2 = 14 \equiv 5 \pmod 9$
$8 \cdot 2 = 16 \equiv 7 \pmod 9$
Replace ? with 7.

69. $? \div ? \equiv 1 \pmod 4$
$0 \div 0$ is undefined.
$1 \div 1 \equiv 1 \pmod 4$
$2 \div 2 \equiv 1 \pmod 4$
$3 \div 3 \equiv 1 \pmod 4$
Replace ? with 1, 2, or 3.

70. $1 \div 2 \equiv ? \pmod 5$
Since $2 \cdot 3 \equiv 6 \equiv 1 \pmod 5$
3 is the inverse of 2. Thus
$1 \div 2 \equiv 1 \cdot 3 \equiv 3 \pmod 5$
Replace ? with 3.

71. $5k \equiv x \pmod 5$

$$\begin{array}{r} K \\ 5 \overline{\smash{\big)}\ 5K} \\ \underline{5K} \\ 0 \end{array}$$

$5k \equiv 0 \pmod 5$

$x = 0$

72. $5k + 4 \equiv x \pmod 5$

$$\begin{array}{r} K \\ 5 \overline{\smash{\big)}\ 5K + 4} \\ \underline{5K} \\ 4 \end{array}$$

$5k + 4 \equiv 4 \pmod 5$

$x = 4$

73. $4k - 2 \equiv x \pmod 4$

$$\begin{array}{r} K - 1 \\ 4 \overline{\smash{\big)}\ 4K - 2} \\ \underline{4K - 4} \\ 2 \end{array}$$

$4k - 2 \equiv 2 \pmod 4$

$x = 2$

74. Check the numbers divisible by 5 until you find one that is also congruent to 2 in modulo 6. $20 \equiv 2 \pmod 6$ and 20 is also divisible by 5.

75. If 10 is subtracted from each number on the wheel,

```
23  11  3  18  10  19  2  10  16  4  24   becomes
13   1  20  8   0   9  19  0   6  21  14   which is equivalent to
 M   A   T  H       I   S      F   U   N
```

Review Exercises

1. A set of elements and at least one binary operation.
2. A binary operation is an operation that can be preformed on two and only two elements of a set. The result is a single element.
3. Yes. The sum of any two integers is always an integer.
4. No. Example: $2 - 3 = -1$, but -1 is not a natural number.
5. $5 + 10 = 3$
6. $5 + 12 = 5$
7. $6 - 10 = 8$
8. $(6 + 7) + 9 = 1 + 9 = 10$
9. $(7 - 4) + 6 = 3 + 6 = 9$
10. $(2 - 8) - 7 = 6 - 7 = 11$

11. a) The system is closed. If the binary operation is $*$, then for any elements a and b in the set, $a * b$ is a member of the set.
   b) There exists an identity element in the set. For any element a in the set, if $a * i = i * a = a$, then i is called the identity element.
   c) Every element in the set has a unique inverse. For any element a in the set, there exists an element b such that $a * b = b * a = i$. Then b is the inverse of a, and a is the inverse of b.
   d) The set is associative under the operation $*$. For any elements a, b, and c in the set, $(a * b) * c = a * (b * c)$.

12. An Abelian group is a group in which the operation has the commutative property.

13. Yes. Closure: The sum of any two integers is an integer. Identity element is zero. Example: $5 + 0 = 0 + 5 = 5$

   Associative property holds: Example: $(2 + 3) + 4 = 2 + (3 + 4)$ Each element has a unique inverse. Example: $6 + (-6) = 0$

14. The set of integers with the operation of multiplication does not form a group since not all elements have an inverse. $4 \times \underline{?} = 1$

15. Yes. Closure: The sum of any two rationals is a rational number.
    Identity element is zero.
       Example: $5 + 0 = 0 + 5 = 5$

    Associative property holds:
       Example: $(2 + 3) + 4 = 2 + (3 + 4)$
    Each element has a unique inverse.
       Example: $6 + (-6) = 0$

16. The set of rational numbers with the operation of multiplication does not form a group since zero does not have an inverse. $0 \times \underline{?} = 1$

17. There is no identity element. Therefore the system does not form a group.

18. The associative property does not hold.
    Example: $(! \smile p) \smile ? \neq ! \smile (p \smile ?)$
    $$p \smile ? \neq ! \smile !$$
    $$! \neq ?$$

19. Not every element has an inverse.
    P does not have an inverse.
    Not associative:
    $(4 ? 4) ? P \neq 4 ? (4 ? P)$
    $$P ? P \neq 4 ? L$$
    $$L \neq \#$$
    Therefore the system does not form a group.

20. a) $\{ \vdash, \odot, ?, \Delta \}$
    c) Yes. All the elements in the table are from the set $\{ \vdash, \odot, ?, \Delta \}$.
    e) Yes.

elem.	inverse	=	identity
$\vdash$	$\vdash$	=	$\vdash$
$\odot$	Δ	=	$\vdash$
$?$	$?$	=	$\vdash$
Δ	$\odot$	=	$\vdash$

    b) ♫
    d) The identity element is $\vdash$.
    f) $(\vdash \text{♫} ?) \text{♫} \Delta = \vdash \text{♫} (? \text{♫} \Delta)$
    $$? \text{♫} \Delta = \vdash \text{♫} \odot$$
    $$\odot = \odot$$

    g) Yes. $\Delta \text{♫} ? = ? \text{♫} \Delta$
    $$\odot = \odot$$
    h) Yes, all five properties are satisfied.

21. $15 \div 4 = 3$, remainder 3
    $15 \equiv 3 \pmod 4$

22. $31 \div 8 = 3$, remainder 7
    $31 \equiv 7 \pmod 8$

23. $27 \div 7 = 3$, remainder 6
    $27 \equiv 6 \pmod 7$

24. $59 \div 8 = 7$, remainder 3
    $59 \equiv 3 \pmod 8$

25. $82 \div 13 = 6$, remainder 4
    $82 \equiv 4 \pmod{13}$

26. $54 \div 4 = 13$, remainder 2
    $54 \equiv 2 \pmod 4$

27. $37 \div 6 = 6$, remainder 1
    $37 \equiv 1 \pmod 6$

28. $54 \div 14 = 3$, remainder 12
    $54 \equiv 12 \pmod{14}$

29. $97 \div 11 = 8$, remainder 9
$97 \equiv 9 \pmod{11}$

30. $42 \div 11 = 3$, remainder 9
$42 \equiv 9 \pmod{11}$

31. $8 + 8 = 16 \equiv 7 \pmod 9$
Thus, replace ? with 7.

32. $? - 3 \equiv 0 \pmod 5$
$0 - 3 \equiv 2 \pmod 5$
$1 - 3 \equiv 3 \pmod 5$
$2 - 3 \equiv 4 \pmod 5$
$\boxed{3 - 3 \equiv 0 \pmod 5}$
Replace ? with 3.

33. $4 \cdot ? \equiv 3 \pmod 6$
$4 \cdot 0 \equiv 0 \pmod 6$
$4 \cdot 1 \equiv 4 \pmod 6$
$4 \cdot 2 = 8 \equiv 2 \pmod 6$
$4 \cdot 3 = 12 \equiv 0 \pmod 6$
$4 \cdot 4 = 16 \equiv 4 \pmod 6$
$4 \cdot 5 = 20 \equiv 2 \pmod 6$
There is no solution. $? = \{\ \}$

34. $3 - ? \equiv 5 \pmod 7$
$3 - 0 \equiv 3 \pmod 7$
$3 - 1 \equiv 2 \pmod 7$
$3 - 2 \equiv 1 \pmod 7$
$3 - 3 \equiv 0 \pmod 7$
$3 - 4 \equiv (3+7) - 4 = 6 \equiv 6 \pmod 7$
$\boxed{3 - 5 \equiv (3+7) - 5 = 5 \equiv 5 \pmod 7}$
Replace ? with 5.

35. $? \cdot 4 \equiv 0 \pmod 8$
$\boxed{0 \cdot 4 \equiv 0 \pmod 8}$
$1 \cdot 4 \equiv 4 \pmod 8$
$\boxed{2 \cdot 4 \equiv 8 \equiv 0 \pmod 8}$
$3 \cdot 4 \equiv 12 \equiv 4 \pmod 8$
$\boxed{4 \cdot 4 \equiv 16 \equiv 0 \pmod 8}$
$5 \cdot 4 \equiv 20 \equiv 4 \pmod 8$
$\boxed{6 \cdot 4 \equiv 24 \equiv 0 \pmod 8}$
$7 \cdot 4 \equiv 28 \equiv 4 \pmod 8$
Replace ? with 0, 2, 4, or 6.

36. $9 \cdot 7 \equiv ? \pmod{12}$
$9 \cdot 7 = 63;$ $63 \div 12 = 5$, remainder 3
Thus, $9 \cdot 7 \equiv 3 \pmod{12}$
Replace ? with 3.

37. $3 - 5 \equiv ? \pmod 7$
$3 - 5 = (3+7) - 5 = 5 \equiv 5 \pmod 7$
Replace ? with 5.

38. $? \cdot 7 \equiv 3 \pmod 6$
$0 \cdot 7 \equiv 0 \pmod 6$
$1 \cdot 7 \equiv 1 \pmod 6$
$2 \cdot 7 \equiv 14 \equiv 2 \pmod 6$
$\boxed{3 \cdot 7 \equiv 21 \equiv 3 \pmod 6}$
Replace ? with 3.

39. $5 \cdot ? \equiv 3 \pmod 8$
    $5 \cdot 0 \equiv 0 \pmod 8$
    $5 \cdot 1 \equiv 5 \pmod 8$
    $5 \cdot 2 \equiv 10 \equiv 2 \pmod 8$
    $5 \cdot 3 \equiv 15 \equiv 7 \pmod 8$
    $5 \cdot 4 \equiv 20 \equiv 4 \pmod 8$
    $5 \cdot 5 \equiv 25 \equiv 1 \pmod 8$
    $5 \cdot 6 \equiv 30 \equiv 6 \pmod 8$
    $\boxed{5 \cdot 7 \equiv 35 \equiv 3 \pmod 8}$
 Replace ? with 7.

40. $7 \cdot ? \equiv 2 \pmod 9$
    $7 \cdot 0 \equiv 0 \pmod 9$
    $7 \cdot 1 \equiv 7 \pmod 9$
    $7 \cdot 2 \equiv 14 \equiv 5 \pmod 9$
    $7 \cdot 3 \equiv 21 \equiv 3 \pmod 9$
    $7 \cdot 4 \equiv 28 \equiv 1 \pmod 9$
    $7 \cdot 5 \equiv 35 \equiv 7 \pmod 9$
    $7 \cdot 6 \equiv 42 \equiv 6 \pmod 9$
    $7 \cdot 7 \equiv 49 \equiv 4 \pmod 9$
    $\boxed{7 \cdot 8 \equiv 56 \equiv 2 \pmod 9}$
 Replace ? with 8.

41.

+	0	1	2	3	4	5
0	0	1	2	3	4	5
1	1	2	3	4	5	0
2	2	3	4	5	0	1
3	3	4	5	0	1	2
4	4	5	0	1	2	3
5	5	0	1	2	3	4

Since all the numbers in the table are elements of {0, 1, 2, 3, 4, 5}, the system has the closure property. The commutative property holds since the elements are symmetric about the main diagonal. The identity element is 0 and the inverses of each element are
    $0 - 0, \; 1 - 5, \; 2 - 4, \; 3 - 3, \; 4 - 2, \; 5 - 1$
If it is assumed the associative property holds as illustrated by the example: $(2 + 3) + 5 = 4 = 2 + (3 + 5)$, then the system is a commutative group.

42.

×	0	1	2	3
0	0	0	0	0
1	0	1	2	3
2	0	2	0	2
3	0	3	2	1

The identity element for the system is 1, but since 0 and 2 do not have inverses, the system does not form a group.

43.

Day (mod 10):	0	1	2	3	4	5	6	7	8	9
Work/off :	w	w	w	o	o	w	w	o	o	o

 a) If today is the first day of her work pattern, day 0, then $18 \equiv 8 \pmod{10}$ indicates Toni will not be working in 18 days.
 b) $38 \equiv 8 \pmod{10}$ indicates that Toni will have the evening off in 38 days.

Chapter Test

1. A mathematical system consists of a set of elements and at least one binary operation.
2. Closure, identity element, inverses, associative property, and commutative property.
3. No, the numbers greater than 0 do not have inverses.

4.

+	1	2	3	4	5
1	2	3	4	5	1
2	3	4	5	1	2
3	4	5	1	2	3
4	5	1	2	3	4
5	1	2	3	4	5

5. Yes. It is closed since the only elements in the table are from the set {1, 2, 3, 4, 5}. The identity element is 5. The inverses are 1 − 4, 2 − 3, 3 − 2, 4 − 1, and 5 − 5. The system is associative. The system is commutative since the table is symmetric about the main diagonal. Thus, all five properties are satisfied.

6. $4 + 3 + 2 = 2 + 2 = 4$

7. $6 − 18 = (15 + 6) − 18 = 21 − 18 = 3$

8. a) The binary operation is □
    b) Yes. All elements in the table are from the set {W, S, T, R}.
    c) The identity element is T, since $T \square x = x = x \square T$, where x is any member of the set {W, S, T, R}.
    d) The inverse of R is S, since $R \square S = T$
    e) $(T \square R) \square W = R \square W = S$

9. The system is not a group. It does not have the closure property since $c * c = d$, and d is not a member of {a, b, c}.

10. Since all the numbers in the table are elements of {1, 2, 3}, the system is closed. The commutative property holds since the elements are symmetric about the main diagonal. The identity element is 2 and the inverses are 1 − 3, 2 − 2, 3 − 1. If it is assumed the associative property holds as illustrated by the example:

    $(1 ? 2) ? 1 = 2 = 1 ? (2 ? 3)$, then the system is a commutative group.

11. Since all the numbers in the table are elements of {@, $, &, %}, the system is closed. The commutative property holds since the elements are symmetric about the main diagonal. The identity element is $ and the inverses are @ − &, $ − $, & − @, % − %. It is assumed the associative property holds as illustrated by the example: $(@ O \$) O \% = \& = @ O (\$ O \%)$, then the system is a commutative group.

12. $73 \div 9 = 8$, remainder 1
    $73 \equiv 1 \pmod 9$

13. $58 \div 11 = 5$, remainder 3
    $58 \equiv 3 \pmod{11}$

14. $6 + 9 = 15$ and $15 \div 7 = 2$, remainder 1
    $6 + 9 \equiv 1 \pmod 7$

15. $? − 9 \equiv 4 \pmod 5$
    $? − 9 \equiv ? − 9 + 10 \equiv ? + 1 \equiv 4 \pmod 5$
    $3 + 1 \equiv 4 \pmod 5$
    Replace ? with 3.

16. $3 − ? \equiv 7 \pmod 9$
    $3 − ? \equiv 3 + 9 − ? \equiv 12 − ? \equiv 7 \pmod 9$
    $12 − 5 \equiv 7 \pmod 9$
    Replace ? with 5.

17. $4 \cdot 2 = 8$ and $8 \div 6 = 1$, remainder 2
    $4 \cdot 2 \equiv 2 \pmod 6$
    Replace ? with 2.

18. $3 \cdot ? \equiv 2 \pmod 6$
    $3 \cdot 0 \equiv 0 \pmod 6$
    $3 \cdot 1 \equiv 3 \pmod 6$
    $3 \cdot 2 \equiv 0 \pmod 6$
    $3 \cdot 3 \equiv 3 \pmod 6$
    $3 \cdot 4 \equiv 0 \pmod 6$
    $3 \cdot 5 \equiv 3 \pmod 6$
    There is no solution for ?
    The answer is { }.

19. $96 \div 7 = 13$, remainder 5
    $96 \equiv 5 \pmod 7$
    Replace ? with 5.

20. a)

×	0	1	2	3	4
0	0	0	0	0	0
1	0	1	2	3	4
2	0	2	4	1	3
3	0	3	1	4	2
4	0	4	3	2	1

b) The system is closed. The identity is 1.
However, 0 does not have an inverse, so
the system is <u>not</u> a group.

Group Projects

1. a) The first three are:

×	0	1	2
0	0	0	0
1	0	1	2
2	0	2	1

×	0	1	2	3
0	0	0	0	0
1	0	1	2	3
2	0	2	0	2
3	0	3	1	2

×	0	1	2	3	4
0	0	0	0	0	0
1	0	1	2	3	4
2	0	2	4	1	3
3	0	3	1	4	2
4	0	4	3	2	1

   b) Modulo 4, modulo 6, and modulo 8
   c) Modulo 3, modulo 5, and modulo 7
   d) If the modulo system is even then the modulo system will have a product of 0 when neither factor is 0.

2. a) Yes, see Group Project exercise 1a.
   b) In the odd modulo system all non zero numbers have multiplicative inverses.
   c) In the even modulo system not all non zero numbers have multiplicative inverses.
   d) If the modulo system is odd, then the modulo system will contain multiplicative inverses for all non zero numbers.

3.

♣	A	B	C	D
A	B	C	D	A
B	C	D	A	B
C	D	A	B	C
D	A	B	C	D

This system forms a commutative group.

CHAPTER ELEVEN

CONSUMER MATHEMATICS

Exercise Set 11.1

1. A percent is a ratio of some number to 100.

2. (i) Divide the number by the denominator.
   (ii) Multiply the quotient by 100 (which has the effect of moving the decimal point two places to the right).
   (iii) Add a percent sign.

3. Multiply the decimal number by 100 and add a percent sign.

4. (i) Divide the number by 100.
   (ii) Remove the percent sign.

5. Percent change = $\dfrac{(\text{Amount in latest period}) - (\text{Amount in previous period})}{\text{Amount in previous period}} \times 100$

6. Percent markup on cost = $\dfrac{\text{Selling Price} - \text{Dealer's Cost}}{\text{Dealer's Cost}} \times 100$

7. $\dfrac{3}{8} = 0.375 = (0.375 \times 100)\% = 37.5\%$

8. $\dfrac{3}{4} = 0.75 = (0.75 \times 100)\% = 75\%$

9. $\dfrac{5}{8} = 0.625 = (0.625 \times 100)\% = 62.5\%$

10. $\dfrac{7}{8} = 0.875 = (0.875 \times 100)\% = 87.5\%$

11. $0.007654 = (0.007654 \times 100)\% = 0.8\%$

12. $0.5688 = (0.5688 \times 100)\% = 56.9\%$

13. $3.78 = (3.78 \times 100)\% = 378\%$

14. $13.678 = (13.678 \times 100)\% = 1367.8\%$

15. $12\% = \dfrac{12}{100} = 0.12$

16. $25.9\% = \dfrac{25.9}{100} = 0.259$

17. $3.75\% = \dfrac{3.75}{100} = 0.0375$

18. $0.0005\% = \dfrac{0.0005}{100} = 0.000005$

19. $\dfrac{1}{4}\% = 0.25\% = \dfrac{0.25}{100} = 0.0025$

20. $\dfrac{3}{8}\% = 0.375\% = \dfrac{0.375}{100} = 0.00375$

21. $\dfrac{1}{5}\% = 0.2\% = \dfrac{0.2}{100} = 0.002$

22. $135.9\% = \dfrac{135.9}{100} = 1.359$

23. $1\% = \dfrac{1}{100} = 0.01$

24. $0.50\% = \dfrac{0.50}{100} = 0.005$

25. $\dfrac{830}{5820} \approx 0.1426 = (0.1426 \times 100)\%$

    $= 14.3\%$ for food

26. $\dfrac{370 \text{ million}}{1.5 \text{ billion}} = \dfrac{370}{1500} \approx 0.247 = (0.247 \times 100)\%$

    $= 24.7\%$ for crest

27. 36% of 693,905 is what number?
    $0.36(693905) = 249,805.8 \approx 249,806$ miles

28. 18.6% of 10,398,000 is what number?
    $0.186(10398000) = 1,934,028$ children

29. 41.4% of $43,281.7 million is what amount?
    $0.414(43281.7) \approx \$17,918.6$ million loss

30. 35.1% of $43,281.7 million is what amount?
    $0.351(43281.7) \approx \$15,191.9$ million loss

31. 10.7% of 148,847,000 is what number?
    $0.107(148847000) = 15,926,629$ A-A workers

32. 11.7% of 148,847,000 is what number?
    $0.117(148847000) = 17,415,099$ Hispanic workers

33. x% of 7534 = 2227
    $0.01x(7534) = 2227$
    $75.34x = 2227$

    $x = \dfrac{2227}{75.34} \approx 29.6\%$

34. x% of 7534 = 1703
    $0.01x(7534) = 1703$
    $75.34x = 1703$

    $x = \dfrac{1703}{75.34} \approx 22.6\%$

35. x% of 13815 = 2491
    $0.01x(13815) = 2491$
    $138.15x = 2491$

    $x = \dfrac{2491}{138.15} \approx 18.0\%$

36. x% of 13815 = 1784
    $0.01x(13815) = 1784$
    $138.15x = 1784$

    $x = \dfrac{1784}{138.15} \approx 12.9\%$

37. a) Percent increase from 1990 to 1998

    $= \dfrac{1998pop. - 1990pop.}{1990pop.} \times 100$

    $= \dfrac{270.3 - 248.7}{248.7} \times 100$

    $= \dfrac{21.6}{248.7} \times 100 = 0.087 \times 100 = 8.7\%$

    b) $270.3 + 0.087(270.3) = 270.3 + 23.5$
        $= 293.8$ million people

38. Percent change from 1996 to 1997 is

    $\dfrac{5.7 - 6.6}{6.6} \times 100 = \dfrac{-0.9}{6.6} \times 100 = -13.6\%$

    or a 13.6% decrease

39. a) percent change $= \dfrac{34467 - 31583}{31583} \times 100$

    $= 0.091 \times 100 = 9.1\%$ increase

    b) percent change $= \dfrac{36820 - 34467}{34467} \times 100$

    $= 0.068 \times 100 = 6.8\%$ increase

    c) percent change $= \dfrac{37005 - 36820}{36820} \times 100$

    $= 0.005 \times 100 = 0.5\%$ increase

    d) percent change $= \dfrac{37005 - 31583}{31583} \times 100$

    $= 0.172 \times 100 = 17.2\%$ increase

40. a) percent change $= \dfrac{7156 - 7123}{7123} \times 100$

    $= 0.005 \times 100 = 0.5\%$ increase

    b) percent change $= \dfrac{6841 - 7156}{7156} \times 100$

    $= -0.044 \times 100 = 4.4\%$ decrease

    c) percent change $= \dfrac{6201 - 6841}{6841} \times 100$

    $= -0.094 \times 100 = 9.4\%$ decrease

    d) percent change $= \dfrac{6201 - 7123}{7123} \times 100$

    $= -0.129 \times 100 = 12.9\%$ decrease

41. a)   increase from 1966 to 1976 is

$$\frac{23.8 - 22.8}{22.8} \times 100 = 4.4\%$$

increase from 1976 to 1986 is

$$\frac{25.7 - 23.8}{23.8} \times 100 = 8.0\%$$

increase from 1986 to 1996 is

$$\frac{27.1 - 25.7}{25.7} \times 100 = 5.4\%$$

Thus, the largest percent increase took place from 1976 to 1986.

b)   increase from 1966 to 1976 is

$$\frac{21.3 - 20.5}{20.5} \times 100 = 3.9\%$$

increase from 1976 to 1986 is

$$\frac{23.1 - 21.3}{21.3} \times 100 = 8.5\%$$

increase from 1986 to 1996 is

$$\frac{24.8 - 23.1}{23.1} \times 100 = 7.4\%$$

The largest percent increase took place from 1976 to 1986.

42. a)   percent change $= \dfrac{3105 - 1528}{1528} \times 100$

= 103.2% increase

b)   percent change $= \dfrac{5761 - 3105}{3105} \times 100$

= 85.5% increase

c)   percent change $= \dfrac{6778 - 1528}{1528} \times 100$

= 343.6% increase

43. $0.18(x) = 54$

$x = \dfrac{54}{0.18}$

$x = 300$

Fifty-four is 18% of 300.

44. $(0.01x)75 = 15$

$0.75x = 15$

$x = \dfrac{15}{0.75} = 20$

20% of 75 is 15.

45. $0.07(9) = x$

$0.63 = x$

0.63 is 7% of 9.

46. $1.34(400) = x$

$536 = x$

134% of 400 is 536.

47. $(0.01x)(346) = 86.5$

$3.46x = 86.5$

$x = \dfrac{86.5}{3.46}$

$x = 25$

Twenty-five percent of 346 is 86.5.

48. $0.20(x) = 11$

$x = \dfrac{11}{0.20}$

$x = 55$

Eleven is 20% of 55.

49. a)   tax = 6% of $43.50 = 0.06(43.50) = $2.61
    b)   total bill before tip= $43.50 + $2.61 = $46.11
    c)   tip = 15% of 46.11 = 0.15(46.11) = $6.92
    d)   total cost = 46.11 + 6.92 = $53.03

50.   25% of what number is 10?

$0.25x = 10$

$x = \dfrac{10}{0.25} = 40$,   original number of crew is 40.

51. $1.50(x) = 18$

$x = \dfrac{18}{1.50}$

$x = 12$

12 students got an A on the 2nd test.

52. $0.30(x) = 57$

$x = \dfrac{57}{0.30}$

$x = 190$

The original no. of employees was 190.

53. Mr. Browns' increase was
0.07(36,500) = $2,555
His new salary = $36,500 + $2,555 = $39,055

54. 0.17(300) = x
51 = x
51 prefer Ranch.

55. Percent change = $\frac{407430}{430} \times 100$

$= \frac{23}{430} \times 100 = -5.3\%$

There was a 5.3% decrease in the number of units sold.

56. Percent markup = $\frac{699320}{320} \times 100$

$= \frac{379}{320} \times 100 = 118.4\%$

57. percent change = $\frac{35.6 - 39.3}{39.3} \times 100 = -9.4\%$, or a 9.4% decrease

58. Percent increase in great grandchildren
$= \frac{12 - 8}{8} \times 100 = 0.50 \times 100 = 50\%$ increase

59. Percent decrease from regular price
$= \frac{\$439539.62}{539.62} \times 100$

$= -0.1864 \times 100 = -18.6\%$

The sale price is 18.6% lower than the regular price.

60. Percent markup = $\frac{\$11.95 - \$7.95}{\$7.95} \times 100$

$= 0.5031 \times 100 = 50.3\%$

61. 0.18(sale price) = $675

sale price = $\frac{\$675}{0.18} = \$3,750$

62. No, 15% of $115 is 0.15($115) = $17.25
The sale price should be
$115 − $17.25 = $97.75 not $100

63. $1000 increased by 10% is $1000 + 0.10($1000) = $1000 + $100 = $1,100.
$1,100 decreased by 10% is $1,100 − 0.10($1,100) = $1,100 − $110 = $990.
Therefore if he sells the car at the reduced price he will lose $10.

64. a) No, the 25% discount is greater. (see part b)
b) 189.99 − 0.10(189.99) = 189.99 − 19.00 = 170.99
170.99 − 0.15(170.99) = 170.99 − 25.65 = $145.34
c) 189.99 − 0.25(189.99) = 189.99 − 47.50 = $142.49
d) Yes

65. Total profit must = 0.40($5901.79) = $2,360.72
Total revenue must = $5901.79 + $2360.72 = $8,262.51
Revenue from first sale = 100 × $9.00 = $900
Revenue from second sale = 150 × $12.50 = $1,875.00
Total Revenue = Rev. from 1st sale + Rev. from 2nd sale + Rev. from final sale
$8262.51 = $900 + $1875 + 250 × (final price)
$5487.51 = 250 × (final price)

$\frac{\$5487.51}{250}$ = final price;   final price = $21.95

Exercise Set 11.2

1. Interest is the money the borrower pays for the use of the lender's money.
2. The amount of money that a bank is willing to lend to a person is called credit.
3. Security is anything of value pledged by the borrower that the lender may sell or keep if the borrower does not repay the loan.
4. A cosigner is a person, other than the person who received the loan, who guarantees that a loan will be repaid.
5. A personal note is an agreement that states the conditions of the loan.
6. i = interest, p = principal, r = interest rate, t = time
   The rate and time must be expressed for the same period of time, i.e. days, months or years.
7. The United States Rule states that if a partial payment is made on a loan, interest is computed on the principal from the first day of the loan (or previous partial payment) up to the date of the partial payment. For each partial payment, the partial payment is used to pay the interest first, then the remainder of the payment is applied to the principle. On the due date of the loan the interest is calculated from the date of the last partial payment.
8. The difference between ordinary interest and interest calculated using the Banker's rule is the way in which time is used in the simple interest formula. Ordinary interest: a month is 30 days and year is 360 days. Banker's rule: any fractional part of a year is the exact number of days, and a year is 360 days.

9. $i = prt = \$420 \times 0.09 \times 3 = \$113.40$

10. $i = \$520 \times 0.065 \times 4 = \$135.20$

11. $i = prt = \$875 \times 0.12 \times \dfrac{30}{360} = \$8.75$

12. $i = \$365.45 \times 0.115 \times \dfrac{8}{12} = \$28.02$

13. $i = prt = \$587 \times 0.00045 \times 60 = \$15.85$

14. $i = \$6,742.75 \times 0.0605 \times \dfrac{90}{360} = \$101.98$

15. $i = \$2,756.78 \times 0.1015 \times \dfrac{103}{360} = \$80.06$

16. $i = \$550.31 \times 0.089 \times \dfrac{67}{360} = \$9.12$

17. $i = \$12,752 \times 0.015 \times 9 = \$1,721.52$

18. $i = \$12,752 \times 0.00055 \times 120 = \$841.63$

19.
$$22.75 = 1300 \times r \times \dfrac{157}{360}$$
$$22.75 = 566.94 \times r$$
$$\dfrac{22.75}{566.94} = r$$
$$r = 0.04 \text{ or } 4\%$$

20.
$$6.00 = p \times 0.06 \times \dfrac{60}{360}$$
$$6.00 = p \times 0.01$$
$$\dfrac{6.00}{0.01} = p$$
$$p = \$600$$

21.
$$12.00 = p \times 0.08 \times \dfrac{3}{12}$$
$$12.00 = p \times 0.02$$
$$\dfrac{12.00}{0.02} = r$$
$$p = \$600$$

22.
$$64.00 = 800 \times 0.06 \times t$$
$$64.00 = 48t$$
$$\dfrac{64.00}{48} = t$$
$$t = 1.\overline{33} \text{ years or 1 yr. 4 months}$$

23.
$$124.49 = 957.62 \times 0.065 \times t$$
$$124.49 = 62.2453t$$
$$\dfrac{124.49}{62.2453} = t$$
$$t = 2 \text{ years}$$

24.
$$343.20 = 1650.00 \times r \times 6.5$$
$$343.20 = 10725r$$
$$\dfrac{343.20}{10725} = r$$
$$r = 0.032 \text{ or } 3.2\% \text{ per year}$$

25. rate: r = 5.08% + 1% = 6.08%

   $i = prt = 2000 \times 0.0608 \times \dfrac{9}{12} = \$91.20$

   amt. due: A = p + i = 2000 + 91.20 = \$2091.20

26. a) i = prt

   $i = 1500 \times 0.065 \times \dfrac{60}{360} = \$16.25$

   b) A = p + i
   A = 1500 + 16.25 = \$1,516.25

27. a) i = prt

   $i = 3500 \times 0.075 \times \dfrac{6}{12}$

   = \$131.25

   b) A = p + i
   A = 3500 + 131.25
   = \$3,631.25

28. a) i = prt

   $= 2500 \times 0.08 \times \dfrac{5}{12}$

   = \$83.33

   b) \$2500.00 − 83.33 = \$2416.67

   c) i = prt

   $83.33 = 2416.67 \times r \times \dfrac{5}{12}$

   83.33 = 1006.95r

   $\dfrac{83.33}{1006.95} = r$

   r = 0.0827 or 8.3%

29. a) i = prt

   $i = \$3650 \times 0.075 \times \dfrac{8}{12} = \$182.50$

   b) \$3650 − 182.50 = \$3467.50 is the amount Julie received.

   c) i = prt

   $182.50 = 3467.50 \times r \times \dfrac{8}{12}$

   182.50 = 2311.67r

   $\dfrac{182.50}{2311.67} = r$

   r = 0.0789 or 7.9%

30. a) 0.80x = 350

   $x = \dfrac{350}{0.80}$

   x = \$437.50
   \$437.50 is needed in savings

   b) $3\dfrac{1}{4}\% + 2\% = 5\dfrac{1}{4}\%$

   c) i = prt
   i = 350 × 0.0525 × 0.5
   = \$9.19
   A = p + i
   = \$350 + \$9.19 = \$359.19

31. Amt. collected = $470 \times \dfrac{4500}{2} = \$1,057,500.$

   $i = prt = 1057500 \times 0.054 \times \dfrac{5}{12} = \$23,793.75$

32. i = 80.25 − 75.00 = 5.25

   $5.25 = 75.00 \times r \times \dfrac{14}{360}$

   5.25 = 2.92r

   $r = \dfrac{5.25}{2.92} = 1.80$ or 180%

33. April 4 is day 94.
   Oct. 11 is day 284.
   284 − 94 = 190 days

34. May 19 is day 139.
   Sept. 17 is day 260.
   260 − 139 = 121 days

35. June 19 is day 170.
   Nov. 5 is day 309.
   309 − 170 = 139 days

36. June 14 is day 165
   January 24 is day 24
   (365 − 165) + 24 = 200 + 24 = 224 days

37. August 24 is day 236
   May 15 is day 135
   (365 − 236) + 135 = 129 + 135 = 264 days

38. December 21 is day 355
   April 28 is day 118
   (365 − 355) + 118 = 10 + 118 = 128 days

39. April 18 is day 108
    108 + 90 = day 198
    Day 198 = July 17

40. June 8 is day 159
    159 + 120 = day 279
    day 279 = October 6

41. November 25 is day 329
    329 + 120 = 449; 449 − 365 = 84
    84 − 1 leap year day = day 83
    day 83 = March 24

42. July 5 is day 186
    186 + 210 = 396; 396 − 365 = day 31
    day 31 = January 31

43. Partial payment on August 1 (31 days)

    i = 2500 × .08 × (31/360) = $17.22

    $300.00 partial payment
    − 17.22 interest
    $282.78 amount applied to principal

    $2500.00 original principal
    − 282.78 amount applied to principal
    $2217.22 principal after Aug.1 payment

    Maturity date is Oct. 15 (75 days)
    i = 2217.22 × .08 × (75/360) = $36.95
    Balance due at maturity is
    $2217.22 + 36.95 = $2254.17

44. Partial payment on May 5 (25 days)
    i = 2400 × .07 × (25/360) = $11.67

    $500.00 partial payment
    − 11.67 interest
    $488.33 amount applied to principal

    $2400.00 original principal
    − 488.33 amount applied to principal
    $1911.67 principal after May 5 payment

    Maturity date is July 7 (63 days)
    i = 1911.67 × .07 × (63/360) = $23.42
    Balance due at maturity is
    $1911.67 + 23.42 = $1,935.09

45. Partial payment on June 15 (45 days)
    i = 8000 × .09 × (45/360) = $90.00
    $2000.00 partial payment
    −   90.00 interest
    $1,910.00 amount applied to principal

    $8000.00 original principal
    − 1910.00 amount applied to principal
    $6090.00 principal after June 15 pmt.

    Maturity date is Nov. 1 (139 days)
    i = 6090.00 × .09 × (139/360)
      = $211.63
    Balance due at maturity is
    $6090.00 + 211.63 = $6,301.63

46. Partial payment on Aug. 1 (108 days)
    i = 7500 × .12 × (108/360) = $270.00
    $1000.00 partial payment
    − 270.00 interest
    $730.00 amount applied to principal

    $7500.00 original principal
    − 730.00 amount applied to principal
    $6770.00 principal after Aug. 1 payment

    Maturity date is Oct. 1 (61 days)
    i = 6770 × .12 × (61/360) = $137.66

    Balance due at maturity is
    $6770.00 + 137.66 = $6,907.66

47. Partial payment on Dec. 27 (165 days)

i = 9000 × 0.06 × (165/360) = $247.50

$4000.00 partial payment
− 247.50 interest
$3752.50 amount applied to principal

$9000.00 original principal
− 3752.50 amount applied to principal
$5247.50 principal after Dec. 27 payment

Maturity date is Feb. 1 (36 days)

i = 5247.50 × 0.06 × (36/360) = $31.49

Balance due at maturity is

$5247.50 + 31.49 = $5278.99

48. Partial payment on Jan. 15 (14 days)

i = 1000 × .125 × (14/360) = $4.86

$300.00 partial payment
− 4.86 interest
$295.14 amount applied to principal

$1000.00 original principal
− 295.14 amount applied to principal
$704.86 principal after Jan. 15 payment

Maturity date is Feb. 15 (31 days)

i = 704.86 × 0.125 × (31/360) = $7.59

Balance due at maturity is

$704.86 + 7.59 = $712.45

49. Partial payment on Sept. 1 (31 days)

i = 1800 × .15 × (31/360) = $23.25

$500.00 partial payment
− 23.25 interest
$476.75 amount applied to principal

$1800.00 original principal
− 476.75 amount applied to principal
$1323.25 principal after Sept.1 payment

Partial payment on Oct. 1 (30 days)

i = 1323.25 × 0.15 × (30/360) = $16.54

$500.00 partial payment

− 16.54 interest

$483.46 amount applied to principal

$1323.25 principal after Sept.1 payment
− 483.46 amount applied to principal
$839.79 principal after Oct. 1 payment

Maturity date is Nov. 1 (31 days)

i = 839.79 × 0.15 × (31/360) = $10.85

Balance due at maturity is

$839.79 + 10.85 = $850.64

50. Partial payment on Nov. 15 (31 days)

i = 5000 × 0.14 × (31/360) = $60.28

$800.00 partial payment
− 60.28 interest
$739.72 amount applied to principal

$5000.00 original principal
− 739.72 amount applied to principal
$4260.28 principal after Nov. 15 payment

Partial payment on Dec. 15 (30 days)

i = 4260.28 × 0.14 × (30/360) = $49.70

$800.00 partial payment
− 49.70 interest
$750.30 amount applied to principal

$4260.28 new principal
− 750.30 amount applied to principal
$3509.98 principal after Dec.15 payment

Maturity date is Jan. 1 (17 days)
i = 3509.98 × 0.14 × (17/360) = $23.20
Balance due at maturity is
$3509.98 + 23.20 = $3,533.18

51. Partial payment on May 1 (61 days)

    $i = 6500 \times 0.105 \times (61/360) = \$115.65$

    $1750.00 partial payment
    $\underline{- \ \ 115.65}$ interest
    $1634.35 amount applied to principal

    $6500.00 original principal
    $\underline{- \ \ 1634.35}$ amount applied to principal
    $4865.65 principal after May 1 payment

    Partial payment on July 1 (61 days)

    $i = 4865.65 \times 0.105 \times (61/360) = \$86.57$

    $2350.00 partial payment
    $\underline{- \ \ 86.57}$ interest
    $2263.43 amount applied to principal

    $4865.65 new principal
    $\underline{- \ \ 2263.43}$ amount applied to principal
    $2602.22 principal after July 1 payment

    On the maturity date (58 days)
    $i = 2602.22 \times 0.105 \times (58/360) = \$44.02$
    Balance due at maturity is
    $2602.22 + 44.02 = \$2,646.24

53. a) May 5 is day 125
        $125 + 182 = 307$
        day 307 is Nov. 3, 1999

    b) $i = 1000 \times 0.0434 \times (182/360) = \$21.94$
        Amt. paid = $1000 - 21.94 = \$978.06$
    c) interest = \$21.94
    d) $r = \dfrac{i}{pt} = \dfrac{21.94}{978.06 \left(\frac{182}{360} \right)} = 0.0444$ or 4.44%

55. a) Amt. received = $743.21 - 39.95 = \$703.26$
        $i = p \times r \times t$
        $39.95 = 703.26 \times r \times (5/360)$
        $39.95 = 9.7675 \times r$
        $r = 39.95/9.7675 = 4.09$ or 409%

    b) $39.95 = 703.26 \times r \times (10/360)$
        $39.95 = 19.535 \times r$
        $r = 39.95/19.535 = 2.045$ or 204.5%

    c) $39.95 = 703.26 \times r \times (20/360)$
        $39.95 = 39.07 \times r$
        $r = 39.95/39.07 = 1.023$ or 102.3%

52. Partial payment on June 15 (31 days)
    $i = 3000 \times 0.11 \times (31/360) = \$28.42$
    $875.00 partial payment
    $\underline{- \ \ 28.42}$ interest
    $846.58 amount applied to principal

    $3000.00 original principal
    $\underline{- \ \ 846.58}$ amount applied to principal
    $2153.42 principal after June 15 payment

    Partial payment on Aug. 1 (47 days)
    $i = 2153.42 \times 0.11 \times (47/360) = \$30.93$
    $940.00 partial payment
    $\underline{- \ \ 30.93}$ interest
    $909.07 amount applied to principal

    $2153.42 principal after June 15 payment
    $\underline{- \ \ 909.07}$ amount applied to principal
    $1244.35 principal after Aug.1 payment

    On maturity Sept. 1 (31 days)
    $i = 1244.35 \times 0.11 \times (31/360) = \$11.79$
    Balance due at maturity is
    $1244.35 + 11.79 = \$1256.14

54. a) Aug. 31 is day 243
        $243 + 364 = 607$
        $(607 - 1) - 365 = 241$
        day 241 is Aug. 29, 2000

    b) $i = 6000 \times 0.044 \times (364/360) = \$266.93$

        Amt. paid = $6000 - 266.93 = \$5,733.07$

    c) $r = \dfrac{266.93}{5733.07 \left(\frac{364}{360} \right)} = 0.0460$ or 4.6%

56. a) At the end of the first month:
        $i = 600 \times 0.105 \times (30/360) = \$5.25$
        His payment = $\$200 + 5.25 = \$205.25$

        At the end of the second month:
        $i = 400 \times 0.11 \times (30/360) = \$3.67$
        His payment = $\$200 + 3.67 = \$203.67$

        At the end of the third month:
        $i = 200 \times 0.12 \times (30/360) = \$2.00$
        His final payment = $\$200 + 2.00 = \$202.00$

    b) total interest = $5.25 + 3.67 + 2.00 = \$10.92$

57. a) interest per $100 = 100 − 93.337 = $6.663
    rate = 6.663/100 = 0.0663 or 6.663%

   b) 0.0663 × 100,000 = $6,663.

   c) 6663 = 93337 × r × 1

   $\dfrac{6663}{93337}$ = r; r = 0.07139 or 7.139%

   d) i = 6663 × 0.05 × 1 = 333.15
      total interest = 6663 + 333.15 = $6,996.15

Exercise Set 11.3

1. An investment is the use of money or capital for income or profit.
2. With a fixed investment the amount invested as principal is guaranteed and the interest is computed at a fixed rate.
3. For a variable investment neither the principal nor the interest is guaranteed.
4. Interest that is computed on the principal and any accumulated interest is called compound interest.
5. The effective annual yield on an investment is the simple interest rate that gives the same amount of interest as a compound rate over the same period of time.
6. The principal that would have to be invested today to have a fixed amount of money in the future.

7. a) n = 1, r = 4.0%, t = 2, p = $4000

   $A = 4000\left(1+\dfrac{0.04}{1}\right)^{1\cdot2} = \$4{,}326.40$

   b) i = $4326.40 − $4000 = $326.40

8. a) n = 2, r = 4.0%, t = 2, p = $4000

   $A = 4000\left(1+\dfrac{0.04}{2}\right)^{2\cdot2} = \$4329.73$

   b) i = $4329.73 − $4000 = $329.73

9. a) n = 2, r = 5.0%, t = 5, p = $3000

   $A = 3000\left(1+\dfrac{0.05}{2}\right)^{2\cdot5} = \$3840.25$

   b) i = $3840.25 − $3000 = $840.25

10. a) n = 1, r = 5.0%, t = 5, p = $3000

   $A = 3000\left(1+\dfrac{0.05}{1}\right)^{1\cdot5} = \$3828.84$

   b) i = $3828.84 − $3000 = $828.84

11. a) n = 4, r = 4.75%, t = 3, p = $1500

   $A = 1500\left(1+\dfrac{0.0475}{4}\right)^{4\cdot3} = \$1728.28$

   b) i = $1728.28 − $1500 = $228.28

12. a) n = 4, r = 4.75%, t = 4, p = $1500

   $A = 1500\left(1+\dfrac{0.0475}{4}\right)^{4\cdot4} = \$1811.85$

   b) i = $1811.85 − $1500 = $311.85

13. a) n = 12, r = 6.25%, t = 2, p = $2500

   $A = 2500\left(1+\dfrac{0.0625}{12}\right)^{12\cdot2} = \$2831.95$

   b) i = $2831.95 − $2500 = $331.95

14. a) n = 12, r = 6.25%, t = 2, p = $3000

   $A = 3000\left(1+\dfrac{0.0625}{12}\right)^{12\cdot2} = \$3398.34$

   b) i = $3398.34 − $3000 = $398.34

15. n = 360, r = 6.75%, t = 5 yr., p = $5000

   a) $A = 5000\left(1+\dfrac{0.0675}{360}\right)^{360\cdot5} = \$7006.98$

   b) i = $7006.98 − $5000 = $2006.98

16. n = 360, r = 6.75%, t = 10 yr., p = $5000

   a) $A = 5000\left(1+\dfrac{0.0675}{360}\right)^{360\cdot10} = \$9819.54$

   b) i = $9819.54 − $5000 = $4819.54

17. $p = 250{,}000 - 10{,}000 = 240{,}000$

$A = 240{,}000\left(1+\dfrac{0.056}{12}\right)^{12\cdot10} = \$419{,}614.45$

18. $p = 25 + 35 + 40 + 50 + 100 + 100 + 200 + 250 + 150 + 300 + 1000 = \$2{,}250.$

$A = 2250\left(1+\dfrac{0.052}{360}\right)^{360\cdot2} = \$2{,}496.58$

19. $A = 5000\left(1+\dfrac{0.06}{4}\right)^{4\cdot5} = \$6{,}734.28$

20. $p = \dfrac{A}{\left(1+\sfrac{i}{n}\right)^{n\cdot t}} = \dfrac{30000}{\left(1+\sfrac{0.0515}{12}\right)^{60}} = \$23{,}202.23$

21. a) $\dfrac{A}{\left(1+\sfrac{i}{n}\right)^{n\cdot t}} = \dfrac{290000}{\left(1+\sfrac{0.0825}{2}\right)^{20}} = \$129{,}210.47$

   b) surcharge $= \dfrac{129210.47}{958} = \$134.88$

22. a) $\dfrac{A}{\left(1+\sfrac{i}{n}\right)^{n\cdot t}} = \dfrac{783000}{\left(1+\sfrac{0.09}{12}\right)^{180}} = \$204{,}010.21$

   b) surcharge $= \dfrac{204010.21 - 50000}{2682} = \$57.42$

23. The amount Troy owes the bank after two years is, $A = 1500\left(1+\sfrac{0.10}{4}\right)^{4\times2} = \$1{,}827.60$

Bank's interest charge: $i = 1827.60 - 1500 = \$327.60$
Grandfather's interest charge: $i = prt = 1500 \times 0.07 \times 2 = \$210.00$
Troy will save $327.60 - 210.00 = \$117.60$

24. a) $A = 2000\left(1+\dfrac{0.05}{2}\right)^{2\cdot15} = \$4{,}195.14$

   b) $A = 2000\left(1+\dfrac{0.05}{4}\right)^{2\cdot15} = \$4{,}214.36$

25. $A = 2000\left(1+\dfrac{0.06}{2}\right)^{2\cdot10}$

   $= \$3612.22$ for first 10 years

   $A = 3612.22\left(1+\dfrac{0.06}{4}\right)^{4\cdot8}$

   $= \$5{,}816.85$ after 18 years

26. $A = 3000\left(1+\dfrac{0.08}{4}\right)^{8} = \$3514.98$

27. $A = 6000\left(1+\dfrac{0.0525}{12}\right)^{24} = \$6{,}662.74$

   $i = \$6662.74 - \$6000 = \$662.74$

28. $A = 6000\left(1+\dfrac{0.08}{4}\right)^{12} = \$7{,}609.45$

29. Let $p = 1.00$. Then

   $A = 1\left(1+\dfrac{0.056}{360}\right)^{360} = \$1.0576$

   $i = 1.0576 - 1.00 = 0.0576$
   The effective annual yield is 5.76%

30. a) $A = 1000\left(1+\dfrac{0.02}{2}\right)^4 = \$1,040.60$

    $i = \$1040.60 - \$1000 = \$40.60$

  b) $A = 1000\left(1+\dfrac{0.04}{2}\right)^4 = \$1,082.43$

    $i = \$1082.43 - \$1000 = \$82.43$

  c) $A = 1000\left(1+\dfrac{0.08}{2}\right)^4 = \$1,169.86$

    $i = \$1169.86 - \$1000 = \$169.86$

  d) No predictable outcome.

31. a) $A = 100\left(1+\dfrac{0.12}{12}\right)^{24} = \$126.97$

    $i = \$126.97 - \$100 = \$26.97$

  b) $A = 200\left(1+\dfrac{0.12}{12}\right)^{24} = \$253.95$

    $i = \$253.95 - \$200 = \$53.95$

  c) $A = 400\left(1+\dfrac{0.12}{12}\right)^{24} = \$507.89$

    $i = \$507.89 - \$400 = \$107.89$

  d) The interest doubles also.

32. a) $A = 1000\left(1+\dfrac{0.06}{2}\right)^4 = \$1,125.51$

    $i = \$1125.51 - \$1000 = \$125.51$

  b) $A = 1000\left(1+\dfrac{0.06}{2}\right)^8 = \$1,266.77$

    $i = \$1266.77 - \$1000 = \$266.77$

  c) $A = 1000\left(1+\dfrac{0.06}{2}\right)^{16} = \$1,604.71$

    $i = \$1604.71 - \$1000 = \$604.71$

  d) New amount $= \dfrac{(\textit{old amount})^2}{1000}$

33. Let $p = 1.00$. Then

    $A = 1\left(1+\dfrac{0.075}{4}\right)^4 = \$1.0771$

    $i = 1.0771 - 1.00 = 0.0771$

    The effective annual yield is 7.71%

34. Let $p = 1.00$. Then

    $A = 1\left(1+\dfrac{0.065}{4}\right)^4 = \$1.0666$

    $i = 1.0666 - 1.00 = 0.0666$

    The effective annual yield is 6.66%

35. Let $p = 1.00$. Then

    $A = 1\left(1+\dfrac{0.0677}{360}\right)^{360} = \$1.0700$

    $i = 1.0700 - 1.00 = 0.0700$ or 7.00%

    The accounts have the same effective rate.

36. The effective rate of the 4.75% account is,

    $A = 1\left(1+\dfrac{0.0475}{12}\right)^{12} = 1.0485$

    $1.0485 - 1.00 = 0.0485$ or 4.85%

    Therefore the 5% simple interest account pays more interest.

37. Present value $= \dfrac{200000}{\left(1+\dfrac{0.075}{4}\right)^{80}} = \$45,250.17$

38. Present value $= \dfrac{50000}{\left(1+\dfrac{0.08}{4}\right)^{72}} = \$12,015.94$

39. Present value $= \dfrac{20000}{\left(1+\dfrac{0.07}{12}\right)^{180}} = \$7,020.14$

40. Present value $= \dfrac{20000}{\left(1+\dfrac{0.07}{4}\right)^{60}} = \$7,062.61$

41. $p = 1.35, r = 0.035, t = 10, n = 1$
     $A = 1.35(1 + 0.035)^{10} = \$1.90$

42. $p = 2000, A = 3586.58, n = 12, t = 5$

$$3586.58 = 2000\left(1 + \frac{r}{12}\right)^{60}$$

$$\frac{3586.58}{2000} = \left(1 + \frac{r}{12}\right)^{60}$$

$$(1.79329)^{1/60} = 1 + \frac{r}{12}$$

$$1.00978 = 1 + \frac{r}{12}$$

$$0.00978 = \frac{r}{12}$$

$$r = 0.00978(12) = 0.117 \text{ or } 11.7\%$$

43. a) $72/3 = 24$ years
     b) $72/6 = 12$ years
     c) $72/8 = 9$ years
     d) $72/12 = 6$ years
     e) $72/r = 22$
     $\quad 72 = 22r$
     $\quad\quad r = 72/22 = 0.0327$
     $\quad\quad r = 3.27\%$

44. $A = 2000 [1 + (.08/2)]^6$
     $\quad = 2000 (1.04)^6 = \$2530.64$
     $i = \$2530.64 - 2500 = \$530.64$
     Simple interest:
     $$i = prt$$
     $$530.64 = 2000(r)(3)$$
     $$530.64 = 6000r$$
     $$r = \frac{530.64}{6000} = 0.0884 \text{ or } 8.84\%$$

45. $R = \$500, r = 5.5\%, n = 2, t = 17$

$$S = 500\frac{\left[\left(1 + \frac{0.055}{2}\right)^{34} - 1\right]}{\frac{0.055}{2}}$$

$$= 500 \, [1.51526] \left(\frac{2}{0.055}\right) = \$27,550.11$$

46. $$S = 50\frac{\left[\left(1 + \frac{0.08}{4}\right)^{120} - 1\right]}{\frac{0.08}{4}} = \$24,412.91$$

47. Use the formula given in exercise 45.
     a) $R = 150, r = 0.056, n = 12, t = 18$
     $\quad$ ans. $S = \$55,726.01$
     b) $R = 900, r = 0.058, n = 2, t = 18$
     $\quad$ ans. $S = \$55,821.15$

48. a) $\left(\dfrac{26600}{12}\right) = \$2,216.67$

     b) $\dfrac{26600}{9} = \$2,955.56$

     c) $\$119.83$

Exercise Set 11.4

1. With an installment plan, the borrower repays the principal plus the interest with weekly or monthly payments that usually begin shortly after the loan is made. With a personal note, the borrower repays the principal plus the interest as a single payment at the end of the specified time period.

2. An open-end installment loan is a loan on which you can make different payment amounts each month. A fixed installment loan is one in which you pay a fixed amount each month for a set number of months.

3. The APR is the true rate of interest charged on a loan.

4. The finance charge is the total amount of money the borrower must pay for the use of the money borrowed.

5. The total installment price is the sum of all the monthly payments and the down payment, if any.

6. The Actuarial method and the Rule of 78's.

7. The unpaid balance method and the average daily balance method.

8. A cash advance is a loan obtained through a credit card.

9. a) Amount financed = 36000 − 0.20(36000) = $28,800
   From table 11.2 the finance charge per $100 at 11% for 60 payments is 30.45.

   Total finance charge = $30.45 \times \dfrac{28,800}{100}$ = $8769.60

   b) Total amount due after down payment = 28800 + 8769.60 = $37,569.60

   monthly payment = $\dfrac{37569.60}{60}$ =$626.16

10. a) Amount financed = 4200 − 0.15(4200) = $3,570.
   From table 11.2, the finance charge per $100 financed at 10.5% for 24 months is 11.30.

   Total finance charge = $11.30 \times \dfrac{3570}{100}$ = $403.41

   b) Total amount due after down payment = 3570 + 403.41 = $3,973.41

   monthly payment = $\dfrac{3973.41}{24}$ = $165.56

11. a) From table 11.2, the finance charge per $100 financed at 7.5% for 60 months is $20.23.

   Total finance charge is $20.23 \times \dfrac{4000}{100}$ = $809.20

   b) Total amount due = 4000 + 809.20 = $4,809.20

   monthly payment = $\dfrac{4809.20}{60}$ = $80.15

12. a) From table 11.2, the finance charge per $100 financed at 9.5% for 48 months is $20.59.

   Total finance charge = $20.59 \times \dfrac{4200}{100}$ =$864.78

   b) Total amount due = 4200 + 864.78 = $5064.78

   monthly payment = $\dfrac{5064.78}{48}$ = $105.52

13. a) down payment = 0.20(3200) = $640.
   Total installment price = 640 + (60 × 53.14) = $3828.40
   Finance charge = 3828.40 − 3200 = $628.40

   b) $\dfrac{finance\ charge}{amt.\ financed} \times 100 = \dfrac{628.40}{2560} \times 100 = 24.55$

   From Table 11.2, for 60 payments, the closest value to 24.55 is 24.55 which corresponds to an APR of 9.0%.

14. a) Total installment price = 500 + (24 × 85.79) = $2558.96
       Finance charge = 2558.96 − 2350 = $208.96

   b) $\dfrac{\textit{finance charge}}{\textit{amt. financed}} \times 100 = \dfrac{208.96}{1850} \times 100 = 11.30$

       From Table 11.2, for 24 payments, the closest value to 11.30 is 11.30 which corresponds to an APR of 10.5%.

15. a) Total installment price = 175 + (12 × 44.66) = $710.92
       Finance charge = 710.92 − 675 = $35.92

   b) $\dfrac{\textit{finance charge}}{\textit{amt. financed}} \times 100 = \dfrac{35.92}{500} \times 100 = 7.18$

       From Table 11.2, for 12 payments, the closest value to 7.18 is 7.18 which corresponds to an APR of 13.0%.

16.   Down payment = (1/3)(3450) = $1150

   a) Installment price = $1150 + (398 × 6) = $3538.00
       Finance charge = $3538 − $3450 = $88.00

   b) $\dfrac{\textit{finance charge}}{\textit{amt. financed}} \times 100 = \dfrac{88}{2300} \times 100 = 3.83$

       From Table 11.2, for 6 payments, the closest value to 3.83 is 3.83 which corresponds to an APR of 13.0%.

17. a) Finance charge = (60 × 260.90) − 12000
                      = $3654.00

   $\dfrac{\textit{finance charge}}{\textit{amt. financed}} \times 100$

   $= \dfrac{3654}{12000} \times 100 = 30.45$

   From Table 11.2, for 60 payments, the APR is 11.0%.

   b) n = 60 − 24 = 36, p = 260.90, v = 17.86

   $u = \dfrac{(36)(260.90)(17.86)}{100 + 17.86} = \$1{,}423.28$

   c)   9392.40   Total of remaining payments
       − 1423.28   Interest saved
         $7969.12   Balance due
       + 260.90   24th monthly payment
         $8,230.02   Total amount due

18. a) Interest = (193.75 × 48) − 7500
                 = $1800

   $\dfrac{\textit{finance charge}}{\textit{amt. financed}} \times 100$

   $= \dfrac{1800}{7500} \times 100 = 24.00$

   From Table 11.2, for 48 payments, the APR is 11.0%.

   b) n = 30, p = 193.75, v = 14.83

   $u = \dfrac{(30)(193.75)(14.83)}{100 + 14.83} = \$750.67$

   c)   5812.50   Total of remaining payments
       − 750.67   Interest saved
         $5061.83   Balance due
       +193.75   18th monthly payment
         $5255.58   Total amount due

19. a) Amount financed = 32000 − 10000 = $22000
From table 11.2, the finance charge per 100 financed at 12% for 36 payments is 19.57.

Total finance charge = $19.57 \times \dfrac{22000}{100} = 4305.40$

b) Total amt. due = 22000 + 4305.40
  = $26,305.40

Monthly payment = $\dfrac{26305.40}{36} = \$730.71$

c) n = 36 − 24 = 12, p = 730.71, v = 6.62

$u = \dfrac{(12)(730.71)(6.62)}{100+6.62} = \$544.43$

d) $8768.52 Total of remaining payments
  − 544.43 Interest saved
  $8224.09 Balance due
  + 730.71 12th monthly payment
  $8954.80 Total amount due

20. a) Amount financed = $6520 − $3962 = $2558
Interest = 3962 + (119.82×24) − 6520 = 317.68

$\dfrac{finance\ charge}{amt.\ financed} \times 100 = \dfrac{317.68}{2558} \times 100 = 12.42$

From Table 11.2, for 24 payments, the closest value to 12.42 is 12.42 which corresponds to an APR of 11.5%.

b) n = 12, p = 119.82, v = 6.34

$u = \dfrac{(12)(119.82)(6.34)}{100+6.34} = \$85.72$

c) $1437.84 Total of remaining payments
  − 85.72 Interest saved
  $1352.12 Balance due
  + 119.82 12th monthly payment
  $1471.94 Total amount due

21. a) From table 11.2, at 12.5% for 48 payments the finance charge per 100 is 27.58.

Finance charge = $27.58 \times \dfrac{7345}{100} = \$2025.75$

b) Total installment price = 7345 + 2025.75
  = $9370.75

Monthly payment = $\dfrac{9370.75}{48} = \$195.22$

c) K = 36, n = 48, f = 2025.75

$u = \dfrac{(2025.75)(36)(37)}{(48)(49)} = \$1,147.24$

d) $7027.92 Total of remaining payments
  − 1147.24 Interest saved
  $5880.68 Balance due
  + 195.22 12th monthly payment
  $6,075.90 Total amount due

22. a) From table 11.2, at 8.5% for 36 payments the finance charge per 100 is 13.64.

Finance charge = $13.64 \times \dfrac{3600}{100} = \$491.04$

b) Total installment price = 3600 + 491.04
  = $4091.04

Monthly payment = $\dfrac{4091.04}{36} = \$113.64$

c) K = 24, n = 36, f = 491.04

$u = \dfrac{(491.04)(24)(25)}{(36)(37)} = \$221.19$

d) $2727.36 Total of remaining payments
  − 221.19 Interest saved
  $2506.17 Balance due
  + 113.64 12th monthly payment
  $2,619.81 Total amount due

23. a) Interest = 500 + (151.39 × 18) − 3000

$$= \$225.02$$

k = 6, n = 18, and f = 225.02

$$u = \frac{(225.02)(6)(6+1)}{18(18+1)} = \frac{9450.84}{342} = \$27.63$$

b) $908.34 Total of remaining payments
− 27.63 Interest saved
$880.71 Balance due
+ 151.39 12th monthly payment
$1032.10 Total amount due

24. a) Interest = 850 +(134.71 × 12) − 2375

$$= \$91.52$$

k = 6, n = 12, and f = 91.52

$$u = \frac{(91.52)(6)(6+1)}{12(12+1)} = \frac{3843.84}{156} = \$24.64$$

b) $808.26 Total of remaining payments
− 24.64 Interest saved
$783.62 Balance due
+134.71 6th monthly payment
$918.33 Total amount due

25. a) Balance due = 365 + 180 + 195 + 84 = $824

$$\text{min. payment} = \frac{bal.\ due}{48} = \frac{824}{48} \approx 17.17 \approx \$18$$

b) Bal. due after Dec. 1 payment = 824 − 200
$$= \$624$$

interest for Dec. = 0.011 × 624 = $6.86
Bal. due Jan. 1 = 624 + 6.86 = $630.86

26. a) Bal. due = 425 + 175 + 450 + 125 = $1175

$$\text{min. payment} = \frac{bal.\ due}{36} = \frac{1175}{36} \approx 32.64 \approx \$33$$

b) Bal. due after Sept. 1 payment = 1175 − 650
$$= \$525$$

interest for Sept. = 0.012 × 525 = $6.30
Bal. due Oct. 1 = 525 + 6.30 = $531.30

27. a) Bal. due = 423 + 36 + 145 + 491 = $1095

$$\text{min. payment} = \frac{bal.\ due}{36} = \frac{1095}{36} \approx 30.42 \approx \$31$$

b) Bal. due after Mar. 1 payment = 1095 − 548
$$= \$547$$

interest for March = 0.011 × 547 = $6.02
Bal. due Apr. 1 = 547 + 6.02 = $553.02

28. a) Bal. due = 512 + 172 + 190 + 350 = $1224

$$\text{min. payment} = \frac{bal.\ due}{36} = \frac{1224}{48} \approx 25.50 \approx \$26$$

b) Bal. due after July 1 payment = 1224 − 500
$$= \$724$$

interest for July = 0.013 × 724 = $9.41
Bal. due Aug. 1 = 724 + 9.41 = $733.41

29. a) Finance charge = 1097.86 × 0.018 × 1
$$= \$19.76$$

b) Bal. due May 5
= 1097.86 + 19.76 + 425.79 − 800 = $743.41

30. a) Finance charge
= 385.75 × 0.0140 × 1 = $5.40

b) 385.75 old balance
+ 5.40 finance charge
− 275.00 payment
+ 330.00 airline ticket
+ 190.80 hotel bill
+ 84.75 clothing
$721.70 new balance

31. a) Finance charge
= 124.78 × 0.0125 × 1 = $1.56

b) 124.78 old balance
+ 1.56 finance charge
− 100.00 payment
+ 25.64 art sup.
+ 67.23 flowers
+ 13.90 music CD
$133.11 new balance, March 3

32. a) Finance charge
= 57.88 × 0.0135 × 1 = $0.78

b) $57.88 old balance
+ .78 finance charge
+ 64.75 paint
− 45.00 payment
+ 72.85 curtains
+ 135.50 chair
$286.76 new balance

33. a)

Date	Balance Due	Number of Days	(Balance)(Days)
May 12	$378.50	1	(378.50)(1) = $378.50
May 13	$508.29	2	(508.29)(2) = $1,016.58
May 15	$458.29	17	(458.29)(17) = $7,790.93
June 1	$594.14	7	(594.14)(7) = $4,158.98
June 8	$631.77	4	(631.77)(4) = $2,527.08
		31	sum = $15,872.07

Average daily balance = $\dfrac{15872.07}{31}$ = $512.00

b) Finance charge = prt = 512.00 × 0.013 × 1 = $6.66
c) Balance due = 631.77 + 6.66 = $638.43

34. a)

Date	Balance Due	Number of Days	(Balance)(Days)
Mar. 23	$1,578.25	3	(1578.25)(3) = $4,734.75
Mar. 26	$1,658.23	4	(1658.23)(4) = $6,632.92
Mar. 30	$1,710.99	4	(1710.99)(4) = $6,843.96
Apr. 3	$1,460.99	12	(1460.99)(12) = $17,531.88
Apr. 15	$1,651.51	7	(1651.51)(7) = $11,560.57
Apr. 22	$1,842.36	1	(1842.36)(1) = $1,842.36
		31	sum = $49,146.44

Average daily balance = $\dfrac{49146.44}{31}$ = $1,585.37

b) Finance charge = prt = 1585.37 × 0.013 × 1 = $20.61
c) Balance due = 1842.36 + 20.61 = $1,862.97

35. a)

Date	Balance Due	Number of Days	(Balance)(Days)
Feb. 3	$124.78	5	(124.78)(5) = $623.90
Feb. 8	$150.42	4	(150.42)(4) = $601.68
Feb. 12	$50.42	2	(50.42)(2) = $100.84
Feb. 14	$117.65	11	(117.65)(11) = $1294.15
Feb. 25	$131.55	6	(131.55)(6) = $789.30
		28	sum = $3,409.87

Average daily balance = $\dfrac{3409.87}{28}$ = $121.78

b) Finance charge = prt = 121.78 × 0.0125 × 1 = $1.52
c) Balance due = 131.55 + 1.52 = $133.07
d) The interest charged using the ave. daily balance method is $0.04 less than the interest charged using the unpaid balance method.

36. a)

Date	Balance Due	Number of Days	(Balance)(Days)		
Sept. 5	$385.75	3	(385.75)(3)	=	$1157.25
Sept. 8	$110.75	13	(110.75)(13)	=	$1439.75
Sept. 21	$440.75	6	(440.75)(6)	=	$2644.50
Sept. 27	$631.55	5	(631.55)(5)	=	$3157.75
Oct. 2	$716.30	3	(716.30)(3)	=	$2148.90
		30		sum =	$10,548.15

Average daily balance $= \dfrac{10548.15}{30} = \$351.61$

b) Finance charge = prt = $351.61 \times 0.014 \times 1 = \$4.92$
c) Balance due = $716.30 + 4.92 = \$721.22$
d) Smaller finance charge on Oct. 5 using the ave. daily balance method.

37. a) Interest charge = prt = $1500 \times 0.0005751 \times 24 = \$20.70$
b) Amount due = $1500 + 20.70 = \$1,520.70$

38. a) $i = 875 \times 0.0004273 \times 32 = \$11.96$

b) $A = 875 + 11.96 = \$886.96$

39. a) ABC interest $= 250 \times 0.074 \times \dfrac{6}{12} = \$9.25$

b) Installment price = $22.19 \times 12 = \$266.28$
XYZ Interest = $266.28 - 250 = \$16.28$

c) $\dfrac{finance\ charge}{amt.\ financed} \times 100 = \dfrac{9.25}{250} \times 100 = 3.7$

From Table 11.2, for 6 payments, the APR is 12.5% for ABC.

d) $\dfrac{finance\ charge}{amt.\ financed} \times 100 = \dfrac{16.28}{250} \times 100 = 6.51$

From Table 11.2, for 12 payments, the APR is 12.0% for XYZ.

40. The interest on $890 at 5.25% annually for 1 month is:

$i = 890 \times 0.0525 \times \dfrac{1}{12} = \$3.89$

She will be saving $3.89 by using her credit card.

41. a) Amount financed = $3450 - 1150 = \$2300$

Month	Finance charge	Payment	Balance
1	None	$384.00	$1,916.00
2	$1916 \times 0.013 = \$24.91$	$408.91	$1,532.00
3	$1532 \times 0.013 = \$19.92$	$403.92	$1,148.00
4	$1148 \times 0.013 = \$14.92$	$398.92	$764.00
5	$764 \times 0.013 = \$9.93$	$393.93	$380.00
6	$380 \times 0.013 = \$4.94$	$384.94	$0.00
	Total = $74.62		

It will take 6 months to repay the loan.

b) The total amount of interest paid is $74.62
c) The finance charge is $13.38 less using the credit card.

42. Let p = amount Ken borrowed

    p + 2500 = purchase price

    Installment price:

    2500 + (379.50 × 36) = $16,162

    Interest = Installment price − purchase price

    $$= 16,162 - (p + 2500)$$
    $$= 16,162 - p - 2500$$
    $$= 13,662 - p$$

Since i = prt we have:

$$13,662 - p = p \times .06 \times 3$$
$$13,662 - p = .18p$$
$$13,662 = .18p + p$$
$$p = 11,577.97$$

purchase price = 11,577.97 + 2500
                = $14,077.97

43. With her billing date on the 25th of the month she can buy the camera during the period of June 26 - June 29 and the purchase will be on the July 25th bill. Purchasing during these dates she can pay the bill on August 5th or later without paying interest.

Exercise Set 11.5

1. A mortgage is a long term loan in which the property is pledged as security for payment of the difference between the down payment and the sale price.

2. The down payment is the amount of cash the buyer must pay the seller before the lending institution will grant the buyer a mortgage.

3. The major difference between these two types of loans is that the interest rate for a conventional loan is fixed for the duration of the loan, whereas the interest rate for a variable-rate loan may change every period, as specified in the loan agreement.

4. a) A point is 1% of the mortgage.
   b) For x points multiply the mortgage by 0.01x.

5. A buyer's adjusted monthly income is found by subtracting any fixed monthly payment with more than 10 months remaining from the gross monthly income.

6. An amortization schedule is a list of the payment number, interest, principal, and balance remaining on the loan.

7. An add on rate, or margin, is the percent added to the interest rate on which the adjustable rate mortgage is based.

8. The FHA insures the loan and a bank provides the money for the loan.

9. Equity is the difference between the appraised value of your home and the loan balance.

10. A home equity loan is a loan in which the equity in your home is used as collateral.

11. a)   down payment = 20% of $90,000
            $= 0.20 \times 90000 = \$18,000.$

    b)   amt. of mortgage = 90000 − 18000= $72,000
         Table 11.4 yields 7.75 per 1000 of mortgage
         monthly payment $= \dfrac{72000}{1000} \times 7.75 = \$558.00$

12. a)   down payment $= 0.20 \times \$97,000 = \$19,400$

    b)   amt. of mortgage
         $= \$97,000 - \$19,400 = \$77,600$
         Table 11.4 yields 7.69 per $1000 of mortgage
         Monthly payment$= \dfrac{77600}{1000} \times 7.69 = \$596.74$

13. a)   down payment $= 0.20 \times \$74,000 = \$14,800$

    b)   amount of mortgage
         $\$74,000 - \$14,800 = \$59,200$
         Table 11.4 yields 8.05 per $1000
         of mortgage.
         Monthly mortgage payment
         $= \dfrac{59200}{1000} \times 8.05 = \$476.56$

14. a)   down payment $= 0.15 \times \$65,000 = \$9,750$

    b)   amount of mortgage
         $\$65,000 - \$9,750 = \$55,250$

    c)   cost of points $= 0.02 \times \$55,250$
                        $= \$1,105.00$

15. a)   down payment $= 0.15 \times \$93,500 = \$14,025$

    b)   amount of mortgage
         $\$93,500 - \$14,025 = \$79,475$

    c)   cost of points $= 0.03 \times \$79,475 = \$2,384.25$

16. a) $2500   gross monthly income
         $\underline{- \$ 95}$ monthly payments
         $2405   adjusted monthly income
         28% of the adjusted monthly income
         $0.28 \times \$2405 = \$673.40$, the amount the
         bank feels he can afford.

    b)   At a rate of 8% for 30 years,
         Table 11.4 yields 7.34.
         monthly mortgage payment
         $\dfrac{52200}{1000} \times 7.34 = \$383.15$
         $383.15 monthly mortgage payment
         $\underline{+\$105.00}$ taxes and insurance
         $488.15   total monthly payment
         Since $488.15 is less than $673.40,
         he qualifies for the loan.

17. a) $7200 gross monthly income

 $-$290 car payment

 $6910 adjusted monthly income

 28% of the adjusted monthly income

 0.28×$6910 = $1,934.80, the amount the bank feels they can afford.

 b) At a rate of 6.5% for 30 years,

 Table 11.4 yields 6.32.

 monthly mortgage payment

 $\dfrac{140000}{1000} \times 6.32 = \$884.80$

 $884.80 monthly mortgage payment

 +$400 taxes and insurance

 $1284.80 total monthly payment

 Since $1,284.80 is less than $1,934.80, they qualify for the loan

18. a) down payment = $75,000 − $63,750

 = $11,250

 Total cost of house:

 $11,250 + (490.24 × 12 × 30)

 = $11,250 + $176,486.40

 = $187,736.40

 b) interest = $187,736.40 − $75,000

 = $112,736.40

 c) interest on first payment

 $i = prt = 63,750 \times 0.085 \times \dfrac{1}{12} = \$451.56$

 amount applied to principal

 $490.24 − $451.56 = $38.68

19. a) down payment:

 $160,000 − $110,000 = $50,000

 Total cost of house:

 $50,000 + (1038.40 × 12 × 25) = $361,520

 b) interest = $361,520 − $160,000 = $201,520

 c) interest on first payment

 $i = prt = 110,000 \times 0.105 \times \dfrac{1}{12} = \$962.50$

 amount applied to principal

 $1,038.40 − $962.50 = $75.90

20. a) down payment = 0.20 × $58,000 = $11,600

 b) amount of mortgage

 $58,000 − $11,600 = $46,400

 cost of two points = 0.02 × $46,400 = $928

 c) At a rate of 9.5% for 35 years,

 Table 11.4 yields 8.22.

 monthly mortgage payment

 $\dfrac{46400}{1000} \times 8.22 = \$381.41$

 d) Total cost of house

 $11,600 + (381.41 × 12 × 35) + $928

 = $172,720.20

 e) total interest paid

 = total cost w/o pts. − price

 $171,792.20 − $58,000 = $113,792.20

 f) interest on first payment

 $i = prt = 46,400 \times 0.095 \times \dfrac{1}{12} = \$367.33$

 amount applied to principal

 $381.41 − $367.33 = $14.08

21. a) down payment = $0.28 \times \$113{,}500 = \$31{,}780$

   b) amount of mortgage
   $\$113{,}500 - \$31{,}780 = \$81{,}720$
   cost of three points
   $= 0.03 \times \$81{,}720 = \$2{,}451.60$

   c) $\$4750$ gross monthly income
   $\underline{-\$420}$ monthly payments
   $\$4330$ adjusted monthly income

   d) maximum monthly payment
   $0.28 \times 4330 = \$1{,}212.40$

   e) At a rate of 10% for 20 years,
   Table 11.4 yields 9.66.
   monthly mortgage payment
   $$\frac{81720}{1000} \times 9.66 = \$789.42$$

   f) $\$789.42$ mortgage payment
   $\underline{+\$126.67}$ taxes and insurance
   $\$916.09$ total monthly payment

   g) Since $\$1{,}212.40$ is greater than
   $\$916.09$, the Yakomo's qualify.

   h) interest on first payment
   $$i = prt = 81{,}720 \times 0.10 \times \frac{1}{12} = \$681.00$$
   amount applied to principal
   $\$789.42 - \$681.00 = \$108.42$

22. a) down payment = $0.20 \times \$95{,}000 = \$19{,}000$

   b) $\$4000$ gross monthly income
   $\underline{-\$135}$ monthly payments
   $\$3865$ adjusted monthly income

   maximum monthly payment
   $0.28 \times 3865 = \$1{,}082.20$

   c) amount of mortgage
   $\$95000 - \$19000 = \$76{,}000$
   At a rate of 9.5% for 35 years,
   Table 11.4 yields 8.22.

   monthly mortgage payment
   $$\frac{76000}{1000} \times 8.22 = \$624.72$$

   d) $\$624.72$ mortgage payment
   $\underline{+\$153.00}$ taxes and insurance
   $\$777.72$ total monthly payment

   e) Since $\$1{,}082.20$ is greater than
   $\$777.72$ she qualifies.

   f) interest on first payment
   $$i = prt = 76000 \times 0.095 \times \frac{1}{12} = \$601.67$$
   amount applied to principal
   $\$624.72 - \$601.67 = \$23.05$

   g) Total cost of condominium
   $19000 + (624.72 \times 12 \times 35) = \$281{,}382.40$

   h) Total interest paid
   $281{,}382.40 - 95{,}000 = \$186{,}382.40$

23. Bank A

down payment = $0.10 \times \$105{,}000 = \$10{,}500$

amount of mortgage

$\$105000 - \$10500 = \$94{,}500$

At a rate of 10% for 30 years,

Table 11.4 yields 8.70.

monthly mortgage payment

$\dfrac{94500}{1000} \times 8.70 = \$822.15$

cost of three points

$0.03 \times 94500 = \$2835$

Total cost of the house

$10500 + 2835 + (822.15 \times 12 \times 30)$

$= \$309{,}309$

Bank B

down payment = $0.20 \times \$105{,}000 = \$21{,}000$

amount of mortgage

$\$105000 - \$21000 = \$84{,}000$

At a rate of 11.5% for 25 years,

Table 11.4 yields 10.16.

monthly mortgage payment

$\dfrac{84000}{1000} \times 10.16 = \$853.44$

Total cost of the house

$21000 + (853.44 \times 12 \times 25) = \$277{,}032$

The Nagrockis should select Bank B.

25. a) $\dfrac{\textit{amount of mortgage}}{1000} \times 8.4 = 950$

amount of mortgage = $\$113{,}095.24$

   b) $0.75(\text{total price}) = 113{,}095.24$
   total price = $\$150{,}793.65$

24. a) amount of mortgage

$\$95000 - \$13000 = \$82{,}000$

At a rate of 8.5% for 30 years,

Table 11.4 yields 7.69.

initial monthly payment

$\dfrac{82000}{1000} \times 7.69 = \$630.58$

   b) effective interest rate

$5.65\% + 3.25\% = 8.9\%$

8.9% is less than 1% above the old rate of

8.5%. Thus, the new rate is 8.9%.

   c) effective interest rate

$4.85\% + 3.25\% = 8.1\%.$

The new rate is 8.1%.

26. a) The variable rate mortgage would be the cheapest.

   b) By choosing the variable rate plan, they

   would save $2,672.64

27. a)   Amount of mortgage = $105000 − $5000 = $100,000

Initial monthly payment = $\dfrac{100000}{1000} \times 8.05 = \$805.00$

b)   Payment

Number	Interest	Principal	Balance of Loan
1	$750.00	$55.00	$99,945.00
2	$749.59	$55.41	$99,889.59
3	$749.17	$55.83	$99,833.76

c)   effective interest rate = 6.13% + 3.25% = 9.38%.
The new rate is 9.38%.

d)   Payment

Number	Interest	Principal	Balance of Loan
4	$780.37	$24.63	$99,809.13
5	$780.17	$24.83	$99,784.30
6	$779.98	$25.02	$99,759.28

e)   New rate = 6.21% + 3.25% = 9.46%

Review Exercises

1. 1/4 = 0.25 = (0.25 × 100)% = 25%

2. 2/3 ≈ 0.667 = (0.667×100)% = 66.7%

3. 5/8 = 0.625 = (0.625 × 100)% = 62.5%

4. 0.039 = (0.039 × 100)% = 3.9%

5. 0.0098 = (0.0098 × 100)% = 0.98%

6. 3.141 = (3.141 × 100)% = 314.1%

7. $26\% = \dfrac{26}{100} = 0.26$

8. $12.1\% = \dfrac{12.1}{100} = 0.121$

9. $123\% = \dfrac{123}{100} = 1.23$

10. $\dfrac{2}{5}\% = 0.4\% = \dfrac{0.4}{100} = 0.004$

11. $\dfrac{5}{6}\% = \dfrac{0.8\overline{3}}{100} = 0.008\overline{3}$

12. $0.00045\% = \dfrac{0.00045}{100} = 0.0000045$

13. percent increase
$\dfrac{13065 - 11916}{11916} \times 100 \approx 9.6\%$

14. percent increase
$\dfrac{51300 - 46200}{46200} \times 100 \approx 11.0\%$
Her salary went up by 11%.

15. $(0.01x)80 = 25$
$0.8x = 25$
$x = \dfrac{25}{0.8} = 31.25$
Twenty-five is 31.25% of 80.

16. $0.16x = 44$
$x = \dfrac{44}{0.16} = 275$
Forty-four is 16% of 275.

17. $0.17(540)\ = x$
          $91.8\ = x$
Seventeen percent of 540 is 91.8.

18. Tip = 15% of $42.79
    Tip = $0.15 \times 42.79 = \$6.42$

19. $0.20(x)\ = 8$

          $x\ = \dfrac{8}{0.20} = 40$

The original number was 40 people.

20. $\dfrac{95 - 75}{75} \times 100 = 26.7$

The increase was 26.7%.

21. $i = 2400 \times 0.07 \times (30/360)$
       $= \$14.00$

22. $41.56\ = 1575 \times r \times (100/360)$

          $41.56\ = \dfrac{157500}{360} \times r$

          $r\ = 0.095 \text{ or } 9.5\%$

23. $114.75\ = p \times 0.085 \times 3$
          $114.75\ = p \times 0.255$
          $\$450\ = p$

24. $316.25\ = 5500 \times 0.115 \times t$
          $316.25\ = 632.50 \times t$
          $t\ = 0.5 \text{ years or 6 months}$

25. $i = 3600 \times 0.1125 \times 2$
       $= \$810.00$

Total amount due at maturity
$3600 + 810 = \$4,410$

26. a) $i = 3000 \times 0.081 \times \dfrac{240}{360} = \$162$

      b) She paid $3000 + 162 = \$3,162$

27. a) $i = 6000 \times 0.115 \times \dfrac{24}{12} = \$1380.00$

      b) amount received:
          $\$6000.00 - \$1380.00 = \$4,620.00$

      c) $i\ = prt$

          $1380 = 4620 \times r \times \dfrac{24}{12}$

          $1380 = 9240r$
              $r = 0.1494 \text{ or } 14.94\%$

28. a) $5\dfrac{1}{2}\% + 2\% = 7\dfrac{1}{2}\%$

      b) $i = 800 \times 0.75 \times \dfrac{6}{12}$

          $= \$30$
          $A = \$800 + \$30$
          $A = \$830.00$

      c) x = amount of money in the account
          85% of $x = 800$
              $0.85x = 800$
                  $x = \$941.18$

29. a) $A = 1500\left(1 + \dfrac{0.06}{1}\right)^{5} = \$2,007.34$

$i = \$2007.34 - \$1500.00 = \$507.34$

      b) $A = 1500\left(1 + \dfrac{0.06}{4}\right)^{4 \cdot 5} = \$2,020.28$

$i = \$2020.28 - \$1500.00 = \$520.28$

      c) $A = 1500\left(1 + \dfrac{0.06}{12}\right)^{12 \cdot 5} = \$2,023.28$

$i = \$2023.28 - \$1500.00 = \$523.28$

30. $A = p\left(1+\dfrac{r}{n}\right)^{nt}$

$A = 2500\left(1+\dfrac{0.0475}{4}\right)^{4 \cdot 15}$

$A = \$5{,}076.35$

31. Let p = 1.00. Then

$A = 1\left(1+\dfrac{0.56}{360}\right)^{360} = 1.05759$

$i = 1.05759 - 1.00 = 0.05759$

The effective annual yield is 5.76%

32. $p\left(1+\dfrac{0.055}{4}\right)^{80} = 40000$

$p = \dfrac{40000}{(1.01375)^{80}} = 13415.00$

You need to invest $13,415.00

33. a) Installment price

$193.75 \times 48 = \$9{,}300$

Finance charge = 9300 − 7500 = $1,800

$\dfrac{finance\ charge}{amt.\ financed} \times 100 = \dfrac{1800}{7500} \times 100 = 24$

From Table 11.2, for 48 payments, the closest value to 24 is 24.06 which corresponds to an APR of 11%.

b) n = 24, p = 193.75, v = 11.86

$u = \dfrac{(24)(193.75)(11.86)}{100+11.86} = \$493.02$

c)
$4650.00	total of remaining payments
− 493.02	interest saved
$4156.98	balance due
+ 193.75	24th payment
$4350.73	total amount due

34. a) Amount financed = $3,500

Finance charge

$= (163.33 \times 24) - 3500 = \$419.92$

f = 419.92, k = 12, n = 24

$u = \dfrac{(419.92)(12)(13)}{(24)(25)} = \$109.18$

b)
$1959.96	total of remaining payments
− 109.18	interest saved
$1850.78	balance due
+ 163.33	12th payment
$2014.11	total amount due

35. a) Amount financed = $3420 − $860 = $2,560

Interest = (119.47 × 24) − 2560 = $307.28

$\dfrac{finance\ charge}{amt.\ financed} \times 100 = \dfrac{307.28}{2560} \times 100 = 12.0$

From Table 11.2, for 24 payments, the closest value to 12.0 is 11.86 which corresponds to an APR of 11.0%.

b) n = 12, p = 119.47, v = 6.06

$u = \dfrac{(12)(119.47)(6.06)}{100+6.06} = \$81.91$

c)
$1433.64	total of remaining payments
− 81.91	interest saved
$1351.73	balance due
+ 119.47	24th payment
$1471.20	total amount due

36. a) finance charge on Dec. 1

$i = 485.75 \times 0.013 \times 1 = \$6.31$

b)
485.75	old balance
+ 6.31	interest
− 375.00	payment
+ 370.00	airline ticket
+ 175.80	hotel bill
+ 184.75	clothing
$847.61	balance on Dec. 1

37. a)

Date	Balance Due	Number of Days	(Balance)(Days)
Mar. 5	185.72	3	(185.72)(3) = 557.16
Mar. 8	271.47	2	(271.47)(2) = 542.94
Mar. 10	196.47	5	(196.47)(5) = 982.35
Mar. 15	269.32	6	(269.32)(6) = 1615.92
Mar. 21	544.32	15	(544.32)(15) = 8164.80
		31	sum = 11,863.17

Average daily balance = $\dfrac{11863.17}{31}$ = \$382.68

Finance charge = 382.68 × 0.014 × 1 = \$5.36

b) Balance due on April 5 = \$544.32 + \$5.36 = \$549.68

38. a) down payment = 0.25 × 14900 = \$3,725

b) amount financed = 14900 − 3725 = \$11,175

c) total interest paid
i = 0.065 × 11175 × 4 = \$2,905.50

d) $\dfrac{2905.50}{11175}$ × 100 = 26

Using Table 11.2, with 48 payments the APR is 12%

39. a) Amt. finance = 135 − 35 = \$100
interest = 8.79 × 12 − 100 = \$5.48

b) $\dfrac{5.48}{100}$ × 100 = 5.48

Using Table 11.2 for 12 payments, the closest value to 5.48 is 5.50 which corresponds to an APR of 10%.

40. a) down payment = 0.25 × 135700 = \$33,925

b) gross monthly income = 64000/12
= \$5,333.33

$5333.33 gross monthly income
− 528.00 total of monthly payments
$4,805.33 adjusted monthly income

c) maximum monthly payment:
0.28 × 4805.33 = \$1,345.49

e) $825.40 mortgage payment
+ 316.67 taxes & insurance
$1,142.07 total monthly payment

f) Yes, \$1345.49 is greater than \$1142.07.

41. a) down payment = 0.15 × 89900 = \$13,485

b) amount of mortgage
\$89,900 − \$13,485 = \$76,415
At 11.5% for 30 years, Table 11.4 yields 9.90.
monthly mortgage payment:
$\dfrac{76415}{1000}$ × 9.90 = \$756.51

c) i = prt = 76415 × 0.115 × $\dfrac{1}{12}$ = \$732.31

amount applied to principal:
756.51 − 732.51 = \$24.20

d) total cost of house:
13485 + (756.51 × 12 × 30) = \$285,828.60

e) total interest paid:
285,828.60 − 89900 = \$195,928.60

42. a) amount of mortgage:
$105,000 − $26,250 = $78,750

First payment = $\frac{78750}{1000} \times 6.99$ = $550.46

b) 5.00% + 3.00% = 8.00%

c) 4.75% + 3.00% = 7.75%

Chapter Test

1. i = 1500 × 0.08 × (8/12)
= $80.00

2. 288 = 1200 × 0.08 × t
288 = 96t
t = 3 years

3. i = prt = 5000 × 0.085 × (18/12)
= $637.50

4. Total amount paid to the bank
$5000 + $637.50 = $5,637.50

5. down payment = 0.15(2350) = $352.50
loan amount = $2350 − $352.50
= $1,997.50

6. finance charge
= 352.50 + (94.50 × 24) − 2350
= $270.50

7. $\dfrac{finance\ charge}{amt.\ financed} \times 100$

$\dfrac{270.50}{1997.50} \times 100 = 13.54$

From Table 11.2 for 24 payments, the closest value to 13.54 is 13.54 which corresponds to an APR of 12.50%.

8. a) original finance charge
= 1550 + (465.85 × 12) − 6750 = $390.20

k = 6, n = 12, f = 390.20
u = $\dfrac{(390.20)(6)(7)}{(12)(13)}$ = $105.05

b)
2795.10	total of remaining payments
− 105.05	interest saved
2690.05	balance due
+465.85	6th monthly payment
$3,155.90	total amount due

9. a)

Date	Balance Due	Number of Days	(Balance)(Days)
May 8	378.50	5	(378.50)(5) = 1892.50
May 13	655.29	2	(655.29)(2) = 1310.58
May 15	405.29	3	(405.29)(3) = 1215.87
May 18	550.14	11	(550.14)(11) = 6051.54
May 29	605.77	10	(605.77)(10) = 6057.70
		31	sum = $16,528.19

Average daily balance = $\dfrac{16528.19}{31}$ = $533.17

Finance charge = 533.17 × 0.013 × 1 = $6.93

b) Remaining balance on June 8 is (605.77 + 6.93) = $612.70

10. a) Finance charge
    = 878.25 × 0.014 × 1 = $12.30

   b) 878.25   old balance
      + 706.02   total of charges
      − 450.00   payment
       1134.27
      + 12.30   interest
      $1146.57   new balance

12. Total interest = 84.38 + 38.82 = $123.20

13. $A = 7500 \left(1 + \dfrac{0.08}{4}\right)^{20} = \$11{,}144.61$

   interest = 11144.61 − 7500 = $3,644.61

14. $A = 2500 \left(1 + \dfrac{0.065}{12}\right)^{36} = \$3{,}036.68$

   interest = 3036.68 − 2500 = $536.68

16. gross monthly income = 86500 ÷ 12
                          = $7208.33

    7,208.33   gross monthly income
    − 605.00   total of monthly bills
   $ 6,603.33   adjusted monthly income

18. At 10.5% interest for 30 years,
    Table 11.4 yields 9.15.
    amount of loan = 144500 − 21675 = $122,825

    The monthly payments are:
    $\dfrac{122825}{1000} \times 9.15 = \$1{,}123.85$

20. Yes, the bank feels he can afford $1,848.93 per month and his payments would be $1,428.02.

11. Partial payment on Sept. 15 (45 days)
    i = 5400 × 0.125 × (45/360) = $84.38
    $3000.00   partial payment
    − 84.38   interest
    $2,915.62 amount applied to principal

     $5400.00 original principal
    − 2915.62 amount applied to principal
     $2,484.38 principal after Sept. payment

    Maturity date is Oct. 29 (45 days)
    i = 2484.38 × 0.125 × (45/360)= $38.82
    Amount owed at maturity
    $2484.38 + 38.82 = $2,523.20

15. down payment = 0.15 × 144500
                 = $21,675.00

17. maximum monthly payment is
    0.28 × 6603.33 = $1,848.93

19. 1123.85 monthly mortgage payment
    + 304.17 taxes and ins. per month
    $1,428.02 total monthly payment

21. a) Total cost of the house:
       21675 + (1123.85 × 12 × 30) = $426,261

    b) interest = $426,261 − $144,500
                = $281,761

Group Projects

1.a) $340,860.00   b) $308,420.00
  c) $23,274.33   d) $174.80
  e) $121,135.34
  f) Make a down payment of $20,000 and invest the difference in part (d).

CHAPTER TWELVE

PROBABILITY

Exercise Set 12.1

1. An experiment is a controlled operation that yields a set of results.
2. a) The possible results of an experiment are called its outcomes.
   b) An event is a subcollection of the outcomes of an experiment.
3. Empirical probability is the relative frequency of occurrence of an event. It is determined by actual observation of an experiment.

   $$P(E) = \frac{\text{number of times the event occurred}}{\text{number of times the experiment was performed}}$$

4. The equally likely possible outcomes of an experiment.
5. Relative frequency over the long run can accurately be predicted, not individual events or totals.
6. The best way to determine the likelihood of death for a person is to observe others with similar characteristics.
7. The official definition by the Weather Service is (d). The specific location is the place where the rain gauge is. The Weather Service uses sophisticated mathematical equations to calculate these probabilities.
8. No, it means that if a die were rolled many times, about 1/6 of the outcomes would be twos.
9. The "average" man in Mr. Reebe's category will live another 42.94 years. Some will die sooner, others will live longer.
10. a) Roll a die many times and then find the relative frequency of three's to the total number of rolls.

11. Student activity exercise.
12. Student activity exercise.
13. Student activity exercise.
14. Student activity exercise.

15. a) $P(\text{red hair}) = \dfrac{5}{60} = \dfrac{1}{12}$

    b) $P(\text{brown hair}) = \dfrac{28}{60} = \dfrac{7}{15}$

    c) $P(\text{blond hair}) = \dfrac{12}{60} = \dfrac{1}{5}$

16. a) $P(\text{finch}) = \dfrac{10}{20} = \dfrac{1}{2}$

    b) $P(\text{cardinal}) = \dfrac{7}{20}$

    c) $P(\text{blue jay}) = \dfrac{3}{20}$

17. a) $P(\text{grouper}) = \dfrac{18}{62} = \dfrac{9}{31}$

    b) $P(\text{shark}) = \dfrac{6}{62} = \dfrac{3}{31}$

    c) $P(\text{flounder}) = \dfrac{30}{62} = \dfrac{15}{31}$

18. $P(\text{P.W. syndrome}) = \dfrac{3}{45000} = \dfrac{1}{15000}$

19. a) P(AT&T) = 0.372

    b) P(MCI) = 0.294

    c) 22.4% of 500 = 0.224 × 500 = 112 people

21. a) P(increase) = $\dfrac{\text{freq. of increases}}{\text{no. of observations}} = \dfrac{12}{12} = 1$

    b) Yes, the answer in part (a) is only an estimate based on observation.

23. a) P(age 15-24 in 1950) = 0.147
    b) P(age 15-24 in 1996) = 0.130
    c) P(age 65+ in 1950) = 0.085
    d) P(age 65+ in 1996) = 0.147

25. a) P(bulls-eye) = $\dfrac{6}{20} = \dfrac{3}{10}$

    b) P(not bulls-eye) = $\dfrac{14}{20} = \dfrac{7}{10}$

    c) P(at least 20 pts.) = $\dfrac{14}{20} = \dfrac{7}{10}$

    d) P(does not score) = $\dfrac{2}{20} = \dfrac{1}{10}$

27. a) P(affecting circular) = $\dfrac{0}{150} = 0$

    b) P(affecting elliptical) = $\dfrac{50}{250} = 0.2$

    c) P(affecting irregular) = $\dfrac{100}{100} = 1$

29. a) P(white flowers) = $\dfrac{224}{929} = 0.24$

    b) P(purple flowers) = $\dfrac{705}{929} = 0.76$

20. a) P(field goal) = $\dfrac{10962}{21686} \approx 0.50549$

    b) P(free throw) = $\dfrac{6798}{8115} \approx 0.83771$

22. a) P(A) = $\dfrac{43}{645} \approx 0.067$

    b) P(C) = $\dfrac{260}{645} \approx 0.403$

    c) P(D or higher) = $\dfrac{90 + 260 + 182 + 43}{645} = 0.891$

24. a) It is based on the observed frequency of an event occurring.

    b) P(KitchenAid has problems) ≈ 0.10

26.   P(side 4) = $\dfrac{13}{100} = 0.13$

28. a) P(male) = $\dfrac{2264031}{4451450} = 0.5086$

    b) P(female) = $\dfrac{2187419}{4451450} = 0.4914$

30. a) P(tall plant) = $\dfrac{787}{1064} = 0.74$

    b) P(short plant) = $\dfrac{277}{1064} = 0.26$

Exercise Set 12.2

1. If each outcome of an experiment has the same chance of occurring as any other outcome, they are said to be equally likely outcomes.

2. P(event) = $\dfrac{\text{no. of outcomes favorable to the event}}{\text{total number of possible outcomes}}$

3. P(A) + P(not A) = 1

4. a) 52   b) 13   c) 26   d) 4   e) 26   f) 12
    g) 4   h) 4

5. None of the possible outcomes is the event in question.

6. The event must include all possible outcomes.

7. All probabilities are between 0 and 1.

8. The sum of the probabilities of all possible outcomes must equal 1.

9. a) P(correct) = 1/5   b) P(correct) = 1/4

10. a) P(channel 3) = 1/10   b) P(even channel) = 5/10 = 1/2
    c) P(less than 7) = 7/10

11. P(you win) = $\dfrac{one \text{ choice}}{48 \text{ } possible \text{ choices}} = \dfrac{1}{48}$

12. P(you win) = $\dfrac{one \text{ choice}}{52 \text{ } possible \text{ choices}} = \dfrac{1}{52}$

13. P(4) = $\dfrac{4}{52} = \dfrac{1}{13}$

14. P(4 or 5) = $\dfrac{8}{52} = \dfrac{2}{13}$

15. P (not a 4) = 1 − P(4) = $1 - \dfrac{1}{13} = \dfrac{12}{13}$

16. P(queen of hearts) = $\dfrac{1}{52}$

17. P(heart) = $\dfrac{13}{52} = \dfrac{1}{4}$

18. P(red card) = $\dfrac{26}{52} = \dfrac{1}{2}$

19. P(red or black card) = $\dfrac{52}{52} = 1$

20. P(red and black) = $\dfrac{0}{52} = 0$

21. P(greater than 6 and less than 10) = $\dfrac{12}{52} = \dfrac{3}{13}$

22. P(king and diamond) = $\dfrac{1}{52}$

23. a) P(red) = $\dfrac{2}{4} = \dfrac{1}{2}$

    b) P(blue) = $\dfrac{1}{4}$

    c) P(yellow) = $\dfrac{1}{4}$

24. a) P(red) = $\dfrac{1}{4}$

    b) P(blue) = $\dfrac{1}{2}$

    c) P(yellow) = $\dfrac{1}{4}$

25. a) P(red) = $\dfrac{2}{6} = \dfrac{1}{3}$

    b) P(blue) = $\dfrac{2}{6} = \dfrac{1}{3}$

    c) P(yellow) = $\dfrac{1}{3}$

26. a) P(red) = $\dfrac{4}{8} = \dfrac{1}{2}$

    b) P(blue) = $\dfrac{3}{8}$

    c) P(yellow) = $\dfrac{1}{8}$

27. P(Duracell) = $\dfrac{25}{100} = \dfrac{1}{4} = 0.25$

28. P(Duracell or Eveready) = $\dfrac{25+40}{100} = \dfrac{65}{100}$

    $= \dfrac{13}{20} = 0.65$

29. P(Duracell or Eveready or Kodak)

    $= \dfrac{25+40+20}{100} = \dfrac{85}{100} = \dfrac{17}{20} = 0.85$

30. P(Fuji) = $\dfrac{0}{100} = 0$

31. P($400) = $\dfrac{1}{12}$

32. P(lose turn or bankrupt) = $\dfrac{2}{12} = \dfrac{1}{6}$

33. P(more than $500) = $\dfrac{4}{12} = \dfrac{1}{3}$

34. P($2500 or Surprise) = $\dfrac{2}{12} = \dfrac{1}{6}$

35. P(Penn) = $\dfrac{12}{40} = \dfrac{3}{10} = 0.3$

36. P(Wilson) = $\dfrac{18}{40} = \dfrac{9}{20} = 0.45$

37. P(not Penn) = 1 − P(Penn)
$$= 1 - \frac{3}{10} = \frac{7}{10} = 0.7$$

38. $P(\text{Wilson or Penn}) = \frac{18+12}{40} = \frac{30}{40} = \frac{3}{4} = 0.75$

39. $P(\text{light is red}) = \frac{30}{75} = \frac{2}{5}$

40. $P(\text{light is yellow}) = \frac{5}{75} = \frac{1}{15}$

41. $P(\text{light is not red}) = 1 - \frac{2}{5} = \frac{3}{5}$

42. $P(\text{not red or yellow}) = \frac{40}{75} = \frac{8}{15}$

43. $P(a) = \frac{3}{10} = 0.3$

44. $P(\text{not } a) = 1 - \frac{3}{10} = \frac{7}{10} = 0.7$

45. $P(\text{vowel}) = \frac{6}{10} = \frac{3}{5} = 0.6$

46. $P(q \text{ or } u) = \frac{4}{10} = \frac{2}{5} = 0.4$

47. $P(\text{not } t) = \frac{9}{10} = 0.9$

48. $P(r) = \frac{0}{10} = 0$

49. $P(\text{exactly 80 sites}) = \frac{1}{8}$

50. $P(\text{greater than 80 sites}) = \frac{3}{8}$

51. $P(\text{Florida site}) = \frac{55}{603} \approx 0.09$

52. $P(\text{New Jersey or New York site}) = \frac{110+80}{603}$
$$= \frac{190}{603} \approx 0.32$$

53. $P(25) = \frac{1}{26}$

54. $P(\text{green area}) = \frac{13}{26} = \frac{1}{2}$

55. $P(\text{greater than or equal to 24}) = \frac{3}{26}$

56. $P(\text{greater than 6 but less or equal to 9}) = \frac{3}{26}$

57. $P(\text{female}) = \frac{310}{575} \approx 0.54$

58. $P(\text{male}) = \frac{265}{575} \approx 0.46$

59. $P(\text{public college}) = \frac{396}{575} \approx 0.69$

60. $P(\text{private college}) = \frac{179}{575} \approx 0.31$

61. $P(\text{male and private college}) = \frac{73}{575} \approx 0.13$

62. $P(\text{female and public college}) = \frac{204}{575} \approx 0.35$

63. 159

64. $P(\text{Jiff}) = \frac{50}{159} \approx 0.31$

65. $P(\text{Skippy}) = \frac{39}{159} = \frac{13}{53} \approx 0.25$

66. $P(\text{chunky}) = \frac{66}{159} = \frac{22}{53} \approx 0.42$

67. $P(\text{smooth}) = \frac{93}{159} = \frac{31}{53} \approx 0.58$

68. P(not Peter Pan smooth)
$$= \frac{159-30}{159} = \frac{129}{159} = \frac{43}{53} \approx 0.81$$

69. $P(\text{red}) = \frac{2}{18} + \frac{1}{12} + \frac{1}{6} = \frac{4}{36} + \frac{3}{36} + \frac{6}{36} = \frac{13}{36}$

70. $P(\text{green}) = \frac{1}{18} + \frac{2}{12} + \frac{1}{12} = \frac{1}{18} + \frac{3}{12} = \frac{2}{36} + \frac{9}{36} = \frac{11}{36}$

71. $P(\text{yellow}) = \frac{1}{6} + \frac{1}{12} + \frac{1}{12} = \frac{2}{12} + \frac{2}{12} = \frac{4}{12} = \frac{1}{3}$

72. $P(\text{red or green}) = \frac{13}{36} + \frac{11}{36} = \frac{24}{36} = \frac{2}{3}$

73. $P(\text{yellow or green}) = \frac{1}{3} + \frac{11}{36} = \frac{23}{36}$

74.

	c	c
c	Cc	Cc
c	Cc	Cc

a) $P(cc) = \dfrac{0}{4} = 0$

b) $P(Cc) = \dfrac{4}{4} = 1$

75.

	S_1	S_2
S_1	S_1S_1	S_1S_2
S_2	S_1S_2	S_2S_2

a) $P(S_2S_2) = \dfrac{1}{4}$

b) $P(S_1S_2) = \dfrac{2}{4} = \dfrac{1}{2}$

c) $P(S_1S_1) = \dfrac{1}{4}$

76. a) $P(\text{red}) = \dfrac{13}{26} = \dfrac{1}{2}$

b) $P(\text{even}) = \dfrac{13}{26} = \dfrac{1}{2}$

c) $P(\text{red and even}) = \dfrac{7}{26}$

d) $P(\text{red or even}) = \dfrac{19}{26}$

e) $P(\text{red or even}) = P(\text{red}) + P(\text{even}) - P(\text{red and even})$

77. a) $P(\text{red and red}) = P(\text{red}) \cdot P(\text{red}) = \dfrac{2}{4} \cdot \dfrac{2}{4} = \dfrac{1}{2} \cdot \dfrac{1}{2} = \dfrac{1}{4}$

b) $P(\text{green and green}) = P(\text{green}) \cdot P(\text{green}) = \dfrac{2}{4} \cdot \dfrac{2}{4} = \dfrac{1}{2} \cdot \dfrac{1}{2} = \dfrac{1}{4}$

c) $P(\text{1st red and 2nd green}) = P(\text{red}) \cdot P(\text{green}) = \dfrac{2}{4} \cdot \dfrac{2}{4} = \dfrac{1}{2} \cdot \dfrac{1}{2} = \dfrac{1}{4}$

78. a) $P(\text{sparrow, given the bird has low attraction to peanut kernels}) = \dfrac{2}{7}$

b) $P(\text{high attraction to cracked corn, given bird has low attraction to peanut kernels}) = 0$

c) $P(\text{high attraction to black striped sunflower seeds, given has low attraction to peanut kernels}) = \dfrac{4}{7}$

Exercise Set 12.3

1. The odds against an event are found by dividing the probability that the event does not occur by the probability that the event does occur. The probabilities used should be expressed in fractional form.

2. The odds in favor of an event are found by dividing the probability that the event does occur by the probability that the event does not occur. The probabilities used should be expressed in fractional form.

3. Odds against are more commonly used.

4. If the odds against an event are a to b, then P(event occurs) = $\dfrac{b}{a+b}$ and

P(event does not occur) = $\dfrac{a}{a+b}$.

5. 15 to 2

6. 2:5

7. a) P(event occurs) = $\dfrac{1}{1+1} = \dfrac{1}{2}$

b) P(event fails to occur) = $\dfrac{1}{1+1} = \dfrac{1}{2}$

8. a) P(event fails to occur) = 1 − P(event occurs) = $1 - \dfrac{1}{2} = \dfrac{1}{2}$

    b) odds against the event = $\dfrac{P(event\ fails\ to\ occur)}{P(event\ occurs)} = \dfrac{\frac{1}{2}}{\frac{1}{2}} = \dfrac{1}{2} \cdot \dfrac{2}{1} = \dfrac{1}{1}$ or 1:1

    c) odds in favor of the event are 1:1.

9. a) P(tie goes well) = $\dfrac{11}{24}$

    b) P(tie does not go well) = $\dfrac{13}{24}$

    c) odds against tie going well = $\dfrac{P(tie\ does\ not\ go\ well)}{P(tie\ goes\ well)} = \dfrac{\frac{13}{24}}{\frac{11}{24}} = \dfrac{13}{24} \cdot \dfrac{24}{11} = \dfrac{13}{11}$ or 13:11

    d) odds in favor of it going well are 11:13.

10. a) P($5) = $\dfrac{2}{12} = \dfrac{1}{6}$ b) P(not a $5) = $\dfrac{10}{12} = \dfrac{5}{6}$

    c) odds in favor of selecting a $5 = $\dfrac{P(\$5)}{P(not\ \$5)} = \dfrac{\frac{1}{6}}{\frac{5}{6}} = \dfrac{1}{6} \cdot \dfrac{6}{5} = \dfrac{1}{5}$ or 1:5

    d) odds against selecting a $5 are 5:1.

11. odds against rolling a 5 = $\dfrac{P(failure\ to\ roll\ a\ 5)}{P(roll\ a\ 5)} = \dfrac{5/6}{1/6} = \dfrac{5}{6} \cdot \dfrac{6}{1} = \dfrac{5}{1}$ or 5:1

12. odds against rolling odd = $\dfrac{P(failure\ to\ roll\ an\ odd)}{P(roll\ an\ odd)} = \dfrac{3/6}{3/6} = \dfrac{3}{6} \cdot \dfrac{6}{3} = \dfrac{1}{1}$ or 1:1

13. odds against rolling greater than 4 = $\dfrac{P(failure\ to\ roll\ greater\ than\ 4)}{P(roll\ greater\ than\ 4)} = \dfrac{4/6}{2/6} = \dfrac{4}{6} \cdot \dfrac{6}{2} = \dfrac{4}{2} = \dfrac{2}{1}$ or 2:1

14. odds against rolling less than 3 = $\dfrac{P(3\ or\ greater)}{P(less\ than\ 3)} = \dfrac{4/6}{2/6} = \dfrac{4}{6} \cdot \dfrac{6}{2} = \dfrac{4}{2} = \dfrac{2}{1}$ or 2:1

15. odds against a 6 = $\dfrac{P(failure\ to\ pick\ a\ 6)}{P(pick\ a\ 6)} = \dfrac{48/52}{4/52} = \dfrac{48}{52} \cdot \dfrac{52}{4} = \dfrac{12}{1}$ or 12:1

    Therefore, odds in favor of picking a 6 are 1:12.

16. odds against a heart = $\dfrac{P(failure\ to\ pick\ a\ heart)}{P(pick\ a\ heart)} = \dfrac{39/52}{13/52} = \dfrac{39}{52} \cdot \dfrac{52}{13} = \dfrac{39}{13} = \dfrac{3}{1}$ or 3:1

    Therefore, odds in favor of picking a heart are 1:3.

17. odds against a picture card = $\dfrac{P(failure\ to\ pick\ a\ picture)}{P(pick\ a\ picture)} = \dfrac{40/52}{12/52} = \dfrac{40}{52} \cdot \dfrac{52}{12} = \dfrac{40}{12} = \dfrac{10}{3}$ or 10:3

    Therefore, odds in favor of picking a picture card are 3:10.

18. odds against card greater than 5 = $\dfrac{\text{P(failure to pick a card greater than 5)}}{\text{P(pick a card greater than 5)}}$

$$= \dfrac{20/52}{32/52} = \dfrac{20}{52} \cdot \dfrac{52}{32} = \dfrac{20}{32} = \dfrac{5}{8} \text{ or 5:8}$$

Therefore, odds against picking a card greater than 5 are 5:8.

19. odds against red = $\dfrac{\text{P(not red)}}{\text{P(red)}} = \dfrac{1/2}{1/2} = \dfrac{1}{2} \cdot \dfrac{2}{1} = \dfrac{1}{1} \text{ or } 1{:}1$

20. odds against red = $\dfrac{\text{P(not red)}}{\text{P(red)}} = \dfrac{2/3}{1/3} = \dfrac{2}{3} \cdot \dfrac{3}{1} = \dfrac{2}{1} \text{ or } 2{:}1$

21. odds against red = $\dfrac{\text{P(not red)}}{\text{P(red)}} = \dfrac{5/8}{3/8} = \dfrac{5}{8} \cdot \dfrac{8}{3} = \dfrac{5}{3} \text{ or } 5{:}3$

22. odds against red = $\dfrac{\text{P(not red)}}{\text{P(red)}} = \dfrac{5/8}{3/8} = \dfrac{5}{8} \cdot \dfrac{8}{3} = \dfrac{5}{3} \text{ or } 5{:}3$

23. a) odds against selecting female = $\dfrac{\text{P(failure to select female)}}{\text{P(select female)}} = \dfrac{15/27}{12/27} = \dfrac{15}{12} = \dfrac{5}{4} \text{ or } 5{:}4.$

   b) odds against selecting male = $\dfrac{\text{P(failure to select male)}}{\text{P(select male)}} = \dfrac{12/27}{15/27} = \dfrac{12}{15} = \dfrac{4}{5} \text{ or } 4{:}5.$

24. a) odds against winning = $\dfrac{\text{P(failure to win)}}{\text{P(win)}} = \dfrac{999999/1000000}{1/1000000} = 999{,}999{:}1$

   b) odds against winning = $\dfrac{\text{P(failure to win)}}{\text{P(win)}} = \dfrac{999990/1000000}{10/1000000} = \dfrac{99999}{1} \text{ or } 99{,}999{:}1$

25. odds against a stripe = $\dfrac{\text{P(not a stripe)}}{\text{P(stripe)}} = \dfrac{8/15}{7/15} = \dfrac{8}{15} \cdot \dfrac{15}{7} = \dfrac{8}{7} \text{ or } 8{:}7$

26. odds in favor of even are $\dfrac{\text{P(even)}}{\text{P(not even)}} = \dfrac{7/15}{8/15} = \dfrac{7}{15} \cdot \dfrac{15}{8} = \dfrac{7}{8} \text{ or } 7{:}8$

27. odds in favor of not the 8 ball are $\dfrac{\text{P(not the 8 ball)}}{\text{P(the 8 ball)}} = \dfrac{14/15}{1/15} = \dfrac{14}{15} \cdot \dfrac{15}{1} = \dfrac{14}{1} \text{ or } 14{:}1$

28. odds against a ball with yellow are $\dfrac{\text{P(no yellow)}}{\text{P(yellow)}} = \dfrac{13/15}{2/15} = \dfrac{13}{15} \cdot \dfrac{15}{2} = \dfrac{13}{2} \text{ or } 13{:}2$

29. odds against a ball with 9 or greater are $\dfrac{\text{P(less than 9)}}{\text{P(9 or greater)}} = \dfrac{8/15}{7/15} = \dfrac{8}{15} \cdot \dfrac{15}{7} = \dfrac{8}{7} \text{ or } 8{:}7$

30. The odds in favor of two digits = $\dfrac{P(\text{two digits})}{P(\text{not two digits})} = \dfrac{6/15}{9/15} = \dfrac{6}{9} = \dfrac{2}{3}$ or 2:3

31. The odds against testing negative = $\dfrac{P(\text{test positive})}{P(\text{test negative})} = \dfrac{2/72}{70/72} = \dfrac{2}{70} = \dfrac{1}{35}$ or 1:35

32. The odds against red = $\dfrac{P(\text{red})}{P(\text{not red})} = \dfrac{2/11}{9/11} = \dfrac{2}{9}$ or 2:9

33. a)   P(Carrie wins) = $\dfrac{7}{7+5} = \dfrac{7}{12}$ b) P(Carrie loses) = $\dfrac{5}{7+5} = \dfrac{5}{12}$

34. a)   P(Claire wins) = $\dfrac{1}{1+6} = \dfrac{1}{7}$ b) P(Carrie loses) = $\dfrac{6}{1+6} = \dfrac{6}{7}$

35. P(promoted) = $\dfrac{9}{5+9} = \dfrac{9}{14}$

36. a)   P(Paul wins) = $\dfrac{2}{5+2} = \dfrac{2}{7}$ b) P(Paul does not win) = $\dfrac{5}{5+2} = \dfrac{5}{7}$

37. P(N) = $\dfrac{15}{75} = \dfrac{1}{5}$ 38. P(not N) = $1 - \dfrac{1}{5} = \dfrac{4}{5}$

39. Odds in favor of N = $\dfrac{P(N)}{P(\text{not N})} = \dfrac{1/5}{4/5} = \dfrac{1}{4}$ or 1:4   40. Odds against N are 4:1

41. Odds against I-27 = $\dfrac{P(\text{not I-27})}{P(\text{I-27})} = \dfrac{74/75}{1/75} = \dfrac{74}{75} \cdot \dfrac{75}{1} = \dfrac{74}{1}$ or 74:1

42. Odds in favor of I-27 are 1:74

43. P(absence for stress in 1995) = 0.06

44. P(absence not for stress in 1995) = 1 − 0.06 = 0.94 or 94/100

45. Odds against absence for stress in 1995 = $\dfrac{P(\text{not stress})}{P(\text{stress})} = \dfrac{94/100}{6/100} = \dfrac{94}{6} = \dfrac{47}{3}$ or 47:3

46. Odds in favor of absence for stress in 1995 are 3:47.

47. Odds in favor of absence for entitlement in 1998 = $\dfrac{P(\text{for entitlement})}{P(\text{not for entitlement})} = \dfrac{16/100}{84/100} = \dfrac{16}{84} = \dfrac{4}{21}$ or 4:21

48. Odds against absence for entitlement in 1998 are 21:4.

49. If P(sell your car this week) $= 0.4 = \dfrac{4}{10} = \dfrac{2}{5}$, then P(do not sell your car this week) $= 1 - \dfrac{2}{5} = \dfrac{3}{5}$.

   The odds against selling your car this week $= \dfrac{3/5}{2/5} = \dfrac{3}{2}$ or 3:2.

50. If P(overtime) $= \dfrac{3}{8}$, then P(no overtime) $= 1 - \dfrac{3}{8} = \dfrac{5}{8}$

   The odds in favor of being asked to work overtime $= \dfrac{3/8}{5/8} = \dfrac{3}{5}$ or 3:5

51. If P(fixes car right the first time) $= 0.8 = \dfrac{8}{10} = \dfrac{4}{5}$, then P(does not fix the car right the first time) $= \dfrac{1}{5}$

   The odds against the car being fixed right the first time $= \dfrac{1/5}{4/5} = \dfrac{1}{4}$ or 1:4.

52. a) The 1 in 40 statement indicates that probability is being discussed. The probability that Mr. Frank is audited is 1/40.

   b) The probability that Mr. Frank is not audited is 1 − 1/40 = 39/40.

   odds against being audited $= \dfrac{\text{P(no audit)}}{\text{P(audit)}} = \dfrac{39/40}{1/40} = \dfrac{39}{1}$ or 39:1.

53. a) The male to female ratio of gout is 20 to 1. The 20 to 1 indicates that this is actually an odds statement. Thus, the odds against J. Douglas being male are 1:20, and the odds against J. Douglas being female are 20:1.

   b) odds against female $= \dfrac{\text{P(not female)}}{\text{P(female)}} = \dfrac{20/21}{1/21}$. The probability of being a male is 20/21.

54. odds against even or greater than 3 are $\dfrac{\text{P(not even and not greater than 3)}}{\text{P(even or greater than 3)}} = \dfrac{2/6}{4/6} = \dfrac{2}{6} \cdot \dfrac{6}{4} = \dfrac{2}{4} = \dfrac{1}{2}$ or 1:2

55. P(# 1 wins) $= \dfrac{2}{7+2} = \dfrac{2}{9}$, P(# 2 wins) $= \dfrac{1}{2+1} = \dfrac{1}{3}$, P(# 3 wins) $= \dfrac{1}{15+1} = \dfrac{1}{16}$,

   P(# 4 wins) $= \dfrac{5}{7+5} = \dfrac{5}{12}$, P(# 5 wins) $= \dfrac{1}{1+1} = \dfrac{1}{2}$

56. a) P(black) $= \dfrac{18}{38} = \dfrac{9}{19}$

   b) odds against black are $\dfrac{\text{P(not black)}}{\text{P(black)}} = \dfrac{10/19}{9/19} = \dfrac{10}{19} \cdot \dfrac{19}{9} = \dfrac{10}{9}$ or 10:9

   c) P(0 or 00) $= \dfrac{2}{38} = \dfrac{1}{19}$

   d) odds in favor of 0 or 00 are $\dfrac{\text{P(0 or 00)}}{\text{P(not 0 and not 00)}} = \dfrac{1/19}{18/19} = \dfrac{1}{19} \cdot \dfrac{19}{18} = \dfrac{1}{18}$ or 1:18

Exercise Set 12.4

1. Expected value is used to determine the average gain or loss of an experiment over the long run.
2. An expected value of 0 indicates that the individual would break even over the long run.
3. The fair price is the amount charged for the game to be fair and result in an expected value of 0.
4. a) $E = P_1A_1 + P_2A_2$ b) $E = P_1A_1 + P_2A_2 + P_3A_3$
5. No, fair price is the price to pay to make the expected value 0. The expected value is the expected outcome of an experiment when the experiment is performed many times.
6. To obtain fair price, add the cost to play to the expected value.
7. $0.50. Since you would lose $1.00 on average for each game you played, the fair price of the game should be $1.00 less. Then the expected value would be 0, and the game would be fair.
8. Fair price = $P_1G_1 + P_2G_2 + P_3G_3$
9. a) A $10 bet is the same as five $2 bets, thus Marty's expected value is $5(-0.40) = -\$2.00$
   b) On average he can expect to lose $2.00
10. a) Paul's expected value on a $5 bet is $5(0.20) = \$1.00$.
    b) If he makes many $5 bets he can expect to win, on average, $1.00 per bet.

11. $E = P_1A_1 + P_2A_2 = 0.65(70000) + 0.35(-30000) = 45500 - 10500 = \$35,000$
12. $E = P_1A_1 + P_2A_2 = 0.40(20) + 0.60(12) = 8 + 7.2 = \$15.2$ people
13. $E = P_1A_1 + P_2A_2 = 0.50(78) + 0.50(62) = 39 + 31 = 70$ points
14. $E = P_1A_1 + P_2A_2 = 0.30(12000) + 0.70(-3000) = 3600 - 2100 = \$1,500$.

15. a) $E = P(\text{sunny})(1/2) + P(\text{cloudy})(1/4)$
       $E = 0.75(1/2) + 0.25(1/4) = 0.375 + 0.0625 = 0.4375$ inches per day
    b) (0.4375 inches per day)(31 days) = 13.5625 inches of growth during July is expected

16. $E = P_1A_1 + P_2A_2 + P_3A_3 = 0.60(8000) + 0.10(0) + 0.30(-6200) = 4800 + 0 - 1860 = \$2,940$.

17. a) $E = P_1A_1 + P_2A_2 = \dfrac{7}{10}(20\%) + \dfrac{3}{10}(30\%) = 14\% + 9\% = 23\%$

    b) Expected amount = $100 - 0.23(100) = 100 - 23 = \$77$.

18. a) $E_{\text{Mike}} = P(\text{heart})(\text{amount won}) + P(\text{not heart})(\text{amount lost})$

       $= \dfrac{13}{52} \cdot (\$5) + \dfrac{39}{52} \cdot (-\$2) = \dfrac{1}{4} \cdot (\$5) + \dfrac{3}{4} \cdot (-\$2) = \$1.25 - \$1.50 = -\$0.25$
    b) Since Mike's expectation is $-\$0.25$, Dave's expectation must be $+\$0.25$.

19. a) $E_{\text{guess}} = P(\text{guess correct})(\text{points gained}) + P(\text{guess incorrect})(\text{points lost})$

       $= \dfrac{1}{4}(5) + \dfrac{3}{4}(-2) = \dfrac{5}{4} - \dfrac{6}{4} = -\dfrac{1}{4}$

    Since $E_{\text{guess}} = -\dfrac{1}{4}$ point, it is to your advantage to leave a question blank.

    b) $E_{\text{guess}} = P(\text{guess correct})(\text{points gained}) + P(\text{guess incorrect})(\text{points lost})$

       $= \dfrac{1}{3}(5) + \dfrac{2}{3}(-2) = \dfrac{5}{3} - \dfrac{4}{3} = \dfrac{1}{3}$ point

    Therefore if you can eliminate one possible choice, it is to your advantage to guess.

20. $E = P_1A_1 + P_2A_2 + P_3A_3 = P(\$1 \text{ off})(\$1) + P(\$2 \text{ off})(\$2) + P(\$5 \text{ off})(\$5)$

    $= \dfrac{7}{10}(\$1) + \dfrac{2}{10}(\$2) + \dfrac{1}{10}(\$5) = \dfrac{7}{10} + \dfrac{4}{10} + \dfrac{5}{10} = \dfrac{16}{10} = \$1.60$

21. a)   E = P(wins)(amount won) + P(loses)(amount lost)

$$= \frac{1}{1000}(\$499) + \frac{999}{1000}(-\$1) = \frac{499}{1000} - \frac{999}{1000} = \frac{500}{1000} = -\$0.50$$

   b)   A fair price for the ticket = cost to play + expectation = $1.00 + (- $0.50) = $0.50

   c)   Profit = 1000($0.50) = $500

22. a) $E = P_1A_1 + P_2A_2 + P_3A_3 + P_4A_4$

   = P($10,000 win)(net amt.)+P($5,000 win)(net amt.)+P($1,000)(net amt.)+P(lose)(amt. lost)

$$= \frac{1}{10000}(\$9,995) + \frac{1}{10000}(\$4,995) + \frac{2}{10000}(\$995) + \frac{9996}{10000}(-\$5)$$

$$= \frac{9995}{10000} + \frac{4995}{10000} + \frac{1990}{10000} + \frac{49980}{10000} = \frac{33000}{10000} = -\$3.30$$

   b)   A fair price for the ticket = cost to play + expectation = $5.00 - $3.30 = $1.70.

23. a)   fair price = P($1)($1) + P($5)($5) = $\frac{1}{2}(1) + \frac{1}{2}(5)$ = 0.50 + 2.50 = $3.00

   b)   expectation = fair price - cost to play = $3.00 - $2.00 = $1.00

24. a)   fair price = P($1) · ($1) + P($5) · ($5) + P($10) · ($10)

$$= \frac{1}{4} \cdot (1) + \frac{1}{4} \cdot (5) + \frac{1}{2} \cdot (10) = 0.25 + 1.25 + 5.00 = \$6.50$$

   b)   expectation = fair price - cost to play = $6.50 - $2.00 = $4.50

25. a)   fair price = P($1) · ($1) + P($5) · ($5) + P($10) · ($10)

$$= \frac{1}{2} \cdot (1) + \frac{1}{4} \cdot (5) + \frac{1}{4} \cdot (10) = 0.50 + 1.25 + 2.50 = \$4.25$$

   b)   expectation = fair price - cost to play = $4.25 - $2.00 = $2.25

26. a)   fair price = P($1) · ($1) + P($5) · ($5) + P($10) · ($10)

$$= \frac{3}{8} \cdot (1) + \frac{2}{8} \cdot (5) + \frac{3}{8} \cdot (10) = 0.375 + 1.25 + 3.75 = \$5.38$$

   b)   expectation = fair price - cost to play = $5.38 - $2.00 = $3.38

27. $E_{company}$ = P(insured lives) · (amount gained) + P(insured dies) · (amount lost)

= 0.994 · ($100) + 0.006 · (-$9,900) = 99.4 - 59.4 = $40

   Thus, the company gains $40 on this type of policy.

28. $E = P_1A_1 + P_2A_2 + P_3A_3 + P_4A_4 + P_5A_5$ = 0.17(1) + 0.10(2) + 0.02(3) + 0.08(4) + 0.63(0) = 0.75 base

29. a) $E = P_1A_1 + P_2A_2 + P_3A_3 = \frac{3}{10}(4) + \frac{5}{10}(3) + \frac{2}{10}(1)$ = 1.2 + 1.5 + 0.2 = 2.9 points

   b)   Fair price = 2.9 points

   c)   3 × E = 3(2.9) = 8.7 points

30. a) $E = P_1A_1 + P_2A_2 + P_3A_3 = \dfrac{3}{10}(5) + \dfrac{5}{10}(2) + \dfrac{2}{10}(-3) = 1.5 + 1.0 - 0.6 = 1.9$ points

    b) Fair price = 1.9 points

    c) $3 \times E = 3(1.9) = 5.7$ points

31. $E = P_1A_1 + P_2A_2 + P_3A_3$

    $= P(\text{hit oil}) \cdot (\text{oil profits}) + P(\text{hit gas}) \cdot (\text{gas profits}) + P(\text{hit nothing}) \cdot (\text{loss})$

    $= 0.08 \cdot (\$500,000) + 0.20 \cdot (\$100,000) + 0.72 \cdot (-\$30,000)$

    $= \$40,000 + \$20,000 - \$21,600 = \$38,400$

    Yes, if the company drills many of these wells, they can expect to make an average of $38,400 per well drilled.

32. $E = P_1A_1 + P_2A_2 + P_3A_3$

    $= 0.5 \cdot (\$350,000) + 0.30 \cdot (\$140,000) + 0.2 \cdot (-\$420,000)$

    $= \$175,000 + \$42,000 - \$84,000 = \$133,000$

    Therefore she has an expected gain of $133,000.

33. $E = P_1A_1 + P_2A_2$

    $= P(\text{granted new routes})(\text{\# of new employees}) + P(\text{not granted})(\text{\# of new employees})$

    $= 0.36 \cdot (920) + 0.64 \cdot (170) = 331.2 + 108.8 = 440$

34. $E = P(1) \cdot (1) + P(2) \cdot (2) + P(3) \cdot (3) + P(4) \cdot (4) + P(5) \cdot (5) + P(6) \cdot (6)$

    $= \dfrac{1}{6}(1) + \dfrac{1}{6}(2) + \dfrac{1}{6}(3) + \dfrac{1}{6}(4) + \dfrac{1}{6}(5) + \dfrac{1}{6}(6) = \dfrac{1}{6} + \dfrac{2}{6} + \dfrac{3}{6} + \dfrac{4}{6} + \dfrac{5}{6} + \dfrac{6}{6} = \dfrac{21}{6} = 3.5$

35. $E = P_1A_1 + P_2A_2 + P_3A_3$

    $= 0.70(40,000) + 0.10(0) + 0.20(-30,000) = 28,000 + 0 - 6,000 = \$22,000$

36. $E = P_1A_1 + P_2A_2 + P_3A_3$

    $= \dfrac{200}{365}(110) + \dfrac{100}{365}(160) + \dfrac{65}{365}(210) = 60.27 + 43.84 + 37.40 = 141.51$ calls/day

37. Profit if Jorge sells the house = $0.06(100,000) = \$6,000$

    Profit if another Realtor sells the house = $0.03(100,000) = \$3,00$

    $E = P_1A_1 + P_2A_2 + P_3A_3$

    $= 0.2 \cdot (\$5,000) + 0.5 \cdot (\$2,000) + 0.3 \cdot (-\$1,000)$

    $= \$1,000 + \$1,000 - \$300 = \$1,700$ gain

    Yes, in the long run if Jorge lists many of these $100,000 homes, he can expect to make, on average, $1,700 per listing.

38. The insurance company can expect to pay out:

    $200(0.002)(10,000) + 400(0.002)(5000) + 1000(0.002)(1000)$

    $= \$4,000 + \$4,000 + \$2,000 = \$10,000$

39. a) $P(\$1) = \frac{1}{2} + \frac{1}{16} = \frac{8}{16} + \frac{1}{16} = \frac{9}{16}$, $P(\$10) = \frac{1}{4} = \frac{4}{16}$, $P(\$20) = \frac{1}{8} = \frac{2}{16}$, $P(\$100) = \frac{1}{16}$

   b) $E = P_1A_1 + P_2A_2 + P_3A_3 + P_4A_4$

   $$= \frac{9}{16}(\$1) + \frac{4}{16}(\$10) + \frac{2}{16}(\$20) + \frac{1}{16}(\$100) = \frac{9}{16} + \frac{40}{16} + \frac{40}{16} + \frac{100}{16} = \frac{189}{16} = \$11.81$$

   c) fair price = expected value − cost to play = $11.81 − 0 = $11.81

40. a) $P(\$1) = \frac{1}{6} + \frac{1}{4} = \frac{2}{12} + \frac{3}{12} = \frac{5}{12} = \frac{10}{24}$, $P(\$10) = \frac{1}{6} = \frac{4}{24}$, $P(\$20) = \frac{1}{6} + \frac{1}{8} = \frac{4}{24} + \frac{3}{24} = \frac{7}{24}$, $P(\$100) = \frac{1}{8} = \frac{3}{24}$

   b) $E = P_1A_1 + P_2A_2 + P_3A_3 + P_4A_4$

   $$= \frac{10}{24}(1) + \frac{4}{24}(10) + \frac{7}{24}(20) + \frac{3}{24}(100) = \frac{10}{24} + \frac{40}{24} + \frac{140}{24} + \frac{300}{24} = \frac{490}{24} = \$20.42$$

   c) fair price = expected value − cost to play = $20.42 − 0 = $20.42

41. E = P(insured lives) · (cost) + P(insured dies) · (cost − $40,000)
    = 0.97(cost) + 0.03(cost − 40,000) = 0.97(cost) + 0.03(cost) − 1200
    = 1.00(cost) − 1200
    Thus, in order for the company to make a profit, the cost must exceed $1,200.

42. E = P(win) · (amount won) + P(lose) · (amount lost)

   $$= \frac{1}{38} \cdot (35) + \frac{37}{38} \cdot (-1) = \frac{35}{38} - \frac{37}{38} = -\frac{2}{38} = -5.3¢$$

43. E = P(red) · (amount won) + P(not red) · (amount lost)

   $$= \frac{18}{38} \cdot (1) + \frac{20}{38} \cdot (-1) = \frac{18}{38} - \frac{20}{38} = -\frac{2}{38} = -5.3¢$$

44. $P(\text{both black}) = \frac{5}{10} \cdot \frac{4}{9} = \frac{20}{90} = \frac{2}{9}$ and $P(\text{both red}) = \frac{2}{9}$

   $$E = \frac{4}{9} \cdot (\$1) + \frac{5}{9} \cdot (-\$1) = \frac{4}{9} - \frac{5}{9} = -\frac{1}{9} = -\$0.11$$

   Since your expectation is negative, the game favors the dealer.

45. a) $E = \frac{1}{12}(100) + \frac{1}{12}(200) + \frac{1}{12}(300) + \frac{1}{12}(400) + \frac{1}{12}(500) + \frac{1}{12}(600) + \frac{1}{12}(700)$

   $$+ \frac{1}{12}(800) + \frac{1}{12}(900) + \frac{1}{12}(1000) + \frac{1}{12}(0) = \frac{550}{12} = \$458.33$$

   b) $E = \frac{1}{12}(5500) + \frac{1}{12}(-1800) = \frac{3700}{12} = \$308.33$

46. No, you don't know how many others are selecting the same numbers that you are selecting.

Exercise Set 12.5

1. If a first experiment can be performed in M distinct way and a second experiment can be performed in N distinct ways, then the two experiments in that specific order can be performed in M · N distinct ways.

2. a) A list of all the possible outcomes of an experiment.

   b) Each individual outcome in a sample space is a sample point.

3. 3 × 5 = 15 ways. Using the counting principle.

4. Answers will vary.

5. The first selection is made. Then the second selection is made before the first selection is returned to the group of items being selected.

6. 8, each branch represents a sample point.

7. a) 50 × 50 = 2500 possibilities
   b) 50 × 49 = 2450 possibilities

8. a) 365 × 365 = 133,225
   b) 365 × 364 = 132,860

9. a) 5 × 5 = 25 sample points
   b) 5 × 4 = 20 sample points

10. a) 6 × 5 × 4 = 120
    b) 6 × 6 × 6 = 216

11. a) 2 × 2 = 4 points
    b)

Coin 1	Coin 2	Sample Space
H	H	H, H
	T	H, T
T	H	T, H
	T	T, T

    c) P(no heads) = $\dfrac{1}{4}$

    d) P(exactly one head) = $\dfrac{2}{4}$ = $\dfrac{1}{2}$

    e) P(two heads) = $\dfrac{1}{4}$

12. a) 3 × 3 = 9 points
    b)

    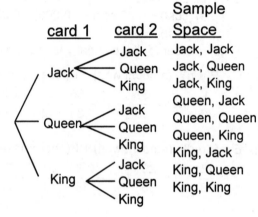

card 1	card 2	Sample Space
Jack	Jack	Jack, Jack
	Queen	Jack, Queen
	King	Jack, King
Queen	Jack	Queen, Jack
	Queen	Queen, Queen
	King	Queen, King
King	Jack	King, Jack
	Queen	King, Queen
	King	King, King

    c) P(two Jacks) = $\dfrac{1}{9}$

    d) P(Jack and then Queen) = $\dfrac{1}{9}$

    e) P(at least one King) = $\dfrac{5}{9}$

13. a) 3 × 2 = 6 points

b)

Card 1	Card 2	Sample Space
Jack	Queen	Jack, Queen
	King	Jack, King
Queen	Jack	Queen, Jack
	King	Queen, King
King	Jack	King, Jack
	Queen	King, Queen

c) P(two Jacks) = $\frac{0}{6}$ = 0

d) P(Jack and then Queen) = $\frac{1}{6}$

e) P(at least one King) = $\frac{4}{6}$ = $\frac{2}{3}$

14. a) 2 × 2 = 4 points

b)

First	Second	Sample Space
boy	boy	boy, boy
	girl	boy, girl
girl	boy	girl, boy
	girl	girl, girl

c) P(two girls) = $\frac{1}{4}$

d) P(at least one girl) = $\frac{3}{4}$

e) P(girl 1st and boy 2nd) = $\frac{1}{4}$

15. a) 4 × 3 = 12 points

b)

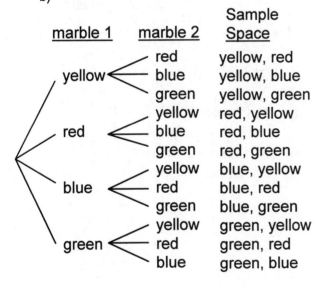

marble 1	marble 2	Sample Space
yellow	red	yellow, red
	blue	yellow, blue
	green	yellow, green
red	yellow	red, yellow
	blue	red, blue
	green	red, green
blue	yellow	blue, yellow
	red	blue, red
	green	blue, green
green	yellow	green, yellow
	red	green, red
	blue	green, blue

c) P(exactly one red) = $\frac{6}{12}$ = $\frac{1}{2}$

d) P(at least one is not red) = $\frac{12}{12}$ = 1

e) P(no green) = $\frac{6}{12}$ = $\frac{1}{2}$

16. a) 2 × 2 × 2 = 8 points

b)

child 1	child 2	child 3	Sample Space
boy	boy	boy	boy, boy, boy
		girl	boy, boy, girl
	girl	boy	boy, girl, boy
		girl	boy, girl, girl
girl	boy	boy	girl, boy, boy
		girl	girl, boy, girl
	girl	boy	girl, girl, boy
		girl	girl, girl, girl

c) P(no boys) = $\frac{1}{8}$

d) P(at least one girl) = $\frac{7}{8}$

e) P(either exactly 2 boys or 2 girls) = $\frac{6}{8}$ = $\frac{3}{4}$

f) P(boy 1st and boy 2nd and girl 3rd) = $\frac{1}{8}$

17. a) $6 \times 6 = 36$ points

b)

1st die	2nd die	Sample Space
1	1	1, 1
	2	1, 2
	3	1, 3
	4	1, 4
	5	1, 5
	6	1, 6
2	1	2, 1
	2	2, 2
	3	2, 3
	4	2, 4
	5	2, 5
	6	2, 6
3	1	3, 1
	2	3, 2
	3	3, 3
	4	3, 4
	5	3, 5
	6	3, 6
4	1	4, 1
	2	4, 2
	3	4, 3
	4	4, 4
	5	4, 5
	6	4, 6
5	1	5, 1
	2	5, 2
	3	5, 3
	4	5, 4
	5	5, 5
	6	5, 6
6	1	6, 1
	2	6, 2
	3	6, 3
	4	6, 4
	5	6, 5
	6	6, 6

17. c) P(double is rolled) $= \dfrac{6}{36} = \dfrac{1}{6}$

d) P(sum of 7) $= \dfrac{6}{36} = \dfrac{1}{6}$

e) P(sum of 2) $= \dfrac{1}{36}$

f) No, there are 6 combinations, out of 36 possibilities, that result in a sum of 7 and only 1 way, out of 36 possibilities, of getting a sum of 2.

18. a) $3 \times 2 \times 1 = 6$ points

b)

pick 1	pick 2	pick 3	Sample Space
E	M	U	E,M,U
	U	M	E,U,M
M	E	U	M,E,U
	U	E	M,U,E
U	E	M	U,E,M
	M	E	U,M,E

c) P(M selected 1st) $= \dfrac{2}{6} = \dfrac{1}{3}$

d) P(E 1st and M 3rd) $= \dfrac{1}{6}$

e) P(M 1st and U 2nd and E 3rd) $= \dfrac{1}{6}$

19. a) $3 \times 3 \times 3 = 27$ points

b)

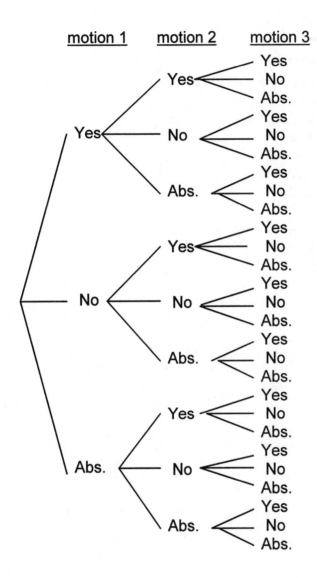

motion 1	motion 2	motion 3	Sample Space
		Yes	yes, yes, yes
	Yes	No	yes, yes, no
		Abs.	yes, yes, abs.
		Yes	yes, no, yes
Yes	No	No	yes, no, no
		Abs.	yes, no abs.
		Yes	yes, abs. yes
	Abs.	No	yes, abs., no
		Abs.	yes, abs., abs.
		Yes	no, yes, yes
	Yes	No	no, yes, no
		Abs.	no, yes, abs.
		Yes	no, no, yes
No	No	No	no, no, no
		Abs.	no, no, abs.
		Yes	no, abs., yes
	Abs.	No	no, abs., no
		Abs.	no, abs., abs.
		Yes	abs., yes, yes
	Yes	No	abs., yes, no
		Abs.	abs., yes, abs.
		Yes	abs., no, yes
Abs.	No	No	abs., no, no
		Abs.	abs., no, abs.
		Yes	abs., abs., yes
	Abs.	No	abs., abs., no
		Abs.	abs., abs., abs.

c)   P(No vote on all three motions) = $\dfrac{1}{27}$

d)   P(Yes vote on exactly two motions) = $\dfrac{6}{27} = \dfrac{2}{9}$

e)   P(at least one yes vote) = $\dfrac{19}{27}$

20. a) $4 \times 3 = 12$ points

b)

	Disney	non-Disney	Sample Space
	M.K.	S.W.	M.K., S.W.
		Univ.	M.K, Univ.
		B.G	M.K., B.G.
	E.C.	S.W.	E.C., S.W.
		Univ.	E.C., Univ.
		B.G.	E.C., B.G.
	MGM	S.W.	MGM, S.W.
		Univ.	MGM, Univ.
		B.G.	MGM, B.G.
	A.K	S.W.	A.K., S.W.
		Univ.	A.K., Univ.
		B.G.	A.K., B.G.

c) $P(\text{M.K. or E.C.}) = \dfrac{6}{12} = \dfrac{1}{2}$

d) $P(\text{MGM or Univ.}) = \dfrac{6}{12} = \dfrac{1}{2}$

e) $P(\text{M.K. and (S.W. or B.G.)}) = \dfrac{2}{12} = \dfrac{1}{6}$

21. a) $3 \times 3 \times 2 = 18$ points

b)

| | | | Sample |
| Bachelors | Masters | Ph.D. | Space |

T, H, E
T, H, C
T, M, E
T, M, C
T, W, E
T, W, C
B, H, E
B, H, C
B, M, E
B, M, C
B, W, E
B, W, C
J, H, E
J, H, C
J, M, E
J, M, C
J, W, E
J, W, C

c) $P(\text{SUNY-B}) = \dfrac{1}{3}$

d) $P(\text{U. Mass. or U. Hawaii for masters}) = \dfrac{2}{3}$

e) $P(\text{U. Texas for B.A. and UCLA for Ph.D.}) = \dfrac{3}{18} = \dfrac{1}{6}$

22. a) $3 \times 3 \times 3 = 27$ points

b)

show 1	show 2	show 3	Sample Space
GMA	St	MS	GMA, St, MS
		SJR	GMA, St, SJR
		DM	GMA, St, DM
	Ma	MS	GMA, Ma, MS
		SJR	GMA, Ma, SJR
		DM	GMA, Ma, DM
	LT	MS	GMA, LT, MS
		SJR	GMA, LT, SJR
		DM	GMA, LT, DM
TM	St	MS	TM, St, MS
		SJR	TM, St, SJR
		DM	TM, St, DM
	Ma	MS	TM, Ma, MS
		SJR	TM, Ma, SJR
		DM	TM, Ma, DM
	LT	MS	TM, LT, MS
		SJR	TM, LT, SJR
		DM	TM, LT, DM
T	St	MS	T, St, MS
		SJR	T, St, SJR
		DM	T, St, DM
	Ma	MS	T, Ma, Ms
		SJR	T, Ma, SJR
		DM	T, Ma, DM
	LT	MS	T, LT, MS
		SJR	T, LT, SJR
		DM	T, LT, DM

c)   P(all NBC shows) = $\dfrac{1}{27}$

d)   P(Today and Martin Short) = $\dfrac{3}{27} = \dfrac{1}{9}$

e)   P(M. Stewart is not watched) = $\dfrac{18}{27} = \dfrac{2}{3}$

23. a) $4 \times 2 \times 2 = 16$ points

b)

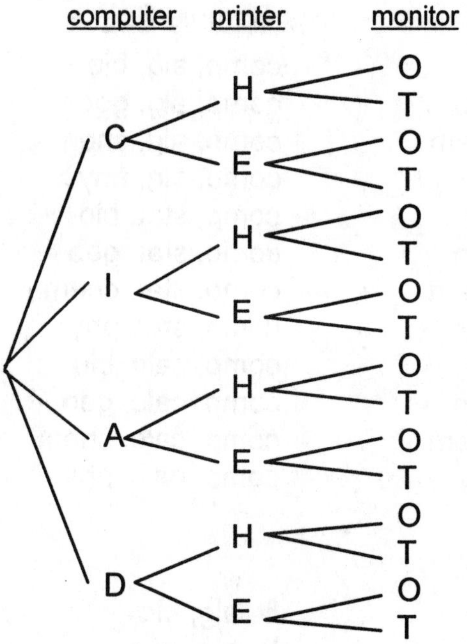

	computer	printer	monitor	Sample Space

C, H, O
C, H, T
C, E, O
C, E, T
I, H, O
I, H, T
I, E, O
I, E, T
A, H, O
A, H, T
A, E, O
A, E, T
D, H, O
D, H, T
D, E, O
D, E, T

c) $P(\text{Apple}) = \dfrac{1}{4}$

d) $P(\text{H-P}) = \dfrac{1}{2}$

e) $P(\text{Apple and H-P}) = \dfrac{2}{16} = \dfrac{1}{8}$

24. a) $2 \times 3 \times 4 = 24$ points

b)

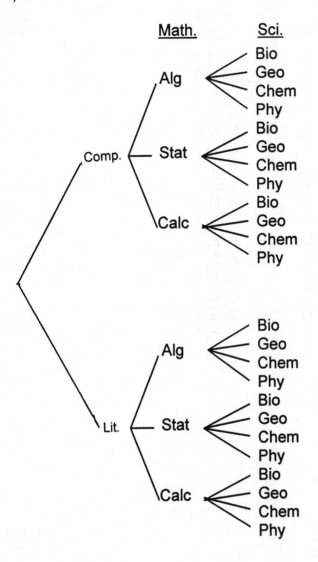

Math.	Sci.	Sample Space
Alg	Bio	comp, alg, bio
	Geo	comp, alg, geo
	Chem	comp, alg, chem
	Phy	comp, alg, phy
Stat	Bio	comp, stat, bio
	Geo	comp, stat, geo
	Chem	comp, stat, chem
	Phy	comp, stat, phy
Calc	Bio	comp, calc, bio
	Geo	comp, calc, geo
	Chem	comp, calc, chem
	Phy	comp, calc, phy
Alg	Bio	lit, alg, bio
	Geo	lit, alg, geo
	Chem	lit, alg, chem
	Phy	lit, alg, phy
Stat	Bio	lit, stat, bio
	Geo	lit, stat, geo
	Chem	lit, stat, chem
	Phy	lit, stat, phy
Calc	Bio	lit, calc, bio
	Geo	lit, calc, geo
	Chem	lit, calc, chem
	Phy	lit, calc, phy

c) $P(\text{geo.}) = \dfrac{1}{4}$

d) $P(\text{geo. or chem.}) = \dfrac{2}{4} = \dfrac{1}{2}$

e) $P(\text{not calc.}) = \dfrac{16}{24} = \dfrac{2}{3}$

25. a) $2 \times 4 \times 3 = 24$ sample points

b)

sex	hair	eyes	Sample Space
		brown	M, red, brown
	red	blue	M, red, blue
		green	M, red, green
		brown	M, brown, brown
	brown	blue	M, brown, blue
		green	M, brown, green
M		brown	M, black, brown
	black	blue	M, black, blue
		green	M, black, green
		brown	M, blonde, brown
	blonde	blue	M, blonde, blue
		green	M, blonde, green
		brown	F, red, brown
	red	blue	F, red, blue
		green	F, red, green
		brown	F, brown, brown
	brown	blue	F, brown, blue
		green	F, brown, green
F		brown	F, black, brown
	black	blue	F, black, blue
		green	F, black, green
		brown	F, blonde, brown
	blonde	blue	F, blonde, blue
		green	F, blonde, green

c) $P(M, black, blue) = \dfrac{1}{24}$

d) $P(F, blonde) = \dfrac{3}{24} = \dfrac{1}{8}$

26. a) $2 \times 2 \times 2 \times 2 = 16$ sample points

b)

height	skin	seeds	peas	Sample Space
		y	wh	s, r, y, wh
			p	s, r, y, p
	r	g	wh	s, r, g, wh
			p	s, r, g, p
s		y	wh	s, w, y, wh
			p	s, w, y, p
	w	g	wh	s, w, g, wh
			p	s, w, g, p
		y	wh	t, r, y, wh
			p	t, r, y, p
	r	g	wh	t, r, g, wh
			p	t, r, g, p
t		y	wh	t, w, y, wh
			p	t, w, y, p
	w	g	wh	t, w, g, wh
			p	t, w, g, p

c) P(round peas) = $\frac{8}{16} = \frac{1}{2}$

d) P(s, w, y, p) = $\frac{1}{16}$

27. a) m or n

b) 3 or 4

c) m, 3
    m, 4
    n, 3
    n, 4

d) No, not unless we know that all outcomes are equally likely.

e) No, not unless we know that all outcomes are equally likely.

f) Yes, each sample point would have the same probability.

Exercise Set 12.6

1. a) "or" means at least one event A or B must occur.
   b) "and" means both events, A and B, must occur.
2. a) P(A or B) = P(A) + P(B) − P(A and B)
3. a) Two events are mutually exclusive if it is impossible for both events to occur simultaneously.
   b) P(A or B) = P(A) + P(B)
4. a) P(A and B) = P(A) • P(B, given that A has occurred)
5. We assume that event A has already occurred.
6. Two events are independent if the occurrence of either event in no way affects the probability of occurrence of the other event. Ex. toss two coins; find P (tails and tails)
7. Two events are dependent if the occurrence of either event affects the probability of occurrence of the other event. Ex. Select two cards from a deck (without replacement); find P (King and King).

8. a) No, it is possible for both to like classical music.
   b) No, if the mother likes classical music the daughter will be more likely to like classical music.

9. a) No, it is possible for an individual to be both happy and healthy at the same time.
   b) No, if you are healthy, you are more likely to be happy.

10. a) No, both mother and father may be teachers.
    b) No, studies have shown that if the husband or wife is a teacher there is an increased probability that their spouse is also a teacher.

11. Student activity problem.

12. If the events are mutually exclusive, the events cannot happen simultaneously and thus P(A and B) = 0.

13. P(A or B) = P(A) + P(B) – P(A and B)
     = 0.4 + 0.5 – 0.2 = 0.7

14. P(A and B) = P(A) + P(B) – P(A or B)
     = 0.5 + 0.6 – 0.9 = 0.2

15. P(B) = P(A or B) + P(A and B) – P(A)
     = 0.8 + 0.1 – 0.4 = 0.5

16. P(A or B) = P(A) + P(B) – P(A and B)
     0.6 = P(A) + 0.3 – 0.1
     0.6 = P(A) + 0.2
     P(A) = 0.4

17. P(3 or 5) = $\frac{2}{6} = \frac{1}{3}$

18. P(odd or greater than 2) = $\frac{5}{6}$

19. P(greater than 5 or less than 3) = $\frac{3}{6} = \frac{1}{2}$

20. All numbers on the die are either greater than 3 or less than 5.

     P(greater than 3 or less than 5) = $\frac{6}{6}$ = 1

21. Since these events are mutually exclusive,
     P(queen or king) = P(queen) + P(king)

     $= \frac{4}{52} + \frac{4}{52} = \frac{8}{52} = \frac{2}{13}$

22. Since it is possible to obtain a card that is both a jack and a diamond when only one card is selected, these events are not mutually exclusive.
     P(jack or diamond)
     = P(jack) + P(diamond) – P(jack and diamond)

     $= \frac{4}{52} + \frac{13}{52} - \frac{1}{52} = \frac{16}{52} = \frac{4}{13}$

23. Since it is possible to obtain a card that is a picture card and a red card, these events are not mutually exclusive.
     P(picture or red)
     = P(pict.) + P(red) – P(pict. and red)

     $= \frac{12}{52} + \frac{26}{52} - \frac{6}{52} = \frac{32}{52} = \frac{8}{13}$

24. Since it is impossible to obtain a card that is both a heart and a black card, these events are mutually exclusive.
     P(heart or black) = P(heart) + P(black)

     $= \frac{13}{52} + \frac{26}{52} = \frac{39}{52} = \frac{3}{4}$

25. Since it is possible to obtain a card less than 9 that is a club, these events are not mutually exclusive.
     P(less than 9 or club)

     $= \frac{32}{52} + \frac{13}{52} - \frac{8}{52} = \frac{37}{52}$

26. Since it is possible to obtain a card greater than 8 that is black, these events are not mutually exclusive.
     P(greater than 8 or black)

     $= \frac{20}{52} + \frac{26}{52} - \frac{10}{52} = \frac{36}{52} = \frac{9}{13}$

27. a) P(3 and 3) = $\frac{4}{20} \cdot \frac{4}{20} = \frac{1}{5} \cdot \frac{1}{5} = \frac{1}{25}$

     b) P(3 and 3) = $\frac{4}{20} \cdot \frac{3}{19} = \frac{1}{5} \cdot \frac{3}{19} = \frac{3}{95}$

28. a) P(frog and frog)= $\dfrac{5}{20}\cdot\dfrac{5}{20}=\dfrac{1}{4}\cdot\dfrac{1}{4}=\dfrac{1}{16}$

   b) P(frog and frog)= $\dfrac{5}{20}\cdot\dfrac{4}{19}=\dfrac{1}{4}\cdot\dfrac{4}{19}=\dfrac{1}{19}$

29. a) P(monkey first and bird second) = $\dfrac{5}{20}\cdot\dfrac{5}{20}=\dfrac{1}{4}\cdot\dfrac{1}{4}=\dfrac{1}{16}$

   b) P(monkey first and bird second) = $\dfrac{5}{20}\cdot\dfrac{5}{19}=\dfrac{1}{4}\cdot\dfrac{5}{19}=\dfrac{5}{76}$

30. a) P(2 first and 4 second) = $\dfrac{4}{20}\cdot\dfrac{4}{20}=\dfrac{1}{5}\cdot\dfrac{1}{5}=\dfrac{1}{25}$

   b) P(2 first and 4 second) = $\dfrac{4}{20}\cdot\dfrac{4}{19}=\dfrac{1}{5}\cdot\dfrac{4}{19}=\dfrac{4}{95}$

31. a) P(frog first and yellow bird second) = $\dfrac{5}{20}\cdot\dfrac{2}{20}=\dfrac{1}{4}\cdot\dfrac{1}{10}=\dfrac{1}{40}$

   b) P(frog first and yellow bird second) = $\dfrac{5}{20}\cdot\dfrac{2}{19}=\dfrac{1}{2}\cdot\dfrac{1}{19}=\dfrac{1}{38}$

32. a) P(odd number and odd number) = $\dfrac{12}{20}\cdot\dfrac{12}{20}=\dfrac{3}{5}\cdot\dfrac{3}{5}=\dfrac{9}{25}$

   b) P(odd number and odd number) = $\dfrac{12}{20}\cdot\dfrac{11}{19}=\dfrac{3}{5}\cdot\dfrac{11}{19}=\dfrac{33}{95}$

33. a) P(not odd and not odd) = $\dfrac{8}{20}\cdot\dfrac{8}{20}=\dfrac{2}{5}\cdot\dfrac{2}{5}=\dfrac{4}{25}$

   b) P(not odd and not odd) = $\dfrac{8}{20}\cdot\dfrac{7}{19}=\dfrac{2}{5}\cdot\dfrac{7}{19}=\dfrac{14}{95}$

34. a) P(lion first and red bird second) = $\dfrac{5}{20}\cdot\dfrac{3}{20}=\dfrac{1}{4}\cdot\dfrac{3}{20}=\dfrac{3}{80}$

   b) P(lion first and red bird second) = $\dfrac{5}{20}\cdot\dfrac{3}{19}=\dfrac{1}{4}\cdot\dfrac{3}{19}=\dfrac{3}{76}$

35. P(frog or odd) = P(frog) + P(odd) – P(frog and odd) = $\dfrac{5}{20}+\dfrac{12}{20}-\dfrac{3}{20}=\dfrac{14}{20}=\dfrac{7}{10}$

36. P(yellow bird or number greater than 4) = P(yellow bird) + P(number greater than 4)

$$= \dfrac{2}{20}+\dfrac{4}{20}=\dfrac{6}{20}=\dfrac{3}{10}$$

37. P(monkey or a 5) = P(monkey) + P(5) – P(monkey and a 5) = $\dfrac{5}{20}+\dfrac{4}{20}-\dfrac{1}{20}=\dfrac{8}{20}=\dfrac{2}{5}$

38. P(lion or even number) = P(lion) + P(even number) – P(lion and even number)

$$= \dfrac{5}{20}+\dfrac{8}{20}-\dfrac{2}{20}=\dfrac{11}{20}$$

39. P(2 yellows) = P(yellow and yellow) = P(yellow) × P(yellow) = $\dfrac{1}{2}\times\dfrac{1}{2}=\dfrac{1}{4}$

40. P(red and then yellow) = P(red) × P(yellow) = $\dfrac{1}{2}\times\dfrac{1}{2}=\dfrac{1}{4}$

41. P(red and then green) = P(red) × P(green) = $\dfrac{1}{4}\times\dfrac{1}{2}=\dfrac{1}{8}$

42. P(2 reds) = P(red and red) = P(red) $\times$ P(red) = $\dfrac{1}{4} \times \dfrac{1}{4} = \dfrac{1}{16}$

43. P(2 yellows) = P(yellow and yellow) = P(yellow) $\times$ P(yellow) = $\dfrac{3}{8} \times \dfrac{3}{8} = \dfrac{9}{64}$

44. P(both not red) = P(not red) $\times$ P(not red) = $\dfrac{5}{8} \times \dfrac{5}{8} = \dfrac{25}{64}$

45. P(2 yellows) = P(yellow on 1st wheel) $\times$ P(yellow on 2nd wheel) = $\dfrac{1}{2} \times \dfrac{1}{4} = \dfrac{1}{8}$

46. P(red and then yellow) = P(red on 1st wheel) $\times$ P(yellow on 2nd wheel) = $\dfrac{1}{2} \times \dfrac{1}{4} = \dfrac{1}{8}$

47. P(both not yellow) = P(not yellow on 1st wheel)$\times$P(not yellow on 2nd wheel) = $\dfrac{1}{2} \times \dfrac{3}{4} = \dfrac{3}{8}$

48. P(yellow and then not yellow) = P(yellow on 1st wheel) $\times$ P(not yellow on 2nd wheel) = $\dfrac{1}{2} \times \dfrac{3}{4} = \dfrac{3}{8}$

49. P(3 girls) = P(1st girl) $\times$ P(2nd girl) $\times$ P(3rd girl) = $\dfrac{1}{2} \times \dfrac{1}{2} \times \dfrac{1}{2} = \dfrac{1}{8}$

50. P(3 boys) = P(1st boy) $\times$ P(2nd boy) $\times$ P(3rd boy) = $\dfrac{1}{2} \times \dfrac{1}{2} \times \dfrac{1}{2} = \dfrac{1}{8}$

51. P(1st girl, 2nd girl, 3rd boy) = P(1st girl) $\times$ P(2nd girl) $\times$ P(3rd boy) = $\dfrac{1}{2} \times \dfrac{1}{2} \times \dfrac{1}{2} = \dfrac{1}{8}$

52. P(1st girl, 2nd boy, 3rd girl) = P(1st girl) $\times$ P(2nd boy) $\times$ P(3rd girl) = $\dfrac{1}{2} \times \dfrac{1}{2} \times \dfrac{1}{2} = \dfrac{1}{8}$

53. a) P(Haefners have 5 boys)

  = P(1st boy) $\times$ P(2nd boy) $\times$ P(3rd boy) $\times$ P(4th boy) $\times$ P(5th boy) = $\dfrac{1}{2} \times \dfrac{1}{2} \times \dfrac{1}{2} \times \dfrac{1}{2} \times \dfrac{1}{2} = \dfrac{1}{32}$

  b) P(next child is a boy) = $\dfrac{1}{2}$

54. a) P(7 girls) = $\dfrac{1}{2} \cdot \dfrac{1}{2} \cdot \dfrac{1}{2} \cdot \dfrac{1}{2} \cdot \dfrac{1}{2} \cdot \dfrac{1}{2} \cdot \dfrac{1}{2} = \dfrac{1}{128}$ b) P(next child is a girl) = $\dfrac{1}{2}$

55. a) P(cola 1st and orange 2nd) = $\dfrac{3}{6} \cdot \dfrac{2}{6} = \dfrac{1}{2} \cdot \dfrac{1}{3} = \dfrac{1}{6}$ b) P(cola 1st and orange 2nd) = $\dfrac{3}{6} \cdot \dfrac{2}{5} = \dfrac{1}{2} \cdot \dfrac{2}{5} = \dfrac{1}{5}$

56. a) P(no colas) = P(not a cola and not a cola) = $\dfrac{3}{6} \cdot \dfrac{3}{6} = \dfrac{1}{2} \cdot \dfrac{1}{2} = \dfrac{1}{4}$

  b) P(no colas) = P(not a cola and not a cola) = $\dfrac{3}{6} \cdot \dfrac{2}{5} = \dfrac{1}{2} \cdot \dfrac{2}{5} = \dfrac{1}{5}$

57. a) P(at least on cola) = P(cola and not cola) + P(not cola and cola) + P(cola and cola)

  $= \dfrac{3}{6} \cdot \dfrac{3}{6} + \dfrac{3}{6} \cdot \dfrac{3}{6} + \dfrac{3}{6} \cdot \dfrac{3}{6} = \dfrac{1}{4} + \dfrac{1}{4} + \dfrac{1}{4} = \dfrac{3}{4}$

  b) P(at least on cola) = P(cola and not cola) + P(not cola and cola) + P(cola and cola)

  $= \dfrac{3}{6} \cdot \dfrac{3}{5} + \dfrac{3}{6} \cdot \dfrac{3}{5} + \dfrac{3}{6} \cdot \dfrac{2}{5} = \dfrac{9}{30} + \dfrac{9}{30} + \dfrac{6}{30} = \dfrac{24}{30} = \dfrac{4}{5}$

58. a) P(at least on orange) = P(orange and not orange) + P(not orange and orange) + P(orange and orange)

$$= \frac{2}{6} \cdot \frac{4}{6} + \frac{4}{6} \cdot \frac{2}{6} + \frac{2}{6} \cdot \frac{2}{6} = \frac{8}{36} + \frac{8}{36} + \frac{4}{36} = \frac{20}{36} = \frac{5}{9}$$

b) P(at least on orange) = P(orange and not orange) + P(not orange and orange) + P(orange and orange)

$$= \frac{2}{6} \cdot \frac{4}{5} + \frac{4}{6} \cdot \frac{2}{5} + \frac{2}{6} \cdot \frac{1}{5} = \frac{8}{30} + \frac{8}{30} + \frac{2}{30} = \frac{18}{30} = \frac{3}{5}$$

59. P(both are 40-59) = (0.23)(0.23) = 0.0529

60. P(first is 60 or older and second is 0-19) = (0.25)(0.27) = 0.0675

61. P(first is 0-19 and second is 20-39) = (0.27)(0.25) = 0.0675

62. P(neither is 0-19) = (0.73)(0.73) = 0.5329

63. P(all three exercise daily) = (0.20)(0.20)(0.20) = 0.008

64. P(once a week and once a week and daily) = (0.15)(0.15)(0.20) = 0.0045

65. P(at least 3 times per week and daily and never) = (0.31)(0.20)(0.11) = 0.00682

66. P(all three exercise once a week or more) = (0.66)(0.66)(0.66) = 0.287496

67. The probability that any individual reacts favorably is 70/100 or 0.7.
    P(Mrs. Rivera reacts favorably) = 0.7

68. Since it is assumed the sample is representative of the entire population, it must be assumed this experiment is done with replacement. If done without replacement, the number in the population must be known. In addition, since the population is so large, reducing the numerator and/or denominator by 1 has no appreciable effect on the answer.
    P(Mr. Rivera and Mrs. Rivera react favorably and Carlos is unaffected)
    = P(Mr. Rivera reacts favorable) × P(Mrs. Rivera reacts favorable) × P(Carlos is unaffected)
    = 0.7 × 0.7 × 0.2 = 0.098

69. P(all 3 react favorably) = 0.7 × 0.7 × 0.7 = 0.343

70. One does not react favorably if the reaction is unfavorable or if it is unaffected.

    P(not favorable) = 0.1 + 0.2 = 0.3. Therefore, P(none reacts favorably) = $(0.3)^3$ = 0.027

71. Since each question has four possible answers of which only one is correct, the probability of guessing correctly on any given question is 1/4.
    P(correct answer on any one question) = 1/4

72. If you have guessed correctly on only the first question, then you have missed the last four. The probability of missing any given question is 3/4.

    P(only the 1st correct)

    =P(1st correct) × P(2nd incorrect) × P(3rd incorrect) × P(4th incorrect) × P(5th incorrect)

    $$= \frac{1}{4} \times \frac{3}{4} \times \frac{3}{4} \times \frac{3}{4} \times \frac{3}{4} = \frac{81}{1024}$$

73. P(only the 3rd and 4th questions correct)= $\frac{3}{4} \times \frac{3}{4} \times \frac{1}{4} \times \frac{1}{4} \times \frac{3}{4} = \frac{27}{1024}$

74. P(all 5 questions correct) = $\frac{1}{4} \times \frac{1}{4} \times \frac{1}{4} \times \frac{1}{4} \times \frac{1}{4} = \frac{1}{1024}$

75. P(none of the 5 questions correct) = $\frac{3}{4} \times \frac{3}{4} \times \frac{3}{4} \times \frac{3}{4} \times \frac{3}{4} = \frac{243}{1024}$

76. P(at least one is correct) = 1 − P(none are correct) = $1 - \frac{243}{1024} = \frac{781}{1024}$

77. P(orange on 1st reel) = $\frac{5}{22}$

78. P(orange on all 3 reels)

= P(orange on 1st reel) $\times$ P(orange on 2nd reel) $\times$ P(orange on 3rd reel)

$= \dfrac{5}{22} \times \dfrac{4}{22} \times \dfrac{5}{22} = \dfrac{100}{10648} = \dfrac{25}{2662}$

79. P(no 7s) = P(not 7 on 1st reel) $\times$ P(not 7 on 2nd reel) $\times$ P(not 7 on 3rd reel) $= \dfrac{21}{22} \times \dfrac{21}{22} \times \dfrac{21}{22} = \dfrac{9261}{10648}$

80. P(three 7s) = P(7 on 1st reel) $\times$ P(7 on 2nd reel) $\times$ P(7 on 3rd reel) $= \dfrac{1}{22} \times \dfrac{1}{22} \times \dfrac{1}{22} = \dfrac{1}{10648}$

81. P(red on outer and red on inner) $= \dfrac{4}{12} \cdot \dfrac{3}{8} = \dfrac{1}{3} \cdot \dfrac{3}{8} = \dfrac{1}{8}$

82. P(red on outer and blue on inner) $= \dfrac{4}{12} \cdot \dfrac{2}{8} = \dfrac{1}{3} \cdot \dfrac{1}{4} = \dfrac{1}{12}$

83. P(not red on outer and not red on inner) $= \dfrac{8}{12} \cdot \dfrac{5}{8} = \dfrac{5}{12}$

84. P(at least one is red) = 1 − P(neither is red) $= 1 - \dfrac{5}{12} = \dfrac{7}{12}$

85. P(both miss) = 0.6 $\times$ 0.6 = 0.36

86. P(1st hit and 2nd miss) = 0.4 $\times$ 0.1 = 0.04

87. P(both hit) = 0.4 $\times$ 0.9 = 0.36

88. P(1st miss and 2nd hit) = 0.6 $\times$ 0.4 = 0.24

89. a) No, they are dependent. Occurrence of the syndrome in the first child increases the probability of the syndrome occurring in the second child.

   b) P(born with affliction) = 0.001

   c) (i) P(both born with affliction) = P(1st afflicted) $\times$ P(2nd afflicted) = 0.001 $\times$ 0.001 = 0.00004

   (ii) P(1st afflicted and 2nd not afflicted) = P(1st afflicted) $\times$ P(2nd not afflicted) = 0.001 $\times$ 0.96 = 0.00096

   (iii) P(1st not afflicted and 2nd is afflicted) = 0.999 $\times$ 0.001 = 0.000999

   (iv) P(neither has affliction) = P(1st not afflicted) $\times$ P(2nd not afflicted) = 0.999 $\times$ 0.999 = 0.998001

90. P(audited this year) = 28/1000 = 0.028

91. P(audited next 2 years) = P(audited this year) $\times$ P(audited next year) = 0.028 $\times$ 0.028 = 0.000784

92. P(audited this year and not next year) = P(audited this year) $\times$ P(not audited next year)

$$= 0.028 \times 0.972 = 0.027216$$

93. P(not audited either of next 2 years)

= P(not audited this year) $\times$ P(not audited next year) = 0.972 $\times$ 0.972 = 0.944784

94. Since there are an equal number of balls marked 0, 1, 2, 3, 4, 5, 6, 7, 8, and 9, the probability of selecting any one of these numbers at random is 1/10 or 0.1.

P(Ms. Jones' number is selected)

= P(1st digit selected 1st) $\times$ P(2nd digit selected 2nd) $\times$ P(3rd digit selected 3rd)

= (0.1) $\times$ (0.1) $\times$ (0.1) = 0.001

95. $P(2) = \dfrac{2}{6} = \dfrac{1}{3}$

96. $P(3) = \dfrac{3}{6} = \dfrac{1}{2}$

97. P(even or less than 3) = P(even) + P(less than 3) − P(even and less than 3) $= \dfrac{2}{6} + \dfrac{3}{6} - \dfrac{2}{6} = \dfrac{3}{6} = \dfrac{1}{2}$

98. P(odd or greater than 1) $= \dfrac{6}{6} = 1$

99. P(2 the same color) = P(2 red) + P(2 blue) + P(2 yellow)

= P(1st red) × P(2nd red) + P(1st blue) × P(2nd blue) + P(1st yellow) × P(2nd yellow)

$$= \frac{5}{10} \times \frac{4}{9} + \frac{3}{10} \times \frac{2}{9} + \frac{2}{10} \times \frac{1}{9} = \frac{20}{90} + \frac{6}{90} + \frac{2}{90} = \frac{28}{90} = \frac{14}{45}$$

100. P(at least one 1-yen coin)

= P(1st is) × P(2nd is not) + P(1st is not) × P(2nd is) + P(1st is) × P(2nd is)

$$= \frac{3}{10} \times \frac{7}{9} + \frac{7}{10} \times \frac{3}{9} + \frac{3}{10} \times \frac{2}{9} = \frac{21}{90} + \frac{21}{90} + \frac{6}{90} = \frac{48}{90} = \frac{8}{15}$$

101. P(2 C and 1 D) = P(C, C, D) + P(C, D, C) + P(D, C, C)

$$= \frac{10}{15} \times \frac{9}{14} \times \frac{5}{13} + \frac{10}{15} \times \frac{5}{14} \times \frac{9}{13} + \frac{5}{15} \times \frac{10}{14} \times \frac{9}{13} = \frac{450}{2730} + \frac{450}{2730} + \frac{450}{2730} = \frac{1350}{2730} = \frac{45}{91}$$

102. P(no diamonds) = P(1st is not) × P(2nd is not) = $\frac{39}{52} \times \frac{38}{51} = \frac{1482}{2652} = 0.56$

The game favors the dealer since the probability of no diamonds is greater than 1/2.

103. The other card could be the ace or the queen and it is equally likely that it is either one. Thus, the probability the card is the queen is 1/2.

Exercise Set 12.7

1. The probability of E_2 given that E_1 has occurred.

2. $P(E_2 | E_1) = \dfrac{n(E_1 \text{ and } E_2)}{n(E_1)}$

3. $P(E_2 | E_1) = \dfrac{n(E_1 \cap E_2)}{n(E_1)} = \dfrac{4}{12} = \dfrac{1}{3}$

4. $P(E_2 | E_1) = \dfrac{5}{22}$

5. $P(3 | \text{orange}) = \dfrac{n(\text{orange and } 3)}{n(\text{orange})} = \dfrac{1}{3}$

6. $P(3 | \text{yellow}) = \dfrac{n(\text{yellow and } 3)}{n(\text{yellow})} = \dfrac{0}{2} = 0$

7. $P(\text{even} | \text{greater than } 2) = \dfrac{n(\text{greater than 2 and even})}{n(\text{greater than 2})} = \dfrac{2}{4} = \dfrac{1}{2}$

8. $P(\text{less than 2} | \text{less than 5}) = \dfrac{n(\text{less than 5 and less than 2})}{n(\text{less than 5})} = \dfrac{1}{4}$

9. $P(\text{green number} | \text{circle is orange}) = \dfrac{n(\text{orange circle and green number})}{n(\text{orange circle})} = \dfrac{2}{3}$

10. $P(\text{greater than 3} | \text{yellow circle}) = \dfrac{n(\text{yellow circle and greater than 3})}{n(\text{yellow circle})} = \dfrac{1}{2}$

11. $P(4 | \text{its purple}) = \dfrac{n(\text{purple and } 4)}{n(\text{purple})} = \dfrac{1}{5}$

12. $P(\text{even} | \text{its red}) = \dfrac{n(\text{red and even})}{n(\text{red})} = \dfrac{1}{3}$

13. $P(\text{purple} | \text{its odd}) = \dfrac{n(\text{odd and purple})}{n(\text{odd})} = \dfrac{2}{6} = \dfrac{1}{3}$

14. P(greater than 4 | its red) = $\dfrac{n(\text{red and greater than 4})}{n(\text{red})} = \dfrac{3}{3} = 1$

15. P(greater than 4 | its purple) = $\dfrac{n(\text{purple and greater than 4})}{n(\text{purple})} = \dfrac{3}{5}$

16. P(even | its red or purple) = $\dfrac{n\big((\text{red or purple}) \text{ and even}\big)}{n(\text{red or purple})} = \dfrac{4}{8} = \dfrac{1}{2}$

17. P(purple | its greater than 5) = $\dfrac{n(\text{greater than 5 and purple})}{n(\text{greater than 5})} = \dfrac{3}{7}$

18. P(yellow | its greater than 10) = $\dfrac{n(\text{greater than 10 and yellow})}{n(\text{greater than 10})} = \dfrac{0}{2} = 0$

19. P(both $5s) = $\dfrac{1}{16}$

20. P(2nd is $5 | 1st is $5) = $\dfrac{1}{4}$

21. P(both $5s | at least one is a $5) = $\dfrac{1}{7}$

22. P(both greater than $5 | 2nd was $10)

    = $\dfrac{2}{4} = \dfrac{1}{2}$

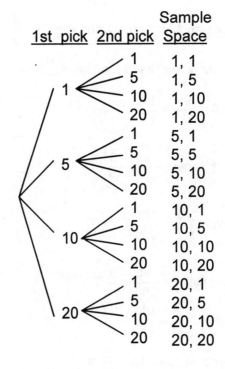

23. P(sum is 7) = $\frac{6}{36} = \frac{1}{6}$

24. P(sum is 7 | first die is a 1) = $\frac{1}{6}$

25. P(sum is 7 | first die is a 3) = $\frac{1}{6}$

26. P(sum is even | 2nd die is a 2) = $\frac{3}{6} = \frac{1}{2}$

27. P(sum is greater than 7 | 2nd die is a 5)

    = $\frac{4}{6} = \frac{2}{3}$

28. P(sum is 7 or 11 | first die is a 5) = $\frac{2}{6} = \frac{1}{3}$

29. P(more than \$1 million) = $\frac{18}{25}$

31. P(more than \$2 million | begins with C) = $\frac{2}{3}$

33. P(dh | earns less than \$1 million) = $\frac{0}{7} = 0$

35. P(good) = $\frac{95}{135} = \frac{19}{27}$

37. P(poor | dinner) = $\frac{25}{70} = \frac{5}{14}$

39. P(back) = $\frac{214}{400} = \frac{107}{200}$

41. P(back | male) = $\frac{180}{200} = \frac{9}{10}$

43. P(good) = $\frac{300}{330} = \frac{10}{11}$

45. P(defective | 20 watts) = $\frac{15}{95} = \frac{3}{19}$

47. P(good | 50 or 100 watts) = $\frac{220}{235} = \frac{44}{47}$

49. P(ABC or NBC) = $\frac{110}{210} = \frac{11}{21}$

51. P(ABC or NBC | man) = $\frac{50}{115} = \frac{10}{23}$

53. P(ABC,NBC,or CBS | man) = $\frac{90}{115} = \frac{18}{23}$

55. P(green circle | +) = $\frac{1}{3}$

Sample space

1 1	3 1	5 1
1 2	3 2	5 2
1 3	3 3	5 3
1 4	3 4	5 4
1 5	3 5	5 5
1 6	3 6	5 6
2 1	4 1	6 1
2 2	4 2	6 2
2 3	4 3	6 3
2 4	4 4	6 4
2 5	4 5	6 5
2 6	4 6	6 6

30. P(more than \$1 million | pitcher) = $\frac{8}{10} = \frac{4}{5}$

32. P(pitcher | earns more than \$3 million) = $\frac{5}{13}$

34. P(of. | earns less than \$300,000) = $\frac{2}{3}$

36. P(good | lunch) = $\frac{50}{65} = \frac{10}{13}$

38. P(poor | lunch) = $\frac{15}{65} = \frac{3}{13}$

40. P(front) = $\frac{186}{400} = \frac{93}{200}$

42. P(front | female) = $\frac{166}{200} = \frac{83}{100}$

44. P(good | 50 watts) = $\frac{100}{105} = \frac{20}{21}$

46. P(good | 100 watts) = $\frac{120}{130} = \frac{12}{13}$

48. P(defective | not 50 watts) = $\frac{25}{225} = \frac{1}{9}$

50. P(ABC | woman) = $\frac{50}{95} = \frac{10}{19}$

52. P(not CBS | woman) = $\frac{75}{95} = \frac{15}{19}$

54. P(NBC or CBS | Woman) = $\frac{30}{95} = \frac{6}{19}$

56. P(+ | orange circle) = $\frac{2}{3}$

57. P(yellow circle | −) = $\frac{1}{3}$

58. P(green + | +) = $\frac{1}{3}$

59. P(green or orange circle | green +) = 1

60. P(orange with green + | +) = $\frac{1}{3}$

61. a) n(A) = 60 + 80 = 140

    b) n(B) = 80 + 40 = 120

    c) P(A) = $\frac{140}{200} = \frac{7}{10}$

    d) P(B) = $\frac{120}{200} = \frac{3}{5}$

    e) P(A | B) = $\frac{n(B \text{ and } A)}{n(B)} = \frac{80}{120} = \frac{2}{3}$

    f) P(B | A) = $\frac{n(A \text{ and } B)}{n(A)} = \frac{80}{140} = \frac{4}{7}$

    g) A and B are not independent events.

62. The denominators of the probabilities will be the same and thus will divide out.

63. a) P(A | B) = $\frac{n(B \text{ and } A)}{n(B)} = \frac{0.12}{0.4} = 0.3$

    b) P(B | A) = $\frac{n(A \text{ and } B)}{n(A)} = \frac{0.12}{0.3} = 0.4$

    c) Yes, P(A) = P(A | B) and P(B) = P(B | A).

Exercise Set 12.8

1. The counting principle is a method for determining the number of ways that multiple experiments can be performed.

2. A permutation is any ordered arrangement of a set of items.

3. Multiply the counting numbers from n down to 1.

4. n! = n(n − 1)(n − 2) · · · 3 · 2 · 1

5. The number of permutations of n items taken r at a time.

6. $_nP_r = \frac{n!}{(n-r)!}$

7. $\frac{n!}{n_1! n_2! \cdots n_r!}$

8. Yes, because 0! = 1! = 1

9. 5! = 5 · 4 · 3 · 2 · 1 = 120

10. 7! = 7 · 6 · 5 · 4 · 3 · 2 · 1 = 5,040

11. 9! = 9 · 8 · 7 · 6 · 5 · 4 · 3 · 2 · 1 = 362,880

12. $_5P_2 = \frac{5!}{(5-2)!} = \frac{5!}{3!} = \frac{5 \cdot 4 \cdot 3 \cdot 2 \cdot 1}{3 \cdot 2 \cdot 1} = 20$

13. 0! = 1

14. $_6P_4 = \frac{6!}{(6-4)!} = \frac{6!}{2!} = \frac{6 \cdot 5 \cdot 4 \cdot 3 \cdot 2 \cdot 1}{2 \cdot 1} = 360$

15. $_8P_0 = \frac{8!}{(8-0)!} = \frac{8!}{8!} = 1$

16. $_5P_0 = \frac{5!}{(5-0)!} = \frac{5!}{5!} = 1$

17. $_8P_7 = \frac{8!}{(8-7)!} = \frac{8!}{1!} = \frac{8 \cdot 7 \cdot 6 \cdot 5 \cdot 4 \cdot 3 \cdot 2 \cdot 1}{1} = 40,320$

18. $_4P_4 = \frac{4!}{(4-4)!} = \frac{4!}{0!} = \frac{4 \cdot 3 \cdot 2 \cdot 1}{1} = 24$

19. $_8P_8 = \frac{8!}{(8-8)!} = \frac{8!}{0!} = \frac{8 \cdot 7 \cdot 6 \cdot 5 \cdot 4 \cdot 3 \cdot 2 \cdot 1}{1} = 40,320$

20. $_9P_6 = \frac{9!}{(9-6)!} = \frac{9!}{3!} = \frac{9 \cdot 8 \cdot 7 \cdot 6 \cdot 5 \cdot 4 \cdot 3 \cdot 2 \cdot 1}{3 \cdot 2 \cdot 1} = 60,480$

21. number of 4 digit codes
$$= 10 \cdot 10 \cdot 10 \cdot 10 = 10^4$$
$$= 10,000 \text{ codes}$$

22. number of tickets
$$= \text{(entries in 1}^{st}\text{ race)(entries in 2}^{nd}\text{ race)}$$
$$= 7 \cdot 8 = 56 \text{ tickets}$$

23. a) number of 5 button possibilities
$$= 5^5 = 3,125$$

  b) P(correct sequence) $= \dfrac{1}{3125} = 0.00032$

24. number of possible S.S. numbers
$$= 10^9 = 1,000,000,000$$

25. a) $7 \times 12 \times 10 = 840$
  b) $12 \times 11 \times 7 = 924$

26. number of ways to select CD's
$$= 7 \cdot 5 \cdot 4 = 140$$

27. number of possible sound systems
$$= 8 \cdot 10 \cdot 9 = 720 \text{ systems}$$

28. number of tickets $= {}_7P_3$
$$= \frac{7!}{(7-3)!} = \frac{7!}{4!} = \frac{7 \cdot 6 \cdot 5 \cdot 4!}{4!} = 210 \text{ tickets}$$

29. a) $5! = 5 \cdot 4 \cdot 3 \cdot 2 \cdot 1 = 120$
  b) $5! = 5 \cdot 4 \cdot 3 \cdot 2 \cdot 1 = 120$
  c) $4 \cdot 3 \cdot 2 \cdot 1 \cdot 1 = 24$
  d) $1 \cdot 3 \cdot 2 \cdot 1 \cdot 1 = 6$

30. a) $6! = 6 \cdot 5 \cdot 4 \cdot 3 \cdot 2 \cdot 1 = 720$
  b) $1 \cdot 5 \cdot 4 \cdot 3 \cdot 2 \cdot 1 = 120$
  c) $1 \cdot 1 \cdot 4 \cdot 3 \cdot 2 \cdot 1 = 24$
  d) $5 \cdot 5 \cdot 4 \cdot 3 \cdot 2 \cdot 1 = 600$

31. ${}_8P_3 = \dfrac{8!}{(8-3)!} = \dfrac{8!}{5!} = \dfrac{8 \cdot 7 \cdot 6 \cdot 5!}{5!} = 336$

32. ${}_8P_3 = \dfrac{8!}{(8-3)!} = \dfrac{8!}{5!} = \dfrac{8 \cdot 7 \cdot 6 \cdot 5!}{5!} = 336$

33. $10^{10} = 10,000,000,000$ possible ISBN numbers

34. a) There are 12 individuals and they can be arranged in $12! = 479,001,600$ ways
  b) $10! = 3,628,800$ different ways
  c) $5! \cdot 5! = 14,400$ different ways

35. $26 \cdot 26 \cdot 10 \cdot 10 \cdot 10 \cdot 10 = 6,760,000$
36. $26 \cdot 25 \cdot 10 \cdot 9 \cdot 8 \cdot 7 = 3,276,000$
37. $4 \cdot 25 \cdot 10 \cdot 9 \cdot 8 \cdot 7 = 504,000$
38. $26 \cdot 1 \cdot 10 \cdot 9 \cdot 8 \cdot 7 = 131,040$
39. $10 \cdot 10 \cdot 10 \cdot 26 \cdot 26 = 676,000$
40. $10 \cdot 9 \cdot 8 \cdot 26 \cdot 25 = 468,000$
41. $5 \cdot 4 \cdot 8 \cdot 26 \cdot 25 = 104,000$
42. $9 \cdot 9 \cdot 8 \cdot 26 \cdot 25 = 421,200$

43. a) $8 \cdot 10 \cdot 10 \cdot 10 \cdot 10 \cdot 10 \cdot 10$
$$= 8,000,000$$
  b) $8 \cdot 10 \cdot 10 \cdot 8,000,000$
$$= 6,400,000,000$$
  c) $8 \cdot 10 \cdot 10 \cdot 8 \cdot 10^{10} = 64 \cdot 10^{12}$
$$= 64,000,000,000,000$$

44. ${}_{30}P_6 = \dfrac{30!}{24!} = \dfrac{30 \cdot 29 \cdot 28 \cdot 27 \cdot 26 \cdot 25 \cdot 24!}{24!}$
$$= 427,518,000$$

45. ${}_{12}P_3 = \dfrac{12!}{9!} = \dfrac{12 \cdot 11 \cdot 10 \cdot 9!}{9!} = 1,320$

46. $10! = 3,628,800$

47. ${}_7P_7 = \dfrac{7!}{0!} = \dfrac{7!}{1} = 7! = 5,040$

48. $3 \cdot 3 \cdot 3 \cdot 3 \cdot 3 \cdot 3 = 3^6 = 729$ ways

49. $5 \cdot 3 \cdot 12 \cdot 4 = 720$

50. $5 \cdot 4 \cdot 7 \cdot 2 = 280$ systems

51. $7! = 7 \cdot 6 \cdot 5 \cdot 4 \cdot 3 \cdot 2 \cdot 1 = 5,040$

52. $9! = 9 \cdot 8 \cdot 7 \cdot 6 \cdot 5 \cdot 4 \cdot 3 \cdot 2 \cdot 1 = 362,880$

53. $\dfrac{9!}{4!3!} = \dfrac{9 \cdot 8 \cdot 7 \cdot 6 \cdot 5 \cdot 4 \cdot 3 \cdot 2 \cdot 1}{4 \cdot 3 \cdot 2 \cdot 1 \cdot 3 \cdot 2 \cdot 1} = 2,520$

54. $\dfrac{11!}{4!4!2!} = 34,650$

55. $\dfrac{7!}{2!2!2!} = \dfrac{7 \cdot 6 \cdot 5 \cdot 4 \cdot 3 \cdot 2 \cdot 1}{2 \cdot 1 \cdot 2 \cdot 1 \cdot 2 \cdot 1} = 630$

56. $\dfrac{7!}{3!2!} = \dfrac{7 \cdot 6 \cdot 5 \cdot 4 \cdot 3!}{3! \cdot 2 \cdot 1} = 420$ (there are 3 2's, 2 3's)

57. The order of the flags is important. Thus, it is a permutation problem.

$_8P_5 = \dfrac{8!}{(8-5)!} = \dfrac{8!}{3!} = 8 \cdot 7 \cdot 6 \cdot 5 \cdot 4 = 6{,}720$

58. Since the order of the answers is important, this is a permutation problem.

$_{10}P_{10} = \dfrac{10!}{(10-10)!} = \dfrac{10!}{0!} = 10 \cdot 9 \cdot 8 \cdot 7 \cdot 6 \cdot 5 \cdot 4 \cdot 3 \cdot 2 \cdot 1 = 3{,}628{,}800$

59. a) Since the pitcher must bat last, there is only one possibility for the last position.

$\underline{\ } \ \underline{\ } \ \underline{\ } \ \underline{\ } \ \underline{\ } \ \underline{\ } \ \underline{\ } \ \underline{\ } \ \underline{1}$

There are 8 possible batters left for the first position. Once the first batter has been selected, there are 7 batters left for the second position, 6 for the third, etc.

$\underline{8} \cdot \underline{7} \cdot \underline{6} \cdot \underline{5} \cdot \underline{4} \cdot \underline{3} \cdot \underline{2} \cdot \underline{1} \cdot \underline{1} = 40{,}320$

b) $9! = 9 \cdot 8 \cdot 7 \cdot 6 \cdot 5 \cdot 4 \cdot 3 \cdot 2 \cdot 1 = 362{,}880$

60. a) Since each arrangement is distinct, this is a permutation. Many problems of this type can be done with both the counting principal and the permutation formula.

counting principal $= 5 \cdot 4 \cdot 3 \cdot 2 \cdot 1 = 120$

permutation formula $= \,_5P_5 = \dfrac{5!}{(5-5)!} = \dfrac{5!}{0!} = \dfrac{5 \cdot 4 \cdot 3 \cdot 2 \cdot 1}{1} = 120$

b) Consider the possible arrangements as indicated by the dashes. $\underline{\ } \ \underline{\ } \ \underline{\ } \ \underline{\ } \ \underline{\ }$
There is only one possibility for the middle position. $\underline{\ } \ \underline{\ } \ \underline{1} \ \underline{\ } \ \underline{\ }$
After the middle one is placed there are 4 possibilities for the first position, 3 for the second, 2 for the fourth, and only 1 for the final position. $\underline{4} \cdot \underline{3} \cdot \underline{1} \cdot \underline{2} \cdot \underline{1} = 24$

61. a) $5^5 = 3125$ different ways   b) $400{,}000 \div 3{,}125 = 128$ cars

c) $\dfrac{128}{400000} = \dfrac{1}{3125} = 0.00032$

62. $_7P_3 + 1 = \dfrac{7!}{4!} + 1 = 7 \cdot 6 \cdot 5 + 1 = 210 + 1 = 211$

63. $_7P_5 = \dfrac{7!}{2!} = \dfrac{7 \cdot 6 \cdot 5 \cdot 4 \cdot 3 \cdot 2!}{2!} = 2{,}520$ different letter permutations

Time $= 2520 \times 5$ sec. $= 12{,}600$ sec. or 210 min. or 3.5 hours

64. $\dfrac{7!}{3!2!} = 420$, Time $= 420 \times 5$ sec. $= 2{,}100$ sec. or 35 min.

65. No, Ex. $_3P_2 \neq \,_3P_{(3-2)}$

$\dfrac{3!}{1!} \neq \dfrac{3!}{2!}$

$6 \neq 3$

Exercise Set 12.9

1. The selection of a certain number of items without regard to their order.

2. The number of combinations possible when r items are selected from n items.

3. $_nC_r = \dfrac{n!}{(n-r)! \cdot r!}$

4. $_nC_r = \dfrac{_nP_r}{r!}$

5. If the order of the items is important then it is a permutation problem. If order is not important then it is a combination problem.

6. There will be more permutations.

7. $_6C_3 = \dfrac{6!}{(6-3)!3!} = \dfrac{6 \cdot 5 \cdot 4 \cdot 3 \cdot 2 \cdot 1}{3 \cdot 2 \cdot 1 \cdot 3 \cdot 2 \cdot 1} = 20$

8. $_6C_2 = \dfrac{6!}{4!2!} = \dfrac{6 \cdot 5 \cdot 4 \cdot 3 \cdot 2 \cdot 1}{4 \cdot 3 \cdot 2 \cdot 1 \cdot 2 \cdot 1} = 15$

9. a) $_7C_3 = \dfrac{7!}{4!3!} = \dfrac{7 \cdot 6 \cdot 5 \cdot 4 \cdot 3 \cdot 2 \cdot 1}{4 \cdot 3 \cdot 2 \cdot 1 \cdot 3 \cdot 2 \cdot 1} = 35$

   b) $_7P_3 = \dfrac{7!}{(7-3)!} = \dfrac{7 \cdot 6 \cdot 5 \cdot 4!}{4!} = 7 \cdot 6 \cdot 5 = 210$

10. a) $_8C_0 = \dfrac{8!}{8!0!} = 1$

    b) $_8P_0 = \dfrac{8!}{(8-0)!} = \dfrac{8!}{8!} = 1$

11. a) $_8C_2 = \dfrac{8!}{(8-2)!2!} = \dfrac{8 \cdot 7 \cdot 6!}{6! \cdot 2!} = \dfrac{8 \cdot 7}{2 \cdot 1} = 28$

    b) $_8P_2 = \dfrac{8!}{(8-2)!} = \dfrac{8 \cdot 7 \cdot 6!}{6!} = 8 \cdot 7 = 56$

12. a) $_{12}C_8 = \dfrac{12!}{4!8!} = \dfrac{12 \cdot 11 \cdot 10 \cdot 9 \cdot 8!}{4 \cdot 3 \cdot 2 \cdot 1 \cdot 8!} = 495$

    b) $_{12}P_8 = \dfrac{12!}{(12-8)!} = \dfrac{12!}{4!} = 19{,}958{,}400$

13. a) $_{10}C_3 = \dfrac{10!}{7!3!} = \dfrac{10 \cdot 9 \cdot 8 \cdot 7!}{7! \cdot 3 \cdot 2 \cdot 1} = 120$

    b) $_{10}P_3 = \dfrac{10!}{(10-3)!} = \dfrac{10 \cdot 9 \cdot 8 \cdot 7!}{7!} = 10 \cdot 9 \cdot 8 = 720$

14. a) $_5C_5 = \dfrac{5!}{0!5!} = \dfrac{5!}{5!} = 1$

    b) $_5P_5 = \dfrac{5!}{(5-5)!} = \dfrac{5!}{1} = 120$

15. $\dfrac{_5C_3}{_5P_3} = \dfrac{\frac{5!}{2!3!}}{\frac{5!}{2!}} = \dfrac{5!}{2!3!} \cdot \dfrac{2!}{5!} = \dfrac{1}{3!} = \dfrac{1}{6}$

16. $\dfrac{_6C_2}{_6P_2} = \dfrac{\frac{6!}{4!2!}}{\frac{6!}{4!}} = \dfrac{6!}{4!2!} \cdot \dfrac{4!}{6!} = \dfrac{1}{2!} = \dfrac{1}{2}$

17. $\dfrac{_8C_5}{_8P_5} = \dfrac{\frac{8!}{3!5!}}{\frac{8!}{6!2!}} = \dfrac{8!}{3!5!} \cdot \dfrac{6!2!}{8!}$

    $= \dfrac{6 \cdot 5 \cdot 4 \cdot 3 \cdot 2 \cdot 1 \cdot 2 \cdot 1}{3 \cdot 2 \cdot 1 \cdot 5 \cdot 4 \cdot 3 \cdot 2 \cdot 1} = 2$

18. $\dfrac{_6C_6}{_8C_0} = \dfrac{\frac{6!}{0!6!}}{\frac{8!}{8!0!}} = \dfrac{1}{1} = 1$

19. $_{20}C_3 = \dfrac{20!}{17!3!} = \dfrac{20 \cdot 19 \cdot 18 \cdot 17!}{17! \cdot 3 \cdot 2 \cdot 1} = 1140$

20. $_9C_6 = \dfrac{9!}{3!6!} = \dfrac{9 \cdot 8 \cdot 7 \cdot 6!}{3 \cdot 2 \cdot 1 \cdot 6!} = \dfrac{504}{6} = 84$ ways

21. $_5C_4 = \dfrac{5!}{1!4!} = 5$

22. $_8C_3 = \dfrac{8!}{5!3!} = \dfrac{8 \cdot 7 \cdot 6}{3 \cdot 2 \cdot 1} = 56$

23. $_{12}C_8 = \dfrac{12!}{4!8!} = \dfrac{12 \cdot 11 \cdot 10 \cdot 9 \cdot 8!}{4 \cdot 3 \cdot 2 \cdot 1 \cdot 8!} = 495$

24. $_8C_4 = \dfrac{8!}{4!4!} = \dfrac{8 \cdot 7 \cdot 6 \cdot 5 \cdot 4!}{4! \cdot 4 \cdot 3 \cdot 2 \cdot 1} = 70$

25. $_8C_4 = \dfrac{8!}{4!4!} = \dfrac{8 \cdot 7 \cdot 6 \cdot 5 \cdot 4!}{4! \cdot 4 \cdot 3 \cdot 2 \cdot 1} = 70$

26. $_{26}C_5 = \dfrac{26!}{21!5!} = \dfrac{26 \cdot 25 \cdots 22 \cdot 21!}{21! \cdot 5 \cdot 4 \cdot 3 \cdot 2 \cdot 1} = 65{,}780$

27. $3 \cdot 2 = 6$

28. $2 \cdot 2 = 4$

29. $3 \cdot 2 = 6$

30. 9; YY, YR, YG, YP, GR, GG, GP, RR, RP

31. $_8C_2 = \dfrac{8!}{6!2!} = \dfrac{8 \cdot 7}{2 \cdot 1} = 28$ tickets

32. Part I:

$_5C_3 = \dfrac{5!}{2!3!} = \dfrac{5 \cdot 4}{2 \cdot 1} = 10$

$10 \cdot 15 = 150$ possible combinations

Part II:

$_6C_4 = \dfrac{6!}{2!4!} = \dfrac{6 \cdot 5}{2 \cdot 1} = 15$

33. Fast songs:

$_{10}C_6 = \dfrac{10!}{4!6!} = \dfrac{10 \cdot 9 \cdot 8 \cdot 7}{4 \cdot 3 \cdot 2 \cdot 1} = 210$

$210 \cdot 35 = 7{,}350$ possible combinations

Slow songs:

$_7C_4 = \dfrac{7!}{3!4!} = \dfrac{7 \cdot 6 \cdot 5}{3 \cdot 2 \cdot 1} = 35$

34. a) $_6C_6 = \dfrac{6!}{0!6!} = \dfrac{1}{1} = 1$

b) $_{51}C_6 = \dfrac{51!}{45!6!} = 18{,}009{,}460$

35. Mathematics:

$_8C_5 = \dfrac{8!}{3!5!} = \dfrac{8 \cdot 7 \cdot 6}{3 \cdot 2 \cdot 1} = 56$

$56 \cdot 10 = 560$ different choices

Computer Science:

$_5C_3 = \dfrac{5!}{2!3!} = \dfrac{5 \cdot 4}{2 \cdot 1} = 10$

36. Regular soda:

$_{10}C_5 = \dfrac{10!}{5!5!} = \dfrac{10 \cdot 9 \cdot 8 \cdot 7 \cdot 6}{5 \cdot 4 \cdot 3 \cdot 2 \cdot 1} = 252$

$252 \cdot 35 = 8{,}820$ ways to select the soda

Diet soda:

$_7C_3 = \dfrac{7!}{4!3!} = \dfrac{7 \cdot 6 \cdot 5}{3 \cdot 2 \cdot 1} = 35$

37. Teachers:

$_6C_2 = \dfrac{6!}{4!2!} = \dfrac{6 \cdot 5}{2 \cdot 1} = 15$

$15 \cdot 19{,}600 = 294{,}000$ ways to select the committee

Students:

$_{50}C_3 = \dfrac{50!}{47!3!} = \dfrac{50 \cdot 49 \cdot 48}{3 \cdot 2 \cdot 1} = 19{,}600$

38. Difficult questions:

$_6C_3 = \dfrac{6!}{3!3!} = \dfrac{6 \cdot 5 \cdot 4}{3 \cdot 2 \cdot 1} = 20$

Easy questions:

$_{12}C_3 = \dfrac{12!}{9!3!} = \dfrac{12 \cdot 11 \cdot 10}{3 \cdot 2 \cdot 1} = 220$

Average questions:

$_{10}C_4 = \dfrac{10!}{6!4!} = \dfrac{10 \cdot 9 \cdot 8 \cdot 7}{4 \cdot 3 \cdot 2 \cdot 1} = 210$

Total number of 10-question tests

$= 20 \cdot 210 \cdot 220 = 924{,}000$

39. Total combinations $= _{12}C_5 \cdot _9C_7 = \dfrac{12!}{4! \cdot 5!} \cdot \dfrac{9!}{2! \cdot 7!} = (792)(36) = 28{,}512$

40. a) $_9C_5 = \dfrac{9!}{4! \cdot 5!} = 126$ b) $_7C_4 = \dfrac{7!}{3! \cdot 4!} = 35$ c) $(126)(35) = 4410$

41. Oat:

$$_6C_3 = \frac{6!}{3!3!} = \frac{6\cdot5\cdot4}{3\cdot2\cdot1} = 20$$

Rice:

$$_4C_2 = \frac{4!}{2!2!} = \frac{4\cdot3}{2\cdot1} = 6$$

Wheat:

$$_5C_2 = \frac{5!}{3!2!} = \frac{5\cdot4}{2\cdot1} = 10$$

Total number of combinations = $20 \cdot 10 \cdot 6 = 1,200$

42. Inexpensive:

$$_7C_3 = \frac{7!}{4!3!} = \frac{7\cdot6\cdot5}{3\cdot2\cdot1} = 35$$

Expensive:

$$_4C_2 = \frac{4!}{2!2!} = \frac{4\cdot3}{2\cdot1} = 6$$

Average:

$$_8C_5 = \frac{8!}{3!5!} = \frac{8\cdot7\cdot6}{3\cdot2\cdot1} = 56$$

Total number of choices = $35 \cdot 56 \cdot 6 = 11,760$

43. a) $_{10}C_8 = \frac{10!}{2!8!} = \frac{10\cdot9}{2\cdot1} = 45$

   b) $_{10}C_8 + {}_{10}C_9 + {}_{10}C_{10} = 45 + 10 + 1 = 56$

44. a) $_4C_2 = 6$ b) $_5C_2 = 10$ c) $_nC_2$

45. a) The order of the numbers is important. For example: if the combination is 12 - 4 - 23, the lock will not open if 4 - 12 - 23 is used. Since repetition is permitted, it is not a true permutation problem.

   b) $40 \cdot 40 \cdot 40 = 64,000$ c) $40 \cdot 39 \cdot 38 = 59,280$

46. a)
```
               1
            1     1
         1     2     1
      1     3     3     1
   1     4     6     4     1
```
   b) 1   5   10   10   5   1

47. a) $_{46}C_6 = \frac{46!}{40!6!} = 9,366,819$

   b) $_{47}C_6 = \frac{47!}{41!6!} = 10,737,573$

   c) $_{48}C_6 = \frac{48!}{42!6!} = 12,271,512$

   d) $_{49}C_6 = \frac{49!}{43!6!} = 13,983,816$

   e) No

48. $$_nC_{(n-r)} = \frac{n!}{(n-(n-r))!(n-r)!}$$

$$= \frac{n!}{(n-n+r)!(n-r)!}$$

$$= \frac{n!}{r!(n-r)!}$$

$$= \frac{n!}{(n-r)!r!} = {}_nC_r$$

49. a) $4! = 24$ b) $4! = 24$

Exercise Set 12.10

1. P(4 red balls) = $\dfrac{\text{no. of 4 red ball comb.}}{\text{no. of 4 ball comb.}} = \dfrac{_6C_4}{_{10}C_4}$

2. P(3 vowels) = $\dfrac{\text{no. of 3 vowel comb.}}{\text{no. of 3 letter comb.}} = \dfrac{_5C_3}{_{26}C_3}$

3. P(12 girls) = $\dfrac{\text{no. of 12 girl comb.}}{\text{no. of 12 children comb.}} = \dfrac{_{19}C_{12}}{_{34}C_{12}}$

4. P(all 70 start with P) =
$\dfrac{\text{no. of 70 P name comb.}}{\text{no. of 70 name comb.}} = \dfrac{_{270}C_{70}}{_{1206}C_{70}}$

5. P(all 8 are wilson) =
$\dfrac{\text{no. of 8 wilson comb.}}{\text{no. of 8 ball comb.}} = \dfrac{_{22}C_{8}}{_{70}C_{8}}$

6. P(all 7 are Palaminos) =
$\dfrac{\text{no. of 7 Palamino comb.}}{\text{no. of 7 horse comb.}} = \dfrac{_{18}C_{7}}{_{24}C_{7}}$

7. P(none of the 9 are oak) =
$\dfrac{\text{no. of 9 non-oak comb.}}{\text{no. of 9 tree comb.}} = \dfrac{_{14}C_{9}}{_{30}C_{9}}$

8. P(none of the 9 are T-I) =
$\dfrac{\text{no. of 9 non-T-I comb.}}{\text{no. of 9 calculator comb.}} = \dfrac{_{23}C_{9}}{_{36}C_{9}}$

9. $_5C_3 = \dfrac{5!}{2!3!} = \dfrac{5\cdot4}{2\cdot1} = 10$

$_9C_3 = \dfrac{9!}{6!3!} = \dfrac{9\cdot8\cdot7}{3\cdot2\cdot1} = 84$

P(3 reds) = $\dfrac{10}{84} = \dfrac{5}{42}$

10. $_3C_2 = \dfrac{3!}{1!2!} = \dfrac{3}{1} = 3$

$_6C_2 = \dfrac{6!}{4!2!} = \dfrac{6\cdot5}{2\cdot1} = 15$

P(2 evens) = $\dfrac{3}{15} = \dfrac{1}{5}$

11. $_4C_3 = \dfrac{4!}{1!3!} = \dfrac{4}{1} = 4$

$_8C_3 = \dfrac{8!}{5!3!} = \dfrac{8\cdot7\cdot6}{3\cdot2\cdot1} = 56$

P(3 good batteries) = $\dfrac{4}{56} = \dfrac{1}{14}$

12. $_4C_2 = \dfrac{4!}{2!2!} = \dfrac{4\cdot3}{2\cdot1} = 6$

$_8C_2 = \dfrac{8!}{6!2!} = \dfrac{8\cdot7}{2\cdot1} = 28$

P(two $5 bills) = $\dfrac{6}{28} = \dfrac{3}{14}$

13. $_5C_3 = \dfrac{5!}{2!3!} = \dfrac{5\cdot4}{2\cdot1} = 10$

$_{10}C_3 = \dfrac{10!}{7!3!} = \dfrac{10\cdot9\cdot8}{3\cdot2\cdot1} = 120$

P(3 greater than 4) = $\dfrac{10}{120} = \dfrac{1}{12}$

14. $_4C_3 = \dfrac{4!}{1!3!} = \dfrac{4\cdot3!}{1\cdot3!} = 4$

$_7C_3 = \dfrac{7!}{4!3!} = 35$

P(3 Democrats) = $\dfrac{4}{35}$

15. $_6C_4 = \dfrac{6!}{2!4!} = \dfrac{6\cdot5}{2\cdot1} = 15$

$_{10}C_4 = \dfrac{10!}{6!4!} = \dfrac{10\cdot9\cdot8\cdot7}{4\cdot3\cdot2\cdot1} = 210$

P(all 4 ride Huffy) = $\dfrac{15}{210} = \dfrac{1}{14}$

16. $_8C_4 = \dfrac{8!}{4!4!} = \dfrac{8\cdot7\cdot6\cdot5}{4\cdot3\cdot2\cdot1} = 70$

$_{15}C_4 = \dfrac{15!}{11!4!} = \dfrac{15\cdot14\cdot13\cdot12}{4\cdot3\cdot2\cdot1} = 1365$

P(4 students) = $\dfrac{70}{1365} = \dfrac{2}{39}$

17. $_{46}C_6 = \dfrac{46!}{40!6!} = 9{,}366{,}819$ $_6C_6 = 1$,   P(win grand prize) = $\dfrac{1}{9{,}366{,}819}$

18. $_{52}C_5 = \dfrac{52!}{47!5!} = \dfrac{52\cdot51\cdot50\cdot49\cdot48}{5\cdot4\cdot3\cdot2\cdot1} = 2{,}598{,}960$

$_{26}C_5 = \dfrac{26!}{21!5!} = \dfrac{26\cdot25\cdot24\cdot23\cdot22}{5\cdot4\cdot3\cdot2\cdot1} = 65{,}700$

P(5 red) = $\dfrac{65700}{2598960} = \dfrac{253}{9996} = 0.0253$

19. $_2C_2 = \dfrac{2!}{0!2!} = 1$

   $_5C_2 = \dfrac{5!}{3!2!} = \dfrac{5 \cdot 4}{2 \cdot 1} = 10$

   P(both cars) = $\dfrac{1}{10}$

20. $_3C_2 = \dfrac{3!}{1!2!} = \dfrac{3}{1} = 3$

   $_5C_2 = \dfrac{5!}{3!2!} = \dfrac{5 \cdot 4}{2 \cdot 1} = 10$

   P(no cars) = $\dfrac{3}{10}$

21. P(at least 1 car) = 1 – P(no cars) = $1 - \dfrac{3}{10} = \dfrac{7}{10}$

22. $_2C_1 = \dfrac{2!}{1! \cdot 1!} = 2$; $\qquad _3C_1 = \dfrac{3!}{2! \cdot 1!} = 3$; $\qquad _5C_2 = \dfrac{5!}{3! \cdot 2!} = 10$

   P(exactly on car) = $\dfrac{2 \cdot 3}{10} = \dfrac{6}{10} = \dfrac{3}{5}$

For problems 23 – 26 we will use the fact that, $_{25}C_3 = \dfrac{25!}{22! \cdot 3!} = 2300$

23. $_{10}C_3 = \dfrac{10!}{7!3!} = 120$

   P(all 3 are pitchers) = $\dfrac{120}{2300} = \dfrac{6}{115}$

24. $_{15}C_3 = \dfrac{15!}{12! \cdot 3!} = 455$

   P(none are pitchers) = $\dfrac{455}{2300} = \dfrac{91}{460}$

25. $_{10}C_2 = \dfrac{10!}{8! \cdot 2!} = 45$; $_6C_1 = \dfrac{6!}{5! \cdot 1!} = 6$

   P(2 pitchers and 1 infielder) = $\dfrac{45 \cdot 6}{2300} = \dfrac{27}{230}$

26. $_{10}C_1 = \dfrac{10!}{9! \cdot 1!} = 10$; $_9C_2 = \dfrac{9!}{7! \cdot 2!} = 36$

   P(1 pitc. and 2 non-pitc. /non-infl.) = $\dfrac{10 \cdot 36}{2300} = \dfrac{18}{115}$

For problems 27 – 30 use the fact that, $_{39}C_{12} = \dfrac{39!}{27!12!} = 3{,}910{,}797{,}436$

27. $_{22}C_{12} = \dfrac{22!}{10!12!} = 646{,}646$

   P(all women) = $\dfrac{646646}{3910797436} = 0.0001653$

28. $_{22}C_8 = \dfrac{22!}{14!8!} = 319{,}770$

   $_{17}C_4 = \dfrac{17!}{13!4!} = 2{,}380$

   P(8 women and 4 men)

   $= \dfrac{(319770)(2380)}{3910797436} = 0.1946$

29. $_{17}C_6 = \dfrac{17!}{11!6!} = 12{,}376$

   $_{22}C_6 = \dfrac{22!}{16!6!} = 74{,}613$

   P(6 men and 6 women)

   $= \dfrac{(12376)(74613)}{3910797436} = 0.236$

30. P(at least one man) = 1 – P(no men)

   $\qquad\qquad\qquad = 1 - $ P(all women)

   $\qquad\qquad\qquad = 1 - 0.0001653$

   $\qquad\qquad\qquad = 0.9998$

For problems 31 – 34 use the fact that, $_{15}C_4 = \dfrac{15!}{11!4!} = \dfrac{15 \cdot 14 \cdot 13 \cdot 12}{4 \cdot 3 \cdot 2 \cdot 1} = 1365$

31. $_5C_2 = \dfrac{5!}{3!2!} = \dfrac{5 \cdot 4}{2 \cdot 1} = 10$

$_6C_2 = \dfrac{6!}{4!2!} = \dfrac{6 \cdot 5}{2 \cdot 1} = 15$

$P(2\ A,\ 2\ B) = \dfrac{10 \cdot 15}{1365} = \dfrac{10}{91}$

32. $_6C_3 = \dfrac{6!}{3!3!} = \dfrac{6 \cdot 5 \cdot 4}{3 \cdot 2 \cdot 1} = 20$

$_5C_1 = \dfrac{5!}{4!1!} = \dfrac{5}{1} = 5$

$P(3\ C,\ 1\ A) = \dfrac{20 \cdot 5}{1365} = \dfrac{20}{273}$

33. $_9C_4 = \dfrac{9!}{5!4!} = \dfrac{9 \cdot 8 \cdot 7 \cdot 6}{4 \cdot 3 \cdot 2 \cdot 1} = 126$

$P(\text{no } C) = \dfrac{126}{1365} = \dfrac{6}{65}$

$P(\text{at least } 1\ C) = 1 - P(\text{no } C) = 1 - \dfrac{6}{65} = \dfrac{59}{65}$

34. $_4C_2 = \dfrac{4!}{2!2!} = \dfrac{4 \cdot 3}{2 \cdot 1} = 6$

$_5C_1 = 5,\ _6C_1 = 6$

$P(1\ A,\ 2\ B,\ 1\ C) = \dfrac{5 \cdot 6 \cdot 6}{1365} = \dfrac{12}{91}$

For problems 35 – 37 use the fact that, $_{11}C_5 = \dfrac{11!}{6!5!} = \dfrac{11 \cdot 10 \cdot 9 \cdot 8 \cdot 7}{5 \cdot 4 \cdot 3 \cdot 2 \cdot 1} = 462$

35. $_6C_5 = \dfrac{6!}{1!5!} = \dfrac{6}{1} = 6$

$P(\text{5 women first}) = \dfrac{6}{462} = \dfrac{1}{77}$

36. $_5C_5 = \dfrac{5!}{0!5!} = 1$

$P(\text{no women first}) = \dfrac{1}{462}$

$P(\text{at least 1 woman 1st}) = 1 - \dfrac{1}{462} = \dfrac{461}{462}$

37. Any one of the 6 women can sit in any one of the five seats - 30 possibilities.

$P(\text{exactly 1 woman}) = \dfrac{30}{462} = \dfrac{5}{77}$

38. $P(\text{3 women and then 2 men})$

$= \dfrac{_6C_3}{_{11}C_3} \cdot \dfrac{_5C_2}{_8C_2} = \dfrac{20}{165} \cdot \dfrac{10}{28} = \dfrac{10}{231}$

39. $_{24}C_6 = \dfrac{24!}{18!6!} = 134{,}596;\ \ _3C_3 = 1;\ \ _{21}C_3 = \dfrac{21!}{18!3!} = 1{,}330$

$P(\text{three brothers are selected}) = \dfrac{_3C_3 \cdot _{21}C_3}{_{24}C_6} = \dfrac{(1)(1330)}{134596} = 0.00988$

40. $_4C_3 = \dfrac{4!}{1!3!} = \dfrac{4}{1} = 4,\ \ _4C_2 = \dfrac{4!}{2!2!} = \dfrac{4 \cdot 3}{2 \cdot 1} = 6$ and from problem 9, $_{52}C_5 = 2{,}598{,}960$

$P(\text{3 kings, 2 five's}) = \dfrac{4 \cdot 6}{2598960} = \dfrac{1}{108290}$

41. $_7C_5 = \dfrac{7!}{2!5!} = \dfrac{7 \cdot 6}{2 \cdot 1} = 21$ and from problem 9, $_{52}C_5 = 2{,}598{,}960$

a) $P(\text{royal spade flush}) = \dfrac{21}{2598960} = \dfrac{1}{123760}$

b) $P(\text{any royal flush}) = \dfrac{4}{123760} = \dfrac{1}{30940}$

For problems 42 – 45 use the fact that, total combinations = $18 \cdot 18 \cdot 18 = 5832$.

42. $_4C_1 \cdot _5C_1 \cdot _4C_1 = 4 \cdot 5 \cdot 4 = 80$

P(3 cherries) = $\dfrac{80}{5832} = \dfrac{10}{729}$

43. $_4C_1 \cdot _5C_1 \cdot _2C_1 = 4 \cdot 5 \cdot 2 = 40$

P(3 cherries) = $\dfrac{40}{5832} = \dfrac{5}{729}$

44. $_1C_1 \cdot _1C_1 \cdot _2C_1 = 1 \cdot 1 \cdot 2 = 2$

P(3 bars) = $\dfrac{2}{5832} = \dfrac{1}{2916}$

45. $_{14}C_1 \cdot _{13}C_1 \cdot _{14}C_1 = 14 \cdot 13 \cdot 14 = 2548$

P(no cherries) = $\dfrac{2548}{5832} = \dfrac{637}{1458}$

P(at least 1 cherry) = $1 - \dfrac{637}{1458} = \dfrac{821}{1458}$

46. Total seating arrangements = $6! = 6 \cdot 5 \cdot 4 \cdot 3 \cdot 2 \cdot 1 = 720$

$\underline{3} \cdot \underline{3} \cdot \underline{2} \cdot \underline{2} \cdot \underline{1} \cdot \underline{1} = 36$ arrangements starting with a male and 36 starting with a female.

Thus, the probability of alternate seating is $\dfrac{72}{720} = \dfrac{1}{10}$

47. A slate of 3 officers can be selected from 15 people in $15 \cdot 14 \cdot 13 = 2730$ ways. From the remaining 12 people, committees of 5 can be selected in

$$_{12}C_5 = \frac{12!}{7!5!} = \frac{12 \cdot 11 \cdot 10 \cdot 9 \cdot 8}{5 \cdot 4 \cdot 3 \cdot 2 \cdot 1} = 792 \text{ ways}$$

Thus, the number of ways to select the officers and committee is $2730 \cdot 792 = 2,162,160$.

a) P(specific slate, specific committee) = $\dfrac{1}{2162160}$

b) P(any 3 of the 8 for officers) = $\dfrac{8 \cdot 7 \cdot 6}{2162160} = \dfrac{1}{6435}$

48. a) $_4C_2 = \dfrac{4!}{2!2!} = \dfrac{4 \cdot 3}{2 \cdot 1} = 6$ and from problem 9, $_{52}C_5 = 2,598,960$

There are 6 ways to choose the aces, 6 ways to choose the 8's and 48 ways to choose the fifth card. Thus, the probability of being dealt a dead man's hand is

$$\frac{6 \cdot 6 \cdot 48}{2598960} = \frac{36}{54145}$$

b) The probability of being dealt the specific dead man's hand is $\dfrac{1}{2598960}$

49. Given any four different numbers, there are $4 \cdot 3 \cdot 2 \cdot 1 = 24$ different ways they can be arranged. One of these is in ascending order. Thus, the probability of the numbers being in ascending order is 1/24.

Exercise Set 12.11

1. A probability distribution shows the probability associated with each specific outcome of an experiment. In a probability distribution every possible outcome must be listed and the sum of all the probabilities must be 1.

2. Each trial has two possible outcomes, success and failure. There are n repeated independent trials.

3. $P(x) = {_nC_x} p^x q^{n-x}$

4. p is the probability of success, $q = 1 - p$ is the probability of failure.

5. $P(1) = {}_4C_1(0.1)^1(0.9)^{4-1}$

   $= 4 \cdot (0.1)^1(0.9)^3$

   $= 0.2916$

6. $P(2) = {}_3C_2(0.6)^2(0.4)^{3-2}$

   $= 3 \cdot (0.6)^2(0.4)^1$

   $= 0.4320$

7. $P(2) = {}_5C_2(0.4)^2(0.6)^{5-2}$

   $= 10 \cdot (0.4)^2(0.6)^3$

   $= 0.3456$

8. $P(3) = {}_3C_3(0.9)^3(0.1)^{3-3}$

   $= 1 \cdot (0.9)^3(0.1)^0$

   $= 0.7290$

9. $P(0) = {}_4C_0(0.5)^0(0.5)^{4-0}$

   $= 1 \cdot (0.5)^0(0.5)^4$

   $= 1 \cdot 1 \cdot (0.5)^4 = 0.0625$

10. $P(3) = {}_5C_3(0.4)^3(0.6)^{5-3}$

    $= 10 \cdot (0.4)^3(0.6)^2$

    $= 0.2304$

11. $p = 0.15$, $q = 1 - p = 1 - 0.15 = 0.85$

    a) $P(x) = {}_nC_x(0.15)^x(0.85)^{n-x}$

    b) $n = 12$, $x = 2$, $p = 0.15$, $q = 0.85$

    $P(2) = {}_{12}C_2(0.15)^2(0.85)^{12-2}$

12. a) $P(x) = {}_nC_x(0.0237)^x(0.9763)^{n-x}$

    b) $P(5) = {}_{20}C_5(0.0237)^5(0.9763)^{20-5}$

13. $P(1) = {}_5C_1(0.2)^1(0.8)^{5-1}$

    $= 5 \cdot (0.2)^1(0.8)^4$

    $= 0.4096$

14. $P(1) = {}_6C_1\left(\frac{1}{6}\right)^1\left(\frac{5}{6}\right)^{6-1}$

    $= 6 \cdot \left(\frac{1}{6}\right)^1\left(\frac{5}{6}\right)^5$

    $= 0.4019$

15. $P(2) = {}_3C_2(0.96)^2(0.04)^{3-2}$

    $= 3 \cdot (0.96)^2(0.04)^1$

    $= 0.1106$

16. $P(4) = {}_6C_4(0.8)^4(0.2)^{6-4}$

    $= 15 \cdot (0.8)^4(0.2)^2$

    $= 0.2458$

17. $P(4) = {}_6C_4(0.92)^4(0.08)^{6-4}$

    $= 15 \cdot (0.92)^4(0.08)^2$

    $= 0.0688$

18. $P(2) = {}_4C_2(0.01)^2(0.99)^{4-2}$

    $= 6 \cdot (0.01)^2(0.99)^2$

    $= 0.00059$

19. $P(3) = {}_4C_3\left(\frac{2}{3}\right)^3\left(\frac{1}{3}\right)^{4-3}$

    $= 4 \cdot \left(\frac{2}{3}\right)^3\left(\frac{1}{3}\right)^1$

    $= \frac{32}{81} = 0.3951$

20. a) $P(0) = {}_4C_0\left(\frac{1}{4}\right)^0\left(\frac{3}{4}\right)^{4-0}$

    $= 1 \cdot 1 \cdot \left(\frac{3}{4}\right)^4 = 0.3164$

    b) $P(\text{at least } 1) = 1 - P(0)$

    $= 1 - 0.3164 = 0.6836$

21. a) $P(0) = {}_5C_0(0.6)^0(0.4)^{5-0}$

    $= 1 \cdot 1 \cdot (0.4)^5$

    $= 0.0102$

    b) $P(\text{at least } 1) = 1 - P(0) = 0.9898$

22. a) $P(3) = {}_5C_3\left(\frac{40}{80}\right)^3\left(\frac{40}{80}\right)^2$

    $= 10 \cdot (0.5)^3(0.5)^2$

    $= 0.3125$

    b) $P(3) = {}_5C_3\left(\frac{20}{80}\right)^3\left(\frac{60}{80}\right)^2$

    $= 10 \cdot (0.25)^3(0.75)^2$

    $= 0.0879$

23. a) $P(3) = {}_6C_3 \left(\frac{12}{52}\right)^3 \left(\frac{40}{52}\right)^3$

$= 20 \cdot \left(\frac{3}{13}\right)^3 \left(\frac{10}{13}\right)^3$

$= 0.1119$

b) $P(2) = {}_6C_2 \left(\frac{13}{52}\right)^2 \left(\frac{39}{52}\right)^4$

$= 15 \cdot \left(\frac{1}{4}\right)^2 \left(\frac{3}{4}\right)^4$

$= 0.2966$

24. a) $P(3) = {}_5C_3 (0.7)^3 (0.3)^2$

$= 10 \cdot (0.7)^3 (0.3)^2$

$= 0.3087$

b) P(at least 3) = P(3) + P(4) + P(5)

$= 0.3087 + 0.3602 + 0.1681$

$= 0.8370$

Review Exercises

1. Relative frequency over the long run can accurately be predicted, not individual events or totals.

2. Roll the die many times then compute the relative frequency of each outcome and compare with the expected probability 1/6.

3. P(heads) = $\frac{55}{60} = \frac{11}{12} = 0.92$

4. Your answer should be close to 0.25.

5. P(male) = $\frac{58}{100} = \frac{29}{50} = 0.58$

6. P(odd) = $\frac{5}{10} = \frac{1}{2}$

7. P(even or greater than 4) = $\frac{8}{10} = \frac{4}{5}$

8. P(greater than 2 or less than 5) = $\frac{10}{10} = 1$

9. P(even and greater than 4) = $\frac{2}{10} = \frac{1}{5}$

10. P(coke) = $\frac{17}{50}$

11. P(Pepsi) = $\frac{15}{50} = \frac{3}{10}$

12. P(Dr. Pepper or 7-up) = $\frac{10+8}{50} = \frac{18}{50} = \frac{9}{25}$

13. P(coke or pepsi or 7-up) = $\frac{17+15+8}{50} = \frac{40}{50} = \frac{4}{5}$

14. P(gold star) = $\frac{1}{10}$, P(not gold star) = $\frac{9}{10}$

a) odds against gold star = $\frac{P(\text{not gold star})}{P(\text{gold star})}$

$= \frac{9/10}{1/10} = \frac{9}{10} \cdot \frac{10}{1} = \frac{9}{1}$ or 9:1

b) odds in favor of gold star are 1:9

15. odds against corn = $\frac{P(\text{not corn})}{P(\text{corn})} = \frac{5/8}{3/8} = \frac{5}{8} \cdot \frac{8}{3} = \frac{5}{3}$ or 5:3

16. P(winning) = $\frac{3}{2+3} = \frac{3}{5}$

17. odds in favor of restaurant succeeding = $\frac{P(\text{succeeds})}{P(\text{not succeed})} = \frac{0.6}{0.4} = \frac{6/10}{4/10} = \frac{6}{10} \cdot \frac{10}{4} = \frac{6}{4} = \frac{3}{2}$ or 3:2

18. a) E = P(win \$200) · \$198 + P(win \$100) · \$98 + P(lose) · (−\$2)

$$= \frac{3}{1000} \cdot 198 + \frac{2}{1000} \cdot 98 - \frac{995}{1000} \cdot 2 = \frac{594}{1000} + \frac{196}{1000} - \frac{1990}{1000} = \frac{1200}{1000} = -\$1.20$$

   b) The expectation of a person who purchases three tickets would be 3(−1.20) = −\$3.60.

   c) Expected value = Fair price − Cost

            −1.20 = Fair price − 2.00

             80¢ = Fair price

19. a) $E_{Cameron}$ = P(picture card)(\$9) + P(not a picture card)(−\$3) = $\frac{12}{52}(9) - \frac{40}{52}(3) = \frac{27}{13} - \frac{30}{13} = \frac{-3}{13} \approx -\$0.23$

   b) $E_{Lindsey}$ = P(picture card)(−\$9) + P(not a picture card)(\$3) = $\frac{-27}{13} + \frac{30}{13} = \frac{3}{13} \approx \$0.23$

   c) Cameron can expect to lose $100 \cdot \left(\frac{3}{13}\right) \approx \$23.08$

20. E = P(sunny)(1000) + P(cloudy)(500) + P(rain)(100)

     = 0.4(1000) + 0.5(500) + 0.1(100) = 400 + 250 + 10 = 660 people

21. a)

b) Sample
<u>President</u> <u>Vice Pres.</u>   <u>Space</u>

```
        ┌ J      T, J
    T ──┼ G      T, G
   ╱    └ C      T, C
  ╱     ┌ T      J, T
 ╱  J ──┼ G      J, G
 │      └ C      J, C
 │      ┌ T      G, T
 │  G ──┼ J      G, J
  ╲     └ C      G, C
   ╲    ┌ T      C, T
    C ──┼ J      C, J
        └ G      C, G
```

   c) P(Gina is Pres. and Jake V.P.) = $\frac{1}{12}$

22. a)

b) Sample
<u>coin</u>   <u>marble</u>   <u>Space</u>

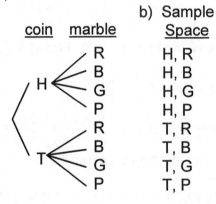

```
        ┌ R      H, R
    H ──┼ B      H, B
   ╱    ├ G      H, G
  ╱     └ P      H, P
  ╲     ┌ R      T, R
   ╲    ├ B      T, B
    T ──┼ G      T, G
        └ P      T, P
```

   c) P(heads, and red or purple) = $\frac{2}{8} = \frac{1}{4}$

23. P(outer is odd and inner is odd) = P(outer is odd) · P(inner is odd) = $\frac{4}{8} \cdot \frac{4}{8} = \frac{1}{2} \cdot \frac{1}{2} = \frac{1}{4}$

24. P(outer is greater than 5 and inner is greater than 5)

   = P(outer is greater than 5) · P(inner is greater than 5) = $\frac{3}{8} \cdot \frac{3}{8} = \frac{9}{64}$

25. P(outer odd and inner less than 6) = P(outer odd) · P(inner less than 6) = $\frac{4}{8} \cdot \frac{5}{8} = \frac{1}{2} \cdot \frac{5}{8} = \frac{5}{16}$

26. P(outer is even or less than 6) = P(even) + P(less than 6) − P(even and less than 6) = $\frac{4}{8} + \frac{5}{8} - \frac{2}{8} = \frac{7}{8}$

27. P(inner is not blue or is even) = P(not blue) + P(even) − P(not blue and even) = $\frac{6}{8} + \frac{4}{8} - \frac{2}{8} = \frac{8}{8} = 1$

28. P(outer is blue and inner is not blue) = P(outer blue) · P(inner not blue) = $\frac{2}{8} \cdot \frac{6}{8} = \frac{1}{4} \cdot \frac{3}{4} = \frac{3}{16}$

29. P(all 3 are Hersheys) = $\frac{5}{12} \cdot \frac{4}{11} \cdot \frac{3}{10} = \frac{60}{1320} = \frac{1}{22}$

30. P(none are Nestle) = $\frac{8}{12} \cdot \frac{7}{11} \cdot \frac{6}{10} = \frac{336}{1320} = \frac{14}{55}$

31. P(at least one is Nestle) = 1 − P(none are Nestle) = $1 - \frac{14}{55} = \frac{55}{55} - \frac{14}{55} = \frac{41}{55}$

32. P(Hershey and Hershey and Reese) = $\frac{5}{12} \cdot \frac{4}{11} \cdot \frac{3}{10} = \frac{60}{1320} = \frac{1}{22}$

33. P(red) = $\frac{1}{4}$

34. odds against red = $\frac{P(\text{not red})}{P(\text{red})} = \frac{3/4}{1/4} = \frac{3}{4} \cdot \frac{4}{1} = \frac{3}{1}$ or 3:1

    The odds in favor of red are then 1:3.

35. fair price = P(red)($5) = $\frac{1}{4}(5) = \frac{5}{4}$ = $1.25

36. P(red and then gray) = P(red) · P(gray) = $\frac{1}{4} \cdot \frac{1}{2} = \frac{1}{8}$

37. P(not gray) = $\frac{1}{4} + \frac{1}{4} + \frac{1}{8} = \frac{5}{8}$

38. odds in favor of gray = $\frac{P(\text{gray})}{P(\text{not gray})} = \frac{3/8}{5/8} = \frac{3}{8} \cdot \frac{8}{5} = \frac{3}{5}$ or 3:5

    The odds against gray are then 5:3.

39. E = P(gray)($10) + P(red)($5) + P(yellow)(−$20) = $\frac{3}{8}(10) + \frac{1}{2}(5) - \frac{1}{8}(20) = \frac{15}{4} + \frac{10}{4} - \frac{10}{4} = \frac{15}{4}$ = $3.75

40. P(at least one red) = 1 − P(none are red) = $1 - \left(\frac{1}{2} \cdot \frac{1}{2} \cdot \frac{1}{2} \right) = 1 - \frac{1}{8} = \frac{7}{8}$

41. P(fewer than 6 defects | American built) = $\frac{89}{106} = 0.84$

42. P(fewer than 6 defects | foreign built) = $\frac{55}{74} = 0.74$

43. P(six or more defects | foreign built) = $\frac{19}{74} = 0.26$

44. P(six or more defects | American built) = $\frac{17}{106} = 0.16$

45. P(right handed) = $\frac{230}{400} = \frac{23}{40}$

46. P(left brained | left handed) = $\frac{30}{170} = \frac{3}{17}$

47. P(right handed | no predominance) = $\frac{60}{80} = \frac{3}{4}$

48. P(right brained | left handed) = $\dfrac{120}{170} = \dfrac{12}{17}$

49. a) $_4P_4 = \dfrac{4!}{(4-4)!} = \dfrac{4!}{0!} = 4! = 4 \cdot 3 \cdot 2 \cdot 1 = 24$ ways

   b) $E = \dfrac{1}{4}(10{,}000) + \dfrac{1}{4}(1{,}000) + \dfrac{1}{4}(500) + \dfrac{1}{4}(100) = \$2{,}900$

50. number of possible arrangements = $_5C_2 \cdot _3C_2 \cdot _1C_1 = \dfrac{5!}{3!2!} \cdot \dfrac{3!}{1!2!} \cdot \dfrac{1!}{0!1!} = 10 \cdot 3 \cdot 1 = 30$

51. $_8P_3 = \dfrac{8!}{(8-3)!} = \dfrac{8!}{5!} = \dfrac{8 \cdot 7 \cdot 6 \cdot 5!}{5!} = 336$

52. $_9P_3 = \dfrac{9!}{(93)!} = \dfrac{9!}{6!} = 9 \cdot 8 \cdot 7 = 504$

53. $_6C_3 = \dfrac{6!}{3!3!} = \dfrac{6 \cdot 5 \cdot 4}{3 \cdot 2 \cdot 1} = 20$

54. a) $_{15}C_{10} = \dfrac{15!}{5!10!} = \dfrac{15 \cdot 14 \cdot 13 \cdot 12 \cdot 11}{5 \cdot 4 \cdot 3 \cdot 2 \cdot 1} = 3{,}003$

   b) number of arrangements = $10! = 3{,}628{,}800$

55. a) P(match 5 numbers) = $\dfrac{1}{_{50}C_5} = \dfrac{1}{\dfrac{50!}{45!5!}} = \dfrac{45!5!}{50!} = \dfrac{1}{2118760}$

   b) P(Big game win) = P(match 5 numbers and match Big number)

   = P(match 5 numbers) • P(match Big number) = $\dfrac{1}{2118760} \cdot \dfrac{1}{36} = \dfrac{1}{76275360}$

56. $_4C_2 \cdot _6C_3 = \dfrac{4!}{2!2!} \cdot \dfrac{6!}{3!3!} = 6 \cdot 20 = 120$ combinations

57. $_8C_3 \cdot _5C_2 = \dfrac{8!}{5!3!} \cdot \dfrac{5!}{3!2!} = \dfrac{8 \cdot 7 \cdot 6}{3 \cdot 2 \cdot 1} \cdot \dfrac{5 \cdot 4}{2 \cdot 1} = 560$

58. P(two aces) = $\dfrac{_4C_2}{_{52}C_2} = \dfrac{\dfrac{4!}{2!2!}}{\dfrac{52!}{50!2!}} = \dfrac{4!}{2!2!} \cdot \dfrac{50!2!}{52!} = \dfrac{1}{221}$

59. P(all three are red) = $\dfrac{5}{10} \cdot \dfrac{4}{9} \cdot \dfrac{3}{8} = \dfrac{1}{12}$

60. P(first two are red and 3rd is blue) = $\dfrac{5}{10} \cdot \dfrac{4}{9} \cdot \dfrac{2}{8} = \dfrac{1}{18}$

61. P(1st red, 2nd white, 3rd blue) = $\dfrac{5}{10} \cdot \dfrac{3}{9} \cdot \dfrac{2}{8} = \dfrac{1}{24}$

62. P(at least one red) = 1 – P(none are red) = $1 - \left(\dfrac{5}{10} \cdot \dfrac{4}{9} \cdot \dfrac{3}{8} \right) = 1 - \dfrac{1}{12} = \dfrac{11}{12}$

63. P(3 maples) = $\dfrac{6}{14} \cdot \dfrac{5}{13} \cdot \dfrac{4}{12} = \dfrac{5}{91}$

64. P(two pines and one maple) = $\dfrac{_5C_2 \cdot _6C_1}{_{14}C_3} = \dfrac{\dfrac{5!}{3!2!} \cdot \dfrac{6!}{5!1!}}{\dfrac{14!}{11!3!}} = \dfrac{15}{91}$

65. P(no pines) = $\dfrac{9}{14} \cdot \dfrac{8}{13} \cdot \dfrac{7}{12} = \dfrac{3}{13}$

66. P(at least one pine) = 1 − P(no pines) = $1 - \frac{3}{13} = \frac{10}{13}$

67. a) $P(x) = {}_nC_x (0.6)^x (0.4)^{n-x}$

    b) $P(75) = {}_{100}C_{75} (0.6)^{75} (0.4)^{25}$

68. n = 5, x = 3, p = 1/5, q = 4/5

$$P(3) = {}_5C_3 \left(\frac{1}{5}\right)^3 \left(\frac{4}{5}\right)^2$$

$$= 10 \cdot \left(\frac{1}{5}\right)^3 \left(\frac{4}{5}\right)^2 = 0.0512$$

69. a) n = 4, p = 0.6, q = 0.4

$$P(0) = {}_4C_0 (0.6)^0 (0.4)^4$$

$$= 1 \cdot 1 \cdot (0.4)^4 = 0.0256$$

   b) P(at least 1) = 1 − P(0)

$$= 1 - 0.0256$$
$$= 0.9744$$

Chapter Test

1. P(fishing for bass) = $\frac{14}{20} = \frac{7}{10} = 0.7$

2. P(greater than 7) = $\frac{2}{9} \approx 0.22$

3. P(odd) = $\frac{5}{9} \approx 0.55$

4. P(even or greater than 4) = $\frac{7}{9} \approx 0.78$

5. P(odd and greater than 4) = $\frac{3}{9} = \frac{1}{3} \approx 0.33$

6. P(both greater than 5) = $\frac{4}{9} \cdot \frac{3}{8} = \frac{12}{72} = \frac{1}{6}$

7. P(both even) = $\frac{4}{9} \cdot \frac{3}{8} = \frac{1 \cdot 1}{3 \cdot 2} = \frac{1}{6}$

8. P(1st odd, 2nd even) = $\frac{5}{9} \cdot \frac{4}{8} = \frac{5}{9} \cdot \frac{1}{2} = \frac{5}{18}$

9. P(neither greater than 6) = $\frac{6}{9} \cdot \frac{5}{8} = \frac{1 \cdot 5}{3 \cdot 4} = \frac{5}{12}$

10. P(red or picture)

    = P(red) + P(picture) − P(red and picture)

    $= \frac{26}{52} + \frac{12}{52} - \frac{6}{52} = \frac{32}{52} = \frac{8}{13}$

11. $6 \cdot 3 = 18$

12.

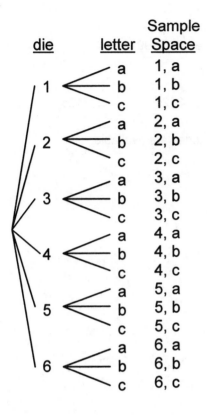

die	letter	Sample Space
1	a	1, a
	b	1, b
	c	1, c
2	a	2, a
	b	2, b
	c	2, c
3	a	3, a
	b	3, b
	c	3, c
4	a	4, a
	b	4, b
	c	4, c
5	a	5, a
	b	5, b
	c	5, c
6	a	6, a
	b	6, b
	c	6, c

13. $P(4 \text{ and a}) = \dfrac{1}{18}$

14. $P(4 \text{ or a}) = \dfrac{8}{18} = \dfrac{4}{9}$

15. $P(\text{even number or b}) = \dfrac{12}{18} = \dfrac{2}{3}$

16. Number of codes $= 9 \cdot 26 \cdot 26 \cdot 10 \cdot 10 = 608{,}400$

17. odds against male $= \dfrac{P(\text{not male})}{P(\text{male})}$

$= \dfrac{3/8}{5/8} = \dfrac{3}{8} \cdot \dfrac{8}{5} = \dfrac{3}{5}$ or $3{:}5$

18. odds against Aimee winning are 5:2 or

$\dfrac{5}{2} = \dfrac{5/7}{2/7} = \dfrac{P(\text{not winning})}{P(\text{winning})}$

Therefore, $P(\text{Aimee wins}) = 2/7$

19. $E = P(\text{club}) (\$8) + P(\text{heart}) (\$4) + P(\text{spade or diamond}) (-\$6)$

$= \dfrac{1}{4}(10) + \dfrac{1}{4}(4) + \dfrac{2}{4}(-6) = \dfrac{8}{4} + \dfrac{4}{4} - \dfrac{12}{4} = \dfrac{0}{4} = \$0$

20. $P(\text{gray squirrel} \mid \text{Yosemite}) = \dfrac{60}{105} = \dfrac{4}{7}$

21. $_6P_3 = \dfrac{6!}{(6-3)!} = \dfrac{6!}{3!} = 6 \cdot 5 \cdot 4 = 120$

22. $P(\text{neither is good}) = \dfrac{8}{20} \cdot \dfrac{7}{19} = \dfrac{2}{5} \cdot \dfrac{7}{19} = \dfrac{14}{95}$

23. $P(\text{at least 1 good})$

$= 1 - P(\text{neither is good}) = 1 - \dfrac{14}{95} = \dfrac{81}{95}$

24. $_7C_3 = \dfrac{7!}{4!3!} = \dfrac{7 \cdot 6 \cdot 5}{3 \cdot 2 \cdot 1} = 35$

$_{10}C_5 = \dfrac{12!}{7!5!} = \dfrac{12 \cdot 11 \cdot 10 \cdot 9 \cdot 8}{5 \cdot 4 \cdot 3 \cdot 2 \cdot 1} = 792$

$_5C_2 = \dfrac{5!}{3!2!} = \dfrac{5 \cdot 4}{2 \cdot 1} = 10$

$P(3 \text{ red and 2 green}) = \dfrac{35 \cdot 10}{792} = \dfrac{175}{396}$

25. $n = 4, x = 3, p = 3/5, q = 2/5$

$P(3) = {_4C_3}\left(\dfrac{3}{5}\right)^3\left(\dfrac{2}{5}\right)^{4-3} = 4 \cdot \left(\dfrac{3}{5}\right)^3\left(\dfrac{2}{5}\right)^1 = 0.3456$

Group Projects

1. 0, no measurement is exact.

2. a) 0.30199   b) 0.10737   c) 0.89263   d) 0.00000   e) 0.30199
   f) They should be the same.

3. a) $10^5 = 100,000$ b) $5^5 = 3125$ c) $\dfrac{1}{3125}$ d) 3125   e) 3125

   f) $\dfrac{1}{3125}$ g) same likelihood   h) More 5 digit codes are available.

CHAPTER THIRTEEN

STATISTICS

Exercise Set 13.1

1. **Descriptive statistics** is concerned with the collection, organization, and analysis of data.
   Inferential statistics is concerned with making generalizations or predictions from the data collected.
2. **Statistics** is the art and science of gathering, analyzing, and making inferences (predictions) from numerical information obtained in an experiment.
3. Answers will vary.
4. Insurance companies, sports, airlines, stock market, medical profession
5. Answers will vary.
6. **Probability** is used to compute the chance of occurrence of a particular event when all possible outcomes are known. **Statistics** is used to draw conclusions about possible outcomes through observations of only a few particular events.
7. a) A **population** consists of all items or people of interest.
   b) A **sample** is a subset of the population.
8. a) A **random sample** is a sample drawn in such a way that each item in the population has an equal chance of being drawn and every sample of a given size has an equal chance of being selected.
   b) Number each item in the population. Write each number on a piece of paper and put each numbered piece of paper in a hat. Select pieces of paper from the hat and use the numbered items selected as your sample.
9. a) A **systematic sample** is a sample obtained by selecting every n^{th} item on a list or production line.
   b) Use a random number table to select the first item, then select every n^{th} item after that.
10. a) A **cluster sample** is a random selection of groups of units.
    b) Selection can be made on a geographical location or by selection of random units.
11. a) A **stratified sample** is obtained when the population is divided into parts, called strata.
    b) Selection can be made by dividing the population into strata and then taking a random sample from each strata.
12. a) A **convenience sample** uses data that is easily or readily obtained.
    b) Select the first 20 students entering a classroom.
13. a) An **unbiased sample** is one that is a small replica of the entire population with regard to income, education, sex, race, religion, political affiliation, age, etc.
14. a) The method used to obtain the sample is biased. In classes where students are seated alphabetically, brothers and sisters could be selected from different classes.
    b) The average will be greater since brothers and sisters from large families would be selected.

15. Random sample
16. Systematic sample
17. Cluster sample
18. Stratified sample
19. Systematic sample
20. Systematic sample
21. Convenience sample
22. Random sample
23. Cluster sample
24. Convenience sample

25. Answers will vary.
26. Biased because the subscribers of *Consumer Reports* are not necessarily representative of the entire population.

Exercise Set 13.2
1. Answers will vary.
2. The graph is misleading because the scale on the horizontal axis is inconsistent.
3. Every employee may not make the average salary. Some may have a salary far below the average or far above the average.
4. Although the cookies are fat free, they still contain calories. Eating many of them can still cause you to gain weight.
5. The fact that Morgan's is the largest department store does not imply it is inexpensive.
6. More people drive on Saturday night. Thus, one might expect more accidents.
7. Most driving is done close to home. Thus, one might expect more accidents close to home.
8. People with asthma may move to Arizona because of its climate. Therefore, more people with asthma may live in Arizona.
9. Averages apply to a set of data. Thus, although the female average score may be greater, some males have higher scores than some females.
10. Just because dermatologists recommend Soft and Smooth does not mean it is the best dry skin lotion.
11. There may be deep sections in the pond, so it may not be safe to go wading.
12. Just because they are the most expensive does not mean they last the longest.
13. Half the students in a population are expected to be below average.
14. Because there are more orange trees in Florida does not mean that Floridians drink the most orange juice.
15. Just because some prefer it does not mean they buy it. Other factors, such as cost, must be considered.
16. Males may drive more miles than females and males may drive in worse driving conditions (like snow).

17. a)

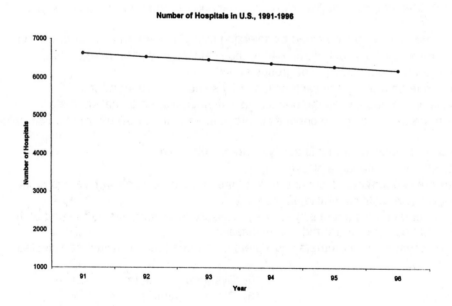

17. b)

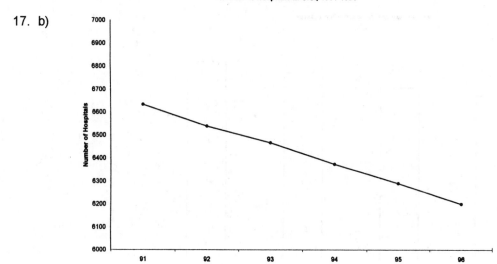

Number of Hospitals in U.S., 1991-1996

18. a)

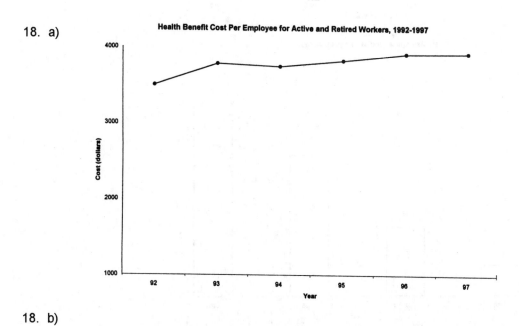

Health Benefit Cost Per Employee for Active and Retired Workers, 1992-1997

18. b)

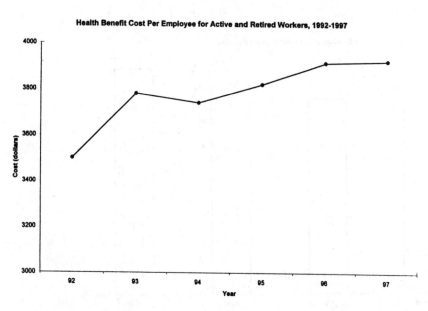

Health Benefit Cost Per Employee for Active and Retired Workers, 1992-1997

19. a)

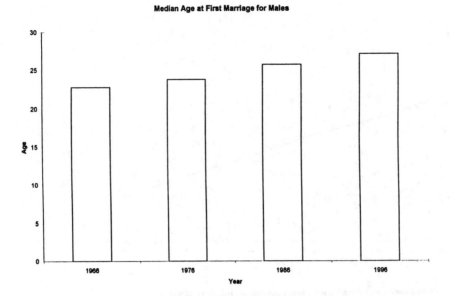

19. b)

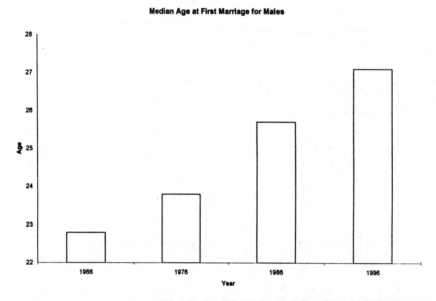

20. a)

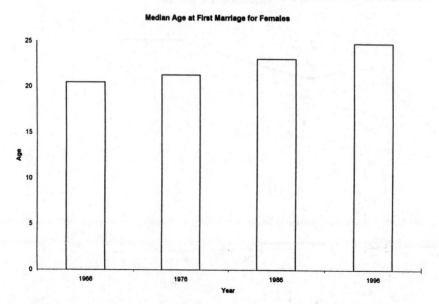

20. b)

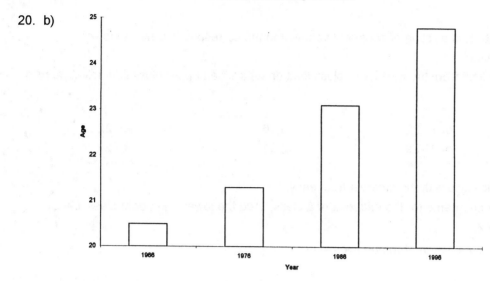

Median Age at First Marriage for Females

21. a)

Gateway Computer Sales

b) Yes, the new graph suggests less growth.

22. a) $\dfrac{394,000,000 - 275,000,000}{275,000,000} = \dfrac{119,000,000}{275,000,000}$

$= 0.43\overline{27} \approx 43.3\%$

c) Radius $= 0.375\, in$

$A = \pi r^2 = \pi(0.375)^2 = 0.140625\pi = 0.441786467$

$\approx 0.442\, in^2$

e) Yes, the percent increase in the size of the area from the first circle to the second is greater than the percent increase in population.

b) Radius $= 0.25\, in$

$A = \pi r^2 = \pi(0.25)^2 = 0.0625\pi = 0.196349541$

$\approx 0.196\, in^2$

d) $\dfrac{0.442 - 0.196}{0.196} = \dfrac{0.246}{0.196} = 1.255102041 \approx 125.5\%$

Exercise Set 13.3

1. A **frequency distribution** is a listing of observed values and the corresponding frequency of occurrence of each value.

2. Subtract a lower class limit from the next lower class limit or subtract an upper class limit from the next upper class limit.

3. a) 7   b) 16-22   c) 16   d) 22

4. a) 9   b) 21-29   c) 21   d) 29

5. The **modal class** is the class with the greatest frequency.

6. The **class mark** is another name for the midpoint of a class. Add the lower and upper class limits and divide the sum by 2.

7. a) Number of observations = sum of frequencies = 17
   b) Width = 14 - 9 = 5
   c) $\dfrac{14+18}{2} = \dfrac{32}{2} = 16$
   d) The modal class is the class with the greatest frequency. Thus, the modal class is 14 - 18.
   e) Since the class widths are 5, the next class would be 39 - 43.

8. a) Number of observations = sum of frequencies = 25
   b) Width = 50 - 40 = 10
   c) $\dfrac{50+59}{2} = \dfrac{109}{2} = 54.5$
   d) 40 - 49 and 80 - 89 both contain 7 pieces of data. Thus, they are both modal classes.
   e) Since the class widths are 10, the next class would be 100 – 109.

9.

Number Sold	Number of Days
0	3
1	8
2	3
3	5
4	2
5	7
6	2
7	3
8	4
9	1
10	2

10.

Number Of Visits	Number of Families
20	3
21	2
22	0
23	3
24	4
25	2
26	6
27	2
28	2
29	1
30	1
31	2
32	2
33	1
34	1

11.

I.Q.	Number of Students
78 - 86	2
87 - 95	15
96 - 104	18
105 - 113	7
114 - 122	6
123 - 131	1
132 - 140	1

12.

I.Q.	Number of Students
80 - 88	4
89 - 97	17
98 - 106	15
107 - 115	8
116 - 124	4
125 - 133	1
134 - 142	1

13.

I.Q.	Number of Students
80 - 90	8
91 - 101	22
102 - 112	11
113 - 123	7
124 - 134	1
135 - 145	1

14.

I.Q.	Number of Students
80 - 92	11
93 - 105	24
106 - 118	9
119 - 131	5
132 - 144	1

15.

Age	Number of Pres.
40 - 45	2
46 - 51	12
52 - 57	16
58 - 63	6
64 - 69	5

16.

Age	Number of Pres.
42 - 47	5
48 - 53	11
54 - 59	15
60 - 65	8
66 - 71	2

17.

Age	Number of Pres.
42 - 46	4
47 - 51	10
52 - 56	12
57 - 61	9
62 - 66	4
67 - 71	2

18.

Age	Number of Pres.
40 - 44	2
45 - 49	6
50 - 54	12
55 - 59	11
60 - 64	7
65 - 69	3

19.

Cost (Millions)	# of Comp.
90 - 199	18
200 - 309	15
310 - 419	5
420 - 529	2
530 - 639	8
640 - 749	0
750 - 859	1
860 - 969	1

20.

Cost (Millions)	# of Comp.
90 - 195	18
196 - 301	15
302 - 407	4
408 - 513	2
514 - 619	8
620 - 725	1
726 - 831	1
832 - 937	0
938 - 1043	1

21.

Cost (Millions)	# of Comp.
50 - 149	12
150 - 249	14
250 - 349	7
350 - 449	5
450 - 549	3
550 - 649	7
650 - 749	0
750 - 849	1
850 - 949	0
950 - 1049	1

22.

Cost (Millions)	# of Comp.
50 - 199	18
200 - 349	15
350 - 499	6
500 - 649	9
650 - 799	1
800 - 949	0
950 - 1099	1

23.

Population (To nearest 100,000)	Number of Cities
5.4 - 7.4	10
7.5 - 9.5	5
9.6 - 11.6	10
11.7 - 13.7	4
13.8 - 15.8	1
15.9 - 17.9	4
18.0 - 20.0	0
20.1 - 22.1	0
22.2 - 24.2	0
24.3 - 26.3	0
26.4 - 28.4	1

24.

Population (To nearest 100,000)	Number of Cities
5.0 - 8.0	11
8.1 - 11.1	12
11.2 - 14.2	7
14.3 - 17.3	4
17.4 - 20.4	0
20.5 - 23.5	0
23.6 - 26.6	0
26.7 - 29.7	1

25.

Population (To nearest 100,000)	Number of Cities
5.1 - 7.6	11
7.7 - 10.2	8
10.3 - 12.8	10
12.9 - 15.4	1
15.5 - 18.0	4
18.1 - 20.6	0
20.7 - 23.2	0
23.3 - 25.8	0
25.9 - 28.4	1

26.

Population (To nearest 100,000)	Number of Cities
5.4 - 7.9	11
8.0 - 10.5	10
10.6 - 13.1	8
13.2 - 15.7	1
15.8 - 18.3	4
18.4 - 20.9	0
21.0 - 23.5	0
23.6 - 26.1	0
26.2 - 28.7	1

27.

Percent with Bachelor's Degree	Number of States
14.6 - 18.5	6
18.6 - 22.5	20
22.6 - 26.5	11
26.6 - 30.5	11
30.6 - 34.5	3

28.

Percent with Bachelor's Degree	Number of States
14.6 - 17.5	4
17.6 - 20.5	11
20.6 - 23.5	14
23.6 - 26.5	8
26.6 - 29.5	10
29.6 - 32.5	2
32.6 - 35.5	2

29.

Percent with Bachelor's Degree	Number of States
14.6 - 18.0	5
18.1 - 21.5	14
21.6 - 25.0	14
25.1 - 28.5	13
28.6 - 32.0	2
32.1 - 35.5	3

30.

Percent with Bachelor's Degree	Number of States
14.6 - 17.0	3
17.1 - 19.5	7
19.6 - 22.0	11
22.1 - 24.5	11
24.6 - 27.0	8
27.1 - 29.5	7
29.6 - 32.0	1
32.1 - 34.5	3

Exercise Set 13.4

1. Answers will vary.
2. a) Observed values   b) Frequency
3. - 4. Answers will vary.

5. a) Answers will vary.

b)

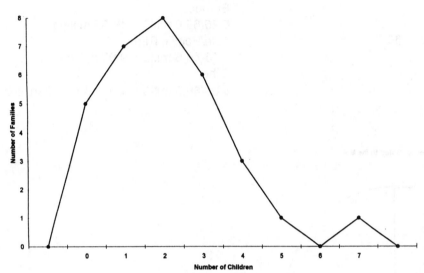

6. a) Answers will vary.

b)

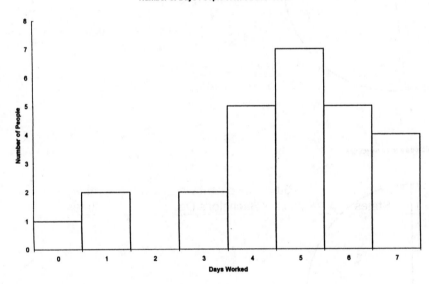

7. a) Answers will vary.

b)

Class	Frequency
45	3
46	0
47	1
48	0
49	1
50	1
51	2

8.

Observed Values	Frequency
16	1
17	2
18	1
19	1
20	0
21	1
22	2
23	1
24	1
25	2

9. None: 0.29(500) = 145
One: 0.31(500) = 155
Two: 0.14(500) = 70
Three: 0.10(500) = 50
Four or more: 0.16(500) = 80

10. North America:
0.57(66.6 mill.) = 37.962 mill. ≈ 37.96 million
Europe:
0.25(66.6 mill.) = 16.65 million
Asia/Pacific Rim:
0.15(66.6 mill.) = 9.99 million
Other:
0.03(66.6 mill.) = 1.998 mill. ≈ 2 million

11.

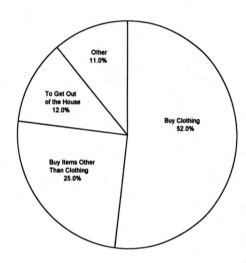

Reasons for Going to the Mall

12.

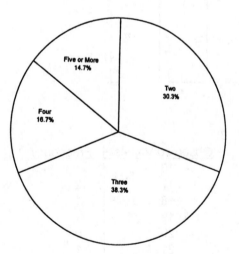

Number of Bedrooms in New Houses

13. a) and b)

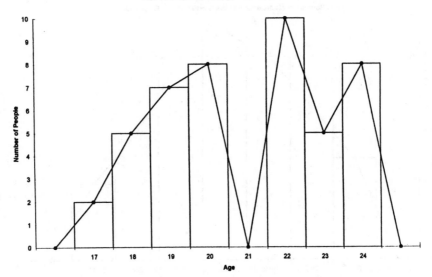

14. a) and b)

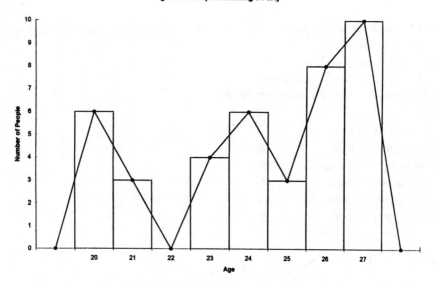

15. a) and b)

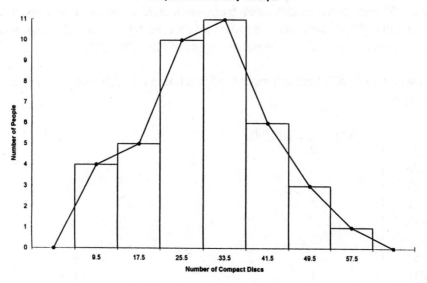

16. a) and b)

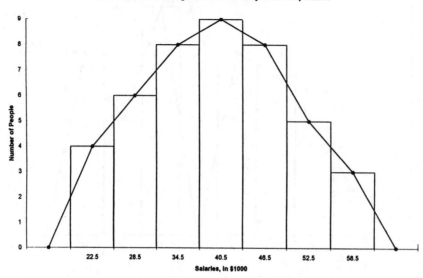

17. a) The total number of people surveyed:
    2 + 5 + 8 + 7 + 4 + 3 + 1 = 30
    b) Four people purchased four books.
    c) The modal class is 2 because more people
    purchased 2 books than any other number of books.
    d) Two people bought 0 books   0
       Five people bought 1 book   5
       Eight people bought 2 books   16
       Seven people bought 3 books   21
       Four people bought 4 books   16
       Three people bought 5 books   15
       One person bought 6 books   6
    Total number of books purchased: 79

e)	Number of Books	Number of People
	0	2
	1	5
	2	8
	3	7
	4	4
	5	3
	6	1

18) a) The total number of students surveyed: 2 + 4 + 6 + 8 + 7 + 3 + 1 = 31
    b) Since there are 51 units between class midpoints, each class width must also be 51 units.
    250 is the midpoint of the first class and there must be 25 units below it and 25 units above it.
    Therefore, the first class is 225 - 275. The second class will be 276 - 326.
    c) Six
    d) The modal class is 378 - 428 because more students had a monthly rent of $378 - $428 than
    any other monthly rent.

e)	Price	Number of Students
	225 - 275	2
	276 - 326	4
	327 - 377	6
	378 - 428	8
	429 - 479	7
	480 - 530	3
	531 - 581	0
	582 - 632	1

19. a) 7 calls

  b) Adding the number of calls responded to in 6, 5, 4, or 3 minutes gives: 4 + 7 + 3 + 2 = 16 calls

  c) The total number of calls surveyed: 2 + 3 + 7 + 4 + 3 + 8 + 6 + 3 = 36

  d)

Response Time (Min.)	Number of Calls
3	2
4	3
5	7
6	4
7	3
8	8
9	6
10	3

  e)

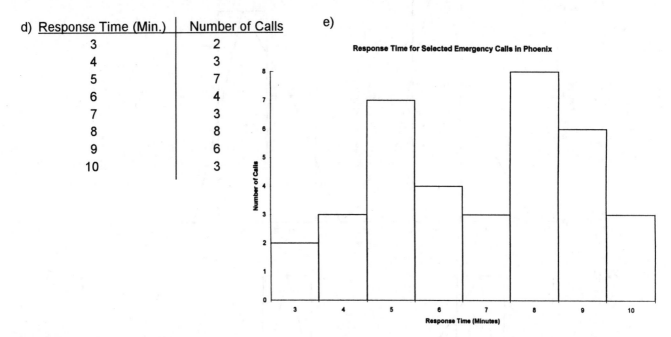

20. a) 8 families

  b) At least six times means six or more times. Adding the families that went 6, 7, 8, 9, or 10 times gives 11 + 9 + 3 + 0 + 1 = 24 families

  c) Total number of families surveyed: 4 + 2 + 8 + 8 + 6 + 11 + 9 + 3 + 0 + 1 = 52 families

  d)

Number of Visits	Number of Families
1	4
2	2
3	8
4	8
5	6
6	11
7	9
8	3
9	0
10	1

  e)

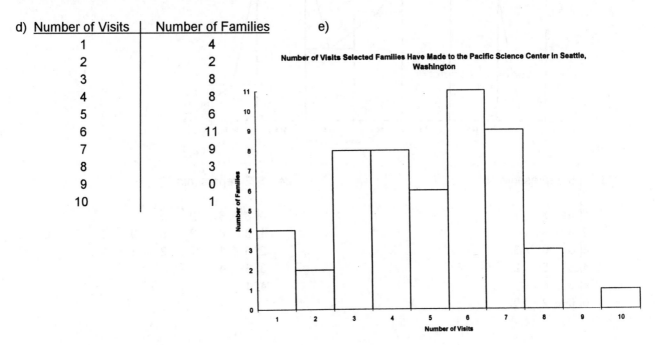

21.

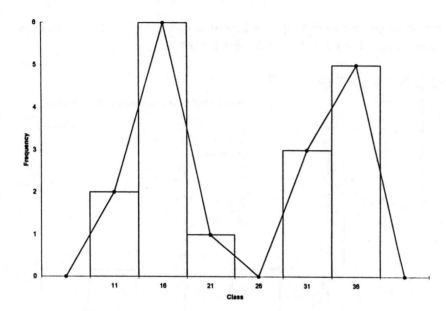

22.

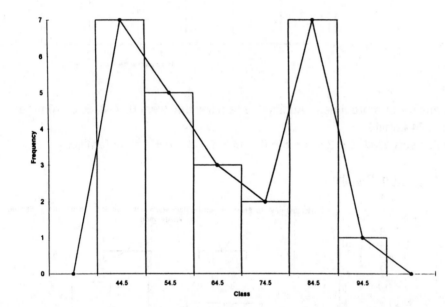

23. 1│5 represents 15

    1│0   5   7
    2│4   4
    3│6   0   3
    4│8   5   2   5   8
    5│3   4
    6│0   2   0

24. 1│2 represents 12

    0│3   8   2   5
    1│2   8   2   5   9   3   7   6
    2│5   1   7   2   3
    3│3   4
    4│1

25. a)

Salaries (in $1000)	Number of Companies
25	1
26	7
27	4
28	3
29	2
30	3
31	3
32	2

b) and c)

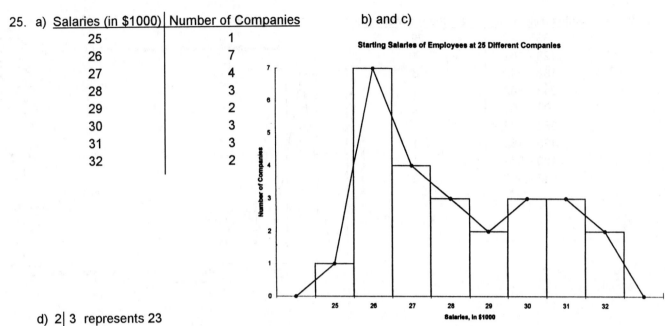

Starting Salaries of Employees at 25 Different Companies

d) 2│3 represents 23

2│5 6 6 6 6 6 6 6 7 7 7 7 8 8 8 9 9
3│0 0 0 1 1 1 2 2

26. a)

Age	Number of People
20 - 24	9
25 - 29	6
30 - 34	10
35 - 39	6
40 - 44	5
45 - 49	4

b) and c)

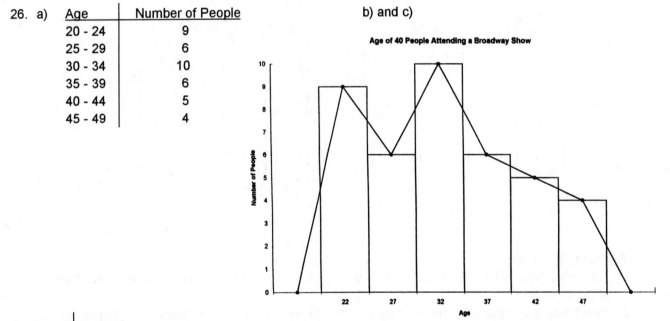

Age of 40 People Attending a Broadway Show

d) 2│3 represents 23

2│0 1 1 2 3 3 3 4 4 5 5 6 7 8 8
3│0 0 0 1 1 2 3 4 4 4 5 5 5 7 8 9
4│0 0 0 2 4 5 5 6 7

27. a)

Sales (Millions)	Number of Magazines
63 - 122	29
123 - 182	4
183 - 242	8
243 - 302	1
303 - 362	2
363 - 422	2
423 - 482	1
483 - 542	1
543 - 602	2

b) and c)

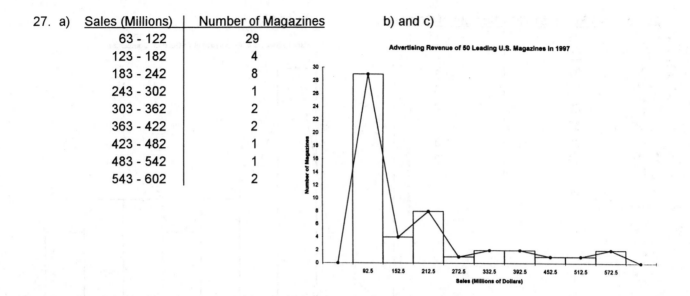

28. a)

Age	Number of Ambassadors
40 - 44	9
45 - 49	6
50 - 54	10
55 - 59	6
60 - 64	5
65 - 69	4

b) and c)

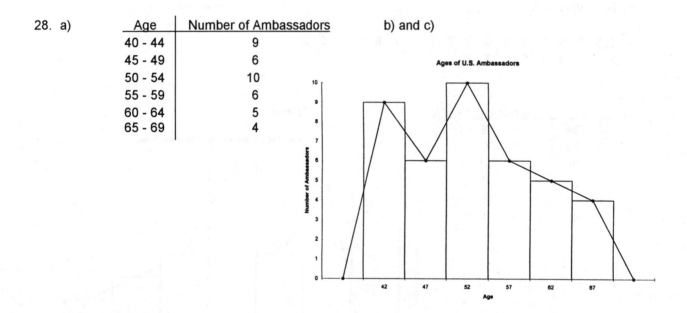

Exercise Set 13. 5

1. The **mean** is the balancing point of a set of data. It is the sum of the data divided by the number of pieces of data.
2. **Ranked data** are data listed from the lowest value to the highest value or from the highest value to the lowest value.
3. The **median** is the value in the middle of a set of ranked data. To find the median, rank the data and select the value in the middle.
4. The **midrange** is the value half way between the lowest and highest values. To find the midrange, add the low and high values and divide the sum by 2.
5. The **mode** is the most common piece of data. The piece of data that occurs most frequently is the mode.
6. The mode may be used when you are primarily interested in the most popular value, or the one that occurs most often, for example, when buying clothing for a store.

7. The median should be used when there are some values that differ greatly from the rest of the values in the set, for example, salaries.
8. The midrange should be used when the item being studied is constantly fluctuating, for example, daily temperature.
9. The mean is used when each piece of data is to be considered and "weighed" equally, for example, weights of adult males.
10. a) $\bar{x}$
    b) μ

	mean	median	mode	midrange
11.	$\dfrac{90}{9}=10$	8	11	$\dfrac{2+36}{2}=19$
12.	$\dfrac{537}{10}=53.7$	$\dfrac{13+13}{2}=13$	13	$\dfrac{7+375}{2}=191$
13.	$\dfrac{523}{7}\approx74.7$	80	none	$\dfrac{45+96}{2}=70.5$
14.	$\dfrac{46}{7}\approx6.6$	6	6	$\dfrac{3+11}{2}=7$
15.	$\dfrac{64}{8}=8$	$\dfrac{7+9}{2}=8$	none	$\dfrac{1+15}{2}=8$
16.	$\dfrac{118}{9}\approx13.1$	11	1	$\dfrac{1+36}{2}=18.5$
17.	$\dfrac{510}{7}\approx72.9$	60	none	$\dfrac{30+140}{2}=85$
18.	$\dfrac{92}{14}\approx6.6$	$\dfrac{4+4}{2}=4$	none	$\dfrac{1+21}{2}=11$
19.	$\dfrac{95}{8}\approx11.9$	$\dfrac{12+13}{2}=12.5$	13	$\dfrac{6+17}{2}=11.5$
20.	$\dfrac{60}{6}=10$	$\dfrac{5+15}{2}=10$	none	$\dfrac{5+15}{2}=10$
21.	$\dfrac{232}{7}\approx33.1$	31	none	$\dfrac{17+51}{2}=34$
22.	$\dfrac{2006}{10}=200.6$	$\dfrac{200+207}{2}=203.5$	none	$\dfrac{132+286}{2}=209$
23. a)	$\dfrac{34}{7}\approx4.9$	5	5	$\dfrac{1+11}{2}=6$
b)	$\dfrac{37}{7}\approx5.3$	5	5	$\dfrac{1+11}{2}=6$
c)	Only the mean			
d)	$\dfrac{33}{7}\approx4.7$	5	5	$\dfrac{1+10}{2}=5.5$

The mean and the midrange

24. Probably the mean since it uses all the data and is the most sensitive to the changes the National Center for Health Statistics wants to document.

25. A 79 average on 10 exams gives a total of 790 points. An 80 average on 10 exams requires a total of 800 points. Thus, Jim missed a B by 10 points not 1 point.

26. a) Mean: $\dfrac{341{,}000}{10} = \$34{,}100$ b) Median: $\dfrac{25{,}000 + 26{,}000}{2} = \$25{,}500$

    c) Mode: $24,000

    d) Midrange: $\dfrac{22{,}000 + 79{,}000}{2} = \$50{,}500$

    e) The median, since it is lower.   f) The mean, since it is higher.

27. a) Mean: $\dfrac{2677}{15} \approx 178.5 \, ft.$ b) Median: $190 \, ft.$

    c) Mode: none

    d) Midrange: $\dfrac{95 + 284}{2} = 189.5 \, ft.$

    e) Median, when there are a few "extreme" values, the median is the best measure of central tendency.

28. a) Mean: $\dfrac{1784.59}{12} \approx \$148.72$ b) Median: $\dfrac{123.72 + 127.96}{2} = \$125.84$

    c) Mode: none

    d) Midrange: $\dfrac{96.27 + 396.81}{2} = \$246.54$

29. a) Mean: $\dfrac{82.2}{10} = 8.22 \approx 8.2$ million   b) Median: $\dfrac{6.0 + 8.9}{2} = 7.45$ million

    c) Mode: none

    d) Midrange: $\dfrac{3.7 + 15.6}{2} = 9.65$ million

30. Let $x =$ the sum of his scores

    $\dfrac{x}{5} = 83$

    $x = 83(5) = 415$

31. Let $x =$ the sum of his scores

    $\dfrac{x}{6} = 78$

    $x = 78(6) = 468$

32. One example is 1, 1, 2, 5, 6. Mode = 1, Median = 2, Mean $= \dfrac{15}{5} = 3$

33. One example is 72, 73, 74, 76, 77, 78.
34. One example is 76, 78, 80, 84, 90, 96.

35. a) Yes
    b) Cannot be found since we do not know the middle two numbers in the ranked list
    c) Cannot be found without knowing all of the numbers
    d) Yes
    e) Mean: $\dfrac{24{,}000}{120} = 200$, Midrange: $\dfrac{20 + 500}{2} = 260$

36. A total of $80 \times 5 = 400$ points are needed for a grade of B. Jorge earned 68 + 78 + 83 + 80 = 309 points on his first four exams. Thus, he needs 400 - 309 = 91 or better to get a B.

37. a) For a mean average of 60 on 7 exams, she must have a total of $60 \times 7 = 420$ points. Sheryl presently has $49 + 72 + 80 + 60 + 57 + 69 = 387$ points. Thus, to pass the course, her last exam must be $420 - 387 = 33$ or greater.
    b) A C average requires a total of $70 \times 7 = 490$ points. Sheryl has 387. Therefore, she would need $490 - 387 = 103$ on her last exam. If the maximum score she can receive is 100, she cannot obtain a C.
    c) For a mean average of 60 on 6 exams, she must have a total of $60 \times 6 = 360$ points. If the lowest score on an exam she has already taken is dropped, she will have a total of $72 + 80 + 60 + 57 + 69 = 338$ points. Thus, to pass the course, her last exam must be $360 - 338 = 22$ or greater.
    d) For a mean average of 70 on 6 exams, she must have a total of $70 \times 6 = 420$ points. If the lowest score on an exam she has already taken is dropped, she will have a total of 338 points. Thus, to obtain a C, her last exam must be $420 - 338 = 82$ or greater.

38. The mode is the only measure which must be an actual piece of data since it is the most frequently occurring piece of data.

39. One example is 1, 2, 3, 3, 4, 5 changed to 1, 2, 3, 4, 4, 5.

40. The mean changes from $\frac{9}{6} = 1.5$ to $\frac{10}{6} = 1.\overline{6}$. The mode changes from no mode to a mode of 1.

    The midrange changes from $\frac{3}{2} = 1.5$ to $\frac{4}{2} = 2$.

41. No, by changing only one piece of data you cannot alter both the median and the midrange.

42. Let $x =$ sum of the values

    $\frac{x}{12} = 85.20$

    $x = 85.20(12) = \$1022.40$

    $\$1022.40 - \$47 + \$74 = \$1049.40$

    $\frac{1049.40}{12} = \$87.45$ is the correct mean

43. The data must be arranged in either ascending or descending order.
44. Josie outscored approximately 73% of all the students who took the test.
45. Kevin was taller than approximately 35% of all kindergarten children.
46. 25% of the workers earn $20,750 or less.
47. Second quartile, median
48. a) No, the percentile only indicated relative position of the score and not the value of it.
    b) Yes, a higher percentile indicates a higher relative position in the respective population.
    Thus, Kendra was in a better relative position.

49. a) $490   b) $500   c) 25%   d) 25%   e) 17%   f) $100 \times \$510 = \$51,000$

50. a) $\frac{56}{7} = 8$, $\frac{26}{4} = 6.5$, $\frac{10}{5} = 2$, $\frac{50}{5} = 10$, $\frac{396}{6} = 66$

    b) $\frac{92.5}{5} = 18.5$ c) $\frac{538}{27} \approx 19.926$ d) No

51. a) Ruth: ≈ 0.290, 0.359, 0.301, 0.272, 0.315

    Mantle: ≈ 0.300, 0.365, 0.304, 0.275, 0.321

    b) Mantle's is greater in every case.

    c) Ruth: $\dfrac{593}{1878} \approx 0.316$, Mantle: $\dfrac{760}{2440} \approx 0.311$, Ruth's is greater.

    d) Answers will vary.

    e) Ruth: $\dfrac{1.537}{5} \approx 0.307$, Mantle: $\dfrac{1.565}{5} = 0.313$, Mantle's is greater.

    f) and g) Answers will vary.

52. a) $\dfrac{707,000}{25} = \$28,280$

    b) $21,000

    c) $17,000

    d) $\dfrac{17,000 + 100,000}{2} = \$58,500$

    e) The median because there are pieces of data that are much greater and much smaller than the rest of the data.

Exercise Set 13.6

1. To find the **range**, subtract the lowest value in the set of data from the highest value.

2. The **standard deviation** measures the spread of the data about the mean.

3. Answers will vary.

4. 0 since the mean is the same value as all of the data values. The spread about the mean is 0.

5. It may be important to determine the consistency of the data.

6. a) s

    b) σ

7. Where one expects to find a large variability such as test scores

8. In manufacturing or anywhere else where a minimum variability is desired

9. The first set of data will have the greater standard deviation because the scores have a greater spread about the mean.

10. They would be the same since the spread of data about each mean is the same.

11. The sum of the values in the (Data – Mean)^2 column will always be greater than or equal to 0.

12. a) The mean is the same for both classes.

    b) The spread of the data is larger for the evening class since the standard deviation is higher in the evening class.

13. Range = 11 − 0 = 11

$$\bar{x} = \frac{25}{5} = 5$$

x	$x - \bar{x}$	$(x - \bar{x})^2$
5	0	0
3	−2	4
0	−5	25
6	1	1
11	6	36
	0	66

$$\frac{66}{4} = 16.5, s = \sqrt{16.5} \approx 4.06$$

14. Range = 14 − 6 = 8

$$\bar{x} = \frac{54}{6} = 9$$

x	$x - \bar{x}$	$(x - \bar{x})^2$
8	−1	1
8	−1	1
12	3	9
14	5	25
6	−3	9
6	−3	9
	0	54

$$\frac{54}{5} = 10.8, s = \sqrt{10.8} \approx 3.29$$

15. Range = 156 − 150 = 6

$$\bar{x} = \frac{1071}{7} = 153$$

x	$x - \bar{x}$	$(x - \bar{x})^2$
150	−3	9
151	−2	4
152	−1	1
153	0	0
154	1	1
155	2	4
156	3	9
	0	28

$$\frac{28}{6} \approx 4.67, s = \sqrt{4.67} \approx 2.16$$

16. Range = 12 − 0 = 12

$$\bar{x} = \frac{50}{10} = 5$$

x	$x - \bar{x}$	$(x - \bar{x})^2$
4	−1	1
0	−5	25
3	−2	4
6	1	1
9	4	16
12	7	49
2	−3	9
3	−2	4
4	−1	1
7	2	4
	0	114

$$\frac{114}{9} \approx 12.67, s = \sqrt{12.67} \approx 3.56$$

17. Range = 9 − 4 = 5

$$\bar{x} = \frac{21}{3} = 7$$

x	$x - \bar{x}$	$(x - \bar{x})^2$
4	−3	9
8	1	1
9	2	4
	0	14

$$\frac{14}{2} = 7, s = \sqrt{7} \approx 2.65$$

18. Range = 9 − 9 = 0

Since all pieces of data are identical,

the standard deviation is 0.

19. Range = 12 − 7 = 5

$\bar{x} = \dfrac{63}{7} = 9$

x	$x - \bar{x}$	$(x - \bar{x})^2$
7	-2	4
9	0	0
7	-2	4
9	0	0
9	0	0
10	1	1
12	3	9
	0	18

$\dfrac{18}{6} = 3, s = \sqrt{3} \approx 1.73$

20. Range = 64 − 40 = 24

$\bar{x} = \dfrac{424}{8} = 53$

x	$x - \bar{x}$	$(x - \bar{x})^2$
52	-1	1
50	-3	9
54	1	1
59	6	36
40	-13	169
43	-10	100
64	11	121
62	9	81
	0	518

$\dfrac{518}{7} = 74, s = \sqrt{74} \approx 8.60$

21. Range = 9 − 2 = 7

$\bar{x} = \dfrac{50}{10} = 5$

x	$x - \bar{x}$	$(x - \bar{x})^2$
3	-2	4
4	-1	1
5	0	0
9	4	16
3	-2	4
7	2	4
4	-1	1
4	-1	1
9	4	16
2	-3	9
	0	56

$\dfrac{56}{9} \approx 6.22, s = \sqrt{6.22} \approx 2.49$

22. Range = 121 − 103 = 18

$\bar{x} = \dfrac{784}{7} = 112$

x	$x - \bar{x}$	$(x - \bar{x})^2$
103	-9	81
106	-6	36
109	-3	9
112	0	0
115	3	9
118	6	36
121	9	81
	0	252

$\dfrac{252}{6} = 42, s = \sqrt{42} \approx 6.48$

23. Range = 50 − 18 = $32

$\bar{x} = \dfrac{360}{10} = \$36$

x	$x - \bar{x}$	$(x - \bar{x})^2$
28	-8	64
28	-8	64
50	14	196
45	9	81
30	-6	36
45	9	81
48	12	144
18	-18	324
45	9	81
23	-13	169
	0	1240

$\dfrac{1240}{9} \approx 137.78, s = \sqrt{137.78} \approx \$11.74$

24. Range = 88 − 43 = $45

$\bar{x} = \dfrac{585}{9} = \$65$

x	$x - \bar{x}$	$(x - \bar{x})^2$
44	-21	441
77	12	144
80	15	225
88	23	529
55	-10	100
44	-21	441
43	-22	484
77	12	144
77	12	144
	0	2652

$\dfrac{2652}{8} = 331.5, s = \sqrt{331.5} \approx \$18.21$

25. a) Range = 68 - 5 = $63

$$\bar{x} = \frac{204}{6} = 34$$

x	$x - \bar{x}$	$(x - \bar{x})^2$
32	-2	4
60	26	676
14	-20	400
25	-9	81
5	-29	841
68	34	1156
	0	3158

$$\frac{3158}{5} = 631.6, s = \sqrt{631.6} \approx \$25.13$$

b) New data: 42, 70, 24, 35, 15, 78

The range and standard deviation will be the same. If each piece of data is increased by the same number, the range and standard deviation will remain the same.

c) Range = 78 - 15 = $63

$$\bar{x} = \frac{264}{6} = 44$$

x	$x - \bar{x}$	$(x - \bar{x})^2$
42	-2	4
70	26	676
24	-20	400
35	-9	81
15	-29	841
78	34	1156
	0	3158

$$\frac{3158}{5} = 631.6, s = \sqrt{631.6} \approx \$25.13$$

d) Yes

26. a) - c) Answers will vary.

d) If each piece of data is increased or decreased by n, the mean is increased or decreased by n. The standard deviation will remain the same.

e) The mean of the first set of numbers is $\frac{63}{7} = 9$. The mean of the second set is $\frac{4193}{7} = 599$.

Standard deviation of first set

x	$x - \bar{x}$	$(x - \bar{x})^2$
6	-3	9
7	-2	4
8	-1	1
9	0	0
10	1	1
11	2	4
12	3	9
	0	28

$$\frac{28}{6} = 4.67, s = \sqrt{4.67} \approx 2.16$$

Standard deviation of second set

x	$x - \bar{x}$	$(x - \bar{x})^2$
596	-3	9
597	-2	4
598	-1	1
599	0	0
600	1	1
601	2	4
602	3	9
	0	28

$$\frac{28}{6} = 4.67, s = \sqrt{4.67} \approx 2.16$$

27. a) - c) Answers will vary.

d) If each number in a distribution is multiplied by n, both the mean and standard deviation of the new distribution will be n times that of the original distribution.

e) The mean of the second set is $5 \times 4 = 20$, and the standard deviation of the second set is $5 \times 2 = 10$.

28. a) Same   b) More

29. a) The standard deviation increases. There is a greater spread from the mean as they get older.

b) $\approx 133\, lb.$

c) $\dfrac{175 - 90}{4} = 21.25 \approx 21\, lb.$

d) The mean weight is about 100 pounds and the normal range is about 60 to 140 pounds.

e) The mean height is about 62 inches and the normal range is about 53 to 68 inches.

f) 100% - 95% = 5%

30. a) - b) Answers will vary.

c) Baseball: $\dfrac{87.3}{10} = \$8.73$ million

Basketball: $\dfrac{146.97}{10} \approx \$14.70$ million

d)

Baseball				Basketball		
x	$x - \bar{x}$	$(x - \bar{x})^2$		x	$x - \bar{x}$	$(x - \bar{x})^2$
10	1.27	1.6129		33.1	18.4	338.56
10	1.27	1.6129		20.5	5.8	33.64
9.6	0.87	0.7569		14.3	-0.4	0.16
8.9	0.17	0.0289		12.9	-1.8	3.24
8.3	-0.43	0.1849		12.4	-2.3	5.29
8.25	-0.48	0.2304		11.26	-3.44	11.8336
8.25	-0.48	0.2304		11.25	-3.45	11.9025
8	-0.73	0.5329		11.16	-3.54	12.5316
8	-0.73	0.5329		10.5	-4.2	17.64
8	-0.73	0.5329		9.6	-5.1	26.01
		6.256				460.8077

$\dfrac{6.256}{9} = 0.695\overline{1}, s = \sqrt{0.695\overline{1}} \approx \$0.83$ million

$\dfrac{460.8077}{9} = 51.20085556, s = \sqrt{51.20085556}$

$\approx \$7.16$ million

31. a)

East			West	
Number of Footware Sold	Number of Weeks		Number of Footware Sold	Number of Weeks
15-20	2		15-20	0
21-26	2		21-26	0
27-32	5		27-32	6
33-38	4		33-38	9
39-44	7		39-44	4
45-50	1		45-50	6
51-56	1		51-56	0
57-62	2		57-62	0
63-68	1		63-68	0

31. b)

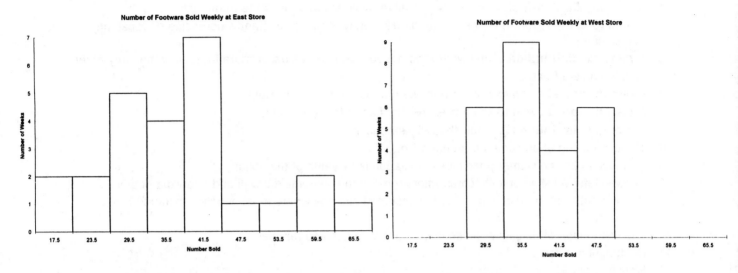

c) They appear to have about the same mean since they are both centered around 38.

d) The distribution for East is more spread out. Therefore, East has a greater standard deviation.

e) East: $\dfrac{950}{25} = 38$, West: $\dfrac{950}{25} = 38$

f)

East				West		
x	$x-\bar{x}$	$(x-\bar{x})^2$		x	$x-\bar{x}$	$(x-\bar{x})^2$
33	-5	25		38	0	0
30	-8	64		38	0	0
25	-13	169		37	-1	1
27	-11	121		36	-2	4
40	2	4		30	-8	64
44	6	36		45	7	49
49	11	121		28	-10	100
52	14	196		47	9	81
42	4	16		30	-8	64
59	21	441		46	8	64
19	-19	361		38	0	0
22	-16	256		39	1	1
57	19	361		40	2	4
67	29	841		34	-4	16
15	-23	529		31	-7	49
41	3	9		45	7	49
43	5	25		29	-9	81
27	-11	121		38	0	0
42	4	16		38	0	0
43	5	25		39	1	1
37	-1	1		37	-1	1
38	0	0		42	4	16
31	-7	49		46	8	64
32	-6	36		31	-7	49
35	-3	9		48	10	100
	0	3832			0	858

$\dfrac{3832}{24} \approx 159.67, s = \sqrt{159.67} \approx \$12.64$ $\dfrac{858}{24} = 35.75, s = \sqrt{35.75} \approx \$5.98$

Exercise Set 13.7

1. A **rectangular distribution** is one where all the values have the same frequency.
2. A **J-shaped distribution** is one where the frequency is either constantly increasing or constantly decreasing.
3. A **bimodal distribution** is one where two nonadjacent values occur more frequently than any other value in a set of data.
4. A **distribution skewed to the right** is one that has "a tail" on its right.
5. A **distribution skewed to the left** is one that has "a tail" on its left.
6. A **normal distribution** is a bell-shaped distribution.
7. The distribution of outcomes from the roll of a die
8. J shaped right - consumer price index; J shaped left - value of the dollar
9. Skewed left - a listing of test scores where most of the students did well and a few did poorly; Skewed right - number of cans of soda consumed in a day where most people consumed a few cans and a few people consumed many cans
10. The distribution of heights of an equal number of males and females
11. Rectangular
12. Skewed right
13. Normal
14. Bimodal
15. The mode is the lowest value, the median is greater than the mode, and the mean is greater than the median. The greatest frequency appears on the left side of the curve. Since the mode is the value with the greatest frequency, the mode would appear on the left side of the curve (where the lowest values are). Every value in the set of data is considered in determining the mean. The values on the far right of the curve would increase the value of the mean. Thus, the value of the mean would be farther to the right than the mode. The median would be between the mode and the mean.
16. The mode is the highest value, the median is lower than the mode, and the mean is lower than the median.
17. Answers will vary.
18. Answers will vary.
19. In a normal distribution the mean, median, and the mode all have the same value.
20. A **z-score** measures how far, in terms of standard deviation, a given score is from the mean.
21. A z-score will be negative when the data is less than the mean.
22. Subtract the mean from the value of the piece of data and divide the difference by the standard deviation.
23. 0

24. a) $\approx 68\%$ b) $\approx 95\%$
25. 0.500
26. 0.500
27. $0.477 + 0.341 = 0.818$
28. $0.464 - 0.364 = 0.100$
29. $0.500 - 0.458 = 0.042$
30. $0.500 + 0.377 = 0.877$
31. $0.500 - 0.463 = 0.037$
32. $0.500 + 0.463 = 0.963$
33. $0.500 - 0.481 = 0.019$
34. $0.500 + 0.475 = 0.975$
35. $0.500 - 0.447 = 0.053$
36. $0.500 - 0.258 = 0.242$
37. $0.282 = 28.2\%$
38. $0.321 - 0.079 = 0.242 = 24.2\%$
39. $0.410 + 0.488 = 0.898 = 89.8\%$
40. $0.500 - 0.471 = 0.029 = 2.9\%$
41. $0.500 + 0.471 = 0.971 = 97.1\%$
42. $0.500 - 0.496 = 0.004 = 0.4\%$
43. $0.500 + 0.475 = 0.975 = 97.5\%$
44. $0.484 - 0.264 = 0.22 = 22\%$
45. $0.466 - 0.437 = 0.029 = 2.9\%$
46. $0.484 + 0.500 = 0.984 = 98.4\%$

47. a) Jake, Sarah, and Carol scored above the mean because their z-scores are positive.
    b) Marie and Kevin scored at the mean because their z-scores are zero
    c) Omar, Justin, and Kim scored below the mean because their z-scores are negative.
48. a) Sarah had the highest score because she had the highest z-score.
    b) Omar had the lowest score because he had the lowest z-score.

49. $z_{75} = \dfrac{75-69}{6} = \dfrac{6}{6} = 1.00;\ 0.341 = 34.1\%$

50. $0.500 + 0.341 = 0.841 = 84.1\%$

51. $z_{63} = \dfrac{63-69}{6} = \dfrac{-6}{6} = -1.00$

    $0.341 + 0.341 = 0.682 = 68.2\%$

52. $z_{72} = \dfrac{72-69}{6} = \dfrac{3}{6} = .50$

    $0.192 + 0.500 = 0.692 = 69.2\%$

    $0.692(1000) = 692$ children

53. $z_{50} = \dfrac{50-48}{4} = \dfrac{2}{4} = .50$

    $0.500 + 0.192 = 0.692 = 69.2\%$

54. $z_{54} = \dfrac{54-48}{4} = \dfrac{6}{4} = 1.50$

    $0.500 - 0.433 = 0.067 = 6.7\%$

55. $z_{54} = \dfrac{54-48}{4} = \dfrac{6}{4} = 1.50$

    $0.433 - 0.192 = 0.241 = 24.1\%$

56. $z_{40} = \dfrac{40-48}{4} = \dfrac{-8}{4} = -2.00$

    $0.500 - 0.477 = 0.023 = 2.3\%$

57. $z_{44} = \dfrac{44-48}{4} = \dfrac{-4}{4} = -1.00$

    $z_{49} = \dfrac{49-48}{4} = \dfrac{1}{4} = 0.25$

    $0.099 + 0.341 = 0.44 = 44.0\%$

58. $z_{41} = \dfrac{41-48}{4} = \dfrac{-7}{4} = -1.75$

    $0.500 + 0.460 = 0.960 = 96.0\%$

59. $z_{30,000} = \dfrac{30,000-35,000}{2500} = \dfrac{-5000}{2500} = -2.00$

    $z_{37,500} = \dfrac{37,500-35,000}{2500} = \dfrac{2500}{2500} = 1.00$

    $0.477 + 0.341 = 0.818 = 81.8\%$

60. At least 39,000 miles means 39,000 miles or more.

    $z_{39,000} = \dfrac{39,000-35,000}{2500} = \dfrac{4000}{2500} = 1.60$

    $0.500 - 0.445 = 0.055 = 5.5\%$

61. The tires that last less than 30,000 miles will fail to live up to the guarantee.

    $0.500 - 0.477 = 0.023 = 2.3\%$

62. $0.055(200,000) = 11,000$ tires

63. 50%

64. $z_{74} = \dfrac{74-80}{8} = \dfrac{-6}{8} = -.75$

    $z_{86} = \dfrac{86-80}{8} = \dfrac{6}{8} = .75$

    $0.273 + 0.273 = 0.546 = 54.6\%$

65. $z_{70} = \dfrac{70-80}{8} = \dfrac{-10}{8} = -1.25$

    $0.500 - 0.394 = 0.106 = 10.6\%$

66. $z_{92} = \dfrac{92-80}{8} = \dfrac{12}{8} = 1.5$

    $0.500 - 0.433 = 0.067 = 6.7\%$

67. $0.106(200) = 21.2 \approx 21$ students

68. $0.067(200) = 13.4 \approx 13$ students

69. $z_{7.4} = \dfrac{7.4 - 7.6}{0.4} = \dfrac{-0.2}{0.4} = -.50$

 $z_{7.7} = \dfrac{7.7 - 7.6}{0.4} = \dfrac{0.1}{0.4} = .25$

 $0.192 + 0.099 = 0.291 = 29.1\%$

70. $z_{7.0} = \dfrac{7.0 - 7.6}{0.4} = \dfrac{-0.6}{0.4} = -1.50$

 $0.500 - 0.433 = 0.067 = 6.7\%$

71. $0.500 + 0.099 = 0.599 = 59.9\%$

72. The 8-oz cup will overflow when the machine dispenses more than 8 oz of hot chocolate.

 $z_{8.0} = \dfrac{8.0 - 7.6}{0.4} = \dfrac{0.4}{0.4} = 1.00$

 $0.500 - 0.341 = 0.159 = 15.9\%$

73. $z_{1450} = \dfrac{1450 - 1500}{100} = \dfrac{-50}{100} = -.50$

 $0.192 + 0.500 = 0.692 = 69.2\%$

74. $z_{1400} = \dfrac{1400 - 1500}{100} = \dfrac{-100}{100} = -1.00$

 $z_{1550} = \dfrac{1550 - 1500}{100} = \dfrac{50}{100} = .50$

 $0.341 + 0.192 = 0.533 = 53.3\%$

75. $z_{1480} = \dfrac{1480 - 1500}{100} = \dfrac{-20}{100} = -.20$

 $0.500 - 0.079 = 0.421 = 42.1\%$

76. 50% will last 1500 hours or more.
 Thus, $0.50(80{,}000) = 40{,}000$ light bulbs

77. $z_{1400} = \dfrac{1400 - 1500}{100} = \dfrac{-100}{100} = -1.00$

 $z_{1600} = \dfrac{1600 - 1500}{100} = \dfrac{100}{100} = 1.00$

 $0.341 + 0.341 = 0.682 = 68.2\%$
 $0.682(80{,}000) = 54{,}560$ light bulbs

78. Customers will be able to claim a refund if they lose less than 5 lb.

 $z_5 = \dfrac{5 - 6.7}{0.81} = \dfrac{-1.7}{0.81} = -2.10$

 $0.500 - 0.482 = 0.018 = 1.8\%$

79. A motor will require repair or replacement if it breaks down in less than 8 years.

 $z_8 = \dfrac{8 - 10.2}{1.8} = \dfrac{-2.2}{1.8} \approx -1.22$

 $0.500 - 0.389 = 0.111 = 11.1\%$

80. The standard deviation is too large.
 There is too much variation.

81. A z-score of 1.8 or higher is required for an A. The area from the mean to 1.8 is 0.464.
 Thus, $0.500 - 0.464 = 0.036 = 3.6\%$ will receive an A.
 A z-score between 1.8 and 1.1 is required for a B. The areas from the mean to these z-scores are 0.464 and 0.364, respectively. Thus, $0.464 - 0.364 = 0.100 = 10.0\%$ will receive a B.
 A z-score between 1.1 and -1.2 is required for a C. The areas from the mean to these z-scores are 0.364 and 0.385, respectively. Thus, $0.364 + 0.385 = 0.749 = 74.9\%$ will receive a C.
 A z-score between -1.2 and -1.9 is required for a D. The areas from the mean to these z-scores are 0.385 and 0.471, respectively. Thus, $0.471 - 0.385 = 0.086 = 8.6\%$ will receive a D.
 A z-score of -1.9 or lower is required for an F. The area from the mean to -1.9 is 0.471.
 Thus, $0.500 - 0.471 = 0.029 = 2.9\%$ will receive an F.

82. a) The grade that corresponds to an A has an area of 0.40 between it and the mean. The z-score corresponding to an area of 0.40 is 1.28. To convert this z-score into a grade:

$$z = \frac{\text{score - mean}}{\text{standard deviation}}$$

$$1.28 = \frac{\text{score - 72}}{8}$$

$$8(1.28) = \text{score - 72}$$

$$10.24 = \text{score - 72}$$

$$\text{score} = 10.24 + 72 = 82.24$$

The minimum score needed for an A is 82.24.

b) The grade that corresponds to a D has an area of 0.40 between it and the mean. The z-score corresponding to an area of 0.40 below the mean is -1.28.

$$-1.28 = \frac{\text{score - 72}}{8}$$

$$8(-1.28) = \text{score - 72}$$

$$-10.24 = \text{score - 72}$$

$$\text{score} = -10.24 + 72 = 61.76$$

The minimum score needed to pass the course is 61.76.

c) The grade that corresponds to a C has an area of 0.20 both above and below the mean. The z-score corresponding to an area of 0.20 is ≈ 0.52.

$$0.52 = \frac{\text{score - 72}}{8}$$

$$8(0.52) = \text{score - 72}$$

$$4.16 = \text{score - 72}$$

$$\text{score} = 4.16 + 72 = 76.16$$

Similarly, below the mean

72 - 4.16 = 67.84

The range of grades resulting in a C:

67.84 - 76.16

83. a) Katie: $z_{28,408} = \dfrac{28,408 - 23,200}{2170} = \dfrac{5208}{2170} = 2.4$

Stella: $z_{29,510} = \dfrac{29,510 - 25,600}{2300} = \dfrac{3910}{2300} = 1.7$

b) Katie. Her z-score is higher than Stella's z-score. This means her sales are further above the mean than Stella's sales.

84. a) $\bar{x} = \dfrac{160}{30} = 5.\overline{3} \approx 5.33$

b)

x	$x-\bar{x}$	$(x-\bar{x})^2$	x	$x-\bar{x}$	$(x-\bar{x})^2$	x	$x-\bar{x}$	$(x-\bar{x})^2$
1	-4.33	18.75	4	-1.33	1.77	7	1.67	2.79
1	-4.33	18.75	4	-1.33	1.77	8	2.67	7.13
1	-4.33	18.75	4	-1.33	1.77	8	2.67	7.13
1	-4.33	18.75	5	-0.33	0.11	8	2.67	7.13
2	-3.33	11.09	6	0.67	0.45	8	2.67	7.13
2	-3.33	11.09	6	0.67	0.45	9	3.67	13.47
2	-3.33	11.09	6	0.67	0.45	9	3.67	13.47
2	-3.33	11.09	7	1.67	2.79	9	3.67	13.47
3	-2.33	5.43	7	1.67	2.79	10	4.67	21.81
3	-2.33	5.43	7	1.67	2.79	10	4.67	21.81
								260.70

$260.70 \div 29 \approx 8.99$ $s = \sqrt{8.99} \approx 3.00$

c) $\bar{x} + 1.1s = 5.33 + 1.1(3) = 8.63$ $\bar{x} - 1.1s = 5.33 - 1.1(3) = 2.03$

$\bar{x} + 1.5s = 5.33 + 1.5(3) = 9.83$ $\bar{x} - 1.15s = 5.33 - 1.5(3) = 0.83$

$\bar{x} + 2.0s = 5.33 + 2.0(3) = 11.33$ $\bar{x} - 2.0s = 5.33 - 2.0(3) = -0.67$

$\bar{x} + 2.5s = 5.33 + 2.5(3) = 12.83$ $\bar{x} - 2.5s = 5.33 - 2.5(3) = -2.17$

84. d) Between -1.1s and 1.1s or between scores of 2.03 and 8.63, there are 17 scores.

$$\frac{17}{30} = 0.5\overline{6} \approx 56.7\%$$

Between -1.5s and 1.5s, or between scores of 0.83 and 9.83, there are 28 scores.

$$\frac{28}{30} = 0.9\overline{3} \approx 93.3\%$$

Between -2.0s and 2.0s, or between scores of -0.67 and 11.33, there are 30 scores.

$$\frac{30}{30} = 1 = 100\%$$

Between -2.5s and 2.5s, or between scores of -2.17 and 12.83, there are 30 scores.

$$\frac{30}{30} = 1 = 100\%$$

e)
Minimum %	K = 1.1	K = 1.5	K = 2.0	K = 2.5
(For any distribution)	17.4%	55.6%	75%	84%
Normal distribution	72.8%	86.6%	95.4%	99.8%
Given distribution	56.7%	93.3%	100%	100%

f) The percent between -1.1s and 1.1s is too low to be considered a normal distribution.

Exercise Set 13.8

1. The **correlation coefficient** measures the strength of the relationship between the quantities.
2. The purpose of **linear regression** is to determine the linear relationship between two variables.

3. 1   4. -1   5. 0

6. A positive correlation indicates as one quantity increases, the other quantity increases.
7. A negative correlation indicates as one quantity increases, the other quantity decreases.
8. The **line of best fit** represents the line such that the sum of the vertical distances between the points and the line is a minimum.
9. The **level of significance** is used to identify the cutoff between results attributed to chance and results attributed to an actual relationship between the two variables.
10. A **scatter diagram** is a plot of data points.

11. No correlation   12. Weak negative
13. Strong positive   14. Strong negative
15. Yes, $|0.73| > 0.684$ 16. Yes, $|0.57| > 0.537$
17. No, $|-0.63| < 0.707$ 18. No, $|-0.49| < 0.602$
19. No, $|-0.23| < 0.254$ 20. No, $|-0.49| < 0.590$
21. No, $|0.82| < 0.917$ 22. Yes, $|0.96| > 0.959$

Note: The answers in the remainder of this section may differ slightly from your answers depending upon how your answers are rounded and which calculator you used.

23. a)

b)

x	y	x^2	y^2	xy
3	6	9	36	18
4	9	16	81	36
5	11	25	121	55
6	11	36	121	66
9	13	81	169	117
27	50	167	528	292

$$r = \frac{5(292) - 27(50)}{\sqrt{5(167) - 729}\sqrt{5(528) - 2500}} = \frac{110}{\sqrt{106}\sqrt{140}} \approx 0.903$$

c) Yes, $|0.903| > 0.878$

d) No, $|0.903| < 0.959$

24. a)

b)

x	y	x^2	y^2	xy
6	10	36	100	60
8	9	64	81	72
11	7	121	49	77
14	8	196	64	112
17	6	289	36	102
56	40	706	330	423

$$r = \frac{5(423) - 56(40)}{\sqrt{5(706) - 3136}\sqrt{5(330) - 1600}} = \frac{-125}{\sqrt{394}\sqrt{50}} \approx -0.891$$

c) Yes, $|-0.891| > 0.878$

d) No, $|-0.891| < 0.959$

25. a)

b)

x	y	x^2	y^2	xy
23	29	529	841	667
35	37	1225	1369	1295
31	26	961	676	806
43	20	1849	400	860
49	39	2401	1521	1911
181	151	6965	4807	5539

$$r = \frac{5(5539) - 181(151)}{\sqrt{5(6965) - 32,761}\sqrt{5(4807) - 22,801}} = \frac{364}{\sqrt{2064}\sqrt{1234}} \approx 0.228$$

c) No, $|0.228| < 0.878$

d) No, $|0.228| < 0.959$

26. a)

b)

x	y	x^2	y^2	xy
90	3	8100	9	270
80	4	6400	16	320
60	6	3600	36	360
60	5	3600	25	300
40	5	1600	25	200
20	7	400	49	140
350	30	23,700	160	1590

$$r = \frac{6(1590) - 350(30)}{\sqrt{6(23,700) - 122,500}\sqrt{6(160) - 900}} = \frac{-960}{\sqrt{19,700}\sqrt{60}} \approx -0.883$$

c) Yes, $|-0.883| > 0.811$

d) No, $|-0.883| < 0.917$

27. a)

b)

x	y	x^2	y^2	xy
5.3	10.3	28.09	106.09	54.59
4.7	9.6	22.09	92.16	45.12
8.4	12.5	70.56	156.25	105
12.7	16.2	161.29	262.44	205.74
4.9	9.8	24.01	96.04	48.02
36	58.4	306.04	712.98	458.47

$$r = \frac{5(458.47) - 36(58.4)}{\sqrt{5(306.04) - 1296}\sqrt{5(712.98) - 3410.56}} = \frac{189.95}{\sqrt{234.2}\sqrt{154.34}} \approx 0.999$$

c) Yes, $|0.999| > 0.878$ **d)** Yes, $|0.999| > 0.959$

28. a)

b)

x	y	x^2	y^2	xy
12	15	144	225	180
16	19	256	361	304
13	45	169	2025	585
24	30	576	900	720
100	60	10,000	3600	6000
50	28	2500	784	1400
215	197	13,645	7895	9189

$$r = \frac{6(9189) - 215(197)}{\sqrt{6(13,645) - 46,225}\sqrt{6(7895) - 38,809}} = \frac{12,779}{\sqrt{35,645}\sqrt{8561}} \approx 0.732$$

c) No, $|0.732| < 0.811$ **d)** No, $|0.732| < 0.917$

29. a)

b)

x	y	x^2	y^2	xy
100	2	10,000	4	200
80	3	6400	9	240
60	5	3600	25	300
60	6	3600	36	360
40	6	1600	36	240
20	8	400	64	160
360	30	25,600	174	1500

$$r = \frac{6(1500) - 360(30)}{\sqrt{6(25,600) - 129,600}\sqrt{6(174) - 900}} = \frac{-1800}{\sqrt{24,000}\sqrt{144}} \approx -0.968$$

c) Yes, $|-0.968| > 0.811$ d) Yes, $|-0.968| > 0.917$

30. a)

b)

x	y	x^2	y^2	xy
90	90	8100	8100	8100
70	70	4900	4900	4900
65	65	4225	4225	4225
60	60	3600	3600	3600
50	50	2500	2500	2500
40	40	1600	1600	1600
15	15	225	225	225
390	390	25,150	25,150	25,150

$$r = \frac{7(25,150) - 390(390)}{\sqrt{7(25,150) - 152,100}\sqrt{7(25,150) - 152,100}} = \frac{23,950}{\sqrt{23,950}\sqrt{23,950}} = 1.00$$

c) Yes, $|1.00| > 0.754$ d) Yes, $|1.00| > 0.875$

31. From # 23: $m = \dfrac{5(292) - 27(50)}{5(167) - 729} = \dfrac{110}{106} \approx 1.0$

$b = \dfrac{50 - \dfrac{110}{106}(27)}{5} \approx 4.4, \quad y = 1.0x + 4.4$

32. From # 24: $m = \dfrac{5(423) - 56(40)}{5(706) - 3136} = \dfrac{-125}{394} \approx -0.3$

$b = \dfrac{40 - \dfrac{-125}{394}(56)}{5} \approx 11.6, \quad y = -0.3x + 11.6$

33. From # 25: $m = \dfrac{5(5539) - 181(151)}{5(6965) - 32{,}761} = \dfrac{364}{2064} \approx 0.2$

$b = \dfrac{151 - \dfrac{364}{2064}(181)}{5} \approx 23.8, \quad y = 0.2x + 23.8$

34. From # 26: $m = \dfrac{6(1590) - 350(30)}{6(23{,}700) - 122{,}500} = \dfrac{-960}{19{,}700} \approx -0.05$

$b = \dfrac{30 - \dfrac{-960}{19{,}700}(350)}{6} \approx 7.8, \quad y = -0.05x + 7.8$

35. From # 27: $m = \dfrac{5(458.47) - 36(58.4)}{5(306.04) - 1296} = \dfrac{189.95}{234.2} \approx 0.8$

$b = \dfrac{58.4 - \dfrac{189.95}{234.2}(36)}{5} \approx 5.8, \quad y = 0.8x + 5.8$

36. From # 28: $m = \dfrac{6(9189) - 215(197)}{6(13{,}645) - 46{,}225} = \dfrac{12{,}779}{35{,}645} \approx 0.4$

$b = \dfrac{197 - \dfrac{12{,}779}{35{,}645}(215)}{6} \approx 20.0, \quad y = 0.4x + 20.0$

37. From # 29: $m = \dfrac{6(1500) - 360(30)}{6(25{,}600) - 129{,}600} = \dfrac{-1800}{24{,}000} \approx -0.1$

$b = \dfrac{30 - \dfrac{-1800}{24{,}000}(360)}{6} \approx 9.5, \quad y = -0.1x + 9.5$

38. From # 30: $m = \dfrac{7(25{,}150) - 390(390)}{7(25{,}150) - 152{,}100} = \dfrac{23{,}950}{23{,}950} = 1$

$b = \dfrac{390 - 1(390)}{7} = 0, \quad y = x$

39. a)

x	y	x^2	y^2	xy
10	37	100	1369	370
15	43	225	1849	645
12	37	144	1369	444
20	49	400	2401	980
25	54	625	2916	1350
17	45	289	2025	765
99	265	1783	11,929	4554

$$r = \frac{6(4554)-99(265)}{\sqrt{6(1783)-9801}\sqrt{6(11,929)-70,225}} = \frac{1089}{\sqrt{897}\sqrt{1349}} \approx 0.990$$

b) Yes, $\left|0.990\right| > 0.811$

c) $m = \dfrac{6(4554)-99(265)}{6(1783)-9801} = \dfrac{1089}{897} \approx 1.2$, $\quad b = \dfrac{265-\dfrac{1089}{897}(99)}{6} \approx 24.1$, $\quad y = 1.2x+24.1$

40. a)

x	y	x^2	y^2	xy
20	40	400	1600	800
40	45	1600	2025	1800
50	70	2500	4900	3500
60	76	3600	5776	4560
80	92	6400	8464	7360
100	95	10,000	9025	9500
350	418	24,500	31,790	27,520

$$r = \frac{6(27,520)-350(418)}{\sqrt{6(24,500)-122,500}\sqrt{6(31,790)-174,724}} = \frac{18,820}{\sqrt{24,500}\sqrt{16,016}} \approx 0.950$$

b) Yes, $\left|0.950\right| > 0.917$

c) $m = \dfrac{6(27,520)-350(418)}{6(24,500)-122,500} = \dfrac{18,820}{24,500} \approx 0.8$, $\quad b = \dfrac{418-\dfrac{18,820}{24,500}(350)}{6} \approx 24.9$, $\quad y = 0.8x+24.9$

41. a)

x	y	x^2	y^2	xy
1	690	1	476,100	690
4	780	16	608,400	3120
7	460	49	211,600	3220
10	280	100	78,400	2800
13	200	169	40,000	2600
16	330	256	108,900	5280
51	2740	591	1,523,400	17,710

$$r = \frac{6(17,710) - 51(2740)}{\sqrt{6(591) - 2601}\sqrt{6(1,523,400) - 7,507,600}} = \frac{-33,480}{\sqrt{945}\sqrt{1,632,800}} \approx -0.852$$

b) Yes, $\left|-0.852\right| > 0.811$

c) $m = \dfrac{6(17,710) - 51(2740)}{6(591) - 2601} = \dfrac{-33,480}{945} \approx -35.4$, $\quad b = \dfrac{2740 - \dfrac{-33,480}{945}(51)}{6} \approx 757.8$, $\quad y = -35.4x + 757.8$

d) $y = -35.4(9) + 757.8 = \$439.20$

42. a)

x	y	x^2	y^2	xy
1	26	1	676	26
2	23.9	4	571.21	47.8
3	21.8	9	475.24	65.4
4	19.5	16	380.25	78
5	15.2	25	231.04	76
6	13.8	36	190.44	82.8
7	12.3	49	151.29	86.1
8	11.1	64	123.21	88.8
36	143.6	204	2798.68	550.9

$$r = \frac{8(550.9) - 36(143.6)}{\sqrt{8(204) - 1296}\sqrt{8(2798.68) - 20,620.96}} = \frac{-762.4}{\sqrt{336}\sqrt{1768.48}} \approx -0.989$$

b) Yes, $\left|-0.989\right| > 0.707$

c) $m = \dfrac{8(550.9) - 36(143.6)}{8(204) - 1296} = \dfrac{-762.4}{336} \approx -2.3$, $\quad b = \dfrac{143.6 - \dfrac{-762.4}{336}(36)}{8} \approx 28.2$, $\quad y = -2.3x + 28.2$

d) $y = -2.3(4.5) + 28.2 = 17.85 = \$17,850$

43. a)

x	y	x^2	y^2	xy
20	8	400	64	160
12	10	144	100	120
18	12	324	144	216
15	9	225	81	135
22	6	484	36	132
10	15	100	225	150
20	7	400	49	140
12	18	144	324	216
129	85	2221	1023	1269

$$r = \frac{8(1269) - 129(85)}{\sqrt{8(2221) - 16{,}641}\sqrt{8(1023) - 7225}} = \frac{-813}{\sqrt{1127}\sqrt{959}} \approx -0.782$$

b) Yes, $|-0.782| > 0.707$

c) $m = \dfrac{8(1269) - 129(85)}{8(2221) - 16{,}641} = \dfrac{-813}{1127} \approx -0.7$, $\quad b = \dfrac{85 - \frac{-813}{1127}(129)}{8} \approx 22.3$, $\quad y = -0.7x + 22.3$

d) $y = -0.7(14) + 22.3 = 12.5$ muggings

44. a)

x	y	x^2	y^2	xy
1	3	1	9	3
2	5	4	25	10
3	5	9	25	15
4	6	16	36	24
5	5	25	25	25
6	7	36	49	42
7	9	49	81	63
28	40	140	250	182

$$r = \frac{7(182) - 28(40)}{\sqrt{7(140) - 784}\sqrt{7(250) - 1600}} = \frac{154}{\sqrt{196}\sqrt{150}} \approx 0.898$$

b) Yes, $|0.898| > 0.754$

c) $m = \dfrac{7(182) - 28(40)}{7(140) - 784} = \dfrac{154}{196} \approx 0.8$, $\quad b = \dfrac{40 - \frac{154}{196}(28)}{7} \approx 2.6$, $\quad y = 0.8x + 2.6$

d) $y = 0.8(5) + 2.6 = 6.6$ lb.

45. a)

x	y	x^2	y^2	xy
89	22	7921	484	1958
110	28	12,100	784	3080
125	30	15,625	900	3750
92	26	8464	676	2392
100	22	10,000	484	2200
95	21	9025	441	1995
108	28	11,664	784	3024
97	25	9409	625	2425
816	202	84,208	5178	20,824

$$r = \frac{8(20,824)-816(202)}{\sqrt{8(84,208)-665,856}\sqrt{8(5178)-40,804}} = \frac{1760}{\sqrt{7808}\sqrt{620}} \approx 0.800$$

b) Yes, $\left|0.800\right| > 0.707$

c) $m = \frac{8(20,824)-816(202)}{8(84,208)-665,856} = \frac{1760}{7808} \approx 0.2$, $b = \frac{202-\frac{1760}{7808}(816)}{8} \approx 2.3$, $y = 0.2x + 2.3$

d) $y = 0.2(115) + 2.3 = 25.3 \approx 25$ units

46. a)

x	y	x^2	y^2	xy
4	100	16	10,000	400
4	67	16	4489	268
3	80	9	6400	240
2	120	4	14,400	240
1	40	1	1600	40
3	90	9	8100	270
4	60	16	3600	240
2	60	4	3600	120
4	90	16	8100	360
1	100	1	10,000	100
28	807	92	70,289	2278

$$r = \frac{10(2278)-28(807)}{\sqrt{10(92)-784}\sqrt{10(70,289)-651,249}} = \frac{184}{\sqrt{136}\sqrt{51,641}} \approx 0.069$$

b) No, $\left|0.069\right| < 0.632$

c) $m = \frac{10(2278)-28(807)}{10(92)-784} = \frac{184}{136} \approx 1.4$, $b = \frac{807-\frac{184}{136}(28)}{10} \approx 76.9$, $y = 1.4x + 76.9$

47. a)

x	y	x^2	y^2	xy
1	80.0	1	6400.0	80.0
2	76.2	4	5806.4	152.4
3	68.7	9	4719.7	206.1
4	50.1	16	2510.0	200.4
5	30.2	25	912.0	151.0
6	20.8	36	432.6	124.8
21	326	91	20,780.7	914.7

$$r = \frac{6(914.7) - 21(326)}{\sqrt{6(91) - 441}\sqrt{6(20,780.7) - 106,276}} = \frac{-1357.8}{\sqrt{105}\sqrt{18,408.2}} \approx -0.977$$

b) Yes, $\left|-0.977\right| > 0.917$

c) $m = \dfrac{6(914.7) - 21(326)}{6(91) - 441} = \dfrac{-1357.8}{105} \approx -12.9$, $\quad b = \dfrac{326 - \frac{-1357.8}{105}(21)}{6} \approx 99.6$, $\quad y = -12.9x + 99.6$

d) $y = -12.9(4.5) + 99.6 = 41.55 \approx 41.6\%$

48. Answers will vary.

49. a) and b) Answers will vary.

c)

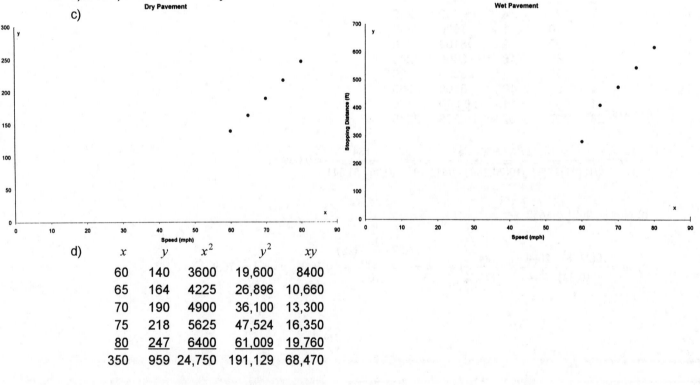

d)

x	y	x^2	y^2	xy
60	140	3600	19,600	8400
65	164	4225	26,896	10,660
70	190	4900	36,100	13,300
75	218	5625	47,524	16,350
80	247	6400	61,009	19,760
350	959	24,750	191,129	68,470

$$r = \frac{5(68,470) - 350(959)}{\sqrt{5(24,750) - 122,500}\sqrt{5(191,129) - 919,681}} = \frac{6700}{\sqrt{1250}\sqrt{35,964}} \approx 0.999$$

49. e)

x	y	x^2	y^2	xy
60	280	3600	78,400	16,800
65	410	4225	168,100	26,650
70	475	4900	225,625	33,250
75	545	5625	297,025	40,875
80	618	6400	381,924	49,440
350	2328	24,750	1,151,074	167,015

$$r = \frac{5(167,015) - 350(2328)}{\sqrt{5(24,750) - 122,500}\sqrt{5(1,151,074) - 5,419,584}} = \frac{20,275}{\sqrt{1250}\sqrt{335,786}} \approx 0.990$$

f) Answers will vary.

g) $m = \dfrac{5(68,470) - 350(959)}{5(24,750) - 122,500} = \dfrac{6700}{1250} \approx 5.4$, $b = \dfrac{959 - \dfrac{6700}{1250}(350)}{5} = -183.4$, $y = 5.4x - 183.4$

h) $m = \dfrac{5(167,015) - 350(2328)}{5(24,750) - 122,500} = \dfrac{20,275}{1250} \approx 16.2$, $b = \dfrac{2328 - \dfrac{20,275}{1250}(350)}{5} = -669.8$, $y = 16.2x - 669.8$

i) Dry: $y = 5.4(77) - 183.4 = 232.4$ ft.

Wet: $y = 16.2(77) - 669.8 = 577.6$ ft.

50. a) The correlation coefficient will not change because $\sum xy = \sum yx$, $\left(\sum x\right)\left(\sum y\right) = \left(\sum y\right)\left(\sum x\right)$,

and the square roots in the denominator will be the same.

b) Answers will vary.

51. Answers will vary.

52. Answers will vary.

53. a)

x	y	x^2	y^2	xy
90	130	8100	16,900	11,700
91	136	8281	18,496	12,376
92	140	8464	19,600	12,880
93	144	8649	20,736	13,392
94	148	8836	21,904	13,912
95	153	9025	23,409	14,535
555	851	51,355	121,045	78,795

$$r = \frac{6(78,795) - 555(851)}{\sqrt{6(51,355) - 308,025}\sqrt{6(121,045) - 724,201}} = \frac{465}{\sqrt{105}\sqrt{2069}} \approx 0.998$$

b) Should be the same

53. c)

x	y	x^2	y^2	xy
0	130	0	16,900	0
1	136	1	18,496	136
2	140	4	19,600	280
3	144	9	20,736	432
4	148	16	21,904	592
5	153	25	23,409	765
15	851	55	121,045	2205

$$r = \frac{6(2205) - 15(851)}{\sqrt{6(55) - 225}\sqrt{6(121,045) - 724,201}} = \frac{465}{\sqrt{105}\sqrt{2069}} \approx 0.998$$

54. a) $SS(xy) = \sum xy - \dfrac{\left(\sum x\right)\left(\sum y\right)}{n} = 2335 - \dfrac{108(147)}{8} = 350.5$

$SS(x) = \sum x^2 - \dfrac{\left(\sum x\right)^2}{n} = 1866 - \dfrac{11,664}{8} = 408$

$SS(y) = \sum y^2 - \dfrac{\left(\sum y\right)^2}{n} = 3055 - \dfrac{21,609}{8} = 353.875$

$r = \dfrac{350.5}{\sqrt{408}\sqrt{353.875}} \approx 0.92$

b) Should be the same

Review Exercises

1. a) A **population** consists of all items or people of interest.

   b) A **sample** is a subset of the population.

2. A **random sample** is one where every item in the population has the same chance of being selected.

3. The candy bars may have lots of calories, or fat, or salt. Therefore, it may not be healthy to eat them.

4. Sales may not necessarily be a good indicator of profit. Expenses must also be considered.

5. a)

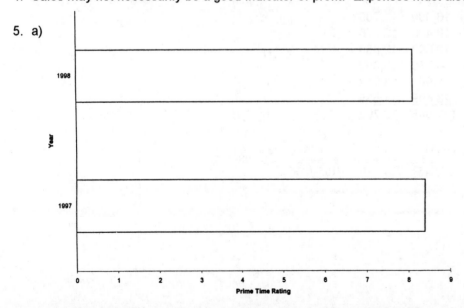

5. b)

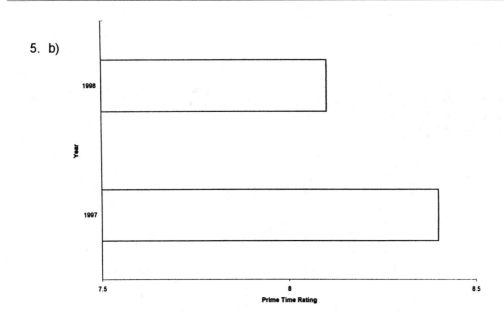

6. a)

Class	Frequency
35	1
36	3
37	6
38	2
39	3
40	0
41	4
42	1
43	3
44	1
45	1

b) and c)

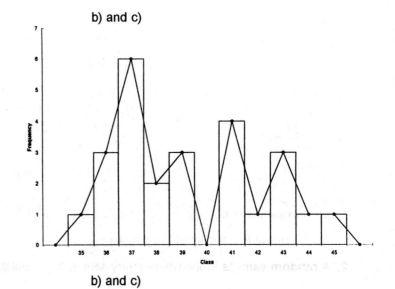

7. a)

High Temps.	Number of Cities
40 - 49	4
50 - 59	11
60 - 69	11
70 - 79	10
80 - 89	4

b) and c)

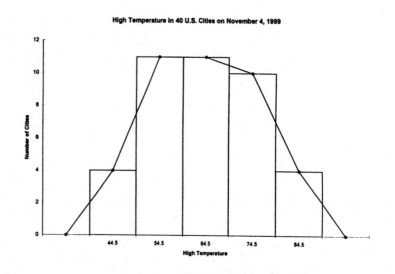

7. d) $4\,|\,6$ represents 46

```
4| 0  6  6  8
5| 0  1  2  3  3  4  4  4  5  6  7
6| 1  4  5  6  6  6  7  8  8  9  9
7| 0  0  1  2  2  2  5  5  5  6
8| 0  1  1  7
```

8. $\bar{x} = \dfrac{480}{6} = 80$

9. $\dfrac{79+83}{2} = 81$

10. None

11. $\dfrac{63+93}{2} = 78$

12. $93 - 63 = 30$

13.

x	$x - \bar{x}$	$(x - \bar{x})^2$
63	-17	289
76	-4	16
79	-1	1
83	3	9
86	6	36
93	13	169
	0	520

$$\frac{520}{5} = 104, \ s = \sqrt{104} \approx 10.20$$

14. $\bar{x} = \dfrac{156}{12} = 13$

15. $\dfrac{12+14}{2} = 13$

16. None

17. $\dfrac{4+23}{2} = 13.5$

18. $23 - 4 = 19$

19.

x	$x - \bar{x}$	$(x - \bar{x})^2$
4	-9	81
5	-8	64
7	-6	36
7	-6	36
12	-1	1
12	-1	1
14	1	1
15	2	4
17	4	16
19	6	36
21	8	64
23	10	100
	0	440

$$\frac{440}{11} = 40, \ s = \sqrt{40} \approx 6.32$$

20. $z_{37} = \dfrac{37-42}{5} = \dfrac{-5}{5} = -1.00$

$z_{47} = \dfrac{47-42}{5} = \dfrac{5}{5} = 1.00$

$0.341 + 0.341 = 0.682 = 68.2\%$

21. $z_{32} = \dfrac{32-42}{5} = \dfrac{-10}{5} = -2.00$

$z_{52} = \dfrac{52-42}{5} = \dfrac{10}{5} = 2.00$

$0.477 + 0.477 = 0.954 = 95.4\%$

22. $z_{50} = \dfrac{50-42}{5} = \dfrac{8}{5} = 1.60$

$0.500 + 0.445 = 0.945 = 94.5\%$

23. $z_{50} = \dfrac{50-42}{5} = \dfrac{8}{5} = 1.60$

$0.500 - 0.445 = 0.055 = 5.5\%$

24. $z_{39} = \dfrac{39-42}{5} = \dfrac{-3}{5} = -.60$

$0.500 + 0.226 = 0.726 = 72.6\%$

25. $z_{4.7} = \dfrac{4.7-4.2}{0.5} = \dfrac{0.5}{0.5} = 1.00$

$0.341 = 34.1\%$

26. $z_4 = \dfrac{4-4.2}{0.5} = \dfrac{-0.2}{0.5} = -.40$

$0.500 - 0.155 = 0.345 = 34.5\%$

27. $z_{4.4} = \dfrac{4.4-4.2}{0.5} = \dfrac{0.2}{0.5} = .40$

$z_{5.4} = \dfrac{5.4-4.2}{0.5} = \dfrac{1.2}{0.5} = 2.40$

$0.492 - 0.155 = 0.337 = 33.7\%$

28. If a CD player lasts less than 3 years, it will need to be replaced.

$z_3 = \dfrac{3-4.2}{0.5} = \dfrac{-1.2}{0.5} = -2.40$

$0.500 - 0.492 = 0.008 = 0.8\%$

29. a)

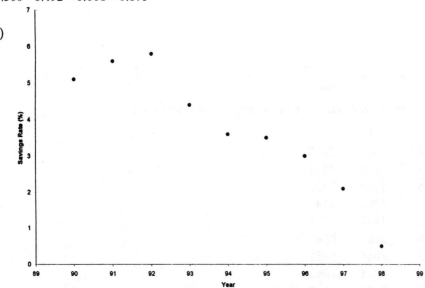

b) Yes, negative because generally as the year increases, the savings rate decreases.

c)

x	y	x^2	y^2	xy
90	5.1	8100	26.01	459.0
91	5.6	8281	31.36	509.6
92	5.8	8464	33.64	533.6
93	4.4	8649	19.36	409.2
94	3.6	8836	12.96	338.4
95	3.5	9025	12.25	332.5
96	3.0	9216	9.00	288.0
97	2.1	9409	4.41	203.7
98	0.5	9604	0.25	49.0
846	33.6	79,584	149.24	3123

$$r = \frac{9(3123) - 846(33.6)}{\sqrt{9(79,584) - 715,716}\sqrt{9(149.24) - 1128.96}} = \frac{-318.6}{\sqrt{540}\sqrt{214.2}} \approx -0.94$$

29. d) Yes, $|-0.94| > 0.666$

e) $m = \dfrac{9(3123) - 846(33.6)}{9(79,584) - 715,716} = \dfrac{-318.6}{540} \approx -0.6$

$b = \dfrac{33.6 - \dfrac{-318.6}{540}(846)}{9} \approx 59.2, \; y = -0.6x + 59.2$

30. a)

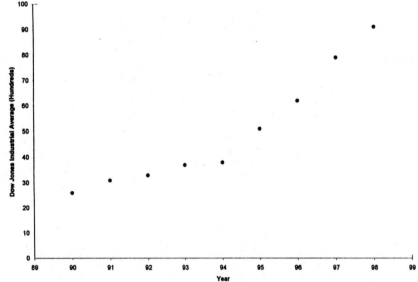

b)   Yes, positive because as the year increases the savings rate increases.

c)

x	y	x^2	y^2	xy
90	26	8100	676	2340
91	31	8281	961	2821
92	33	8464	1089	3036
93	37	8649	1369	3441
94	38	8836	1444	3572
95	51	9025	2601	4845
96	62	9216	3844	5952
97	79	9409	6241	7663
98	91	9604	8281	8918
846	448	79,584	26,506	42,588

$r = \dfrac{9(42,588) - 846(448)}{\sqrt{9(79,584) - 715,716}\sqrt{9(26,506) - 200,704}} = \dfrac{4284}{\sqrt{540}\sqrt{37,850}} \approx 0.95$

d) Yes, $|0.95| > 0.798$

e) $m = \dfrac{9(42,588) - 846(448)}{9(79,584) - 715,716} = \dfrac{4284}{540} \approx 7.9$

$b = \dfrac{448 - \dfrac{4284}{540}(846)}{9} \approx -696.0, \; y = 7.9x - 696.0$

31. a)

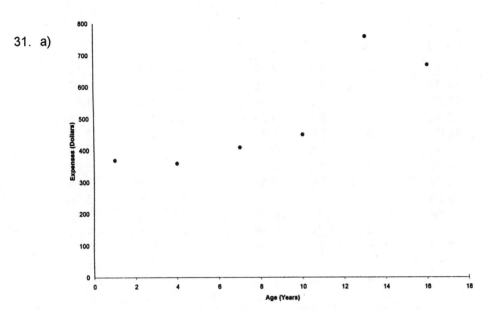

b) Yes, positive because generally as the age increases the expense increases.

c)

x	y	x^2	y^2	xy
1	370	1	136,900	370
4	360	16	129,600	1440
7	410	49	168,100	2870
10	450	100	202,500	4500
13	760	169	577,600	9880
16	670	256	448,900	10,720
51	3020	591	1,663,600	29,780

$$r = \frac{6(29,780) - 51(3020)}{\sqrt{6(591) - 2601}\sqrt{6(1,663,600) - 9,120,400}} = \frac{24,660}{\sqrt{945}\sqrt{861,200}} \approx 0.86$$

d) Yes, $|0.86| > 0.811$

e) $$m = \frac{6(29,780) - 51(3020)}{6(591) - 2601} = \frac{24,660}{945} \approx 26.1$$

$$b = \frac{3020 - \frac{24,660}{945}(51)}{6} \approx 281.5, \ y = 26.1x + 281.5$$

f) $y = 26.1(12) + 281.5 = \$594.70$

32. Mode = 175 lb.

33. Median = 180 lb.

34. 25%

35. 25%

36. 100% - 86% = 14%

37. 100(187) = 18,700 lb.

38. 187 + 2(23) = 233 lb.

39. 187 - 1.8(23) = 145.6 lb.

40. $\bar{x} = \frac{148}{41} \approx 3.610$

41. 2

42. 3

43. $\frac{0 + 14}{2} = 7$

44. 14 - 0 = 14

45.

x	$x-\bar{x}$	$(x-\bar{x})^2$	x	$x-\bar{x}$	$(x-\bar{x})^2$	x	$x-\bar{x}$	$(x-\bar{x})^2$
0	-3.6	12.96	2	-1.6	2.56	4	0.4	0.16
0	-3.6	12.96	2	-1.6	2.56	5	1.4	1.96
0	-3.6	12.96	3	-0.6	0.36	5	1.4	1.96
0	-3.6	12.96	3	-0.6	0.36	5	1.4	1.96
0	-3.6	12.96	3	-0.6	0.36	6	2.4	5.76
0	-3.6	12.96	3	-0.6	0.36	6	2.4	5.76
1	-2.6	6.76	3	-0.6	0.36	6	2.4	5.76
1	-2.6	6.76	3	-0.6	0.36	6	2.4	5.76
2	-1.6	2.56	4	0.4	0.16	6	2.4	5.76
2	-1.6	2.56	4	0.4	0.16	7	3.4	11.56
2	-1.6	2.56	4	0.4	0.16	8	4.4	19.36
2	-1.6	2.56	4	0.4	0.16	10	6.4	40.96
2	-1.6	2.56	4	0.4	0.16	14	10.4	108.16
2	-1.6	2.56	4	0.4	0.16			329.76

$$\frac{329.76}{40} = 8.244, \; s = \sqrt{8.244} \approx 2.87$$

46.

# of Child.	# of Presidents
0 - 1	8
2 - 3	14
4 - 5	10
6 - 7	6
8 - 9	1
10 - 11	1
12 - 13	0
14 - 15	1

47. and 48.

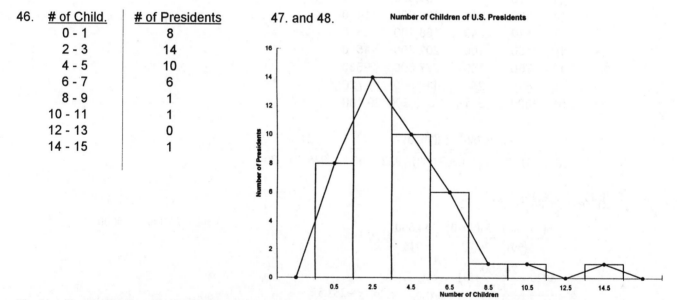

49. No, the distribution is not symmetrical about the mean.
50. No, some families have no children, more have one child, the greatest percent may have two children, fewer have three children, etc.
51. No, the number of children per family has decreased over the years.

Chapter Test

1. $\bar{x} = \dfrac{150}{5} = 30$

2. 31

3. 31

4. $\dfrac{15+40}{2} = 27.5$

5. 40 - 15 = 25

6.

x	$x - \bar{x}$	$(x - \bar{x})^2$
15	-15	225
31	1	1
31	1	1
33	3	9
40	10	100
	0	336

$$\frac{336}{4} = 84, \; s = \sqrt{84} \approx 9.17$$

7.

Class	Frequency
25 - 30	7
31 - 36	5
37 - 42	1
43 - 48	7
49 - 54	5
55 - 60	3
61 - 66	2

8. and 9.

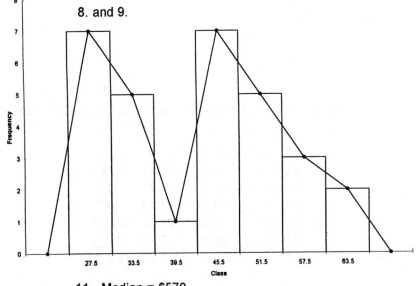

10. Mode = \$595

11. Median = \$570

12. 100% - 25% = 75%

13. 79%

14. 100(600) = \$60,000

15. 600 + 1(40) = \$640

16. 600 - 1.5(40) = \$540

17. $z_{50,000} = \dfrac{50,000 - 75,000}{12,000} = \dfrac{-25,000}{12,000} \approx -2.08$

$z_{70,000} = \dfrac{70,000 - 75,000}{12,000} = \dfrac{-5000}{12,000} = -.42$

$0.481 - 0.163 = 0.318 = 31.8\%$

18. $z_{60,000} = \dfrac{60,000 - 75,000}{12,000} = \dfrac{-15,000}{12,000} = -1.25$

$0.500 + 0.394 = 0.894 = 89.4\%$

19. $z_{90,000} = \dfrac{90,000 - 75,000}{12,000} = \dfrac{15,000}{12,000} = 1.25$

$0.500 - 0.394 = 0.106 = 10.6\%$

20. From #17 and #18,

$z_{60,000} = -1.25$ and $z_{70,000} \approx -.42$

$0.394 - 0.163 = 0.231 = 23.1\%$

$0.231(300) = 69.3 \approx 69$ cars

21. a)

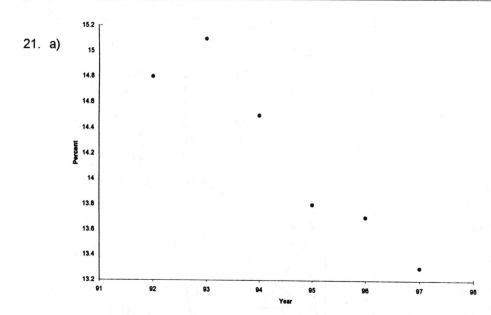

b) Yes, negative because generally as the year increases the percent decreases.

c)

x	y	x^2	y^2	xy
92	14.8	8464	219.04	1361.6
93	15.1	8649	228.01	1404.3
94	14.5	8836	210.25	1363
95	13.8	9025	190.44	1311
96	13.7	9216	187.69	1315.2
97	13.3	9409	176.89	1290.1
567	85.2	53,599	1212.32	8045.2

$$r = \frac{6(8045.2) - 567(85.2)}{\sqrt{6(53,599) - 321,489}\sqrt{6(1212.32) - 7259.04}} = \frac{-37.2}{\sqrt{105}\sqrt{14.88}} \approx -0.94$$

d) Yes, $|-0.94| > 0.811$

e) $m = \dfrac{6(8045.2) - 567(85.2)}{6(53,599) - 321,489} = \dfrac{-37.2}{105} \approx -0.4$

$b = \dfrac{85.2 - \dfrac{-37.2}{105}(567)}{6} = 47.7,\ y = -0.4x + 47.7$

f) $y = -0.4(98) + 47.7 = 8.5\%$

CHAPTER FOURTEEN

GRAPH THEORY

Exercise Set 14.1

1. A **graph** is a finite set of points, called **vertices**, that are connected with a set of line segments, called **edges**.

2.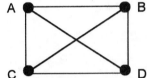

3.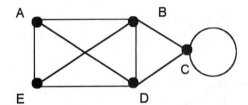

4. The **degree** of a vertex is the number of edges that connect to that vertex.

5. If the number of edges connected to the vertex is even, the vertex is **even**. If the number of edges connected to the vertex is odd, the vertex is **odd**.

6. a) A **path** is a sequence of adjacent vertices and the edges connecting them.
   b) A **circuit** is a path that begins and ends at the same vertex.
   c)

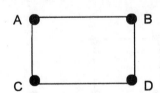

The path A, B, D, C is a path that is not a circuit.
The path A, B, D, C, A is a path that is also a circuit.

7. In the graphs below, the second graph is disconnected since no path connects vertices A, D, and E to vertices B and C.

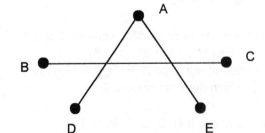

Connected Graph   Disconnected Graph

8. In the following graph, the edge EF is a bridge because if it were removed from the graph the result would be a disconnected graph (i.e., there would be no path from vertices A, B, E, H, and G to vertices C, D, J, I, and F).

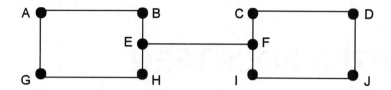

9.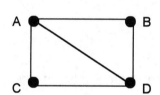

A, B, C, and D are all even.

10.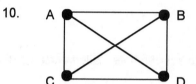

A, B, C, and D are all odd.

11.

B and C are even. A and D are odd.

12.

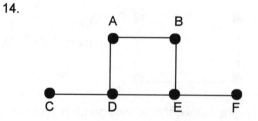

DE is a bridge.

13.

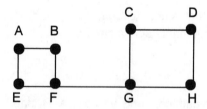

FG is a bridge.

14.

CD and EF are bridges.

15. No. There is no edge connecting vertices C and D. Therefore, A, B, C, D, E is not a path.
16. Edge AE (or EA) and edge BC (or CB)
17. No. One attempt would be A, E, D, B, which does not contain C. A second attempt would be A, E, C, B, which does not contain D.
18. No.
19. Yes. One example is B, D, E, A, B, C, E.
20. No.

21.

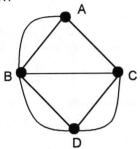

22.

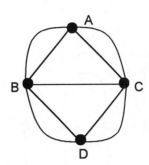

23.

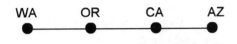

24.

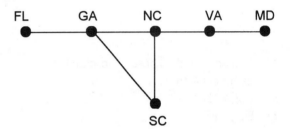

25.

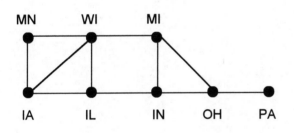

26.

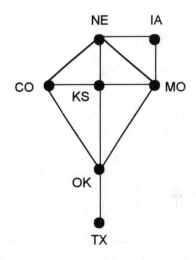

27.

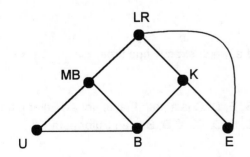

28.

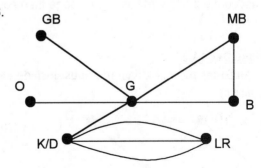

29.

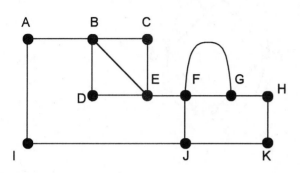

30.

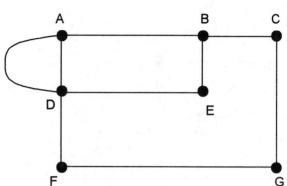

31. Connected

32. Disconnected. There is no path that connects A to C.

33. Disconnected. There is no path that connects A to B.

34. Connected

35. Edge AB

36. Edge EF

37. Edge EF

38. Edge FK and edge HL

39.

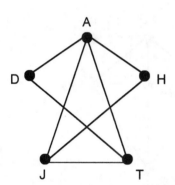

Other answers are possible.

40. Answers will vary.

41. It is impossible to have a graph with an odd number of odd vertices.

42. a) - c) Answers will vary.

d) The sum of the degrees is equal to twice the number of edges. This is true since each edge must connect two vertices. Each edge then contributes two to the sum of the degrees.

Exercise Set 14.2

1. a) An **Euler path** is a path that must include each edge of a graph exactly one time.

b) and c)

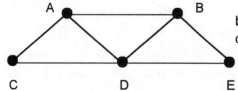

b) The path A, B, E, D, C is a path that is not an Euler path.

c) The path A, B, E, D, C, A, D, B is an Euler path.

2. a) An **Euler circuit** is a circuit that must include each edge of a graph exactly one time and return to the original vertex.

b) and c)

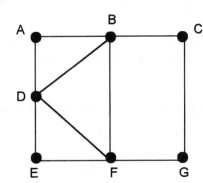

b) The path A, B, C, G, F, E, D, A is a circuit, but not an Euler circuit.

c) The path A, B, C, G, F, B, D, F, E, D, A is an Euler circuit.

3. a) Yes, according to Euler's Theorem.
   b) Yes, according to Euler's Theorem.
   c) No, according to Euler's Theorem.

4. a) Yes, according to Euler's Theorem.
   b) No, according to Euler's Theorem.
   c) No, according to Euler's Theorem.

5. If all of the vertices are even, the graph has an Euler circuit.

6. a) If all the vertices are even, then start with any vertex. If there are two odd vertices, then start with one of the odd vertices. Move from vertex to vertex without tracing any bridges until you have traced each edge of the graph exactly one time. You will finish at the other odd vertex.

   b) If there are any odd vertices, then there is no Euler circuit. If there are all even vertices, then start with any vertex. Move from vertex to vertex without tracing any bridges until you have traced each edge of the graph exactly one time. You will finish at the vertex you started from.

7. D, E, C, B, A, D, B, E; other answers are possible.

8. E, D, B, E, C, B, A, D; other answers are possible.

9. B, C, E, D, B, A, E; other answers are possible.

10. E, A, B, C, E, D, B; other answers are possible.

11. A, B, C, B, F, E, B, D, A; other answers are possible.

12. B, C, B, F, E, B, D, A, B; other answers are possible.

13. C, B, A, D, B, E, F, B, C; other answers are possible.

14. D, B, F, E, B, C, B, A, D; other answers are possible.

15. E, F, B, C, B, A, D, B, E; other answers are possible.

16. F, E, B, A, D, B, C, B, F; other answers are possible.

17. a) Yes. There are zero odd vertices.
    b) Yes. There are zero odd vertices.

18. a) Yes. There are exactly two odd vertices.
    b) No. There are more than zero odd vertices.

19. a) No. There are more than two odd vertices.
    b) No. There are more than zero odd vertices.

20. a) No. There are more than two odd vertices.
    b) No. There are more than zero odd vertices.

21. a) Yes. The land at the top and the island on the left would each correspond to an odd vertex. According to item 2 of Euler's Theorem, a graph with exactly two odd vertices has at least one Euler path, but no Euler circuits.

    b) They could start either on the land at the top of the picture or on the island on the left. If they started on the island, then they would end on the land at the top, and vice versa.

22. a) Yes. Each island would correspond to an odd vertex. According to item 2 of Euler's Theorem, a graph with exactly two odd vertices has at least one Euler path, but no Euler circuit.

    b) They could start on either island and finish at the other.

23. a) Yes. The graph representing the map:

They are seeking an Euler path or an Euler circuit. Note that vertices WA and AZ are both odd. According to item 2 of Euler's Theorem, since there are exactly two odd vertices, at least one Euler path, but no Euler circuits exist.
b) One path is WA, OR, CA, AZ.
c) No. According to Euler's Theorem, each Euler path must begin at one odd vertex and end at the other.

24. a) No. The graph representing the map:

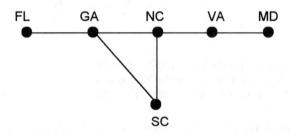

They are seeking an Euler path or an Euler circuit. Note that vertices FL, GA, NC, and MD are all odd. According to item 3 of Euler's Theorem, since there are more than two odd vertices, no Euler path or Euler circuit can exist.

25. a) Yes. The graph representing the map:

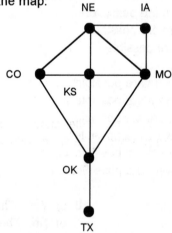

They are seeking an Euler path or an Euler circuit. Note that vertices CO and TX are both odd. According to item 2 of Euler's Theorem, since there are exactly two odd vertices, at least one Euler path, but no Euler circuits exist.
b) One path is TX, OK, MO, IA, NE, MO, KS, NE, CO, KS, OK, CO.
c) No. According to Euler's Theorem, each Euler path must begin at one odd vertex and end at the other.

26. a) Yes. The graph representing the map:

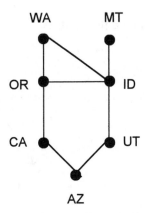

They are seeking an Euler path or an Euler circuit. Note that MT and OR are both odd. According to item 2 of Euler's Theorem, since there are exactly two odd vertices, at least one Euler path, but no Euler circuits exist.

b) One path is MT, ID, UT, AZ, CA, OR, WA, ID, OR.

c) No. According to Euler's Theorem, each Euler path must begin at one odd vertex and end at the other.

27. a) Yes. The graph representing the floor plan:

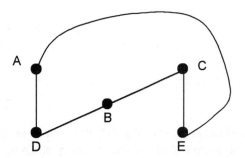

The wood carver is seeking an Euler path or an Euler circuit. Note that there are no odd vertices. According to item 1 of Euler's Theorem, since there are no odd vertices, at least one Euler path (which is also an Euler circuit) must exist.

b) One path (which is also a circuit) is A, D, B, C, E, A.

28. a) No. The graph representing the floor plan:

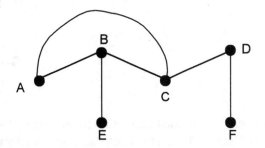

The wood carver is seeking an Euler path or an Euler circuit. Note that vertices B, C, E, and F are all odd. According to item 3 of Euler's Theorem, since there are more than two odd vertices, no Euler path or Euler circuit can exist.

29. a) Yes. The graph representing the floor plan:

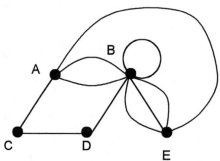

The wood carver is seeking an Euler path or an Euler circuit. Note that there are no odd vertices. According to item 1 of Euler's Theorem, since there are no odd vertices, at least one Euler path (which is also an Euler circuit) must exist.

b) One path (which is also a circuit) is A, C, D, B, E, B, A.

30. a) Yes. The graph representing the floor plan:

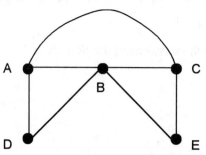

The wood carver is seeking an Euler path or an Euler circuit. Note that vertices A and C are both odd. According to item 2 of Euler's Theorem, since there are exactly two odd vertices, at least one Euler path, but no Euler circuits exist.

b) One path is A, D, B, E, C, B, A, C.

31. a) Yes. The graph representing the map:

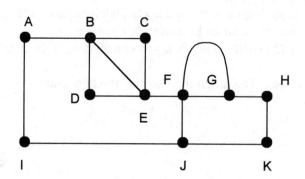

They are seeking an Euler path or an Euler circuit. Note that vertices G and J are both odd. According to item 2 of Euler's Theorem, since there are exactly two odd vertices, at least one Euler path, but no Euler circuits exist.

b) The residents would need to start at one of the two odd vertices.

32. a) Yes. The graph representing the map:

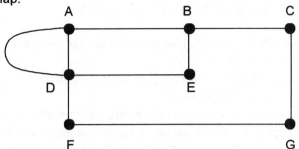

They are seeking an Euler path or an Euler circuit. Note that vertices A and B are both odd. According to item 2 of Euler's Theorem, since there are exactly two odd vertices, at least one Euler path, but no Euler circuits exist.

b) The residents would need to start at one of the two odd vertices.

33. H, I, F, C, B, D, G, H, E, D, A, B, E, F; other answers are possible.
34. F, G, E, F, D, E, B, D, A, B, C, E; other answers are possible.
35. A, B, C, E, F, D, E, B, D, A; other answers are possible.
36. A, B, D, G, B, F, G, I, F, C, E, H, F, E, A; other answers are possible.
37. A, B, C, D, F, C, B, E, F, H, G, E, A; other answers are possible.
38. A, E, B, F, C, G, D, K, G, J, F, I, E, H, A; other answers are possible.
39. A, B, C, E, B, D, E, F, D, A, C, A; other answers are possible.
40. A, B, C, E, B, D, E, F, I, E, H, D, G, H, I, J, F, C, A; other answers are possible.
41. F, C, J, M, P, H, F, M, P; other answers are possible.
42. B, A, E, H, I, J, K, D, C, G, G, J, F, C, B, F, I, E, B; other answers are possible.
43. B, E, I, F, B, C, F, J, G, G, C, D, K, J, I, H, E, A, B; other answers are possibe.
44. J, G, G, C, F, J, K, D, C, B, F, I, E, B, A, E, H, I, J; other answers are possible.
45. J, F, C, B, F, I, E, B, A, E, H, I, J, G, G, C, D, K, J; other answers are possible.

46. No. California, Nevada, and Louisiana (and others) have an odd number of states bordering it. Since a graph of the United States would have more than two odd vertices, no Euler path and no Euler circuit exist.
47. It is impossible to draw a graph with an Euler circuit that has a bridge. Therefore, a graph with an Euler circuit has no bridge.

Exercise Set 14.3
1. A **Hamilton path** is a path that passes through each vertex exactly one time.
2. A **Hamilton path** passes through each *vertex* of a graph exactly once; an **Euler path** passes through each *edge* of a graph exactly once.
3. A **Hamilton circuit** is a path that begins and ends at the same vertex and passes through all other vertices exactly one time.
4. Both **Hamilton** and **Euler circuits** begin and end at the same vertex. A **Hamilton circuit** passes through all other *vertices* of the graph exactly once, while an **Euler circuit** passes through each *edge* of a graph exactly once.
5. A **weighted graph** is a graph with a number, or weight, assigned to each edge.
6. A **complete graph** is a graph in which there is an edge between each pair of vertices.
7. a) The **factorial** is computed by multiplying the given number by each natural number less than the given number.
    b) $8! = 8(7)(6)(5)(4)(3)(2)(1) = 40,320$

8. a) 6! = 6(5)(4)(3)(2)(1) = 720
    b) 10! = 10(9)(8)(7)(6)(5)(4)(3)(2)(1) = 3,628,800

9. To find the number of unique Hamilton circuits, take the factorial of the number which is one less than the number of vertices.

10. The **optimal solution** to a traveling salesman problem is the least expensive way to visit each location exactly one time and return home.

11. To find the optimal solution using the **Brute Force method**, write down all possible Hamilton circuits and then compute the cost or distance associated with each Hamilton circuit. The one with the lowest cost or shortest distance is the optimal solution to the traveling salesman problem.

12. Starting from your current position, choose the cheapest or shortest route to get to the next city. From there choose the cheapest or shortest route to a city you have not already visited. Continue this process until you have visited each city. The path found is the path found using the **Nearest Neighbor method** for approximating the optimal solution

13. F, B, C, A, D, E, G and E, G, D, A, C, F, B; other answers are possible.
14. A, B, C, G, F, E, D and E, D, A, B, F, G, C; other answers are possible.
15. A, B, C, D, H, G, F, E, I, J, K, L and A, E, I, J, F, B, C, G, K, L, H, D; other answers are possible.
16. A, B, C, D, G, F, E, H and E, H, F, G, D, C, A, B; other answers are possible.
17. A, B, C, D, H, L, K, G, F, J, I, E, A and A, E, I, J, K, L, H, D, C, G, F, B, A; other answers are possible.
18. A, B, D, E, G, F, C, A and A, C, F, G, E, D, B, A; other answers are possible.
19. A, B, C, F, I, E, H, G, D, A and A, E, B, C, F, I, H, G, D, A; other answers are possible.
20. A, B, F, G, H, I, E, D, C, A and A, C, D, E, I, H, G, F, B, A; other answers are possible.

21.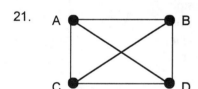

22.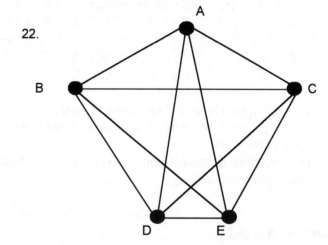

23. The number of unique Hamilton circuits within the complete graph with eight vertices representing this situation is (8 - 1)! = 7! = 7(6)(5)(4)(3)(2)(1) = 5040 ways

24. The number of unique Hamilton circuits within the complete graph with thirteen vertices representing this situation is (13 - 1)! = 12! = 12(11)(10)(9)(8)(7)(6)(5)(4)(3)(2)(1) = 479,001,600 ways

25. The number of unique Hamilton circuits within the complete graph with twelve vertices representing this situation is (12 - 1)! = 11! = 11(10)(9)(8)(7)(6)(5)(4)(3)(2)(1) = 39,916,800 ways

26. The number of unique Hamilton circuits within the complete graph with eleven vertices representing this situation is (11 - 1)! = 10! =10(9)(8)(7)(6)(5)(4)(3)(2)(1) = 3,628,800 ways
    (The vertices are the 10 different farms he has to visit and his starting point.)

27. a)

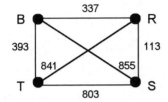

Other graphs are possible.

b)

Hamilton Circuit	First Leg/Cost	Second Leg/Cost	Third Leg/Cost	Fourth Leg/Cost	Total Cost
S, R, B, T, S	113	337	393	803	$1646
S, R, T, B, S	113	841	393	855	$2202
S, T, B, R, S	803	393	337	113	$1646
S, T, R, B, S	803	841	337	855	$2836
S, B, R, T, S	855	337	841	803	$2836
S, B, T, R, S	855	393	841	113	$2202

The least expensive route is S, R, B, T, S or S, T, B, R, S

c) $1646

28. a)

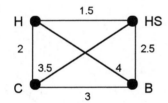

Other graphs are possible.

b)

Hamilton Circuit	First Leg/Distance	Second Leg/Distance	Third Leg/Distance	Fourth Leg/Distance	Total Distance
H, HS, B, C, H	1.5	2.5	3	2	9 miles
H, HS, C, B, H	1.5	3.5	3	4	12 miles
H, B, HS, C, H	4	2.5	3.5	2	12 miles
H, B, C, HS, H	4	3	3.5	1.5	12 miles
H, C, HS, B, H	2	3.5	2.5	4	12 miles
H, C, B, HS, H	2	3	2.5	1.5	9 miles

The shortest route is H, HS, B, C, H or H, C, B, HS, H

c) 9 miles

29. a)

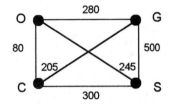

   Other graphs are possible.

b)

Hamilton Circuit	First Leg/Distance	Second Leg/Distance	Third Leg/Distance	Fourth Leg/Distance	Total Distance
C, O, G, S, C	80	280	500	300	1160 miles
C, O, S, G, C	80	245	500	205	1030 miles
C, G, O, S, C	205	280	245	300	1030 miles
C, G, S, O, C	205	500	245	80	1030 miles
C, S, G, O, C	300	500	280	80	1160 miles
C, S, O, G, C	300	245	280	205	1030 miles

   The shortest route is C, O, S, G, C or C, G, O, S, C or C, G, S, O, C or C, S, O, G, C

c) 1030 miles

30. a)

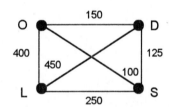

   Other graphs are possible.

b)

Hamilton Circuit	First Leg/Distance	Second Leg/Distance	Third Leg/Distance	Fourth Leg/Distance	Total Distance
O, D, S, L, O	150	125	250	400	925 feet
O, D, L, S, O	150	450	250	100	950 feet
O, L, S, D, O	400	250	125	150	925 feet
O, L, D, S, O	400	450	125	100	1075 feet
O, S, D, L, O	100	125	450	400	1075 feet
O, S, L, D, O	100	250	450	150	950 feet

   The shortest route is O, D, S, L, O or O, L, S, D, O

c) 925 feet

31. a)

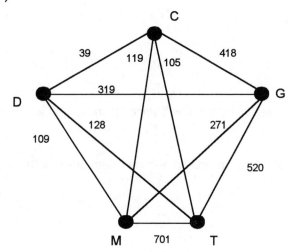

Other graphs are possible.

b) C, D, M, G, T, C for 39 + 109 + 271 + 520 + 105 = $1044
c) Answers will vary.

32. a)

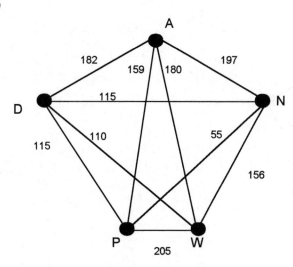

Other graphs are possible.

b) N, P, D, W, A, N for 55 + 115 + 110 + 180 + 197 = $657
c) Answers will vary.

33. Answers will vary.

34. a)

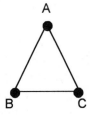

There are two choices for moving to the second vertex. There is one choice for moving to a third vertex.
2(1) = 2
(3 -1)! = 2! = 2(1) = 2
The number obtained is the same as the number of Hamilton circuits in a complete graph with 3 vertices.

b)

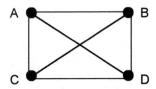

There are three choices for moving to the second vertex. There are two choices for moving to the third vertex. There is one choice for moving to the fourth vertex.
3(2)(1) = 6
(4 - 1)! = 3! = 3(2)(1) = 6
The number obtained is the same as the number of Hamilton circuits in a complete graph with 4 vertices.

c)

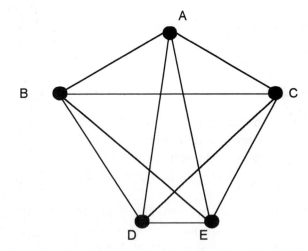

There are four choices for moving to the second vertex. There are three choices for moving to the third vertex. There are two choices for moving to the fourth vertex. There is one choice for moving to the fifth vertex.
4(3)(2)(1) = 24
(5 - 1)! = 4! = 4(3)(2)(1) = 24
The number obtained is the same as the number of Hamilton circuits in a complete graph with 5 vertices.

34. c)

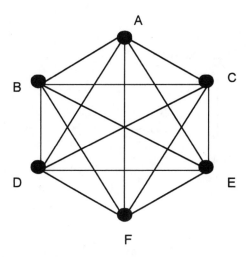

There are five choices for moving to the second vertex. There are four choices for moving to the third vertex. There are three choices for moving to the fourth vertex. There are two choices for moving to the fifth vertex. There is one choice for moving to the sixth vertex.

5(4)(3)(2)(1) = 120

(6 - 1)! = 5! = 5(4)(3)(2)(1) = 120

The number obtained is the same as the number of Hamilton circuits in a complete graph with 6 vertices.

d) When starting at a vertex in a complete graph with n vertices, you have n - 1 choices. At your second vertex, you have one less choice, or n - 2 choices. This process continues until you only have one vertex to choose from.

Exercise Set 14.4

1. A **tree** is a connected graph in which each edge is a bridge.
2. A tree cannot have a circuit unless at least one of the edges is used twice.
3. Yes, because removing the edge would create a disconnected graph.
4. A **spanning tree** is obtained by removing the edges of a graph one at a time, while maintaining a path to each vertex, until the graph is reduced to a tree.
5. A **minimum-cost spanning tree** is a spanning tree that has the lowest cost or shortest distance of all spanning trees for a given graph.
6. To find a minimum-cost spanning tree, choose the lowest cost or shortest distance edge first. Continue to choose the lowest cost or shortest distance edge that does not lead to a circuit until a spanning tree is found.

7.

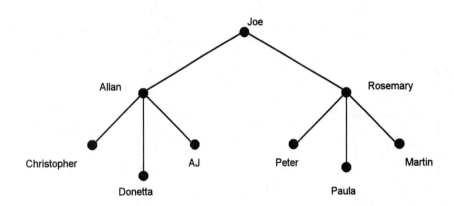

8.

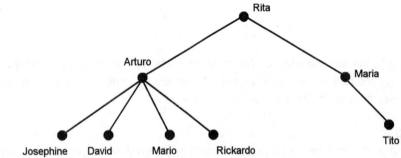

9.

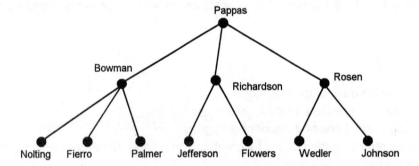

10.

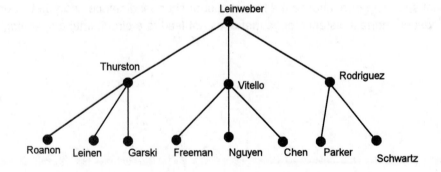

11.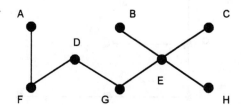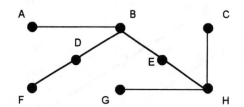

Other answers are possible.

12.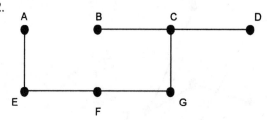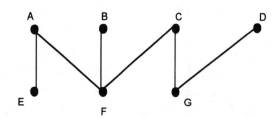

Other answers are possible.

13.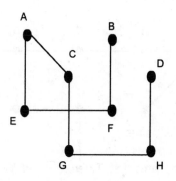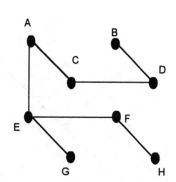

Other answers are possible.

14.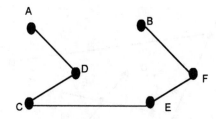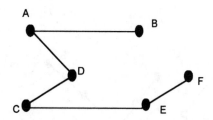

Other answers are possible.

15.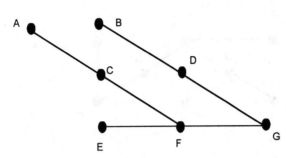

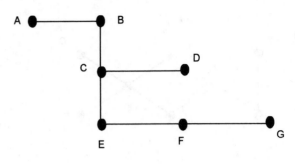

Other answers are possible.

16.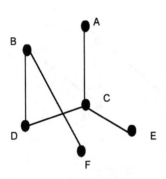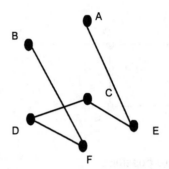

Other answers are possible.

17.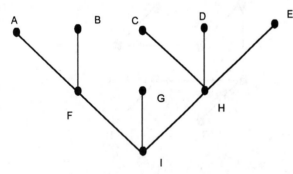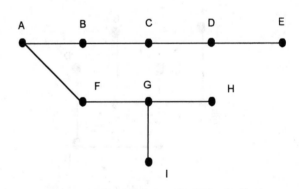

Other answers are possible.

18.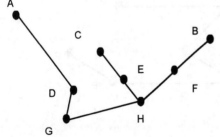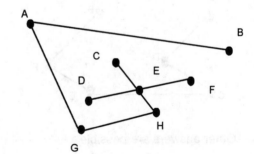

Other answers are possible.

19.

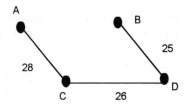

Choose edges in the following order:
BD, CD, AC

20.

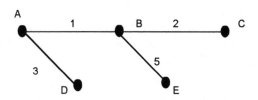

Choose edges in the following order:
AB, BC, AD, BE

21.

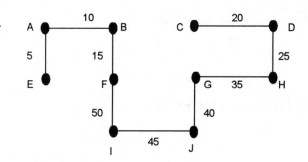

Choose edges in the following order:
AE, AB, BF, CD, DH, GH, GJ, IJ, FI

22.

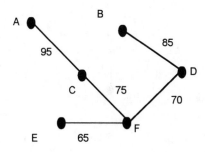

Choose edges in the following order:
EF, FD, FC, BD, AC

23.

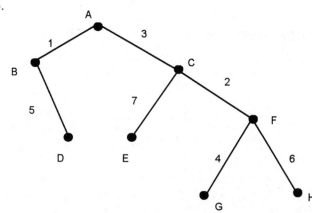

Choose edges in the following order:
AB, CF, AC, FG, BD, FH, EC

24.

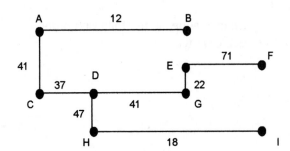

Choose edges in the following order:
AB, HI, EG, CD, AC, DG, EF, DH

25.

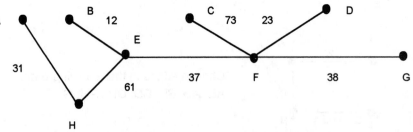

Choose edges in the following order: BE, FD, AH, EF, FG, HE, CF

26.

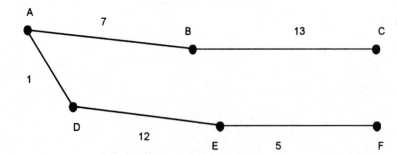

Choose edges in the following order: AD, EF, AB, DE, BC

27. a)

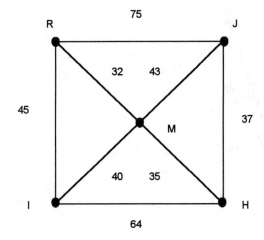

b)

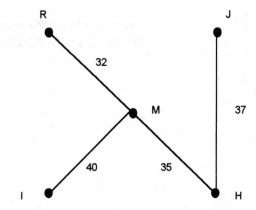

Choose edges in the following order:
RM, MH, JH, IM

c) 15(32 + 35 + 37 + 40) = 15(144) = $2160

28. a)

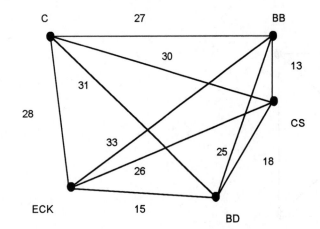

b)

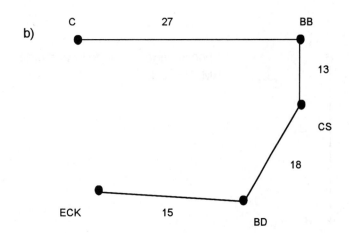

Choose edges in the following order:
BB CS, ECK BD, BD CS, C BB

c) 0.75(13 + 15 + 18 + 27) = 0.75(73) = $54.75

29. a)

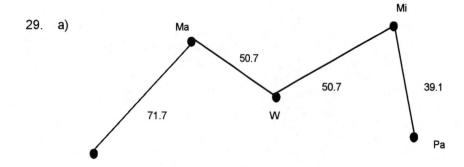

Choose edges in the following order: Mi Pa, W Mi, Ma W, Ma Pl

b) 895(39.1 + 50.7 + 50.7 + 71.7) = 895(212.2) = $189,919

30. a)

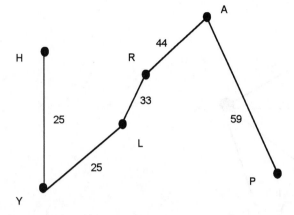

Choose edges in the following order: HY, YL, LR, RA, AP

b) 6800(25 + 25 + 33 + 44 + 59) = 6800(186) = $1,264,800

31. a)

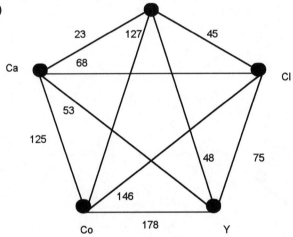

Other graphs are possible.

b)

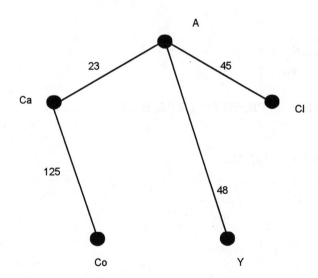

Choose edges in the following order:
ACa, AC, AY, CaCo

c) 2300(23 + 45 + 48 + 125) = 2300(241) = $554,300

32. a)

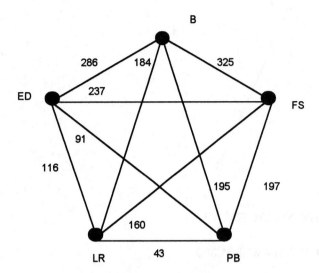

Other graphs are possible.

b)

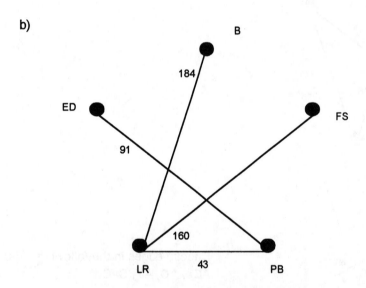

Choose edges in the following order: LR PB, ED PB, LR FS, B LR

c) 2500(43 + 91 + 160 + 184) = 2500(478) = $1,195,000

33. a)

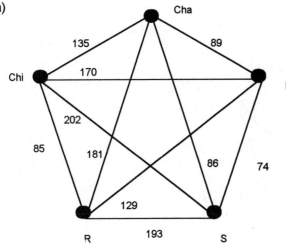

Other graphs are possible.

b)

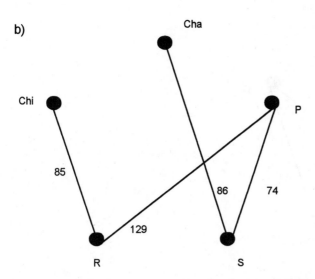

Choose edges in the following order: PS, Chi R, Cha S, RP

c) 74 + 85 + 86 + 129 = 374 miles

34. a)

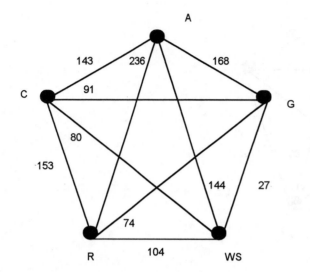

Other graphs are possible.

b)

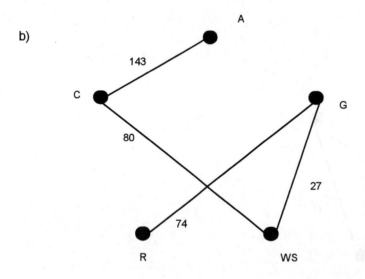

Choose edges in the following order: G WS, RG, C WS, AC

c) 27 + 74 + 80 + 143 = 324 miles

Review Exercises

1.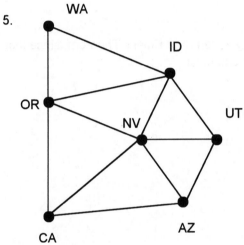

2.

3. One example is D, A, B, D, E, B, C, E.
4. No. To trace each edge in the graph with a path would require you to trace at least one edge twice.

5.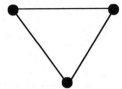

6.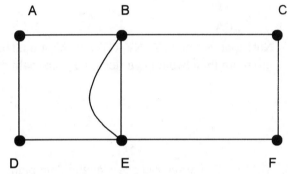

7. Connected
8. Disconnected. There is no path that connects A to C.
9. Edge CD
10. B, A, E, B, C, D, F, C, E, F; Other answers are possible.
11. F, E, A, B, C, D, F, C, E, B; Other answers are possible.
12. B, C, A, D, F, E, C, D, E, B; Other answers are possible.
13. E, F, D, E, C, D, A, C, B, E; Other answers are possible.

14. No. The graph representing the map:

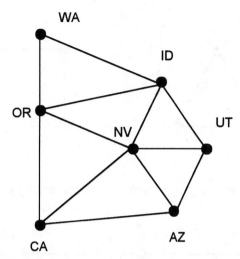

Note that vertices CA, NV, UT, and AZ are all odd. According to item 3 of Euler's Theorem, since there are more than two odd vertices, no Euler path or Euler circuit can exist.

15. a) Yes. The graph representing the floor plan:

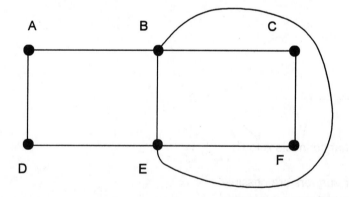

We are seeking an Euler path or an Euler circuit. Note that there are no odd vertices. According to item 1 of Euler's Theorem, since there are no odd vertices, at least one Euler path (which is also an Euler circuit) must exist.

b) You may start in any room and you will end where you started.

16. a) Yes. The graph representing the map:

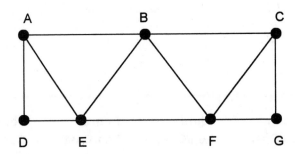

The officer is seeking an Euler path or an Euler circuit. Note that vertices A and C are both odd. According to item 2 of Euler's Theorem, since there are exactly two odd vertices, at least one Euler path but no Euler circuits exist.

   b) The officer would have to start at either the upper left-hand corner or the upper right-hand corner and end at the other one.

17. F, B, A, E, F, G, C, D, H, G; Other answers are possible.
18. A, B, C, D, H, G, C, F, G, B, F, E, A; Other answers are possible.
19. A, C, B, F, E, D, G and A, C, D, G, F, B, E; Other answers are possible.
20. A, B, C, D, F, E, A and A, E, F, B, C, D, A; Other answers are possible.

21.

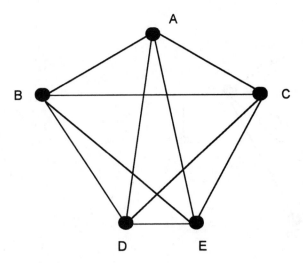

22. The number of unique Hamilton circuits within the complete graph with 5 vertices representing this situation is $(5 - 1)! = 4! = 4(3)(2)(1) = 24$ ways

23. a)

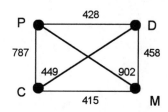

b)

Hamilton Circuit	First Leg/Cost	Second Leg/Cost	Third Leg/Cost	Fourth Leg/Cost	Total Cost
P, D, C, M, P	428	449	415	902	$2194
P, D, M, C, P	428	458	415	787	$2088
P, C, M, D, P	787	415	458	428	$2088
P, C, D, M, P	787	449	458	902	$2596
P, M, D, C, P	902	458	449	787	$2596
P, M, C, D, P	902	415	449	428	$2194

The least expensive route is P, D, M, C, P or P, C, M, D, P

c) $2088

24. a)

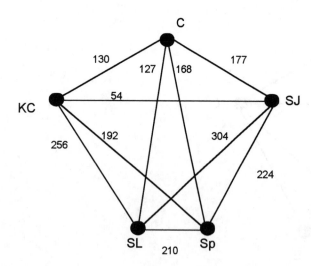

b) SJ, KC, C, SL, Sp, SJ traveling a total of 54 + 130 + 127 + 210 + 224 = 745 miles

c) Sp, C, SL, KC, SJ, Sp traveling a total of 168 + 127 + 256 + 54 + 224 = 829 miles

25.

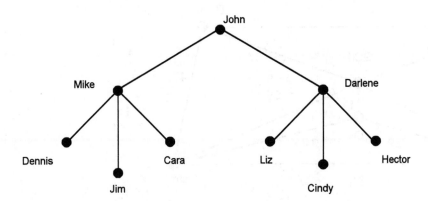

26.

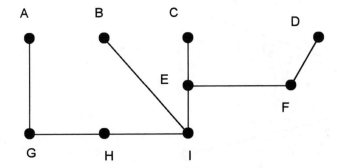

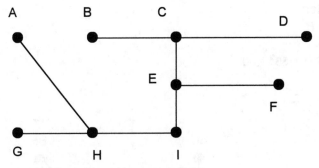

Other answers are possible.

27.

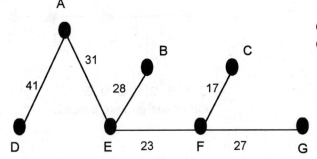

Choose edges in the following order:
CF, EF, FG, BE, AE, AD

28. a)

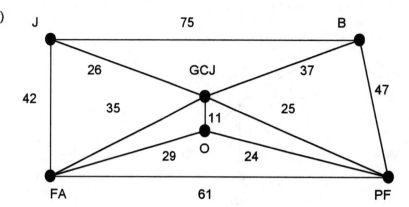

b)

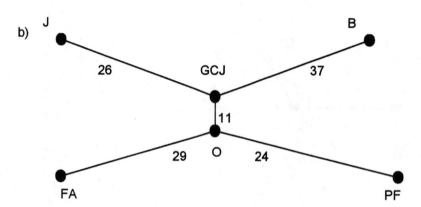

Choose edges in the following order:
O GCJ, O PF, J GCJ, FA O, GCJ B

c) 2.50(11 + 24 + 26 + 29 + 37) = 2.50(127) = $317.50

Chapter Test

1.

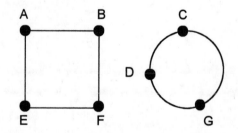

Other answers are possible.

2.

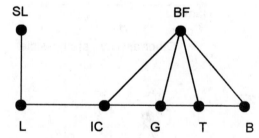

3. One example:

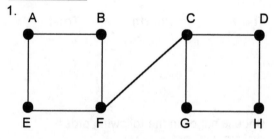

4. D, A, B, C, E, B, D, E;
Other answers are possible.

5.   Yes. The graph representing the floor plan:

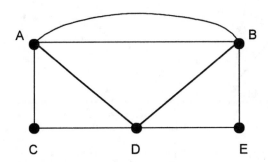

You are seeking an Euler path or an Euler circuit. Note that there are no odd vertices. According to item 1 of Euler's Theorem, since there are no odd vertices, at least one Euler path (which is also an Euler circuit) must exist.

You may start in any room and you will end where you started.

6.   A, D, E, A, F, E, H, F, I, G, F, B, G, C, B, A; Other answers are possible.
7.   A, B, C, D, H, L, K, G, F, J, I, E, A; Other answers are possible.
8.   The number of unique Hamilton circuits within the complete graph with 8 vertices representing this situation is (8 - 1)! = 7! = 7(6)(5)(4)(3)(2)(1) = 5040 ways

9. a)

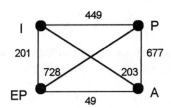

b)

Hamilton Circuit	First Leg/Cost	Second Leg/Cost	Third Leg/Cost	Fourth Leg/Cost	Total Cost
I, P, EP, A, I	449	728	49	203	$1429
I, P, A, EP, I	449	677	49	201	$1376
I, A, P, EP, I	203	677	728	201	$1809
I, A, EP, P, I	203	49	728	449	$1429
I, EP, A, P, I	201	49	677	449	$1376
I, EP, P, A, I	201	728	677	203	$1809

The least expensive route is I, P, A, EP, I or I, EP, A, P, I for $1376.

c) I, EP, A, P, I for $1376.

10.

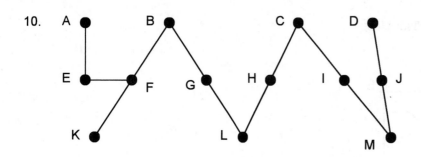

11.

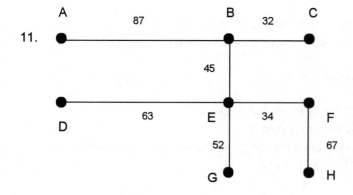

Choose edges in the following order:
BC, EF, BE, EG, DE, FH, AB

12. a)

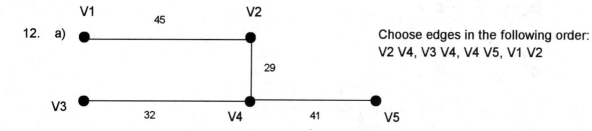

Choose edges in the following order:
V2 V4, V3 V4, V4 V5, V1 V2

b) 1.25(29 + 32 + 41 + 45) = 1.25(147) = $183.75

CHAPTER FIFTEEN

VOTING AND APPORTIONMENT

Exercise Set 15.1

1. When a candidate receives more than 50% of the votes.

2. Each voter votes for one candidate. The candidate receiving the most votes is declared the winner.

3. Voters rank candidates from most favorable to least favorable. Each last place vote is awarded one point, each next to last place vote is awarded two points, each third from last place vote is awarded three points, etc. The candidate receiving the most points is the winner.

4. Each voter votes for one candidate. If a candidate receives a majority of votes, that candidate is declared the winner. If no candidate receives a majority, eliminate the candidate with the fewest votes. (If there is a tie for the fewest votes, eliminate all tied candidates.) Repeat this process until a candidate receives a majority.

5. Voters rank the candidates. A series of comparisons in which each candidate is compared to each of the other candidates follows. If candidate A is preferred to candidate B, then A receives one point. If candidate B is preferred to candidate A, then B receives one point. If the candidates tie, each receives ½ point. The candidate receiving the most points is declared the winner.

6. Different systems can lead to a different winner.

7. a) Felicia is the winner. Felicia received the most votes.

   b) No. $\dfrac{2863}{2192+2562+1671+2863+1959} = \dfrac{2863}{11247} \approx 0.25$ is not a majority.

8. a) Jeter is the winner; he received the most votes.

   b) No. $\dfrac{265128}{192827+210361+265128} = \dfrac{265128}{668316} \approx 0.40$ is not a majority.

9.
Number of votes	3	1	2	2	1
First	B	A	C	C	A
Second	A	B	B	A	C
Third	C	C	A	B	B

10.
Number of votes	2	3	2	1
First	A	C	B	C
Second	B	A	A	B
Third	C	B	C	A

11. $8 + 4 + 3 + 2 = 17$

12. No. J had the most, but $8/17 = 0.47$ is not a majority

13. Votes – (J): 8, (P): $4 + 3 = 7$, (C): 2. Jones wins with the most votes.

14. Choi:
    2 first place votes producing $2 \times 3 = 6$ points
    3 second place votes producing $3 \times 2 = 6$ points
    $8 + 4 = 12$ third place votes producing $12 \times 1 = 12$ points
    Choi receives $6 + 6 + 12 = 24$ points

    Jones:
    8 first place votes producing $8 \times 3 = 24$ points
    4 second place votes producing $4 \times 2 = 8$ points
    $3 + 2 = 5$ third place votes producing $5 \times 1 = 5$ points
    Jones receives $24 + 8 + 5 = 37$ points

    Patterson:
    $4 + 3 = 7$ first place votes producing $7 \times 3 = 21$ points
    $8 + 2 = 10$ second place votes producing $10 \times 2 = 20$ points
    0 third place votes producing $0 \times 1 = 0$ points
    Patterson receives $21 + 20 + 0 = 41$ points

    Patterson wins with the most points

15. A majority out of 17 votes is 9 or more votes.
    First choice votes:
    (C): 2, (J):8, (P): $4 + 3 = 7$ None receives a majority, thus Choi with the least votes is eliminated.

Number of votes	8	4	3	2
First	J	P	P	P
Second	P	J	J	J

    First Choice Votes: (J): 8, (P): $4 + 3 + 2 = 9$ Patterson is the winner with 9 votes – a majority.

16. Choi vs. Jones: Choi: $3 + 2 = 5$ votes, Jones : $8 + 4 = 12$ votes;
    Jones is awarded 1 point.

    Choi vs. Patterson: Choi: 2 votes, Patterson: 15 votes;
    Patterson is awarded 1 point.

    Jones vs. Patterson: Jones: 8 votes; Patterson: 9 votes;
    Patterson is awarded 1 point.

    Since Choi received 0 points, Jones 1 point and Patterson 2 points;
    Patterson is the winner.

17. Grand Canyon
    2 first place votes producing $2 \times 3 = 6$ points
    $3 + 1 = 4$ second place votes producing $4 \times 2 = 8$ points
    $2 + 1 = 3$ third place votes producing $3 \times 1 = 3$ points
    Grand Canyon receives $6 + 8 + 3 = 17$ points

    Disney World
    $2 + 1 = 3$ first place votes producing $3 \times 3 = 9$ points
    $1 + 2 = 3$ second place votes producing $3 \times 2 = 6$ points
    3 third place votes producing $3 \times 1 = 3$ points
    Disney World receives $9 + 6 + 3 = 18$ points

    Beach
    $3 + 1 = 4$ first place votes producing $4 \times 3 = 12$ points
    2 second place votes producing $2 \times 2 = 4$ points
    $2 + 1 = 3$ third place votes producing $3 \times 1 = 3$ points
    The Beach receives $12 + 4 + 3 = 19$ points

    The beach wins with the most points.

18. Votes: (B): $3 + 1 = 4$, (D): $2 + 1 = 3$, (G): 2
    The beach wins with the most votes.

19. Grand Canyon vs. Disney World
    (G): $3 + 2 = 5$, (B): $2 + 1 + 1 = 4$
    Grand Canyon is awarded 1 point.

    Grand Canyon vs. The Beach
    (G): $2 + 1 = 3$, (B): $3 + 2 + 1 = 6$
    The beach is awarded 1 point.

    The Beach vs. Disney World
    (B): $3 + 1 = 4$, (D): $2 + 2 + 1 = 5$
    Disney World receives 1 point.

    Since (G) received 1 point, (D) received 1 point, and (B) received 1 point, There is no winner.

20. A majority out of 9 voters is 5 or more votes.
    First choice votes:
    (B): $3 + 1 = 4$, (D): $2 = 1 = 3$, (G): 2. None received a majority
    Thus (G) with the least votes is eliminated.

Number of votes	3	2	1	2	1
First	B	D	B	D	D
Second	D	B	D	B	B

    First choice votes: (B): $3 + 1 = 4$, (D): $2 + 2 + 1 = 5$
    Disney World is the winner with 5 votes – a majority

21. Votes: (S): $7 + 3 + 2 = 12$, (L): $5 + 3 = 8$, (H): $4 + 3 + 2 = 9$, (T): 1
    San Antonio wins with the most votes.

22. San Antonio:
    7 + 3 + 2 = 12 first place votes producing 12 × 4 = 48 points
    3 + 3 = 5 second place votes producing 5 × 3 = 15 points
    3 + 1 = 4 third place votes producing 4 × 2 = 8 points
    5 + 4 = 9 fourth place votes producing 9 × 1 = 9 points
    San Antonio receives 48 + 15 + 8 + 9 = 80 points

    Los Angeles:
    5 + 3 = 8 first place votes producing 8 × 4 = 32 points
    7 + 4 + 3 + 3 = 17 second place votes producing 17 × 3 = 51 points
    2 + 2 = 4 third place votes producing 4 × 2 = 8 points
    1 fourth place votes producing 1 × 1 = 1 points
    Los Angeles receives 32 + 51 + 8 + 1 = 92 points

    Honolulu:
    4 + 3 + 2 = 9 first place votes producing 9 × 4 = 36 points
    5 + 2 + 1 = 8 second place votes producing 8 × 3 = 24 points
    7 + 3 = 10 third place votes producing 10 × 2 = 20 points
    3 fourth place votes producing 3 × 1 = 1 points
    Honolulu receives 36 + 24 + 20 + 3 = 83 points

    Toronto:
    1 first place votes producing 1 × 4 = 4 points
    0 second place votes producing 0 × 3 = 0 points
    5 + 4 + 3 = 12 third place votes producing 12 × 2 = 24 points
    7 + 3 + 3 + 2 + 2 = 17 fourth place votes producing 17 × 1 = 17 points
    Toronto receives 4 + 0 + 24 + 17 = 45 points

    Los Angeles wins with the most points.

23. Majority out of 30 voters is 16 or more votes.
    First choice votes:
    (S): 7 + 3 + 2 = 12, (L): 5 + 3 = 8, (H): 4 + 3 + 2 = 9, (T): 1
    None receives a majority. Thus (T) with the least is eliminated.

Number of votes	7	5	3	4	3	3	2	1	2
First	S	L	L	H	S	H	S	H	H
Second	L	H	S	L	L	L	H	S	S
Third	H	S	H	S	H	S	L	L	L

    First choice votes: (S): 7 + 3 + 2 = 12, (L): 5 + 3 = 8, (H): 4 + 3 + 1 + 2 = 10
    None receives a majority. Thus (L) with the least is eliminated.

Number of votes	7	5	3	4	3	3	2	1	2
First	S	H	S	H	S	H	S	H	H
Second	H	S	H	S	H	S	H	S	S

    First choice votes: (S): 7 + 3 + 3 + 2 = 15, (H): 5 + 4 + 3 + 1 + 2 = 15
    Since neither has a majority, there is no winner.

24. (S) vs. (L)
(S): 7 + 3 + 2 + 1 + 2 = 15, (L): 5 + 3 + 4 + 3 = 15
Each is awarded ½ point.

(S) vs. (H)
(S): 7 + 3 + 3 + 2 = 15, (H): 5 + 4 + 3 + 1 + 2 = 15
Each is awarded ½ point.

(S) vs. (T)
(S): 7 + 3 + 3 + 3 + 2 + 2 = 20, (T): 5 + 4 + 1 = 10
(S) is awarded 1 point.

(L) vs. (H)
(L): 7 + 5 + 3 + 3 = 18, (H): 4 + 3 + 2 + 1 + 2 = 12
(L) is awarded 1 point.

(L) vs. (T)
(L): 7 + 5 + 3 + 4 + 3 + 3 + 2 + 2 = 29, (T): 1
(L) is awarded 1 point.

(H) vs. (T)
(H): 7 + 5 + 3 + 4 + 3 + 2 + 2 = 26, (T): 3 + 1 = 4
(H) is awarded 1 point.

Since (S) receives 2 points, (L) receives 2½ points, (H) receives 1½ points and (T) receives 0 points, Los Angeles is the winner with the most points.

25. Williams:
5 first place votes producing $5 \times 3 = 15$ points
4 second place votes producing $4 \times 2 = 8$ points
1 + 2 = 3 third place votes producing $3 \times 1 = 3$ points
Williams receives 15 + 8 + 3 = 26 points

Diaz:
1 first place votes producing $1 \times 3 = 3$ points
5 + 2 = 7 second place votes producing $7 \times 2 = 14$ points
4 third place votes producing $4 \times 1 = 4$ points
Diaz receives 3 + 14 + 4 = 21 points

Johnson:
4 + 2 = 6 first place votes producing $6 \times 3 = 18$ points
1 second place votes producing $1 \times 2 = 2$ points
5 third place votes producing $5 \times 1 = 5$ points
Johnson receives 18 + 2 + 5 = 25 points

Williams wins with the most points.

26. Votes: (W): 5, (D): 1, (J): 4 + 2 = 6
Johnson wins with the most votes.

27.
(W) vs. (D)	(W) vs. (J)	(J) vs. (D)
(W): 5 + 4 = 9, (D): 1 + 2 = 3	(W): 5, (J): 1 + 4 + 2 = 7	(J): 4 + 2 = 6, (D): 5 + 1 = 6
(W) is awarded 1 point	(J) is awarded 1 point	Each is awarded ½ point

Johnson is the winner with the most points.

28. A majority out of 12 voters is 7 or more votes. First choice votes: (W): 5, (D): 1, (J): 4 + 2 = 6 None of them receives a majority. Thus eliminate (D)

Number of votes	5	1	4	2
First	W	J	J	J
Second	J	W	W	W

First choice votes: (W): 5, (J): 1 + 4 + 2 = 7. Johnson wins with a majority of the votes.

29. A majority out of 12 voters is 7 or more votes. First choice votes: (W): 5, (D): 1, (J): 4 + 2 = 6 None receives a majority. Thus eliminate Johnson with the most last place votes.

Number of votes	5	1	4	2
First	W	D	W	D
Second	D	W	D	W

First choice votes: (W): 5 + 4 = 9, (D): 1 + 2 = 3. Williams wins with a majority of the votes.

30. Votes: (L): 5, (E): 2, (O): 4. Lehigh Road wins with the most votes.

31. Lehigh Road:
    5 first place votes producing 5 × 3 = 15 points
    0 second place votes producing 0 × 2 = 0 points
    2 + 4 = 6 third place votes producing 6 × 1 = 6 points
    Lehigh Road receives 15 + 6 = 21 points

    Erie Road:
    2 first place votes producing 2 × 3 = 6 points
    5 + 4 = 9 second place votes producing 9 × 2 = 18 points
    0 third place votes producing 0 × 1 = 0 points
    Erie Road receives 6 + 18 = 24 points

    Ontario Road:
    4 first place votes producing 4 × 3 = 12 points
    2 second place votes producing 2 × 2 = 4 points
    5 third place votes producing 5 × 1 = 5 points
    Ontario Road receives 12 + 4 + 5 = 21 points

    Erie Road wins with the most points.

32. A majority out of 11 voters is 6 or more votes. First choice votes: (L): 5, (E): 2, (O): 4 None has a majority, thus (E) is eliminated.

Number of votes	5	2	4
First	L	O	O
Second	O	L	L

First choice votes: (L): 5, (O): 2 + 4 = 6. Ontario Road wins with a majority of the votes.

33. (L) vs. (E)   (L) vs. (O)   (E) vs. (O)
    (L): 5, (E): 2 + 4 = 6   (L): 5, (O): 2 + 4 = 6   (E): 5 + 2 = 7, (O): 4
    (E) is awarded 1 point   (O) is awarded 1 point   (E) is awarded 1 point

    Erie Road wins with the most points.

34. A majority out of 11 voters is 6 or more votes.
    First choice votes: (L): 5, (E): 2, (O): 4
    None has a majority, thus eliminate (L) with the most last place votes.

Number of votes	5	2	4
First	E	E	O
Second	O	O	E

    First choice votes: (E): 5 + 2 = 7, (O): 4
    Erie Road wins with a majority of the votes.

35. a) Votes: (TI): 6 + 4 = 10, (C): 3, (HP): 2, (S): 0
       TI wins with the most votes

    b) TI:
       6 + 4 = 10 first place votes producing 10 × 4 = 40 points
       3 + 2 = 5 second place votes producing 5 × 3 = 15 points
       0 third place votes producing 0 × 2 = 0 points
       0 fourth place votes producing 0 × 1 = 0 points
       TI receives 40 + 15 = 55 points

       (C):
       3 first place votes producing 3 × 4 = 12 points
       6 second place votes producing 6 × 3 = 18 points
       4 + 2 = 6 third place votes producing 6 × 2 = 12 points
       0 fourth place votes producing 0 × 1 = 0 points
       (C) receives 12 + 18 + 12 = 42 points

       (HP):
       2 first place votes producing 2 × 4 = 8 points
       4 second place votes producing 4 × 3 = 12 points
       0 third place votes producing 0 × 2 = 0 points
       6 + 3 = 9 fourth place votes producing 9 × 1 = 9 points
       (HP) receives 8 + 12 + 9 = 29 points

       (S):
       0 first place votes producing 0 × 4 = 0 points
       0 second place votes producing 0 × 3 = 0 points
       6 + 3 = 9 third place votes producing 9 × 2 = 18 points
       4 + 2 = 6 fourth place votes producing 6 × 1 = 6 points
       (S) receives 18 + 6 = 24 points

       TI is the winner with the most points.

    c) A majority out of 15 voters is 8 or more votes.
       First choice votes: (TI): 6 + 4 = 10, (C): 3, (HP): 2. (S): 0
       TI wins with a majority of the votes.

   d) (TI) vs. (C)

      (TI): 6 + 4 + 2 = 12, (C): 3

      (TI) is awarded 1 point

      (TI) vs. (HP)

      (TI): 6 + 4 + 3 = 13, (HP): 2

      (TI) is awarded 1 point

      (TI) vs. (S)

      (TI): 6 + 4 + 3 + 2 = 15, (S): 0

      (TI) is awarded 1 point

      (C) vs. (HP)

      (C): 6 + 3 = 9, (HP): 2 + 4 = 6

      (C) is awarded 1 point

      (C) vs. (S)

      (C): 6 + 4 + 3 + 2 = 15, (S): 0

      (C) is awarded 1 point

      (S) vs. (HP)

      (S): 6 + 3 = 9, (HP): 4 + 2 = 6

      (S) is awarded 1 point

      TI wins with the most points.

36. a) Votes: (L): 8, (A): 4, (B): 3, (M): 2

      I Love Lucy with the most votes

   b) A:

      4 first place votes producing 4 × 4 = 16 points

      0 second place votes producing 0 × 3 = 0 points

      3 + 2 = 5 third place votes producing 5 × 2 = 10 points

      8 fourth place votes producing 8 × 1 = 8 points

      (A) receives 16 + 10 + 8 = 34 points

      (B):

      3 first place votes producing 3 × 4 = 12 points

      2 second place votes producing 2 × 3 = 6 points

      8 + 4 = 12 third place votes producing 12 × 2 = 24 points

      0 fourth place votes producing 0 × 1 = 0 points

      (B) receives 12 + 6 + 24 = 42 points

      (L):

      8 first place votes producing 8 × 4 = 32 points

      0 second place votes producing 0 × 3 = 0 points

      0 third place votes producing 0 × 2 = 0 points

      4 + 3 + 2 = 9 fourth place votes producing 9 × 1 = 9 points

      (L) receives 32 + 9 = 41 points

      (M):

      2 first place votes producing 2 × 4 = 8 points

      8 + 4 + 3 = 15 second place votes producing 15 × 3 = 45 points

      0 third place votes producing 0 × 2 = 0 points

      0 fourth place votes producing 0 × 1 = 0 points

      (M) receives 8 + 45 = 53 points

      Mash wins with the most points.

c) A majority out of 17 voters is 9 or more votes. First choice votes: (L): 8, (A): 4, (B): 3, (M): 2
None has a majority, thus eliminate (M) with the least votes.

Number of votes	8	4	3	2
First	L	A	B	B
Second	B	B	A	A
Third	A	L	L	L

First choice votes: (L): 8, (A): 4, (B): 3 + 2 = 5
None has the majority, thus eliminate (A) with the least votes.

Number of votes	8	4	3	2
First	L	B	B	B
Second	B	L	L	L

First choice votes: (L): 8, (B): 4 + 3 + 2 = 9
Barney Miller wins with a majority of the votes.

d) (L) vs. (A)
(L): 8, (A): 4 + 3 + 2 = 9
(A) is awarded 1 point.

(L) vs. (B)
(L): 8, (B): 4 + 3 + 2 = 9
(B) is awarded 1 point.

(L) vs. (M)
(L): 8, (M): 4 + 3 + 2 = 9
(M) is awarded 1 point.

(A) vs. (B)
(A): 4, (B): 8 + 3 + 2 = 13
(B) is awarded 1 point.

(A) vs. (M)
(A): 4, (M): 8 + 3 + 2 = 13
(M) is awarded 1 point.

(B) vs. (M)
(B): 3, (M): 8 + 4 + 2 = 14
(M) is awarded 1 point.

Mash wins with the most points.

37. a) (ND) vs. (YS)
(ND): 7 + 2 = 9, (YS): 3 + 1 = 4
(ND) is awarded 1 point

(ND) vs. (GK)
(ND): 7 + 3 + 1 = 11, (GK): 2
(ND) is awarded 1 point

(ND) vs. (MR)
(ND): 7 + 2 + 1 = 10, (MR): 3
(ND) is awarded 1 point

(YS) vs. (GK)
(YS): 7 + 3 + 1 = 11, (GK): 2
(YS) is awarded 1 point

(YS) vs. (MR)
(YS): 3 + 1 = 4, (MR): 7 + 2 = 9
(MR) is awarded 1 point

(GK) vs. (MR)
(GK): 2 + 1 = 3, (MR): 7 + 3 = 10
(MR) is awarded 1 point

(ND): 3 points, (YS): 1 point, (GK): 0, (MR): 2 points
(ND) wins with the most points.

b) A majority out of 13 voters is 7 or more votes.

First choice votes: (ND): 7, (YS): 3 + 1 = 4, (GK): 2, (MR): 0

None has a majority, thus eliminate (MR) with the least votes.

Number of votes	7	3	2	1
First	ND	YS	GK	YS
Second	YS	ND	ND	ND
Third	GK	GK	YS	GK

First choice votes: (ND): 7, (YS): 3 + 1 = 4, (GK): 2

None has the majority, thus eliminate (GK) with the least votes.

Number of votes	7	3	2	1
First	ND	YS	ND	YS
Second	YS	ND	YS	ND

First choice votes: (ND): 7 + 2 = 9, (YS): 3 + 1 = 4

(ND) wins with a majority of the votes.

c) (ND):

7 first place votes producing 7 × 4 = 28 points

2 + 1 = 3 second place votes producing 3 × 3 = 9 points

3 third place votes producing 3 × 2 = 6 points

0 fourth place votes producing 0 × 1 = 0 points

(ND) receives 28 + 9 + 6 = 43 points

(YS):

3 + 1 = 4 first place votes producing 4 × 4 = 16 points

0 second place votes producing 0 × 3 = 0 points

7 third place votes producing 7 × 2 = 14 points

2 fourth place votes producing 2 × 1 = 2 points

(YS) receives 16 + 14 + 2 = 32 points

(GK):

2 first place votes producing 2 × 4 = 8 points

0 second place votes producing 0 × 3 = 0 points

1 third place votes producing 1 × 2 = 2 points

7 + 3 = 10 fourth place votes producing 10 × 1 = 10 points

(GK) receives 8 + 2 + 10 = 20 points

(MR):

0 first place votes producing 0 × 4 = 0 points

7 + 3 = 10 second place votes producing 10 × 3 = 30 points

2 third place votes producing 2 × 2 = 4 points

1 fourth place votes producing 1 × 1 = 1 points

(MR) receives 30 + 4 + 1 = 35 points

(ND) wins with the most points.

d) Votes: (ND): 7, (YS): 3 + 1 = 4, (GK): 2, (MR): 0

(ND) wins with the most votes.

38. a) (G) vs. (A)

(G): 43 + 26 = 69, (A): 30 + 29 + 14 = 73

(A) is awarded 1 point

(G) vs. (C)

(G): 43, (C): 30 + 29 + 26 + 14 = 99

(C) is awarded 1 point

(G) vs. (D)

(G): 43, (D): 30 + 29 +26 + 14 = 99

(D) is awarded 1 point

(A) vs. (C)

(A): 42 + 30 = 73, (C): 29 + 26 + 14 + = 69

(A) is awarded 1 point

(A) vs. (D)

(A): 43 + 30 = 73, (D): 29 + 26 + 14 + = 69

(A) is awarded 1 point

(C) vs. (D)

(C): 43 + 29 = 72, (D): 30 + 26 + 14 = 70

(C) is awarded 1 point

Apple wins with the most points.

b) A majority out of 142 voters is 72 or more votes.

First choice votes: (G): 43, (A): 30, (C): 29, (D): 26 + 14 = 40

None has a majority, thus eliminate (C) with the least votes.

Number of votes	43	30	29	26	14
First	G	A	D	D	D
Second	A	D	A	G	A
Third	D	G	G	A	G

First choice votes: (G): 43, (A): 30, (D): 29 + 26 + 14 = 69

None has the majority, thus eliminate (A) with the most votes.

Number of votes	43	30	29	26	14
First	G	D	D	D	D
Second	D	G	G	G	G

First choice votes: (G): 43, (D): 30 + 29 + 26 + 14 = 99

Dell wins with a majority of the votes.

c) (G):

43 first place votes producing $43 \times 4 = 172$ points

0 second place votes producing $0 \times 3 = 0$ points

26 third place votes producing $26 \times 2 = 52$ points

$30 + 29 + 14 = 73$ fourth place votes producing $73 \times 1 = 73$ points

(G) receives $172 + 52 + 73 = 297$ points

(A):

30 first place votes producing $30 \times 4 = 120$ points

43 second place votes producing $43 \times 3 = 129$ points

$29 + 14 = 43$ third place votes producing $43 \times 2 = 86$ points

26 fourth place votes producing $26 \times 1 = 26$ points

(A) receives $130 + 129 + 86 + 26 = 361$ points

(C):

29 first place votes producing $29 \times 4 = 116$ points

$26 + 14 = 40$ second place votes producing $40 \times 3 = 120$ points

$43 + 30 = 73$ third place votes producing $73 \times 2 = 146$ points

0 fourth place votes producing $0 \times 1 = 0$ points

(C) receives $116 + 120 + 146 = 382$ points

(D):

$26 + 14 = 40$ first place votes producing $40 \times 4 = 160$ points

$30 + 29 = 59$ second place votes producing $59 \times 3 = 177$ points

0 third place votes producing $0 \times 2 = 0$ points

43 fourth place votes producing $43 \times 1 = 43$ points

(D) receives $160 + 177 + 43 = 380$ points

Compaq wins with the most points.

d) Votes: (G): 43, (A): 30, (C): 29, (D): $26 + 14 = 40$
Gateway wins with the most votes

e) Different methods of selection may produce different outcomes.

39. a) If there were only two columns then only two of the candidates were the first choice of the voters. If each of the 15 voters cast a ballot, then one of the voters must have received a majority of votes because 15 cannot be split evenly.

b) An odd number cannot be divided evenly so one of the two first choice candidates must receive more than half of the votes.

40. a) (A):
　　　　0 first place votes producing $0 \times 4 = 0$ points
　　　　1 second place votes producing $1 \times 3 = 3$ points
　　　　2 third place votes producing $2 \times 2 = 4$ points
　　　　1 fourth place votes producing $1 \times 1 = 1$ point
　　　　(A) receives $3 + 4 + 1 = 8$ points

　　　　(B):
　　　　1 first place votes producing $1 \times 4 = 4$ points
　　　　2 second place votes producing $2 \times 3 = 6$ points
　　　　0 third place votes producing $0 \times 2 = 0$ points
　　　　1 fourth place votes producing $1 \times 1 = 1$ point
　　　　(B) receives $4 + 6 + 1 = 11$ points

　　　　(C):
　　　　2 first place votes producing $2 \times 4 = 8$ points
　　　　0 second place votes producing $0 \times 3 = 0$ points
　　　　0 third place votes producing $0 \times 2 = 0$ points
　　　　2 fourth place votes producing $2 \times 1 = 2$ points
　　　　(C) receives $8 + 2 = 10$ points

　　　　(D):
　　　　1 first place votes producing $1 \times 4 = 4$ points
　　　　1 second place votes producing $1 \times 3 = 3$ points
　　　　2 third place votes producing $2 \times 2 = 4$ points
　　　　0 fourth place votes producing $0 \times 1 = 0$ points
　　　　(D) receives $4 + 3 + 4 = 11$ points

　　　　Tie between (B) and (D).

　　b) (B):
　　　　1 first place votes producing $1 \times 5 = 5$ points
　　　　2 second place votes producing $2 \times 3 = 6$ points
　　　　0 third place votes producing $0 \times 2 = 0$ points
　　　　0 fourth place votes producing $0 \times 1 = 0$ points
　　　　(B) receives $5 + 6 = 11$ points

　　　　(D):
　　　　1 first place votes producing $1 \times 5 = 5$ points
　　　　1 second place votes producing $1 \times 3 = 3$ points
　　　　2 third place votes producing $2 \times 1 = 2$ points
　　　　0 fourth place votes producing $0 \times 1 = 0$ points
　　　　(D) receives $5 + 3 + 2 = 10$ points
　　　　(B) wins with the most points.

41. a) Comets:

   1 first place votes producing $1 \times 4 = 4$ points
   0 second place votes producing $0 \times 3 = 0$ points
   0 third place votes producing $0 \times 2 = 0$ points
   2 fourth place votes producing $2 \times 1 = 2$ points
   Comets receives $4 + 2 = 6$ points

   Rams:

   2 first place votes producing $2 \times 4 = 8$ points
   1 second place votes producing $1 \times 3 = 3$ points
   0 third place votes producing $0 \times 2 = 0$ points
   0 fourth place votes producing $0 \times 1 = 0$ points
   Rams receives $8 + 3 = 11$ points

   Warriors:

   0 first place votes producing $0 \times 4 = 0$ points
   2 second place votes producing $2 \times 3 = 6$ points
   2 third place votes producing $2 \times 2 = 4$ points
   2 fourth place votes producing $2 \times 1 = 2$ points
   Warriors receives $6 + 4 + 2 = 12$ points

   Tigers:

   1 first place votes producing $1 \times 4 = 4$ points
   1 second place votes producing $1 \times 3 = 3$ points
   2 third place votes producing $2 \times 2 = 4$ points
   0 fourth place votes producing $0 \times 1 = 0$ points
   Tigers receives $4 + 3 + 4 = 11$ points

   Warriors are first, Rams and Tigers are tied and Comets are last.

   b) Comets would receive 5 points.
   Rams would receive 13 points.
   Warriors would receive 8 points.
   Tigers would receive 10 points.
   The new rank would be Rams first, Tigers second, Warriors third, and Comets fourth.

42. a) 15 first place votes producing 4 points = 60
   15 second place votes producing 3 points = 45
   15 third place votes producing 2 points = 30
   15 fourth place votes producing 1 point = 15
   Total = 150 points.

   b) $150 - (35 + 40 + 25) = 150 - 100 = 50$ points.

   c) Yes. It depends on the method used.

43. Votes: (A): 10, (B): 7, (C): 5, (D): 9
   A and D would win since they received the most votes.

Exercise Set 15.2

1. If a candidate receives a majority of first place votes, then that candidate should be declared the winner.

2. If a candidate is favored when compared individually with every other candidate, then that candidate should be declared the winner.

3. A candidate who wins a first election and then gains additional support without losing any of the original support should also win a second election.

4. If a candidate is declared the winner of an election, and in a second election, one or more of the other candidates is removed, then the previous winner should still be declared the winner.

5. A candidate that is preferred to all others will win each pairwise comparison and be selected with the pairwise comparison method.

6. A candidate that holds a majority of first place votes wins each pairwise comparison and is selected with the pairwise comparison method.

7. (F) receives 25 points, (S) receives 23 points and (M) receives 18 points
   (F) wins with the Borda count method but S has 6 votes which is a majority out of the 11 voters.

8. (A) receives 19 points, (B) receives 24 points, (C) receives 15 points and (D) receives 12 points
   B wins with the Borda count method but A has 4 votes which is a majority out of 7 voters. Thus, the majority criterion is <u>not</u> satisfied.

9. Votes: A:4, B:2, C:5; C wins with the plurality method.
   However, A is favored over the others using a head-to-head comparison.
   Thus, the head-to-head criterion is <u>not</u> satisfied.

10. Votes: A:12, B:3, C:6, D:4; A wins with the plurality method.
    A is also favored in a head-to-head comparison.
    Thus, the head-to-head criterion is satisfied.

11. A receives 19 points, B receives 15 points, C receives 20 points; C wins with the Borda count method.
    However, A is favored over B and C in a head-to-head comparison.
    Thus, the head-to-head criterion is <u>not</u> satisfied.

12. A receives 20 points, B receives 15 points, C receives 19 points; A wins with the Borda count method.
    However, C is favored over A and B in a head-to-head comparison.
    Thus, the head-to-head criterion is <u>not</u> satisfied.

13. A majority out of 25 voters is 13 or more votes.
    B wins with a majority of the votes.
    B also wins in a head-to-head comparison with the others.
    Thus, the head-to-head criterion is satisfied.

14. A majority out of 25 voters is 13 or more votes.
    Votes: A:10, B:2, C:8, D:5, thus eliminate B.
    Votes: A:10, C: 2 + 8 = 10, D:5, thus eliminate D.
    Votes: A:10, C: 2 + 5 + 8 = 15, D:5, thus C wins.
    However, B wins in a head-to-head comparison.
    Thus, the head-to-head criterion is <u>not</u> satisfied.

15. Votes: A:8, B:4, C:5; thus A wins
    If B drops out we get the following:
    Votes: A:8, B:4 + 5 = 9, thus B would win.
    The irrelevant alternatives criterion is <u>not</u> satisfied.

16. Votes: A:3, B:4, C:5; thus B wins
    If C drops out we get the following:
    Votes: A:3 + 5 = 8, B:6, thus A would win.
    The irrelevant alternatives criterion is <u>not</u> satisfied.

17. A receives 38 points, B receives 35 points, C receives 35 points
    Thus, A wins using the Borda count method.
    If B drops out we get the following:
    A receives 25 points, C receives 29 points
    Thus, C wins the second vote.
    The irrelevant alternatives criterion is <u>not</u> satisfied.

18. A receives 53 points, B receives 56 points, C receives 53 points
    Thus, B wins using the Borda count method.
    If A drops out we get the following:
    B receives 37 points, C receives 44 points
    Thus, C wins the second vote.
    The irrelevant alternatives criterion is <u>not</u> satisfied.

19. A majority out of 21 voters is 11 or more votes.
    Votes: A:5 + 3 = 8, B:6, C:7; none has a majority, thus eliminate B.
    Votes: A:5 + 3 = 8, C: 6 + 7 = 13, thus C wins.
    If the three voters who voted for A,C,B change to C,A,B the table become:

Number of votes	5	6	10
First	A	B	C
Second	B	C	A
Third	C	A	B

    The new set of votes is
    Votes: A:5, B:6, C:10; none has a majority, thus eliminate A.
    Votes: B:5 + 6 = 11, D:10, thus B wins this time.
    Thus, the monotonicity criterion is <u>not</u> satisfied.

20. A majority out of 29 voters is 15 or more votes.
    Votes: A:8, B:10, C:11; none has a majority, thus eliminate A.
    Votes: B:8 + 10 = 18, C: 7 + 4 = 11, thus B wins.
    After the four votes change their votes the new table is:

Number of votes	7	8	14
First	C	A	B
Second	A	B	C
Third	B	C	A

    The new set of votes is
    Votes: A:8, B:14., C:7; none has a majority, thus eliminate C.
    Votes: A: 7+ 8 = 15, B:14; thus A wins this time.
    Thus, the monotonicity criterion is <u>not</u> satisfied.

21. A majority out of 23 voters is 12 votes.
    Votes: A:10, B:8, C:5; none has a majority, thus eliminate C.
    Votes: B:10, B:8 + 5 = 13; thus B wins.
    After A drops out the new table is:

Number of votes	10	8	5
First	C	B	C
Second	B	C	B

Votes: B:8, C:10 + 5 = 15; thus C wins this time.
The irrelevant alternatives criterion is <u>not</u> satisfied.

22. A majority out of 13 voters is 7 votes.
    Votes: A:3, B:6, C:4; none has a majority, thus eliminate A.
    Votes: B:6, C:4 + 3 = 7; thus C wins.
    After B drops out the new table is:

Number of votes	6	4	3
First	A	C	A
Second	C	A	C

Votes: A:6 + 3 = 9, C:4; thus A wins this time.
The irrelevant alternatives criterion is <u>not</u> satisfied

23. A receives 2 points
    B receives 3 points
    C receives 2 points
    D receives 1 point
    E receives 2 points
    Thus, B wins.

    After A, C and E drop out the new table is

Number of votes	1	1	1	1	1
First	B	B	D	D	D
Second	D	D	B	B	B

(B) vs. (D)
Votes: (B):2, (D):3; thus D wins this time.
The irrelevant alternatives criterion is <u>not</u> satisfied.

24. A receives 3 points
    B receives 1 point
    C receives 3 points
    D receives 1 point
    E receives 2 points
    A and C tie, but when A vs. C, C wins and thus we declare C the winner

    After A, B and E drop out the new table is

Number of votes	2	1	1	1	1	1
First	C	C	D	D	D	D
Second	D	D	C	C	C	C

Votes: C:2 + 1 = 3, D:4, thus D wins this time.
The irrelevant alternatives criterion is <u>not</u> satisfied.

25. a) A majority out of 23 votes is 12 votes.
    First place votes: C:8, G:0, H:3, S:12
    (S) holds a majority of first place votes.

    b) Votes: C:8, G:0, H:3, S:12. Thus, (S) wins.

    c) C receives 62 points, G receives 63 points, H receives 40 points, S receives 65 points. Thus, (S) wins.

    d) A majority out of 23 votes is 12 votes. In part (a) we find that (S) holds a majority. Thus, (S) wins.

    e) C receives 1 point, G receives 2 points, H receives 0 points, S receives 3 points. Thus, (S) wins.

    f) None, since (S) wins in every case.

26. a) A receives 0 points, B receives 2 points, C receives 3 points, D receives 3½ points,
    E receives 1½ points. Thus, D wins.

    b) The new table is:

Number of votes	12	8	8	8	4	2	2
First	B	B	E	A	D	B	E
Second	D	D	D	E	E	D	D
Third	E	E	A	B	B	E	B
Fourth	A	A	B	D	A	A	A

    B wins the second vote with the most points.

    c) Yes.

27. a) A majority out of 82 votes is 42 votes or more.
    Votes: A:28, B:24, C:20 + 10 = 30; none has a majority, thus, eliminate B
    Votes: A:28 + 24 = 52, G:20 + 10 = 30; A has a majority; thus A wins

    b) Votes: A:36, B:24, C:20 + 2 = 22; none has a majority; thus eliminate C
    Votes: A:35 + 2 = 38, B:24 + 20 = 44; thus B wins

    c) Yes. There is a new winner.

28. a) A receives 1 point, B receives 2½ points, C receives 1½ points, D receives 3 points,
    E receives 2 points. Thus, (D) wins

    b) A receives 0 points, B receives 2½ points, D receives 2 points, E receives 1½ points.
    Thus, B wins.

    c) Yes.

29. If a candidate receives a majority of votes, that candidate will also have the most votes.

30. A candidate who holds a plurality will only gain strength and hold and even larger lead if more
    favorable votes are added.

31. If there is a candidate that is the first choice of a majority of voters, that candidate will be declared the
    winner in the first round of the plurality with elimination method.

32. A majority out of 11 voters is 6 or more votes.
    a) Votes: A:9, B:2; thus A wins.
    b) Votes: A:4 + 2 = 6, C:5; Yes, A wins.
    c) The five voters who favor C should vote C, B, A instead of C, A, B.

Exercise Set 15.3

1. If we divide the total population by the number of items to be apportioned we obtain a number called the standard divisor.

2. The standard quota is found by dividing each group's population by the standard divisor.

3. The standard quota rounded up to the nearest whole number.

4. The standard quota rounded down to the nearest whole number.

5. An apportionment should always be either the upper quota or the lower quota.

6. Hamilton's method

7. Jefferson's method, Webster's method, Adams's method

8. Jefferson's method, Webster's method, Adams's method

9. a) Standard divisor = $\dfrac{7500000}{150} = 50,000$

b & c)

State	A	B	C	D	Total
Population	1,222,000	2,730,000	857,000	2,693,000	7,500,000
Standard Quota	24.40	54.60	17.14	53.86	
Lower Quota	24	54	17	53	148
Hamilton's Apportionment	24	55	17	54	150

10. a & b)

State	A	B	C	D	Total
Population	1,222,000	2,730,000	857,000	2,693,000	7,500,000
Modified Quota	24.65	55.15	17.31	54.40	
Jefferson's Apportionment (round down)	24	55	17	54	150

11. a & b)

State	A	B	C	D	Total
Population	1,222,000	2,730,000	857,000	2,693,000	7,500,000
Modified Quota	24.70	55.26	17.35	54.51	
Jefferson's Apportionment (round down)	24	55	17	54	150

12. a & b)

State	A	B	C	D	Total
Population	1,222,000	2,730,000	857,000	2,693,000	7,500,000
Modified Quota	24.11	53.95	16.94	53.22	
Adams' Apportionment (round up)	25	54	17	54	150

13. a & b)

State	A	B	C	D	Total
Population	1,222,000	2,730,000	857,000	2,693,000	7,500,000
Modified Quota	24.06	53.85	16.90	53.12	
Adams' Apportionment (round up)	25	54	17	54	150

14.

State	A	B	C	D	Total
Population	1,222,000	2,730,000	857,000	2,693,000	7,500,000
Standard Quota	24.40	54.60	17.14	53.86	
Webster's Apportionment (standard rounding)	24	55	17	54	150

15. a & b)

State	A	B	C	D	Total
Population	1,222,000	2,730,000	857,000	2,693,000	7,500,000
Modified Quota	24.38	54.55	17.12	53.81	
Webster's Apportionment	24	55	17	54	150

16. a) Standard divisor = $\dfrac{\text{total}}{60} = \dfrac{1350}{30} = 45$

b & c)

Person	Al	Bob	Charlie	Total
Amount	350	530	470	1350
Standard Quota	7.78	11.78	10.44	
Lower Quota	7	11	10	28
Hamilton's Apportionment	8	12	10	30

17. a & b)

Person	Al	Bob	Charlie	Total
Amount	350	530	470	1350
Modified Quota	8.05	12.18	10.84	
Jefferson's Apportionment (rounded down)	8	12	10	30

18. a & b)

Person	Al	Bob	Charlie	Total
Amount	350	530	470	1350
Modified Quota	8.14	12.33	10.93	
Jefferson's Apportionment	8	12	10	30

19. a & b)

Person	Al	Bob	Charlie	Total
Amount	350	530	470	1350
Modified Quota	7.45	11.28	10.00	
Adam's Apportionment (rounded up)	8	12	10	30

20. a & b)

Person	Al	Bob	Charlie	Total
Amount	350	530	470	1350
Modified Quota	7.29	11.04	9.79	
Adam's Apportionment (rounded up)	8	12	10	30

21. a & b)

Person	Al	Bob	Charlie	Total
Amount	350	530	470	1350
Standard Quota	7.78	11.78	10.44	
Webster's Apportionment (standard rounding)	8	12	10	30

22. a & b)

Person	Al	Bob	Charlie	Total
Amount	350	530	470	1350
Modified Quota	7.61	11.52	10.22	
Webster's Apportionment	8	12	10	30

23. a) A standard divisor $= \dfrac{\text{total}}{60} = \dfrac{1260}{60} = 21$

b)

State	A	B	C	D	Total
Population	123	484	382	271	1260
Standard Quota	5.86	23.05	18.19	12.90	

24.

State	A	B	C	D	Total
Population	123	484	382	271	1260
Standard Quota	5.86	23.05	18.19	12.90	
Lower Quota	5	23	18	12	58
Hamilton's Apportionment	6	23	18	13	60

25. A divisor of 20.5 was used.

State	A	B	C	D	Total
Population	123	484	382	271	1260
Modified Quota	6.00	23.61	18.63	13.22	
Jefferson's Apportionment (round down)	6	23	18	13	60

26. A divisor of 21.5 was used.

State	A	B	C	D	Total
Population	123	484	382	271	1260
Modified Quota	5.72	27.51	17.77	12.60	
Adams' Apportionment (round up)	6	23	18	13	60

27.

State	A	B	C	D	Total
Population	123	484	382	271	1260
Standard Quota	5.86	23.05	18.19	12.90	
Webster's Apportionment	6	23	18	13	60

28. a) Standard divisor = $\dfrac{\text{total}}{250} = \dfrac{13000}{250} = 52$

   b)

School	LA	Sci.	Eng.	Bus.	Hum	Total
Enrollment	1746	7095	2131	937	1091	13000
Standard Quota	33.58	136.44	40.98	18.02	20.98	

29.

School	LA	Sci.	Eng.	Bus.	Hum	Total
Enrollment	1746	7095	2131	937	1091	13000
Standard Quota	33.58	136.44	40.98	18.02	20.98	
Lower Quota	33	136	40	18	20	247
Hamilton's Apportionment	34	136	41	18	21	250

30. A divisor of 51.5 was used.

School	LA	Sci.	Eng.	Bus.	Hum	Total
Enrollment	1746	7095	2131	937	1091	13000
Modified Quota	33.90	137.77	41.38	18.19	21.18	
Jefferson's Apportionment (round down)	33	137	41	18	21	250

31. A divisor of 52.5 was used.

School	LA	Sci.	Eng.	Bus.	Hum	Total
Enrollment	1746	7095	2131	937	1091	13000
Modified Quota	33.26	135.14	40.59	17.85	20.78	
Adam's Apportionment (round up)	34	136	41	18	21	250

32.

School	LA	Sci.	Eng.	Bus.	Hum	Total
Enrollment	1746	7095	2131	937	1091	13000
Standard Quota	33.58	136.44	40.98	18.02	20.98	
Webster's Apportionment (standard rounding)	34	136	41	18	21	250

33. a) Standard divisor = $\dfrac{\text{total}}{50} = \dfrac{400}{50} = 8$

   b)

Division	LA	Sci.	Bus.	Hum	Total
Faculty	130	175	46	49	
Standard Quota	16.25	21.88	5.75	6.13	

34.

Division	LA	Sci.	Bus.	Hum	Total
Faculty	130	175	46	49	
Standard Quota	16.25	21.88	5.75	6.13	
Lower Quota	16	21	5	6	48
Hamilton's Apportionment	16	22	6	6	50

35. The divisor of 7.65 was used.

Division	LA	Sci.	Bus.	Hum	Total
Faculty	130	175	46	49	
Modified Quota	16.99	22.88	6.01	6.41	
Jefferson's Apportionment (round down)	16	22	6	6	50

36. The divisor 8.25 was used.

Division	LA	Sci.	Bus.	Hum	Total
Faculty	130	175	46	49	
Modified Quota	15.76	21.21	5.58	5.94	
Adam's Apportionment (round down)	16	22	6	6	50

37.

Division	LA	Sci.	Bus.	Hum	Total
Faculty	130	175	46	49	
Standard Quota	15.76	21.21	5.58	5.94	
Webster's Apportionment (standard rounding)	16	22	6	6	50

38. a) Standard divisor = $\dfrac{\text{total}}{210} = \dfrac{2940}{210} = 14$

b)

Precinct	A	B	C	D	E	F	Total
Crimes	743	367	432	491	519	388	2940
Standard Quota	53.07	26.21	30.86	35.07	37.07	27.71	

39.

Precinct	A	B	C	D	E	F	Total
Crimes	743	367	432	491	519	388	2940
Standard Quota	53.07	26.21	30.86	35.07	37.07	27.71	
Lower Quota	53	26	30	35	37	27	208
Hamilton's Apportionment	53	26	31	35	37	28	210

40. The divisor 3.8 as used.

Precinct	A	B	C	D	E	F	Total
Crimes	743	367	432	491	519	388	2940
Modified Quota	53.84	26.59	31.30	35.58	37.61	28.12	
Jefferson's Apportionment (round down)	53	26	31	35	37	28	210

41. The divisor 14.2 as used.

Precinct	A	B	C	D	E	F	Total
Crimes	743	367	432	491	519	388	2940
Modified Quota	52.32	22.85	30.42	34.58	36.55	27.32	
Adam's Apportionment (round up)	53	26	31	35	37	28	210

42.

Precinct	A	B	C	D	E	F	Total
Crimes	743	367	432	491	519	388	2940
Standard Quota	52.32	22.85	30.42	34.58	36.55	27.32	
Webster's Apportionment (standard rounding)	53	26	31	35	37	28	210

43. a) Standard divisor = $\dfrac{\text{total}}{200} = \dfrac{2400}{200} = 12$

b)

Shift	A	B	C	D	Total
Room calls	751	980	503	166	2400
Standard Quota	62.58	81.67	41.92	13.83	

44.

Shift	A	B	C	D	Total
Room calls	751	980	503	166	2400
Standard Quota	62.58	81.67	41.92	13.83	
Lower Quota	62	81	41	13	197
Hamilton's Apportionment	62	82	42	14	200

45. The divisor 11.9 was used.

Shift	A	B	C	D	Total
Room calls	751	980	503	166	2400
Modified Quota	63.11	82.35	42.27	13.95	
Jefferson's Apportionment (round down)	63	82	42	13	200

46. The divisor 12.1 was used.

Shift	A	B	C	D	Total
Room calls	751	980	503	166	2400
Modified Quota	62.07	80.99	41.57	13.72	
Adam's Apportionment	63	81	42	14	200
(round up)					

47. The divisor 12.02 was used.

Shift	A	B	C	D	Total
Room calls	751	980	503	166	2400
Modified Quota	62.48	81.53	41.85	13.81	
Webster's Apportionment	62	82	42	14	200
(standard rounding)					

48.   Standard divisor = $\dfrac{3615920}{105} = 34437.33$

a) Hamilton's Apportionment: 7, 2, 2, 2, 8, 14, 4, 5, 10, 10, 13, 2, 6, 2, 18
b) Jefferson's Apportionment: 7, 1, 2, 2, 8, 14, 4, 5, 10, 10, 13, 2, 6, 2, 19

c) States that Benefited: Virginia
    States Disadvantaged: Delaware

Exercise set 15.4

1. The Alabama paradox occurs when an increase in the total number of items results in a loss of items for a group.
2. The population paradox occurs when group A loses items to group B, although group A's population grew at a higher rate than group B's.
3. The new-sates paradox occurs when the addition of a new group changes the apportionment of another group.
4. Yes, it can produce the Alabama paradox, population paradox, and new-states paradox.
5. New divisor = $\dfrac{900}{51} = 17.65$

School	A	B	C	D	E	Total
Standard Quota	11.90	9.35	9.07	9.92	10.76	
Lower Quota	11	9	9	9	10	48
Hamilton's Apportionment	12	9	9	10	11	51

No. No school suffers a loss so the Alabama paradox does not occur.

6. a) Standard divisor = $\dfrac{3312}{184} = 18$

School	A	B	C	D	Total
Population	919	457	798	1138	3312
Standard Quota	51.06	23.39	44.33	63.22	
Lower Quota	51	25	44	63	183
Hamilton's Apportionment	51	26	44	63	184

b) New divisor = $\dfrac{3312}{185} = 17.9$

School	A	B	C	D	Total
Population	919	457	798	1138	3312
Standard Quota	51.34	25.53	44.58	63.58	
Lower Quota	51	25	44	63	183
Hamilton's Apportionment	51	25	45	64	185

Yes. School B <u>loses</u> a chair while schools C and D each gain a chair.

7. a) Standard divisor = $\dfrac{900}{30} = 30$

State	A	B	C	Total
Population	161	250	489	900
Standard Quota	5.37	8.33	16.30	
Lower Quota	5	8	16	29
Hamilton's Apportionment	6	8	16	30

b) new divisor = $\dfrac{900}{31} = 29.03$

State	A	B	C	Total
Population	161	250	489	900
Standard Quota	5.55	8.61	16.84	
Lower Quota	5	8	16	29
Hamilton's Apportionment	5	9	17	31

Yes. State A loses a seat while states B and C each gain a seat.

8. a) Standard divisor = $\dfrac{1000000}{200} = 5000$

State	A	B	C	Total
Population	233,000	461,000	306,000	1,000,000
Standard Quota	46.60	92.20	61.20	
Lower Quota	46	92	61	199
Hamilton's Apportionment	47	92	61	200

b) New divisor = $\dfrac{1000000}{201} = 4975.12$

State	A	B	C	Total
Population	233,000	461,000	306,000	1,000,000
Standard Quota	46.83	92.66	61.51	
Lower Quota	46	92	61	199
Hamilton's Apportionment	47	93	61	201

No. None of the States lost a seat.

9. a) Standard divisor = $\dfrac{20000}{200} = 100$

City	A	B	C	Total
Population	7130	2030	10,840	20,000
Standard Quota	71.3	20.3	108.4	
Lower Quota	71	20	108	199
Hamilton's Apportionment	71	20	109	200

b) New divisor = $\dfrac{20010}{200} = 100.05$

City	A	B	C	Total
New Population	7135	2030	10,845	20,010
Standard Quota	71.31	20.29	108.40	
Lower Quota	71	20	108	199
Hamilton's Apportionment	71	20	109	200

No. None of the Cities loses a bonus.

10. a) Standard divisor = $\dfrac{900}{30} = 30$

College	A	B	C	Total
Faculty	162	249	489	900
Standard Quota	5.40	8.30	16.30	
Lower Quota	5	8	16	29
Hamilton's Apportionment	6	8	16	30

b) New divisor = $\dfrac{965}{30} = 32.167$

College	A	B	C	Total
Faculty	178	269	518	965
Standard Quota	5.53	8.36	16.10	
Lower Quota	5	8	16	29
Hamilton's Apportionment	6	8	16	30

No. The opportionment is the same.

11. a) Standard divisor = $\dfrac{5400}{54} = 100$

Division	A	B	C	D	E	Total
Population	733	1538	933	1133	1063	5400
Standard Quota	7.33	15.38	9.33	11.33	10.63	
Lower Quota	7	15	9	11	10	52
Hamilton's Apportionment	7	16	9	11	11	54

b) New divisor = $\dfrac{5454}{54} = 101$

Division	A	B	C	D	E	Total
Population	733	1539	933	1133	1116	
Standard Quota	7.26	15.238	9.238	11.22	11.05	
Lower Quota	7	15	9	11	11	53
Hamilton's Apportionment	8	15	9	11	11	54

Yes. Division B loses a seat to division A even though the population of division B grew faster than the population of division A.

12. a) Standard divisor = $\dfrac{30000}{300} = 100$

State	A	B	C	Total
Population	459	10551	18990	30000
Standard Quota	4.59	105.51	189.90	
Lower Quota	4	105	189	298
Hamilton's Apportionment	5	105	190	300

b) New divisor = $\dfrac{30110}{300} = 100.37$

State	A	B	C	Total
Population	459	10551	18990	30000
Standard Quota	4.57	105.12	189.20	
Lower Quota	4	105	189	298
Hamilton's Apportionment	5	105	190	300

No. The opportionment is the same.

13. a) Standard divisor = $\dfrac{4800}{48} = 100$

Tech. Data	A	B	Total
Employees	844	3956	4800
Standard Quota	8.44	39.56	
Lower Quota	8	39	47
Hamilton's Apportionment	8	40	48

b) New divisor = $\dfrac{5524}{55} = 100.44$

Tech. Data	A	B	C	Total
Employees	844	3956	724	5524
Standard Quota	8.40	39.39	7.21	
Lower Quota	8	39	7	54
Hamilton's Apportionment	9	39	7	55

Yes. The US lost an employee to Europe.

14. a) Standard divisor = $\dfrac{900000}{60} = 15,000$

State	A	B	C	Total
Population	62700	230700	606,600	900,000
Standard Quota	4.18	15.38	40.44	
Lower Quota	4	15	40	59
Hamilton's Apportionment	4	15	41	60

b) New divisor = $\dfrac{978000}{65} = 15,046.15$

State	A	B	C	D	Total
Population	62700	230700	606,600	78,000	978000
Standard Quota	4.17	15.33	40.32	5.18	
Lower Quota	4	15	40	5	64
Hamilton's Apportionment	4	16	40	5	65

Yes. State C loses a seat to State B.

15. a) Standard divisor = $\dfrac{10000}{100} = 100$

State	A	B	Total
Population	11.35	8865	10,000
Standard Quota	11.35	88.65	
Lower Quota	11	88	99
Hamilton's Apportionment	11	89	100

b) New divisor = $\dfrac{10625}{106} = 100.24$

State	A	B	C	Total
Population	11.35	8865	625	5524
Standard Quota	11.32	88.44	6.24	
Lower Quota	11	88	6	105
Hamilton's Apportionment	11	89	6	106

No. The apportionment is the same.

16. a) Standard divisor = $\dfrac{3300}{33} = 100$

State	A	B	Total
Population	744	2556	3300
Standard Quota	7.44	25.56	
Lower Quota	7	25	32
Hamilton's Apportionment	7	26	33

b) New divisor = $\dfrac{4010}{40} = 100.25$

State	A	B	C	Total
Population	744	2556	710	4010
Standard Quota	7.42	25.50	7.08	
Lower Quota	7	25	7	39
Hamilton's Apportionment	7	26	7	40

No. The apportionment is the same.

Review Exercises

1. a) Robert Rivera wins with the most votes (12).
   b) A majority out of 24 voters is 13 or more votes. Robert Rivera does not have a majority.
2. a) Michelle MacDougal wins with the most votes (224).
   b) Yes. A majority out of 421 voters is 211 or more votes.

3.

Number of votes	3	2	1	3	1
First	B	A	D	C	D
Second	A	C	C	B	A
Third	C	D	A	A	B
Fourth	D	B	B	D	C

4.

Number of votes	2	2	2	1
First	C	A	B	C
Second	A	B	C	B
Third	B	C	A	A

5. Number of votes = 6 + 4 + 3 + 2 + 1 + 1 = 17

6. Votes: P:6 + 1 = 7, D:4, M:3 + 2 = 5, B:1. Pizza Hut wins.

7. P:50 points, D:47 points, M:35 points, B:38 points. Pizza Hut wins.

8. A majority out 17 voters is 9 or more votes.
   Votes: P:6 + 1 = 7, D:4, M: 3 + 2 = 5, B:1. None has a majority, thus eliminate B.
   Votes: P:6 + 1 = 7, D:4, M: 3 + 2 + 1 = 6. None has a majority, thus eliminate D.
   Votes: P:6 + 4 + 1 = 11, M: 3 + 2 + 1 = 6. Pizza Hut wins.

9. P:3 points, D:2 points, M:0 points, B:1 point; Pizza Hut wins.

10. Votes: P:7, D:4, M:5, B:1
    None has a majority, thus eliminate M with most last place votes.
    Votes: P:10, D:4, B:3; Pizza Hut wins.

11. Voters: 38 + 30 + 25 + 7 + 10 = 110

12. Votes: S:38, V:30 + 10 = 40, B:25 + 7 = 32; Volleyball wins.

13. S:223 points, V:215 points, B:222 points; Soccer wins.

14. A majority out of 110 voters is 56 or more votes.
    Votes: S:38, V:40, B:32; None has a majority, thus eliminate B
    Votes: S:45, V:65; Volleyball wins.

15. S:1 point, V:1 point, B:1 point; A 3-way tie.

16. Votes: S:38, V:40, B:32; none has a majority, thus eliminate V with the most last place votes.
    Votes: S:68, B:42; Soccer wins.

17. a) Votes: A:150 + 123 = 273, F:45, M:3, P:0; A wins.
    b) Yes. A majority out of 321 voters is 161 or more votes. A receives a majority.
    c) A:1230 points, F:609 points, M:621 points, P:750 points. A wins.
    d) 161 or more votes is needed for a majority. Votes: A:273, F:45, M:3, P::0; A wins.
    e) A:3 points, F:1 point, M:1 point, P:1 point; A wins.

18. a) Votes – (C):30, (D):45, (I):60 + 10 = 70, (M):55. Indianapolis wins.
    b) A majority out of 200 voters is 101 or more votes. None of the cities has a majority.
    c) (C):495 points, (D):495 pints, (I):410 points, (M):600 points. Milwaukee wins.
    d) Votes: C:30, D:45, I:70, M:55; None has a majority, thus eliminate C.
       Votes: D:45, I:70, M:55 + 30 = 85; None has a majority, thus eliminate D.
       Votes: I:70, M:130; Milwaukee wins.
    e) C:1 point, D:2 points, I:0 points, M:3 points; Milwaukee wins.

19. a) A majority out of 16 voters is 9 or more votes.
       Votes: (EB):4 + 3+ = 7, (FW): 1 + 1 – 2, (G):0, (WB): 6 + 1 = 7;
       None has a majority, thus eliminate G.
       Votes: (EB):4 + 3 = 7, (FW):1 + 1 = 2, (WB): 6 + 1 = 7;
       None has a majority, thus eliminate FW
       Votes: (EB): 4 + 3 + 1 = 8, (WB): 6 + 1 + 1 = 8. Thus, EB and WB tie.

    b) Use the Borda count method to break the tie.
       (EB) has 46 points, (WB) has 50 points; World Book wins.

    c) (EB) vs. (WB)
       EB:4 + 3 + 1 = 8 points, (WB):6 + 1 + 1 = 8 points. EB and WB tie again.

20. A:23 points, B:26 points, C:18 points, D:13 points.   Using the Borda count method B wins. However, B only has 2 first place votes, thus the majority criterion is <u>not</u> satisfied.

21. In a head-to-head comparison B must win over all the others. For (B vs. A) A wins. The head-to-head criterion is <u>not</u> satisfied.

22. a) A majority out of 42 voters is 22 or more votes.
    Votes: A:12, B:10 + 6 = 16, C:14; None has the majority, thus eliminate A.
    Votes: B:10 + 6 = 16, C:14 + 12 = 26; C wins.

   b) The new preference table is

Number of votes	10	20	12
First	B	C	A
Second	A	B	C
Third	C	A	B

   Votes: A:12, B:10, C:20; None has a majority, thus eliminate B.
   Votes: A:22, C:20; A wins.
   When the order is changed A wins. Therefore, the monotonicity criterion is <u>not</u> satisfied.

   c) If B drops out the new table is

Number of votes	10	14	6	12
First	A	C	C	A
Second	C	A	A	C

   Votes: A:10 + 12 = 22, C:14 + 6 = 20; A wins.
   Since C won the first election and then after B dropped out A won, the irrelevant criterion is not satisfied.

23. a) Yes. (C) Rene Descartes is favored when compared to each of the other candidates.
   b) Votes: (A):29, (B)43, (C):26 + 14 = 40, (D):30. (B) Bernhard Bolzano wins.

   c) A:422, B:297, C:380, D:361; (A) Maria Agnesi wins.

   d) A majority out of 142 voters is 72 or more votes.
      Votes: A:29, B:43, C:26 + 14 = 40, D:30; None has a majority, thus eliminate A.
      Votes: B:432, C:29 + 26 + 14 = 69, D:30; None has a majority, thus eliminate D.
      Votes: B:43, C:69 + 30 = 99; (C) Marquis deCondorcet wins.

   e) A received 2 points, B receive 0 points, C receives 1 point, D receives 3 points; D wins.

   f) From part (a) we see that Rene Descartes is favored over each of the others when compared head-to-head. However, Renee Descartes does not win when the <u>plurality method</u>, <u>Borda count method</u> and <u>plurality with elimination method</u> are used. Thus, these methods violate the head-to-head criterion.

24. a) Yes. (D) Dire Straits is favored when compared to each of the other bands.

   b) Votes: A:15, B:34, C:9 + 4 = 13, D:25; (B) Boston wins.

   c) A:217 points, B:198 points, C:206 points, D:249 points; (D) Dire Straits wins.

   d) A majority out of 87 voters is 44 or more votes.
      Votes: A:15, B:34, C:13, D:25; None has a majority, thus eliminate C.
      Votes: A:15 + 9 +4 = 28, B:34, D:25; None has a majority, thus eliminate D.
      Votes: A:28 + 25 = 53, B:34; (A) Abba wins.

   e) A receives 2 points, B receives 0 points, C receives 1 point, D receives 3 points; thus (D) Dire Straits wins.

   f) The plurality method and the plurality with elimination method.

25. A majority out of 70 voters is 36 or more votes. Candidate A has a majority of the votes.
   Using plurality A wins. Using Borda count B wins. Using plurality with elimination A wins, Using Pairwise A wins. The only method to violate the majority criterion is the Borda count method.

26. The only methods that violate the monotonicity criterion are the plurality method and the plurality with elimination method.

27. Using the plurality method, B wins with D included and B wins after D drops out.
   Using the Borda count method, A wins with D included but E wins after D drops out.
   Using plurality with elimination, B wins with D included and B wins after D drops out.
   Using the pairwise method, B wins with D include but E wins after D drops out.
   The Borda count and pairwise comparison methods violate the irrelevant alternatives criterion.

28. Standard divisor = $\dfrac{6000}{10} = 600$

Region	A	B	C	Total
Number of Houses	2592	1428	1980	6000
Standard Quota	4.32	2.38	3.30	
Lower Quota	4	2	3	9
Hamilton's Apportionment	4	3	3	10

29. Using the modified divisor 500.

Region	A	B	C	Total
Number of Houses	2592	1428	1980	6000
Modified Quota	5.18	2.86	3.96	
Jefferson's Apportionment (rounded down)	5	2	3	10

30. Using the modified divisor 700.

Region	A	B	C	Total
Number of Houses	2592	1428	1980	6000
Modified Quota	3.70	2.04	2.83	
Adam's Apportionment (rounded up)	4	3	3	10

31. Using the modified divisor 575.

Region	A	B	C	Total
Number of Houses	2592	1428	1980	6000
Modified Quota	4.51	2.48	3.4	
Webster's Apportionment (normal rounding)	5	2	3	10

32. Yes. Hamilton's Apportionment becomes 5, 2, 4.
   Region B loses one truck.

33. Standard divisor = $\dfrac{690}{23} = 30$

Course	A	B	C	Total
Number of Students	311	219	160	690
Standard Quota	10.37	7.30	5.33	
Lower Quota	10	7	5	22
Hamilton's Apportionment	11	7	5	23

34. Use the modified divisor 28

Course	A	B	C	Total
Number of Students	311	219	160	690
Modified Quota	11.12	7.82	5.71	
Jefferson's Apportionment (round down)	11	7	5	23

35. Use the modified divisor 31.5

Course	A	B	C	Total
Number of Students	311	219	160	690
Modified Quota	9.87	6.95	5.08	
Adam's Apportionment (round up)	10	7	6	23

36. Use the modified divisor 29.5

Course	A	B	C	Total
Number of Students	311	219	160	690
Modified Quota	10.54	7.42	5.42	
Webster's Apportionment (standard rounding)	11	7	5	23

37. The new divisor is $\dfrac{698}{23} = 30.35$

Course	A	B	C	Total
Number of Students	317	219	162	698
Standard Quota	10.44	7.22	5.34	
Lower Quota	10	7	5	22
Hamilton's Apportionment	11	7	5	23

No. The apportionment remains the same.

38. The Standard divisor = $\dfrac{50000}{50} = 1000$

State	A	B	Total
Population	4420	45580	50,000
Standard Quota	4.42	45.58	
Lower Quota	4	45	49
Hamilton's Apportionment	4	46	50

39. Use the modified divisor 975

State	A	B	Total
Population	4420	45580	50,000
Modified Quota	4.53	46.75	
Jefferson's Apportionment (round down)	4	46	50

40. Use the modified divisor 1025

State	A	B	Total
Population	4420	45580	50,000
Modified Quota	4.31	44.47	
Adam's Apportionment (round up)	5	45	50

41. Use the standard divisor 1000

State	A	B	Total
Population	4420	45580	50,000
Standard Quota	4.42	45.58	
Webster's Apportionment (standard rounding)	4	46	50

42. The new divisor is $\dfrac{55400}{55} = 1007.27$

State	A	B	C	Total
Population	4420	45580	5400	55,400
Standard Quota	4.39	45.25	5.36	
Lower Quota	4	45	5	54
Hamilton's Apportionment	5	45	5	55

Yes. State A. gains a seat while State B loses a seat.

Chapter Test

1. Number of voters = 4 + 3 + 3 + 2 = 12.
2. A majority out of 12 voters is 7 or more votes.
   Votes: D:4, C: 3 + 2 = 5, S:3; None of them has a majority.
3. Chris wins with the most votes.

4. Chris (C)- First: $5 \times 3 = 15$ points
        Second: $4 \times 2 = \ 8$ points
        Third: $3 \times 1 = \ 3$ points

   C receives 26 points.

   Donyall (D) - First: $4 \times 3 = 12$ points
        Second: $5 \times 2 = 10$ points
        Third: $3 \times 1 = \ 3$ points

   D receives 25 points.

   Sam (S) - First: $3 \times 3 = \ 9$ points
        Second: $3 \times 2 = \ 6$ points
        Third: $6 \times 1 = \ 6$ points

   S receives 21 points.
   Chris is the winner with 26 points.

5. A majority of 7 or more votes is required to win.
   Votes: D:4, C:3 + 2 = 5, S:3; None has a majority, thus eliminate (S) with the lease votes.

Number of votes	4	3	3	2
First	D	C	D	C
Second	C	D	C	D

   Votes: D:4 + 3 = 7, C = 3 + 2 = 5; Donyall (D) wins.

6. D vs. C, D:7, C:5; D is awarded 1 point.
   D vs. S, D:6, S:6; D and S are awarded ½ point each.
   C vs. S, C:9, S:3; C is awarded 1 point.
   Donyall (D) has the most points, thus D wins.

7. a) Votes: H:26 + 14 = 40, I:29, L:30, S:43; thus hamster (H) wins.

   b) Hamster (H) - First: $40 \times 4 =$ 160 points
                  Second: $59 \times 3 =$ 177 points
                  Third: $0 \times 2 =$ 0 points
                  Fourth: $43 \times 1 =$ 43 points

   H receives 380 points.

   Iguana (I) -   First: $29 \times 4 =$ 116 points
               Second: $40 \times 3 =$ 120 points
               Third: $73 \times 2 =$ 146 points
               Fourth: $0 \times 1 =$ 0 points

   I receives 382 points

   Ladybug (L) - First: $30 \times 4 =$ 120 points
               Second: $43 \times 3 =$ 129 points
               Third: $43 \times 2 =$ 86 points
               Fourth: $26 \times 1 =$ 26 points

   L receives 361 points

   Snail (S) -   First: $43 \times 4 =$ 172 points
               Second: $0 \times 3 =$ 0 points
               Third: $26 \times 2 =$ 52 points
               Fourth: $73 \times 1 =$ 73 points

   S receives 297 points.

   The iguana (I) wins with the most points.

   c) A majority out of 142 voters is 72 or more votes.
      Votes: H:40, I:29, L:30, S:43; None has a majority, thus eliminate I.
      Votes: H:40 + 29 = 69, L:30, S:43; None has a majority, thus eliminate L.
      Votes: H:69 + 30 = 99, S:43; hamster (H) wins.

   d) H vs. I: I is awarded 1 point
      H vs. L: L is awarded 1 point
      H vs. S: H is awarded 1 point
      I vs. L: L is awarded 1 point
      I vs. S: I is awarded 1 point
      L vs. S: L is awarded 1 point

      H: 1 point, I:2 points, L:3 points, S: 0 points; ladybug (L) wins.

8. Plurality:
    Votes: W: 86, X:52 + 28 = 80, Y:60, Z:58; W wins.

    Borda count:
    W receives 594 points, X receives 760 points, Y receives 722 points, Z receives 764 points; Z wins

    Plurality with elimination:
    A majority out of 284 voters is 143 or more votes.
    Votes: W:86, X:80, Y:60, Z:58; None has a majority, thus eliminate Z.
    Votes: W:86, X:80 + 58 = 138, Y:60; None has a majority, thus eliminate Y.
    Votes: W:86, S:1328 + 60 = 198; X wins.

    Head-to-Head:
    When Y is compared to each of the others, Y is favored. Thus Y wins the head-to-head comparison.

    Plurality, Borda count and Plurality with elimination each violate the head-to-head criterion. The pairwise Method never violates the head-to-head criterion.

9. A majority out of 35 voters is 18 or more votes. Louisiana (L) has a majority.
    However, Mississippi (M) wins using the Borda count method. Thus the majority criterion is violated.

10. a) The standard divisor = $\dfrac{30000}{30} = 1000$

State	A	B	C	Total
Population	6,100	8,700	15,200	30,000
Standard Quota	6.10	8.70	15.20	
Lower Quota	6	8	15	29
Hamilton's Apportionment	6	9	15	30

    b) Use the modified divisor 960.

State	A	B	C	Total
Population	6,100	8,700	15,200	30,000
Modified Quota	6.35	9.06	15.83	
Jefferson's Apportionment (round down)	6	9	15	30

    c) The new divisor 967.74.

State	A	B	C	Total
Population	6,100	8,700	15,200	30,000
Standard Quota	6.30	8.99	15.71	
Lower Quota	6	8	15	29
Hamilton's Apportionment	6	9	16	31

    The Alabama paradox does not occur, sine none of the states loses a seat.

APPENDIX

GRAPH THEORY

Exercise Set

1. A **vertex** is a designated point.
2. An **edge** (or an **arc**) is any line, either straight or curved, that begins and ends at a vertex.
3. To determine whether a vertex is odd or even, count the number of edges attached to the vertex. If the number of edges is odd, the vertex is **odd**. If the number of edges is even, the vertex is **even**.
4. Answers will vary.

5. 5 vertices, 7 edges
6. 6 vertices, 8 edges
7. 7 vertices, 11 edges
8. 5 vertices, 6 edges
9. Each graph has the same number of edges from the corresponding vertices
10. Each graph has the same number of edges from the corresponding vertices.
11. Odd vertices: C, D
    Even vertices: A, B
12. Odd vertices: A, C, E, F
    Even vertices: B, D

13. Yes. The figure has exactly two odd vertices, namely C and D. Therefore, the figure is traversable. You may start at C and end at D, or start at D and end at C.
14. No. All four vertices are odd. There are more than two odd vertices. Therefore, the figure is not traversable.
15. Yes. The figure has no odd vertices. Therefore, the figure is traversable. You may start at any point and end where you started.
16. Yes. The figure has no odd vertices. Therefore, the figure is traversable. You may start at any point and end where you started.
17. No. The figure has four odd vertices, namely A, B, E, and F. There are more than two odd vertices. Therefore, the figure is not traversable.
18. Yes. The figure has exactly two odd vertices, namely C and G. Therefore, the figure is traversable. You may start at C and end at G, or start at G and end at C.
19. Yes. The figure has exactly two odd vertices, namely A and C. Therefore, the figure is traversable. You may start at A and end at C, or start at C and end at A.
20. Yes. The figure has no odd vertices. Therefore, the figure is traversable. You may start at any point and end where you started.

21. a) 0 rooms have an odd number of doors.
       5 rooms have an even number of doors.
    b) Yes because the figure would have no odd vertices.
    c) Start in any room and end where you began. For example: A to D to B to C to E to A.
22. a) 4 rooms have an odd number of doors.
       1 room has an even number of doors.
    b) No because the figure would have more than two odd vertices.

23. a) 2 rooms have an odd number of doors.
    4 rooms have an even number of doors.
    b) Yes because the figure would have exactly two odd vertices.
    c) Start at B and end at F, or start at F and end at B.
    For example: B to C to F to E to D to A to B to E to F
24. a) 2 rooms have an odd number of doors.
    4 rooms have an even number of doors.
    b) Yes because the figure would have exactly two odd vertices.
    c) Start at B and end at E, or start at E and end at B. For example: B to A to D to E to F to C to B to E
25. a) 4 rooms have an odd number of doors.
    1 room has an even number of doors.
    b) No because the figure would have more than two odd vertices.
26. a) 5 rooms have an odd number of doors.
    1 room has an even number of doors.
    b) No because the figure would have more than two odd vertices.
27. a) 3 rooms have an odd number of doors.
    2 rooms have an even number of doors.
    b) No because the figure would have more than two odd vertices.
28 a) 3 rooms have an odd number of doors.
    4 rooms have an even number of doors.
    b) No because the figure would have more than two odd vertices.

29. The door must be placed in room D. Adding a door to any other room would create two rooms with an odd number of vertices. You would then be unable to enter the building through the door marked "enter" and exit through the new door without going through a door at least twice.
30. The door must be placed in room D. Adding a door to any other room would create two rooms with an odd number of vertices. You would then be unable to enter the building through the door marked "enter" and exit through the new door without going through a door at least twice.

31. Yes because the figure would have exactly two odd vertices. Begin at either the island on the left or on the right and end at the other island.
32. Yes because the figure would have exactly two odd vertices. Begin at the island on the right and end on the land below the island, or vice versa.

33.

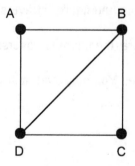

34.

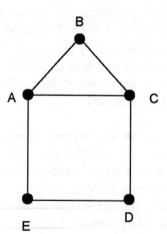

35. a) Kentucky, Virginia, North Carolina, Georgia, Alabama, Mississippi, Arkansas, Missouri
    b) Illinois, Arkansas, Tennessee
36. a) French Guiana, Surinam, Guyana, Venezuela, Columbia, Peru, Bolivia, Paraguay, Argentina, Uruguay
    b) Peru, Chile, Argentina, Paraguay, Brazil

37. a) 4
    b) 4
    c) 11

38.

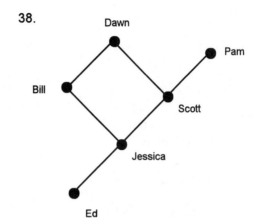

39.

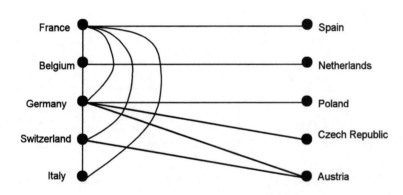

40. No, it is not possible, assuming that your starting and ending points are considered vertices.
41. a) Yes, the graph has exactly two odd vertices, namely C and G.
    b) C, A, B, E, F, D, G, C
42. Number of Edges = Number of Vertices + Number of Regions - 2